THE BEGINNER'S GUIDE TO LONELINESS

After a tragic event left Tori Williamson isolated from her loved ones, she's been struggling. That's why she set up her blog, The Beginner's Guide to Loneliness, as a way of — *anonymously* — reaching others who just need a little help sometimes. When she's offered a free spot on a wellbeing retreat, Tori is anxious about opening herself up to new surroundings. But after her three closest friends — who she talks to online but has never actually met — convince her it'll do her some good, she reluctantly agrees and heads off for three weeks in the wild (well, a farm in Wales). From the moment she arrives, Tori is sceptical and quickly finds herself drawn to fellow sceptic Than, the retreat's mysterious latecomer. But as the beauty of The Farm slowly comes to light she realizes that opening herself up might not be the worst thing.

LAURA BAMBREY

THE BEGINNER'S GUIDE TO LONELINESS

Complete and Unabridged

ISIS
Leicester

First published in Great Britain in 2020 by
Simon & Schuster UK Ltd
London

First Isis Edition
published 2021
by arrangement with
Simon & Schuster UK Ltd
London

This book is a work of fiction. Names, characters, places and incidents are either a product of the author's imagination or are used fictitiously. Any resemblance to actual people, living or dead, events or locales is entirely coincidental.

A catalogue record for this book is available from the British Library.

ISBN 978–1–78541–991–1

Published by
Ulverscroft Limited
Anstey, Leicestershire

Printed and bound in Great Britain by
TJ Books Ltd., Padstow, Cornwall

This book is printed on acid-free paper

For Jules

Prologue

Tackling the Taboo

Dear Readers,

Today marks the second anniversary of The Beginner's Guide to Loneliness. I can't express how grateful I am for all of your messages telling me how my blog has helped you navigate your own personal journeys. It makes me incredibly proud to know that so many people have benefited from this site.

Admitting that you are lonely remains one of the biggest taboos in our society. That's why all of the recent publicity the blog has received has been so welcome. The mixture of newspaper, magazine and online coverage has helped thousands of new readers to find their way here. If you're one of them, then welcome! The more able people feel to talk about being lonely, the easier it becomes to seek the support that's needed.

One of the greatest misconceptions is that loneliness stems from a character trait, or even a character flaw. Listen to me: **you don't have to be broken to be lonely**. I've heard it so many times: 'But you're so friendly . . . ' 'You seem to get on with people so easily . . . ' 'But you know lots of people . . . ' etc. I hope I am friendly, but that doesn't mean I can't feel isolated at times too; it doesn't mean I don't find it difficult to connect with people.

The truth is, you can be alone and not at all lonely — happy and content in your own company. Or you can be at the centre of a huge crowd and feel so lonely it's like a physical ache.

Sudden life changes can sometimes cause connections with other people to fall away. A bereavement, change of job or even the disintegration of a relationship are just a few of the catalysts. Should more than one of these things hit you at the same time, as they did for me, you can end up feeling not just lonely, but completely stuck, searching for the way out.

So no, you don't have to be broken to be lonely — but loneliness can, eventually, break you.

Let's keep talking about it. Let's keep looking at ways to heal. Let's keep supporting each other. Here's to the next two years of TheBeginnersGuideToLoneliness.com.

Thank you for being here.
TBGTL

P.S. A note to the press: thank you so much for your interest in the site! Should you wish to reach me about my work, please use the contact page. I will, however, be maintaining my anonymity. From this point onwards please note that I will not respond to any communications that include the request to 'come out' to my readers.

1

True Friends Will Always Be There

Warriors Chat Group. April 30. 10.48pm

WriterTori: Guys, help!
Nathalie33: Hey Tori! What's occurring?
WriterTori: Gah. Gah. GAH!
Nathalie33: Drama. Drama. DRAMA ;) Come on. Tell Aunty Nat . . .
WriterTori: Are Sue and Hugh online?
Nathalie33: Who knows . . . who cares . . . ?
WriterTori: Nat!!
Nathalie33: Kidding! Anyway, talk to me. What's up?
SueSue52: Oi, Nat, you cheeky mare! I'm here Tori. Managed to place any of your articles yet?
WriterTori: No, and that's half the problem.
Nathalie33: What's the other half?
WriterTori: Paying my rent! My landlord is being patient, but he said he wants the money the next time he sees me.
SueSue52: Ah, the joys of life as a self-employed writer. I thought you were going to look for a part-time job?
Nathalie33: Nah, she gave up that idea to focus!
SueSue52: How's that working out?
Nathalie33: How do you think it's working out? Her landlord's chasing her . . .
WriterTori: Jeez, thanks guys . . . But seriously — I'm skint. I have a million ideas for articles out, but so

far, no interest. AND I'm struggling for rent, hence the landlord issue. Also, I haven't been paid by puddle.com, even though I wrote six weeks' worth of content for them before they went under!

SueSue52: Nightmare! Wish I could help you out, but with the twins' birthday coming up and OH's hours cut, we're tight too. Maybe think again about getting that part-time job?

WriterTori: Cheers Sue, but I wouldn't want to borrow from you guys anyway. And I don't want to give in and look for a job yet. Would seem like admitting defeat . . . Anyway, this one opportunity has come up, and I need your advice about whether or not to go for it.

Nathalie33: Spill . . .

WriterTori: You know I don't accept any advertising on the blog?

Nathalie33: If you did, you wouldn't be having these problems. The Beginner's Guide to Loneliness is so insanely popular — you'd be raking it in, especially after the recent publicity you've been getting. And don't get me started on all the interview opportunities you've turned down . . . !

WriterTori: That's not what the site's about! The blog's anonymous and I want to keep it that way. But, this place in Wales called The Farm made contact a couple of weeks ago. They run wellness retreats and they've offered me a spot on the latest course in exchange for a review.

SueSue52: What's the course?

WriterTori: It's a mixture of mindfulness and counselling, designed to teach people how to improve their mental health and wellbeing. You work on building authentic relationships, self-acceptance, with a bit of yoga thrown in there for good measure. They reckon my readers are their target audience.

Nathalie33: Erm, yep — I can see their point! So are they going to pay you?

WriterTori: No, but it's a free three-week course that normally costs £3k, and they provide food, somewhere to stay and they'd cover travel costs too. What do you think? I'm not sure if I should go . . .

Nathalie33: Why the hell not? It sounds like it's practically tailor-made for you!

WriterTori: 1. Because the site's *anonymous*! 2. Because it feels a bit like I'd be selling out.

SueSue52: The anonymity thing is easy enough to get around. Just contact them via the blog's generic email address and say you'll send 'one of the site's reviewers'. Stops them knowing that you're the face behind all the articles.

WriterTori: Oh. Actually, that's a good plan.

Nathalie33: And you wouldn't be selling out by writing about an experience that could benefit so many of your readers.

SueSue52: Have you got a link?

WriterTori: Sure, two secs . . .

I paste the retreat's website address into the chat for Sue and Nat to peruse and then slump back on my sofa. With my computer balanced precariously on my lap, I reach over for my glass of wine and take a gulp. It's not just my need to stay anonymous that's making me hesitate. The thought of sharing my problems, face to face, makes me feel a bit sick. That's why I need the Warriors' second (and third and fourth) opinions.

I really don't know where I'd be without this lot. Nat, Sue and Hugh have been my one constant for the past two years, ever since I lost my mum. Things got . . . desperate. I didn't have anyone I could talk to about how I was really feeling, so I went online and found a grief support group. Nat came to my rescue within minutes of me posting to the communal chat. We talked so much that we were clogging up the thread, and it was gently suggested by a moderator that we shift over to our own private message channel. We chatted for hours on end, and she was just amazing. I credit her with single-handedly saving my sanity that first week.

I was still posting to the communal chat too, desperate for as much support as possible, and that's where I met Hugh and Sue. Sue had lost a baby the previous month and Hugh's brother had end-stage terminal cancer. We clicked so well that I invited them into the private channel too. I don't think Nat was very happy that our chats were now between four of us, but I'd found my life raft. I could be completely open with these three, and within just a few weeks, they became my family.

That was two years ago, and we've been inseparable ever since. Online at least. I've never met them in real life as we're spread all over the country. I've tried to meet up with Nat a couple of times as she's not that far away from London, just along the south coast, but something always crops up at the last minute and we still haven't managed it.

But just because we've never met in person doesn't stop me classing Sue, Nat and Hugh as my best friends. They held me together after Mum's accident. They were there through the long nights of tears when my relationship with my fiancé, Markus, imploded. They stop me from feeling completely alone and are my loudest and best cheerleaders.

Nat's actually the one who encouraged me to start up The Beginner's Guide. It started out as my way of coping with everything that had happened to me, but it's grown way past that. I write anonymous essays on grief, loss, depression and loneliness. I know — they hardly sound like the most cheering of subjects, but losing myself in the research and looking at the behaviours and patterns that everyone shares helps me to see that I'm not completely alone. Or, at least, I am, but everyone is at some stage.

Anyway, the site has really struck a chord. I receive an astonishing number of hits some days and, like Nat said, even the glossies and newspapers have picked up on my pieces recently — though they rather went to town on the whole 'who's behind the blog?' angle. This makes me even more grateful that I kept it anonymous — I'm not sure I'm up for becoming 'the face of loneliness'. As it is, I'm safe in the knowledge that it's only the Warriors who know that I'm the one behind the words.

My computer makes a chirruping sound and I nearly spill my wine in my haste to see what they both think.

Nathalie33: Sorry, I don't get why you're hesitating. This looks incredible!
SueSue52: It does look like an amazing opportunity Tori. But no pay? Not sure how that's going to help your current situation . . .
Nathalie33: Of course it is! She'll get fed and watered for free so won't need to spend any money,
and she'll have the chance to take a break from everything else, including the big bad landlord. Tori,

it'll give you some really interesting new content for the blog on top of the review they've asked for. And, let's face it, you could do with the help, what with everything you've been dealing with. Get some of that shit sorted, and all sorts of good things could happen for you.

I feel like I've been slapped. I shoot to my feet, plonk the laptop down unceremoniously on the coffee table and start to pace around my tiny living room.

Maybe Nat's got a point. I do need a break from everything, and getting some help to keep my head straight would be a massive bonus.

My heart's hammering, and I pause in my stomping to steady myself against the wall. I suck in a deep breath and try to calm down.

The laptop chirrups. They can wait. Just for a moment. I flop back down onto the sofa and, ignoring the chat, click back onto the tab for the retreat.

The words jump out at me: Healing, Mindfulness, Relationships, Grief. I scroll through some of the photos and gasp. Their beautiful stone farmhouse is set among green fields and wild flowers. There are photos of orchards in bloom, cosy campfires and a table laden with a gorgeous feast.

Three weeks.

What if other work comes through during that time? I'd risk missing out on paid jobs by being away. I drain my wine glass.

Perhaps I need to sleep on this. Again. The request's been in my inbox, unanswered, for at least a couple of weeks.

I click back through to the email and scan it again. Shit. I can't sleep on this. The bloody thing starts on

Monday. It's currently Thursday — *night*. Balls. I'm so not good at making snap decisions. *Any* decisions actually.

Chirrup.

Nathalie33: You okay?
Nathalie33: Tori, I'm sorry. I didn't mean to upset you. Just thought it could be good for you.
HughTypesLikeAFlamingo: Subtle as ever, Nat! Nice job.
HughTypesLikeAFlamingo: Hi by the way :)
Nathalie33: Get lost, Hugh! Tori? Come back! Don't leave me hanging . . .
WriterTori: Sorry, I was just having another look at that link.
SueSue52: So? What do you think? Gonna go for it? These guys look like they know their stuff.
WriterTori: Don't think so. I can't afford to be out of action for 3 weeks.
Nathalie33: Ah, come on Tori, what have you got to lose?! It's the 21st century. You can keep on top of emails and everything while you're there, and if something new comes in, just fit it in around the course. Isn't that the joy of being self-employed?!
WriterTori: I don't know . . .
HughTypesLikeAFlamingo: Do it do it do it!
WriterTori: You really think so?
HughTypesLikeAFlamingo: Hell yeah! Like Nat said, you've got nothing to lose!
WriterTori: Okay, okay. Three against one. I'm in! I'll shoot them an email in the morning and see if it's still available.
Nathalie33: Why wait? Let them know now. You've been sitting on this long enough by the sound of

it. Then they'll get it first thing tomorrow and you can organize everything ASAP.

SueSue52: Woohoo! Good for you Tori :) You have to promise to share all the gory details with us though . . .

WriterTori: Of course — you guys have to promise to be my lifeline.

HughTypesLikeAFlamingo: Aren't we always? ;)

WriterTori: Well, yeah. You're family and I don't know what I'd do without you.

Nathalie33: Let me know as soon as it's all confirmed!

WriterTori: Of course! Right, I'm off to write the email and then to bed . . . Looks like I'll be spending the weekend packing for a trip to Wales.

SueSue52: Whatever you do, don't forget your wellies!

I grin as I close down the chat tab. The smile feels unfamiliar on my face. It's been a while. Firing off a quick email to The Farm, I tell them that one of the blog's reviewers has agreed to attend the course if their offer is still open. I hold my breath as I hit send.

Scrolling through the photographs of the retreat for one last time, I gaze at the beautiful countryside, fresh food and all that green. Yes. This could be perfect. Out of the city, away from my grumpy landlord and away from all those crappy memories.

I pad through to my bedroom, determined to get a decent night's sleep for once. If this works out, I've got a seriously busy couple of days ahead of me, and an even busier three weeks. I need to be ready to head off and leave everything for a while. But, then, that's the joy of still being footloose and fancy free at the grand old age of thirty-three.

Just as I'm snuggling down into my pillows, my phone buzzes with a new email alert. I fumble for it in the dark and glance at the screen, fully expecting it to be junk about erectile dysfunction or offering me hot sex with a Colombian beauty.

But no. It's the retreat centre. I sit up and swipe it open.

They're looking forward to welcoming the reviewer on Monday, and they want said reviewer to call The Farm in the morning to confirm details.

Holy shit, what have I let myself in for?

2

Positive Is as Positive Does

'Every dawn brings a new challenge, but by going into the day with a positive mindset, you'll colour everything that follows with positivity.'
©TheBeginnersGuideToLoneliness.com

I hate trains.

Do you want to know what I hate even more than trains? Coaches.

I had to swap to what must be the most uncomfortable version of public transport available when my train terminated in Carmarthen, and for the past hour I've been trundling through the soggy depths of deepest, darkest Wales as if I'm on some kind of urgent mission.

I really don't want to be here.

'*Rhyn-Yr-Eithin* will be our next stop,' the driver mumbles into his microphone. 'Make sure you gather all your belongings, ladies and gents!'

About bloody time. I reach up and stretch out my spine, wincing slightly at every single crackle and pop that comes from sitting in one position for too long. Catching sight of my reflection in the grubby window, I rake my hands through my hair and try to tame my wayward mop.

Oh God, where have I landed myself?

All I've seen from the windows for the past hour has been green, green, green, sheep, more green . . .

Green is a highly overrated colour in my opinion.

As we come to a standstill, I struggle to my feet and thrust the course handbook I've been trying to binge-read into my handbag. I yank it roughly onto my shoulder and try not to bash people on the back of the head as I struggle down the narrow aisle. I manoeuvre my feet gingerly down the steep steps, conscious of my high heels and the looming gap between the coach and the kerb edge.

I really should stop taking fashion advice from people I've never met.

Sue thought it would be a good idea for me to turn up looking professional so that they take me seriously when I arrive. I've opted for a smart, slightly funky outfit. I haven't worn heels since I left my job at the ad agency and, frankly, if I'd had my way, I'd be in a pair of grubby Converse, but Sue nearly had a meltdown at the idea. As usual, I'd ended up trusting someone else's judgement above my own and Sue won. Hence the ridiculous heels that, right now, couldn't be more out of place if they tried.

Landing safely on the pavement, I look around to see the driver hauling my little wheelie case out of the hold before dumping it onto the tarmac. I totter over and thank him. He simply raises his hand, hops back on the coach and, without ceremony, closes the door and drives away.

I can't help but quietly fume as I make my way over to the crumbling wooden bus shelter and lower myself down onto a cracked, plastic seat.

I sigh. This is exactly why I hate being given lifts. You always end up waiting around for hours for people to turn up. Plus, it's cold and I'm hungry and . . . well, I just feel like whining right now. And I need to pee.

Why would anyone leave the comfort of London and come to bloody Wales? It's cold, it's raining and people are late.

I called The Farm as soon as was polite on Friday morning. I'm not too proud to admit that I begged them to be allowed to drive, and when that was refused because they're 'trying to do their bit for the environment', I tried arguing against being picked up from the bus stop, telling the man that I'd be happier getting a cab. This caused so much hilarity that I'd had to give in and agree to the lift. Now I can see why it was quite so funny: the idea of there being a taxi anywhere near here is . . . remote.

It's so quiet it's almost scary. Quiet, but very windy. I may as well have been airlifted into this green, hill-lined valley, because apart from this little shelter, there sure as hell isn't any other hint of civilization to be seen.

For what must be the hundredth time already, I glance back down the road, which snakes away between two grey-green hills that are clearly hoping to be mountains when they grow up.

There's a small cloud of dust, but nothing much else to see. I huddle down into my collar, trying to escape the chilly wind, and cross my legs tighter. There's no way I'm going to pee in a hedge, not on my first day living wild, and not on the last day either. I'm just not an al fresco pisser. The day that happens, this little trip has gone too far and I'll be making a break for freedom.

Ah, wait a minute, I think, that cloud of dust is getting closer. Could it be?

As I watch, a beaten-up Land Rover materializes and swings itself gracelessly onto the patch of gravel next to the bus stop.

'Victoria!' A huge smile followed by an awful lot of white whiskers appears from the driver's side of the vehicle.

'Yes, that's me. But it's Tori.' I smile tightly at this ill-groomed Father Christmas. I hold out my hand as he steps towards me, my heels causing me to tower over him. He catches my hand in both of his and gives it a rough-skinned squeeze.

'Great shoes!' he smiles down at my feet as if mesmerized.

'Erm . . . thanks.'

'I'm Ted. This is Frank,' he pats the side of the Land Rover. 'Let's get you back to the ranch,' he says, grabbing my case.

When they'd said 'Land Rover' on the phone, I'd pictured a lovely shiny Chelsea Chariot, the kind of vehicle that glamorous, platinum-blond mums use to drop their kids off at their very expensive private schools.

This is not one of those. There are only two words to describe it: Rust. Bucket.

It used to be khaki green, but has been repaired and patched so many times that the surface looks like it has bad acne scarring. There are patches of rusty red paint and blobs of white, presumably covering some botched mending. It looks as though there may be a fair bit of household gloss paint on there too. The canvas back is just as bad and appears to be mainly held together by moss and gaffer tape.

'Your carriage, madam . . .' To my horror, Ted yanks at the handle, throws open the door at the back of the vehicle and waves me in. 'Don't worry, it's not too far. I'd let you sit up front, but Dennis is in there and he won't move for man nor beast.'

'It's fine, no problem.' I force a smile. *He's got to be kidding?!*

The floor is covered with bits of straw and, well, poo. Dried poo, but still. Waving and nodding at me are four other people. Okay, so three are waving and nodding and the fourth one has his head back and appears to be fast asleep with his mouth open. Either that or he's dead and no one has noticed the smell yet.

'Everyone, this is Tori. Tori, everyone.' Ted smiles at me and swings my case up onto the floor.

'Do you need a boost?' asks Ted.

'Oh, right . . . err . . . no thanks, I'm fine.' I can't find any convenient handholds, so I try not to pull a face as I rest them on top of the filthy floor and attempt to get a foot up. But the shoes aren't helping, slipping and sliding on the rusted metal, the heel threatening to snag at any moment. I'm really starting to struggle when a hand appears in front of me. Without looking up, I grasp it. Just as it gives me a tug, I feel Ted's palm plant firmly on my behind and he gives me a hefty shove upwards.

I practically fly into the back of the Land Rover and land straight on top of the owner of the helping hand.

There's a grunt from the warm tangle of clothes and skin from underneath me.

I scramble backwards hastily.

'Hey, watch it!' comes an angry growl from a skinny teenager I just managed to pin against the canvas side.

'I'm so sorry!' I mutter, trying to keep my head down and my sweaty, horrifed face to myself. *Shit, shit, shit.* Not the calm entrance I'd been hoping for.

'Hey. It's okay. Here, take a pew.' The pile of clothing I winded moments ago takes shape, shifts a beaten-up rucksack from the seat next to him and dumps it on the floor.

'Thanks,' I mutter. 'And sorry.'

'Don't worry.'

I'm relieved to hear a smile in his voice.

'I'm Bay.'

'Hi . . . I'm sorry about . . . your . . . uh . . . ' I tail off. I am sorry, but I'm not sure which part of his anatomy I should be sorry about.

'It's fine. Stop apologizing. Frankly, I blame your shoes.'

'So, what—?' I start, but I'm interrupted by the spluttering of the engine being forced into life. And then the rattling starts. Bone-splintering vibrations run through the decrepit metal skeleton and threaten to dislocate my coccyx.

'Brace yourself!' shouts Bay, and I wonder what he means.

'For what?'

I can barely hear him over the engine, but, glancing around at the others, I can see that they're all stiffening in their seats.

Catching on just a moment too late, I pitch sideways as Ted guns the vehicle into a dizzying reversed arc.

'Twice in one day?' Bay yells in my ear, an amused look on his face. I peel myself out of his lap and resolutely try to anchor myself to the hard metal bench.

'Sorry . . . again!' I yell. My face is so hot it feels like it's on fire.

Bay rolls his eyes at me and shrugs goodnaturedly. I look away, mortified.

In a desperate attempt to distract myself from the constant rattling playing tom-toms on my bladder, I look around at the other passengers.

The guy in the corner still has his head tilted back against the canvas, mouth wide open and fast asleep. The woman next to him looks to be somewhere in her late seventies. Her long silver hair is plaited and coiled all the way around her head. She is wearing an oversized, bright yellow jumper with a massive daisy on the front. Beneath this is a pair of faded, threadbare cord flares. Her hands are busy knitting something in a repulsive bright green, the yarn snaking from her needles and down to a huge ball that lies nestled in a wicker basket at her feet.

I look cautiously towards the girl I managed to trample and meet a pair of very stroppy brown eyes. I smile at her, but she simply blinks at me and continues to stare, her eyes wandering leisurely down over my fitted blazer and skinny black jeans. She lingers on the offending shoes that caused her the grievous bodily trampling just now.

Oh God, oh God, oh God! What have I let myself in for? I'm going to get Nat back for talking me into this, if it's the last thing I do.

⋆ ⋆ ⋆

Twenty minutes and six aborted attempts at conversation later, my knuckles have turned from white to blue in a bid to stay put in my pew-of-torture. My bum is completely numb, in beautiful contrast to the base of my spine, which is on fire from the continuous vibrations and multiple bashings, courtesy of every bump and stone on this godforsaken stretch of road. I'm considering screaming for mercy, or maybe even making a mad dash for the back door and hotfooting it back to Carmarthen in time to catch the next train back to London, when Bay leans in close.

'ALMOST HOME!' he yells in my ear. I nod and bite down firmly on my lip, letting out a tiny moan that instantly gets lost under the hammering of the engine.

Ted swings sharply to the right, hits the brakes and abruptly kills the engine. Two seconds later his face appears at the back of the cab.

'Okay, campers. I need two willing volunteers to walk the rest of the way. Frank can't take this amount of weight on his suspension going down the track.' He grins as if this is the best news he has given all day. Bay immediately jumps down.

'Of course, when I say volunteers, I mean you, Tori. It's all in the handbook.' He glances at my feet, looking a bit concerned.

'Come on,' Bay says, holding out his hand to me.

'Handbook? Wait! What?'

'New arrivals walk the driveway. It's important that they enter the aura of the place in peace, so that their spirit fully integrates with the new surroundings,' Ted recites by rote. At least he has the decency to look a little bit sheepish.

'But . . . ' I look down at the muddy puddles surrounding my perch. Two seconds ago I would have given anything to get out of the Land Rover. Now, I'm not so sure.

'Have you not read your handbook?' Bay asks me, a definite twinkle in his eye.

'Of course I have . . . most of it, anyway,' I say. Perhaps it would have been a good idea to spend less time arguing about clothes with Sue and more time reading all the material The Farm sent through to me after I spoke to them on Friday. I mean, I did scan through it on the way here, but I'm guessing I missed a few key points.

Ted's smile slips. 'Oh dear. Well, you have to walk on your first time. It's really important.'

'Come on,' Bay says impatiently.

I will be fine. My shoes, on the other hand, are about to die a horrible, muddy death and my Converse are buried right at the bottom of my bag.

'Here, borrow my boots.'

A pair of grim wellies land in my lap. Dead-guy is awake and in his socks. The boots reek and are covered in . . . crap. That's the only word for it.

'Um, thanks. I don't think these will fit you though,' I waggle one of my heels for him to see.

The guy peers curiously at me, obviously trying to figure out where I've come from and whether I'm sane. He seems to come to a conclusion fast enough as he starts to howl with laughter, his head thrown back.

An eerie sound echoes his howl from somewhere in the front of the Land Rover.

'Dennis!!!' bellow five people as one. The howling stops.

'Great. You have boots. Job done.' Ted beams and hurries back to the driver's seat. As he coaxes the engine back to life, my spine instantly sets up a protest. Slip-sliding to my feet, boots in one hand and handbag in the other, I shuffle across to the doorway, but before I can even begin to negotiate my way down, Bay reaches up and jumps me down like a five-year-old.

3

A is for Approachable

> 'One of the biggest challenges in escaping isolation is breaking free of habits. What started out as useful defence mechanisms are now patterns that play a large part in keeping the world out — and may be preventing you from forming new bonds and friendships.'
>
> ©TheBeginnersGuideToLoneliness.com

'Come on then, princess, let's be having you,' Bay grins as he sets me down. 'Do you need a hand?' He holds his arm out, ready to steady me so that I can slip the wellingtons on more easily.

'Thanks, princess, but I'll be fine on my own!' I snap. Why does my inner bitch always show up when I meet new people? I really wanted to start out on a better note. Too late now.

'Fine. Holler if you need me. I'll go on ahead.' Bay shoots me a tight smile that really doesn't reach his eyes. Oops. He turns his back and trudges off, following the trail of blue smoke from the Land Rover.

For a second, I just stand and stare at his departing back. Half of me wants to call after him, to apologize, to introduce myself properly and let him get to know the real me rather than this prissy little madam that seems to have body-snatched me. The other half of me, however, the one that is that prissy little madam, is still desperate to show him that she's fine without his stupid help. This part of me wins, like it always does when I'm feeling nervous and out of my depth. It's my version of body armour.

I dump the disgusting wellington boots down into the mud in front of me and wobble as I prise one of my hot, over-travelled feet out of a heel and plunge it into the loaned boot. I manage to gather a decent toe-scoop of mud while I'm at it. Great. Just bloody great. Go it alone and get covered in mud. Typical.

Thrusting on the other boot unceremoniously, I cuddle my heels to me and follow Bay. I really don't want to get lost on top of everything else. Slipping and sliding in the mud, I keep my eyes firmly on the ground to stop myself from going arse-over-tit. I'm so intent on what I'm doing that I suddenly slam with full force into something solid.

'Do I have 'hurt me' stamped on my forehead or something?' asks Bay as he catches hold of my arm, stopping me from face-planting as I lose my balance.

'Sorry! Sorry!' I wheeze, winded from the impact. I glare at him, unsure whether to let rip with anger or give in to giggles, as both seem to be bubbling. A pair of moss-green eyes are twinkling at me from under his mop of dark, wavy hair. I quickly decide anger is the safest route. 'I wasn't expecting there to be a human pillar in my path, doing absolutely nothing.'

'See, that's the problem with you city girls. Your eyes are always down, watching your feet or your phone.'

'What's that supposed to mean?' I snap. Like he knows anything about me. Git.

'It means that you run headlong into a lot of trouble without seeing it coming. And, worse than that, it means you miss the view.'

I scowl at him and then look around. The lane is

flanked on one side by a steep wall of slate and mud, with the occasional tree just about managing to cling to it. But Bay is looking in the opposite direction, to where the ground just seems to disappear. What looks like a cliff edge is actually the side of a steep valley. I find myself looking out over a rooftop of trees that must be growing on the lower edges of the slope. Piles of steely clouds march off into the distance, creating a blanket under which nestles a patchwork of fields. A narrow, leaden ribbon of river snakes its way across the valley floor. I shiver and rub my arms. As if in response, a ray of sunshine pierces the clouds just for a second, turning a bend in the river to silver and illuminating everything around it.

'You see, I wasn't 'doing nothing'. I was looking. It's a perfectly wonderful thing to be doing. Until you're walked into by an angry Londoner.'

I choose to ignore the dig. I can't believe I almost missed this.

'Thank you.' The words come out of my mouth, but, trust me, they are completely unintentional. I quickly make up for them: 'Do you mind if we get on with it though?' That's more like it.

Bay rolls his eyes at me. 'Sure. Come on. It's not far.' He continues his trudge and I slide along behind him, desperately trying to keep one eye on where I place my feet while I continue to sneak peeks at the view.

⋆ ⋆ ⋆

Pretty soon, the lane begins to descend steeply, carving its way through an avenue of giant trees. I catch up to Bay's side.

'So, is this your first time here too?' I ask, trying to start again.

He laughs. 'Nah, I've been coming here for years, at least once every six months. It's the perfect way to reset myself.'

'So you walked because . . . ?'

'Because I didn't want Frank to fall apart on the lane,' he smiles back at me.

'So the others have been before too?'

'Moth has — she was the one knitting. And Russ, the guy who lent you the boots, he's one of the instructors.'

I nod and swallow nervously. Surely I'm not going to be the only one new to this?

'So . . . ah . . . where are all the others?'

'Oh, they've been arriving since yesterday morning. I think they're only waiting for one more newbie now that you're here, and then everyone's present and correct.'

As we come to the edge of the woodland and reach the valley floor, we pass through a huge, five-barred gate.

'To keep the inmates in?' I ask with raised eyebrows.

Bay grins at me. 'To keep the world out, more like.' He swings the gate back into place and secures it with a loop of plaited, orange twine.

'So this is it? We're here?' There's a note of desperation in my voice. My bladder is now officially at breaking point. I need to empty it in the next two minutes to avoid sustaining a horrific injury.

'Almost. This path runs straight up to the main house. You carry on. I need to head off this way to sort a few things out,' he points to a field to our left.

'Oh. Okay. Thanks for your help.' *He's leaving me*

alone now? Seriously?

'Sure thing. See you later!' And with that, Bay strides off, following the line of the trees.

I watch him go and shift my weight from foot to foot. It would be great to take a look around while I've got a moment to myself (who knows whether I'm going to get any peace over the next three weeks?), but the call of my bladder has now gone from an annoying mutter to a constant scream. I let out a defeated sigh and head off up the pathway in search of the house.

It's not long before I spot it. It's absolutely massive and looks a bit like it's grown straight up out of the ground. Built from heavy grey stone, it's two storeys high with a navy front door that stands open underneath a slate-roofed porch. This is flanked by stone pillars, and at either side of the porch are large mullioned windows. The top floor boasts three more windows in a straight line. As deep as it is wide, this is a proper, old-fashioned farmhouse like something straight out of a kids' book, an impression that's only strengthened by the fact that the place is surrounded by brown and white chickens, all scratching around on the front lawn.

I wander up to the front door, side-stepping a couple of the braver birds who aren't about to get out of my way, and pause. What should I do? Knock? Go straight in? Call out? Deciding on two of the three, I hammer on the open door and shout.

'Hello? It's Tori!'

No one appears. Oh, for heaven's sake.

'Hello?!' I yell a bit louder. *I can't just walk in, can I?*

There's a creaking sound behind me followed by a crash that makes me jump in fright. I take a shaky step backwards to see what made the noise and notice that the window to my left has just been thrown open with so much force it bashed straight into the wall and is now swinging on its hinges. Ted's smiling face appears and regards me with some curiosity.

'Hello. Can I help?'

I laugh. 'Oh, thank God, it is the right place!'

Ted raises his eyebrows. 'Right place for what?'

'It's Tori?' I say slowly. 'You just picked me up from the bus stop?'

He stares at me blankly. *What, does he have amnesia or something?*

'Yes?' he sounds unconvinced.

'I'm here for the retreat?' I say.

'And what do you want to do that for?'

Good question, Ted. Right now, all I want is to be back in my flat where the world makes sense behind my computer screen. I chew my lip and consider my options for escape.

'Well?' Ted asks, watching me closely, as if I might trample his flower beds and steal a chicken or two while I'm at it.

'I want . . . I want . . .' Oh shit, what was that line I spotted in the handbook earlier? I wrack my brain. 'I want to . . . to find inner peace?' Nope, that wasn't it. 'I want to start moving mountains by picking up the small stones in my life.' Yes . . . that was it.

Ted is beaming at me. 'That is a good answer. I know because I wrote it . . . Well, actually, Confucius did first and I borrowed it . . . But what's *your* answer?'

Oh great. A comedian. I let out a long sigh as it dawns on me in a rush exactly what I've let myself in for. I'm actually going to have to share stuff with these people. Personal stuff. The stuff that hurts. Something deep inside me feels like it caves in.

'I would like to find out what you're all about here. And if I can learn even one tiny thing that makes my life better, I'll count it a worthwhile stay.'

'That is an honest and humble answer, Victoria. Welcome. Come on in.'

I bristle at the use of my full name, but as I go to correct him, I find that the window has closed and the smiling face has disappeared.

Not wanting to be the one to tread inches of crap into my host's house, I'm just slipping off my borrowed boots in the porch when a figure looms in front of me.

'I'm sorry about Ted,' says a soft voice. 'He can be a tad overly dramatic at times, but I guess that's why I love him! I'm Lizzie.'

I straighten up and come face to face with a breathtakingly beautiful woman. She has a mass of strawberry-blond hair that tumbles around her face and down her back. Here and there I can see combs in it that appear to be losing a desperate battle to keep the heavy strands in some kind of order. She has clear, blue eyes and is absolutely massive. At least eight months pregnant. So pregnant, in fact, that I find myself holding my breath just in case breathing might set her off.

'I'm Tori,' I smile at her. It's impossible not to, really. I hold out my hand, but Lizzie grabs it and pulls me in for a hug. Unused to random strangers demanding physical contact, I stiffen in the awkward embrace, desperate to avoid the unexploded time-bomb between us.

Lizzie laughs. 'Sorry, this is getting in the way more and more.' She pulls away and pats her bump affectionately. 'Do you have little ones?'

'*No. No. Not really.*' *Not really? What kind of answer is that? What, are there imaginary kids following me around?* 'I mean, no. I've not met the right man and I'm just not ready and . . . ' This is getting worse. *Stop. Talking.* 'Erm, how long . . . ?' I stare worriedly at the bump.

'Due any time after the end of next week. Hey, you might be here! That's so exciting!'

My smile freezes on my face. *What? I'm going to be here?* Okay . . . I'll be here. That's got to be at least thirty miles away from the nearest hospital. That's a decent distance from all the pain and screaming. Thirty miles should just about muffle the noise.

As if it's responding with advanced sympathy pains, my bladder gives an agonizing twitch.

'Sorry . . . do you mind if I use your bathroom? I've been on that coach for what feels like an eternity . . . '

'Gosh, you poor thing. And then Ted's driving! I'd have peed myself. I'm in there every five minutes at the moment. When I was pregnant with my first . . . '

Argh, I'm going to have to gag the woman before I find the bloody toilet. 'I'm kind of desperate,' I interrupt, mortified, but I guess a puddle would be a lot worse.

'Sorry! Just at the end of the hall there. Read the instructions!'

I shoot off as fast as my desperate waddle will allow.

'Come and join us in the kitchen and meet the other guys as soon as you're done,' I hear her call after me.

Desperately hoping my bladder hasn't ruptured, I push my way through the doorway and plonk myself onto the loo with a sigh of relief.

The relief is short-lived, though. I do up my jeans and turn to reach for the flush . . . which isn't there. What on earth? Lizzie's words come back to me.

'*Read the instructions.*' Peering around, I spot a hand-painted wooden sign hanging from a nail in the wall. It reads: 'Lovely visitor, you are relieved. Press the orange button for pee, the red for poo. This system uses rainwater harvested from our roof.' *Orange button . . . orange button* . . . Ah, there it is. I press it and an almighty racket of groaning pipes forces me to cover my ears and back away as a torrent of slightly discoloured water pours into the bowl.

I catch sight of myself in the mirror as I carefully wash my hands and sigh at the bedraggled reflection that stares back at me. I hastily pull my hair back into a spare elastic from my pocket.

While I'm here, I may as well let the guys know I've arrived safely.

WriterTori: Here safe. What a palaver!
Nathalie33: What's everyone like?
WriterTori: Don't know. Haven't met them yet. Currently hiding in the loo. Flushes with rainwater!! ;)
SueSue52: Too cool! Go on then, Tori, get out there and meet all the other weirdos.
WriterTori: Calling me a weirdo?
Nathalie33: Well, if the shoe fits . . .
WriterTori: Don't talk to me about shoes, I had to borrow a pair of wellies.
SueSue52: I told you to pack some!
WriterTori: You also told me to wear heels to make a good impression, so you don't get to comment! Wish you guys were here.
SueSue52: We'll be with you every step of the way.
Nathalie33: Heads up, busy few weeks ahead of me, will be a bit quieter on here than normal.
WriterTori: You're going to abandon me in my hour

of need?!

Nathalie33: Of course not, I'll be right by your side. Just didn't want you to worry about me if you notice I'm not online as much :)

WriterTori: Thanks, Nat!

SueSue52: Have fun!

Nathalie33: Good luck, keep us posted!

WriterTori: Catch you later.

I slip my phone back in my pocket and unlock the door. Here goes nothing . . .

4

Be the Change

> 'To make a change, you have to be the change. Do something differently. Take a different route, visit a new coffee shop, speak to someone new. Every little change you make is an opportunity to set your day on a different path.'
>
> ©TheBeginnersGuideToLoneliness.com

I head back out into the hallway and follow the muffled hum of conversation to what I assume must be the kitchen. Taking a deep breath, an all-too familiar sensation washes over me and settles in my chest: nerves. Horrible, crippling nerves. I swallow down the urge to run and, pushing open the door, step into a large kitchen.

It's like something straight out of a magazine's design pages . . . or it would be if it were tarted up a bit. As it stands, its beautiful slate floor is almost entirely covered with old rag-rugs, thrown down higgledy-piggledy between the mismatched furniture. There's an ancient Aga sandwiched between cupboards topped with different work surfaces, one side marble, the other an offcut of melamine. The cupboard doors have a random assortment of handles, from intricate wrought-iron affairs to small lengths of rope. Here and there, just a bare, rusty screw sticks out.

Over in the corner is a hulking, dark wooden

dresser, groaning under the weight of family photographs, thank-you cards and assorted odds and ends.

My heart flutters uncomfortably as I turn to meet the dozen or so pairs of eyes trained on me from around the long, scrubbed pine table that dominates the centre of the room. This is it then.

I'm not really sure where to look, but I force a smile, painfully aware that it probably looks like I've got a bad case of wind.

'Everyone, this is Victoria,' says Ted from his perch at the table. 'Budge up and make room for her so we can get started.'

I flinch. Mum was the only one who ever used my full name, and it still makes my skin prickle. Now's not the time to start thinking about Mum. I've already got enough to deal with. I wipe my sweaty palms on my jeans.

'Hi,' I squeak, and slip into a chair that has been pulled up to a tiny gap at the table. 'It's Tori . . . at least to friends,' I say. God, I sound like such a knob.

'Tori it is then,' says Lizzie, coming up behind me and passing a mug of some kind of strong-smelling herbal tea over my shoulder. 'We're all friends here from day one.'

'Okay, guys,' Ted says, drawing himself up, his hand-knitted, bobbly brown jumper pulling tight across his rounded stomach. 'I'm not going to go around and introduce everyone now; we can save that for our welcoming circle this evening. But just so that you're all aware, we're still missing one person from our group, but he'll be here in time for this evening's session. Oh, and Bay is off sorting out a couple of last-minute errands — but you've met him already. He's done this course so many times that he could recite this little meet-up by heart!

'Now, I just want to go over a few practicalities about your stay with us. There shouldn't be too many surprises as it's all in your handbooks, but there are a couple of things I'd like to clarify.'

I clasp my hands tightly around my mug of tea. Truth time. I wonder how many more little gems I managed to miss during my skim-read earlier.

'Lizzie,' continues Ted, 'why don't you start, my love, and we'll take it in turns?' Ted smiles at his wife and I can see that he's glad to be at the start of a well-rehearsed routine.

'Okay then,' says Lizzie, easing herself down into a chair. 'Number one. As you know, you won't be staying in the house with us. This retreat is all about self-discovery and self-acceptance — re-connecting with yourself so that you can move forward in your relationships and forge new, authentic connections. To start to do this, you need to live in the wild with your own thoughts. I know some of you have opted for the camping option, which is lovely. We've gone through your course questionnaires and have allocated sites for you. We've done our best to match up your location with your personal and emotional needs.'

A buzz of excitement runs around the table. Moth, the long-haired knitter, nudges my elbow and grins at me. I smile back.

I wonder if she can see the pure terror on my face.

'Sam and Emma,' Ted smiles at an extremely young couple that exude the kind of shiny, happy beauty that only comes from being in your late teens, 'as you guys are here on honeymoon, you've been given the eco-build. We hope that this special space will help you connect for a long and happy future.'

Emma throws her arm around Sam's shoulders and snuggles her face into his neck. Sam flushes bright red, looking decidedly uncomfortable at the public display of affection.

'You three will be in South Wood,' continues Ted, gesturing to the three guys directly opposite me. All of them have impressive beards, two have dreadlocks, and there's an awful lot of hemp and leather on display. 'The materials you need to create your own shelters are there, as requested.' A cloud of patchouli wafts across the table as all three of them quiver with excitement.

Heart. Now. Hammering. *Build* our own shelters? Holy crap . . . there's no way I'm up for that. It's probably going to be even worse for me, I was so late getting back to them. Ted did mention on the phone that they might need to make some special arrangements. *Oh no, it's going to be sharing a sleeping bag with the chickens, isn't it?!*

'Tori, I know you don't have the energy for camping . . .'

They got that from my questionnaire? I bristle a bit as my natural competitive streak starts to kick in, but then I give a little mental shrug. Does it really matter as long as it means I don't have to build my own earth hut or sleep in a leaky tent?

'We've decided that the best thing for you is to take the yurt in Seven Acre field. You won't be on your own, though, as we'd already offered the space to one of our regulars, so you'll be sharing.'

'Sharing? Oh, okay . . . um . . . okay . . .' Shit, I wasn't expecting that. Then again, maybe a bit of company isn't the worst thing in the world, considering I'm going to be stuck in the middle of nowhere for three weeks.

As Lizzie and Ted continue to dole out the camp sites, I brood on how I'm going to cope with the whole sharing thing. I haven't lived with anyone since I left home, and I did that as promptly as I possibly could, so you could say that it's been quite a while since I've had to deal with anyone in my space. Markus and I never quite got around to actually living together before everything went tits up.

'Okay, so that's everyone!' Ted smiles. 'When we're done here we'll go for a walk and drop you off at your sites. Then you can make yourselves at home, or, in some cases, *make* your homes, before we all meet up again this evening.' I roll my eyes as he beams at his own joke. 'All food is supplied, and you will be expected to cook together at the outdoor station most evenings. You will not be permitted entry into the house again during your stay, except for in an emergency. There are basic facilities located close to all of your sites, except for those of you in the woods — you will make your own.' The trio opposite me, whom I promptly dub the Beardy Weirdies, all nod eagerly, clearly excited at the thought of crapping in a hole.

'We would like to request that you refrain from using any scented deodorant, antiperspirant, perfumes or chemical-based lotions while you're here. No cosmetics please. These will impede your progress and are disrespectful to the land and to each other.'

No. Nonononononono. Just as I think they can't get any worse, I feel my nerves ramp up another notch. I guess I could deal with the lack of make-up — after all, it's not like there's anyone here who's going to care what I look like, but moisturizer and deodorant? Surely they are basic human rights?

'Finally, I need you all to turn in your phones, blackcurrants, laptops . . .'

'Ted, love, I think you mean BlackBerries,' Lizzie interrupts, rolling her eyes.

'Right, right. Well, turn in all electrical gadgets, whether named after fruit or not.'

My eyes widen in shock. *What? WHAT?*

'*What?*' Damn, one of them has escaped.

Everyone's eyes swivel in my direction, and I'm pretty sure I spot a few raised eyebrows. I definitely spot a look exchanged between Ted and Lizzie.

'Sorry, I . . . erm . . . I meant to say, could you tell us a bit more about what made you decide to bring in this rule?' There. I think I've just about managed to cover my behind . . . maybe.

'First of all, we don't really do rules. Think of them more as suggestions that we hope you'll take on board while accepting our hospitality,' Lizzie says, sounding a lot less earth mother and a lot more like a slightly pissed off librarian. 'But yes, I can certainly explain the idea,' she continues, her voice settling back into its honeyed tones. 'Each of you is here for some form of healing. You all have blocks that are preventing you from connecting fully and authentically to your lives. These might be emotional, creative,' she looks around the table, 'or mental,' she adds, turning back to me.

Way to out us all in one breath! I peep around at the others, and pretty much everyone is fixated on the table in front of them.

'You have decided to take this retreat from your lives in order to concentrate on your healing. It is our responsibility to remove the uncentring influences of the outside world. We do not want your progress impaired by the constant flow of bile that runs through communications devices. Whether you're watching the news, talking to work colleagues or being harassed by family members, your thought processes are changed by each interaction. And so we remove this interruption to your healing.'

'What if we need to check on someone . . . family . . . ?' asks a woman from across the table. She looks decidedly out of place with her tight perm and fuchsia lipstick, sandwiched in between one of the Beardy Weirdies and Ted. A few of the others shift uncomfortably. Seems I'm not the only one who's not completely thrilled with the idea of being cut off from civilization.

'The handbook says to leave the main house number here as your emergency contact,' says Lizzie smoothly.

'I did. But my mother's in a home. She often gets confused. They might need to call us,' says the woman tremulously.

'If they do call, we are here to help,' smiles Lizzie. 'If someone calls for any of you, we will decide if it's a matter of importance strong enough to interrupt your healing process.'

The woman smiles and nods at Lizzie, visibly relaxing in the knowledge that someone else is taking the responsibility out of her hands. I'm not so sure I'd be so chilled about it if it were me, but then I haven't got a single soul who'll worry about me while I'm away other than the Warriors. Crap. I hadn't thought of that. How am I going to keep them updated without an internet connection?

Ted stands and makes his way around the table, handing everyone a cotton bag and a paper luggage label. 'Okay, before you all head back outside, please make sure that all of your gadgets go in here. We advise you to leave all of your valuables in these bags too. We can all trust each other here, but we can't guarantee the safety of any belongings apart from those stored in these bags, which will be placed in our safe this afternoon and returned to you when you leave.'

Everyone starts to rummage in pockets and bags, placing items in the little cloth sacks before handing them over and heading back outside. I heave a huge sigh and place my wallet, mobile and iPad into the sack. I'm not wearing any jewellery, but I reach down, pick up my shoes and place them gently on top of the gadgets. Then a flash of inspiration hits. Glancing around me to double-check I'm not going to be overheard, I edge my way over to Lizzie.

'Erm, I know you said you'd supply stock photos to protect everyone's privacy, but as a reviewer, will I be able to keep hold of my iPad to take notes?' I ask hopefully.

'We've thought about that,' she says with a smile and passes me a bag. I take a quick peep. *Seriously?* I've just been handed a notebook and pen.

'There you go!' she smiles at me triumphantly.

Damn. Well, I'll just have to figure it out later. There's bound to be a computer somewhere around here that I can sneak onto to send a quick message when no one's looking.

5

Go with the Flow

> 'Isolation can cause you to overthink. Every single step of the day is inspected for anything that might go wrong. Ultimately, this can mean that you don't take many steps at all. Learn to go with the flow, take one step at a time and set yourself free.'
>
> ©TheBeginnersGuideToLoneliness.com

The group ahead of me comes to a halt. We've reached a wooden cabin which sits in a small clearing at the edge of the apple orchard. The sight and the scent of the apple blossom is quite something, and we've all been wandering along, looking upwards with smiles on our faces. Smiling's not something I was expecting to be doing quite so soon after being forcibly parted from my phone. But this really is beautiful.

The hut looks a little bit like a rustic woodshed, but, in comparison to a leaky tent, it's practically a palace. In front of us are the remains of a little outdoor fire within a ring of stones, over which hangs a blackened kettle from a metal frame. Perfect, as long as you're not after a quick cuppa . . .

'Geoff and Doreen, welcome to your new home. I hope you'll find everything you need for a very comfortable stay with us. There's running water just around the side of the cabin.'

The woman with the perm and the fuchsia lipstick

hurries forward to take a look around, her husband following at a more leisurely pace. Around me, there's a lot of excited muttering and nodding. It's clear that everyone's looking forward to seeing their own quarters if they're all going to be as nice as this.

'Ted, it's lovely,' Doreen grins, coming to stand at the doorway after a quick scout around her new home. 'One thing. Where's the loo?'

'Very good question. I always forget that part. See over there?' he points off into the trees a little way. 'There's a little hut? That's your toilet. It's a composting loo. Just dump a handful of wood shavings in after . . . well . . . '

'Dumping?' provides Doreen, her perm quivering.

'Precisely,' Ted beams at her. A little titter runs around the group. I don't see it as a laughing matter, frankly. What did I say about al fresco pooing?

'Right, we'd better get going. Everyone needs to be settled in with enough time to spare before this evening's session. You two get comfy. See you later.'

As we leave Doreen and Geoff behind, I somehow feel like I've lost my last link to the real world. Rather than gossiping with the others, I walk quietly, trying to keep my bearings while tuning in and out of everyone else's conversations.

We soon head uphill and make our way through a patch of woodland. It's a little bit like the newly planted woods we walked through earlier, but fast-forwarded by twenty years. The grass between the trees is gone and the ground is covered by a soft, leafy litter, dotted here and there with clusters of tiny flowers.

Soon we're in a circular clearing with a fire pit at its centre, but there's no hut to be seen.

'Right, the three of you who've opted for the

self-build option, this is where we leave you,' Ted says. He looks over at the Beardy Weirdies.

'There are only two rules. Set up more than fifteen paces away from the fire, and absolutely no felling of any live wood. I planted this woodland by hand over twenty years ago when we first came here. It's my first love and anyone who damages it will feel my wrath.'

I force down a giggle at the thought of the smiley, slightly distracted Ted smiting anyone down with his wrath. It's not an image that comes to mind readily.

Ted's still glaring around, and he does briefly seem to lose his fuzzy, hand-knitted edges, but still, hardly the thing of nightmares.

'There are plenty of stacks of seasoned firewood and brash piles for you to make your homes out of. Next to the fire pit, there's a limited supply of rope and a few tools to get you started. I've marked the site for your bog over there. I didn't want you to accidentally come across the one from the last group! Have fun, guys. See you later.'

Next we drop Moth off at a campsite, where there are already a couple of tents pitched, followed by Emma and Sam at their eco-build cabin. Finally, I'm left on my own with Ted.

'What if the weather changes?' I ask. It's something I've been wondering about as we've been walking. 'What will those guys in the wood do if it gets bad?'

'The closeness to the elements adds a deeper note of connection to the soul for those who choose to look for it.' He clears his throat and I see him glance sideways at me. 'We've found that if the weather gets really bad, everyone makes very good friends very quickly, as the loan of a cabin floor becomes rather sought after.' He grins at me, eyes twinkling, evidently aware of the mischief that these sleeping arrangements can lead to.

'Now then, let's get you to your abode.'

'Great,' I reply lamely. I've still got to meet my roommate, and I've got a knot of anxiety building in my stomach.

'It's a big space, and can easily be divided up by hanging some sheets if you need to.'

'Great, that's great.' I seem to have got stuck on a loop.

We come to the top of a little rise and I spot it: my home for the next three weeks. I let out a breath. I can handle this. It's a large round tent with a domed roof covered in canvas. In front of it, a collection of handmade, wooden furniture sits around the obligatory fire pit.

As we approach, I spot another little hut some distance away. That must be the toilet.

'You should find the yurt very comfortable. There are a couple of rules that come with living here, but I've got quite a bit to do before this evening — Lizzie can barely waddle at the moment! — so I'm going to leave you in Bay's very capable hands.'

WHAT?

Ted turns and begins to head back in what I assume is the direction of the main house. I'm too shocked to say anything and so I just stare, open-mouthed at his retreating back, digesting this new piece of information. *Bay?* As in, the guy I've already managed to injure *three times*?

'Ted,' I call, 'did you say Bay?'

Ted swings around, looking anxious. 'Yup. He said that he wouldn't mind sharing, and as we had no more cabins left, it was either this or make you camp.

We thought you'd be happier staying here.'

'Is there no way I can stay in the house with you guys?' I'm aware I sound a bit pathetic, but there's no way I want to share with Bay.

'Nope. Sorry. That would completely undermine the whole purpose of this exercise. This is perfect for you. Unless you really do want to camp? We have spare roll-mats, tents and sleeping bags . . . '

I can see his eyes twinkling, and for a second I'm tempted to accept, just to wipe the smile off of his face. But I can't. Composting toilets *and* a tent? Not happening.

'No, this is fine,' I concede gracelessly.

'Great.' Ted twinkles at me, turns and continues on his way.

'I promise I won't bite.'

The new voice makes me jump. I swing around and see Bay's head sticking out of the little front door flap of the yurt.

'You'd better not, or I'll sue!' I shoot back. It's meant to be a joke, but comes out of my mouth more like a spear. Bay doesn't seem to care, though. He shrugs and gives me an easy grin.

'Come on in and make yourself comfortable.' His head disappears back inside, leaving me with no other option but to follow him.

* * *

Great. This is just *great*. No sooner have I got my poor little brain around the fact that I'm going to be sharing my living space with another human being, I find out I've got to share with a man. Okay, I'm an adult, I can get over that fact. But why does it have to be *this* man, who's already made it clear that he finds me incredibly annoying, and . . .

Oh wow.

As I stick my head through the flap, my jaw drops, cartoon style. It is absolutely beautiful in here. The curved sides are made from a concertina of honey-coloured wood and the roof is held up with a hooped structure of the same stuff. The floor is covered by about fifty brightly patterned rugs. There are sleeping areas at either side of the space complete with two futon-style beds. In the middle of the yurt, there's a squashy old settee with a low table in front of it.

'Welcome to my humble abode!' smiles Bay, noticing that I've let my guard down. 'Your humble abode too for the next few weeks.'

I smile at him weakly, not really knowing what to say or do next. 'Uh, thanks . . . ' I start, rather lamely. 'Sorry, I didn't realize I'd be staying with you . . . I mean . . . I . . . '

'It's fine, don't worry,' he cuts me off. 'It was all a little bit last minute and this was the best solution.' He smiles at me warmly and I just nod.

'Ted said there are some rules?'

'Sure. It's simple really. Don't wear outdoor shoes in here because of all of the rugs. A bit of chicken shit takes forever to locate. Don't smoke inside. Don't go to the loo inside. That's about it. Oh, and preferably don't wake the dog. He hates being disturbed.'

'Dog?' I squeak.

'Ah. Didn't they check that with you?'

'Um, no.'

It's not that I'm scared of dogs, I just have a healthy respect for them. I respect the fact that they'll bite me if I go anywhere near them. When I was little, I begged Mum over and over again for a dog. I had no brothers or sisters, and it was just me and Mum in the house. I was desperate for someone to play with, and the idea of a furry friend took root in my imagination. That lasted until it got on my mum's nerves and she decided to tell me all about the horrors of rabies, scaring me senseless with tales of infected dog bites and horrific injuries that needed stitches. All of her stories ended up with the dog being shot. I went off the idea pretty quickly after that.

'You're not just sharing with me, I'm afraid. You're sharing with Dennis too,' says Bay. 'He's usually a big softy, but I think he's going to be a bit put out. See, your bed is usually *his* bed. I keep trying to get him off of it, but he's stubborn like that.'

'Oh great. So which one's supposed to be my bed?'

'The one with the great big dog on it?' he smiles at me apologetically and nods to the far side of the yurt.

I hadn't spotted him before because he is stretched out on a brown blanket and is so relaxed that he has moulded into the bed and has become a part of the furniture.

'Dennis! Here!' Bay pats his leg, but the dog doesn't budge. 'Dennis, don't make me come over there!' Bay lets out a sharp whistle, making me jump. Dennis deigns to lift his head. His piggy little eyes glance in our direction, his tail thumps on the blanket once and then he flops back down and appears to be asleep again almost instantly.

'Ah, what can you do? He knows who's boss here, and it sure as hell isn't me,' Bay smiles indulgently and shrugs.

Great. I'm going to have to do battle with a canine roadblock. This is hardly going to be 'restful on the spirit'.

'What kind of dog is he?' I ask, not because I'm that interested, but because it seems like the polite thing to say.

'English bull terrier. Beautiful, isn't he? I couldn't resist that much attitude piled into one dog. Anyway, make yourself at home.'

I smile tightly at him, cross over to the bed and stare down at the unwelcome guest.

Correction: *I'm* the unwelcome guest.

He's a chunky mish-mash of brown and white splotches, with a bent snout and funny little eyes.

'Bay, why don't we just swap beds? At least then you'll be sharing with someone you know,' I say hopefully.

'I can't sleep on the west side. Sorry.'

'Oh. Um. Okay.'

'It's fine, don't worry. I'll make sure he gets down when you want to go to bed. He's house-trained, you don't need to worry about that. And he's been in the river today, so he's fairly clean.'

* * *

I dither around, wondering what exactly I'm supposed to do until the mythical welcoming ceremony in a couple of hours. After the initial, obligatory small talk with Bay, we've both fallen silent. I don't want to bug him. After all, I'm in his space and he's probably far from happy about it, even though he has been pretty gracious so far.

Eventually, Bay makes his excuses, saying that he'd better go and help Ted get everything ready. Before he leaves, he checks that I'm going to be able to find my way back to the little courtyard behind the house in time for six o'clock.

After he's gone, it's a couple of seconds before I realize that, as well as telling a complete lie about knowing my way back to the house, my only method of telling the time was my phone. I hotfoot it back outside and shout after him.

Bay looks back at me, amusement dancing in his eyes.

'Don't tell me you've already forgotten how to get back down there?'

'Of course not.' I'm not going to give him any such pleasure. 'You don't have a clock in any of your stuff, do you? My phone's in the safe . . . '

'You don't have a watch?'

'Uh . . . nope . . . '

'And I'm taking it that you can't tell the time by the position of the sun?' he continues, the corner of his lips twitching up into a half smile.

'See previous answer,' I huff.

Bay raises his arm and begins to fumble with the battered strap of an old-fashioned man's watch. 'Here, wear this. Look after it, though. It used to be my father's.'

Before I have the time to register my surprise, he's reaching for my hand and proceeds to gently fasten the worn leather around my wrist.

'How will you know when it's time?' I ask, my voice all husky. I cringe. Oh, for heaven's sakes. A little bit of physical contact and I'm all wibbly? *Really?*

'See previous question,' he shoots back cheekily, and sets off again.

'Thank you!' I call after him, but rather quieter than is necessary to actually reach his ears.

As I turn back to the yurt, my mind is racing. I'm not used to random acts of kindness, especially not from a complete stranger whose home I've invaded. I gaze around, still trying to fathom how on earth I'm going to manage to share the space with Bay for a whole three weeks. We've got nothing in common and nothing to talk about. The last few hours of almost complete silence have proved that.

Maybe I should ask him if we can divide the space like Ted suggested earlier. It was an absolute nightmare trying to change just now without giving him an eyeful.

And then, of course, there's the dog.

Shit! The dog! Dennis is still asleep on my bed, completely oblivious to the fact that his master has gone off without him. How could Bay forget him?

I dash back out of the tent to call Bay back again, but he's long gone and nowhere to be seen.

'Damn!' I turn and stomp back into the yurt to face my newly inherited, rather hairy problem . . . who is now wide awake.

Okay, this is going from bad to worse. Or maybe not. At least now I don't have to decide whether to wake him up or not.

'Hello. Hi, boy,' I croon, my voice wavering. I try to stay as still as possible, but he's now regarding me with grudging interest through those piggy little eyes. 'Hi, boy . . .' I say again, edging one step in his direction.

The dog thumps his tail twice on the bedspread and, yawning widely, begins to pant, his tongue leisurely flopping out of the side of his mouth. He looks exactly like he's grinning at me, and I can't help but smile back. Maybe he's not going to be so bad to have around after all.

6

Finding Friends in Unlikely Places

> 'Often we are guilty of having an infexible image of what new relationships might look like, usually as a result of unconscious expectations that lurk in the mind, narrowing our chances of new and exciting connections before they've even started.'
> ©TheBeginnersGuideToLoneliness.com

'Get off you idiot, get off!' I yell, not sure if I want to laugh or cry. I quickly realize that I don't have the energy or breath left in my body to do either. 'Dennis, bloody well get off!' I wheeze, pushing at him and trying to lever myself up off the multicoloured rug at the same time. He bounces straight back on top of me.

'Help! Help!' I shout. I start to giggle, but it quickly becomes hysterical as I struggle to get the mutt off me.

'Dennis, HEEL!'

The shout from the doorway makes us both jump. The reaction from the dog is amazing. He immediately slinks away from me, giving me these little backwards glances as if I'd started the game just to get him into trouble.

'Don't give her that look, you naughty hound. I'll tell Bay and then you'll be in trouble. Are you okay?'

I scramble to my feet, wondering who this angel of mercy is. Whoever she is, she's only about thirteen years old. Thirteen and extremely sure of herself.

Standing in the doorway of the yurt, petting the ears of a now cowering Dennis, is the teenager I nearly sat on in the back of the Land Rover earlier. With her long, shiny black hair drawn over one shoulder, her large, melting brown eyes stare back at me as I struggle to my feet and attempt to dust myself off. She may be dressed like the bad fairy out of a pantomime, but there's something in the girl's look that makes me feel incredibly inadequate.

'Erm. Hi there. Thanks for that!'

'S'okay.' She leans against the wooden prop, jutting out a bony hip. 'You okay? Not hurt?' She doesn't look particularly worried, more like she feels like she has to ask.

'I'm fine, a little bit damp around the edges. I'm Tori by the way.' I hold out my hand. The girl simply stares at it until I start to feel mildly stupid, and let it drop to my side. Please can I go back to being mauled by the dog now? That was way more comfortable.

'I'm Rowan. I thought I'd come and say hi and just let you know that if you need anything, I'm your man.' She gives a tiny, casually indifferent shrug of the shoulders.

'Rowan? You're Ted and Lizzie's daughter?'

'Yep.'

'Oh, well that's really kind, thanks. Your parents have been great so far.' I feel wrong-footed.

'No, I don't think you get it. If you *need* anything . . .'

Is this kid trying to sell me drugs? I stare at Rowan, mouth open slightly, wondering what to say next. Rowan rolls her eyes at me.

'I mean, if you want to send an email, want some decent shampoo, a bit of non-perfumed deodorant. Basically, anything on the banned list.' She smiles, obviously proud of herself. 'Course, I don't offer my services to everyone, only a chosen few, but when I saw your shoes I knew you'd be interested. Just don't tell anyone else unless you clear it with me first.'

I smile. I can't help it. Rowan is going to make an excellent businesswoman. Identify a niche, find your captive audience, make your products available.

'Here's my price list. I can get you practically anything that's not on the list too, provided that it's legal, but there'll be an extra charge.'

I take the handwritten photocopy, plainly done in a stolen moment at school, and glance down the list. Coffee, deodorant, mobile phone use billed by the (extortionate) minute, email checking and printing service, mobile internet access. There's no end to the everyday needs of the average product-deprived, technology-starved guest that Rowan isn't catering to.

'Tell my parents, I'll deny everything and you'll likely be lynched by my other customers.' She treats me to a brief moment of the pure evils before giving me a quick smile. 'Anyway, if you need me, let me know.'

'Uh, right. Great. Thanks . . . ' I'm so taken aback by this old, cynical head on such young shoulders, I find myself at a loss for words for a couple of seconds.

'And if I do need you?' I finally ask.

'Leave me a note in the crack of the gatepost at the bottom of the field. Oh, and don't let Dennis give you any shit. Bay makes out like he's such a big, scary dog, but he's a complete softy . . . like any man if you know how to handle him. See ya!'

With her piece said, Rowan turns on her heel and heads out again, no doubt to continue making the rounds of all the most likely candidates to take her up on her offer. I'm guessing that she's well-versed enough to avoid the open-air sleepers like the plague. They seem so diehard about the whole experience that they'd probably drop her in it straight away and try to forcibly cleanse her aura while they were at it. As for me, I've got a feeling that Rowan's services might come in handy at some point in the very near future.

I glance over to where Dennis is still sitting, gazing out of the yurt entrance, tail slowly wagging from side to side.

'So, you're a softy after all. Who'd have thought?' I murmur. I wander over to him and place a tentative hand on top of his head.

* * *

I spend the next couple of hours curled up on my bed and, with Dennis snoring away on one of the many coloured rugs, I finally read the course handbook properly, from cover to cover. By the time I've finished, the knot of fear that has been lurking in my chest ever since I arrived seems to be trying to throttle me. I thought knowing exactly what I was in for over the next three weeks might calm me down. I thought wrong.

I mean, I knew when I accepted the offer to come here and take the course that parts of it would be challenging, but what these guys do is serious. Basically, it's a chance to reprogramme any behaviour that's holding you back. I somehow thought I might be able to get away with watching it all unfold for everyone else without really having to deep-dive into my own issues too far. But, from what I've just read, and with such a small group of us, there seems to be fat chance of that!

The retreat is divided up into three themes, one per week. Week one is spent getting to know and trust each other; week two is all about discovering where we're stuck and breaking down barriers; and week three looks at how we can use what we've learned in our day-to-day lives. I mean . . . gulp.

Of course, I also came across all of the bits I'd missed before about handing over phones and iPads, and the fact that you have to walk down the lane the first time you come here. The other major discovery is that every day there's a session called 'Bodywork'. Yes, it's exactly like it sounds. These guys are fans of exercise — especially first thing in the morning. *Gah!* I take a deep breath and try to stem the wave of panic. I just need to take all of this one step at a time.

I check Bay's watch and realize that I'd better start trying to find my way back towards the house and, as Bay hasn't reappeared, I guess I'd better take Dennis with me. It's not like I can just abandon him here.

I look everywhere for a lead to attach to his collar. Either Bay doesn't own one, he's got it with him or he doesn't believe in them and will give me grief about imprisoning his dog. I quickly give up the search, mainly because Dennis is shadowing my every move, wagging his tail madly and pushing his nose into everything I touch. I pull a long, silk scarf out of my case and wind it around his collar a couple of times to use instead.

To my huge surprise, Dennis instantly becomes a model citizen. He doesn't pull, sits at my feet waiting patiently until I give him the nod that we're leaving and then trots daintily to heel. He looks so incredibly snooty on the end of his scarf that I can't help but laugh. Maybe I could learn to love dogs after all.

⋆ ⋆ ⋆

I'm finding it surprisingly difficult to navigate my way to the farmhouse. Just as I consider retracing my steps and starting again — or calling out until help finds me — Dennis begins to pull very decidedly to our right. I've got nothing to lose at this point, so let him take the lead and follow his nose. I'm guessing there's a good chance that he's heading in the direction of food, which makes it likely that he'll find the farmhouse a lot faster than I will.

Pretty soon, instead of ending up where we need to be, we're crossing yet another muddy field, completely lost.

'You idiot, Dennis!'

The dog carries on pulling ahead and, to my relief, I spot a tall figure climbing the gate at the opposite side of the field. I might be lost, but the dog certainly isn't.

'Dennis, what on earth are you wearing?' laughs Bay as he strides over towards us. 'Tori, I see you two've made friends? I'm glad. If Dennis likes someone enough to let them put him on a lead, it usually means I'll get on okay with them too.'

'I think we've called a truce, but only after he pinned me and practically drowned me in slobber!'

'I'm sorry, he does get a bit overexcited sometimes. How did you get out of that? It's his favourite game . . . usually goes on for hours.'

'Rowan saved me.'

'Ah. Well no doubt she'll bill you for it later,' Bay

laughs. 'Poor old Dennis is terrified of her. So am I a little bit!'

'I don't blame you!' I laugh.

'So what services did she offer you then?' he asks, giving me a sly look.

'How do you know about that?'

'Oh, come on, I've been doing this for years,' Bay grins.

I just shrug at him.

'Anyway,' he says, 'why on earth are you all the way out here? Surely it must be about time for the meeting? If not, I'm completely out of whack and need my head seeing to.' He reaches out and takes my hand, raising the watch up to take a look. 'Yup, just as I thought, time to be heading homeward. And don't let Dennis lead you astray, he'll take you off on a jaunt any time of the day or night, depending on what he fancies!'

'You are a bad, bad dog,' I smile, bending down to ruffle his ears. Dennis raises his chin for a tickle and thumps his tail on the ground.

'I still can't believe you managed to get him on a lead. All joking aside, he usually goes ballistic and then refuses to budge an inch.'

⋆ ⋆ ⋆

I've been so focused on finding my way back to the farmhouse, and then actually enjoying the quiet stroll with Bay, Dennis trotting along between us, that I'd briefly forgotten where we're going and the fact that I'm completely dreading this evening. After reading the handbook, I know that the welcoming ceremony is an important part of the process. But right now, I'd much rather be back in the yurt than headed towards an evening with a group of people I don't know.

'You're really quiet. Everything okay?' Bay asks, dragging me out of my rapidly spiralling panic. I realize that I've been walking along, chewing my lip in silence for a good ten minutes.

'Just a bit nervous about this evening.'

Bay nods. 'Fair enough.'

Silence lands heavily between us again, and I feel like it's my turn to try to make some kind of small talk.

'I thought we weren't allowed back into the main house?' I ask as we reach the field gate and head into the yard.

'The meeting's not in the house. It usually starts in the old hayloft and goes on from there,' he says, leading the way around behind the house and into a cobbled courtyard. Directly opposite us, a wide flight of stone steps runs up the side of one of the barns. The rest of the group are already gathered below, and there's the hum of low conversation as we head towards them.

'Are you going to be okay?' Bay asks gently, lowering his voice.

'Sure, fine.' I bend down and rub the top of Dennis's head. He really is better than a teddy bear right now.

'He never misses the welcoming ceremony, you know,' Bay says, nodding at the dog. 'He likes to know who's around as much as the rest of us.'

I nod, feeling oddly relieved that my newfound friend will be a part of the proceedings. I hand the lead over to Bay and he unwinds it from Dennis's collar.

'Thanks for the loan,' he smiles, handing the scarf back to me. I stuff it in my pocket, feeling a bit daft. Clearly Dennis doesn't really need a lead, and there he was trotting to heel all the way down the field.

'Sorry, I wasn't sure if he was allowed to roam free or not.'

'It's fine, and probably a good job you did, otherwise he'd have just pottered off and left you up in the fields. He's pretty much got the run of this place as he's so placid, and he always turns up when he's hungry.'

As if on cue, Dennis looks up at us both, wags his fat little tail a couple of times and disappears off to check everyone else out.

'I'd better go and see if they need any last-minute help setting up.'

'Of course,' I nod, swallowing.

'Catch you later, then,' Bay smiles and jogs lightly up the steps.

Just as my nerves ramp up another notch, I feel a warm hand on my shoulder and turn to find Doreen grinning at me, though she looks so different I do a bit of a double take. She's removed her fuchsia lipstick and what must have been liberal coatings of foundation, mascara and eye shadow. She looks soft, and friendly, and so much younger.

'Hi! Tori, isn't it?'

I nod.

'I'm Doreen, and my hubby's called Geoff, though goodness knows who he's gossiping with at the moment!'

'Nice to meet you,' I croak.

'So what's your place like? I've been dying to ask but didn't want to interrupt you and that rather tasty young man . . . '

'Tasty?' I laugh. I can't help it. 'I booked my spot right at the last minute, so I'm sharing a yurt . . . '

'Oh, gorgeous! That'll be really cosy, I bet. Who're you sharing with? What's she like?'

'Erm. That was him. Your tasty little morsel. And that little devil polishing your hand is his dog.'

Doreen looks down at Dennis and pats him on the head. 'That's so unfair. I get landed with Geoff for three weeks in a tiny wooden cabin and you end up in a luxury canvas palace with a sex god and his minion . . . '

'What's this?' chuckles Geoff, materializing at my side.

'Tori was just telling me how she's living in a palace with a sex god, while I have to put up with you!'

'I never said . . . '

'Don't mind her, love. She reads a lot of steamy romance,' Geoff stage-whispers in my ear.

Doreen sticks her tongue out at him good-naturedly.

'But you're all right, are you? Happy with where you're staying?' Geoff asks.

'Sure, it's okay. Me and Dennis are already friends.'

* * *

Everyone around us seems to have teamed up into little groups. There's a great deal of earnest talking, nodding and beard-scratching going on over in the Beardy Weirdies' corner. It seems these guys are serious about being serious and, by the sound of the snatches of conversation I'm able to pick up, they're playing an eco version of 'who's got the biggest willy?'.

In this instance, 'who's got the smallest carbon footprint?'.

'Hello, Tori. How are you settling in?'

I jump. Lizzie's standing right next to me. How is it that this woman, who is currently the size of a house, is able to sneak up unheard? It's unnerving.

'Very well, thanks. It's a beautiful place.'

Lizzie swells with pride. I wish she wouldn't. I really don't want her to explode.

'Thank you. We try. We pride ourselves on the energies we have encouraged from the land. All our visitors leave us in a better place than they arrived. And you're happy in the yurt?'

'Yes, thanks,' I reply on autopilot.

'And the company?' Lizzie's voice seems to take on a slightly sharper edge.

'It'll be great to have someone around who knows what direction he's going in,' I reply.

Lizzie claps her hands like a three-year-old. 'That's what I told Ted. You need a strong, warming influence. Someone who knows their place in the world and their spirit's destination. You are very perceptive, Tori. Bay has exactly what you say: direction.'

I smile tightly and keep my mouth closed. Lizzie smiles back at me, nods happily and floats off to interrogate the Beardy Weirdies.

'Not quite what you meant, that, was it?' Doreen asks, grinning wickedly.

'Erm . . . no. I just meant that it'll be great to have someone around who knows which direction the bog is in and where to find the next session.'

'Thought as much. So, have you finally read the handbook?'

'How did you know I hadn't already?' I demand.

Geoff laughs. 'You should have seen your face when they told you to hand over your phone.'

'I tried to cram it in on the journey here, but seems I missed quite a few important details. Anyway, I had the chance to read it all the way through this afternoon.' Just mentioning it makes the butterflies start to swoop in my stomach again.

'That's good . . . You'd be in for a few shocks over the next couple of weeks otherwise!' says Doreen.

I reckon we're all in for a shock or two whether we've read the handbook or not, but I keep that thought to myself.

7

Learning to Trust Again

> 'There are a lot of factors that contribute to loneliness. Some come from inside us, and some come from external influences beyond our control. It's natural to withdraw into yourself after being treated badly. How can we trust someone not to hurt us like we've been hurt before?'
> ©TheBeginnersGuideToLoneliness.com

'Friends. Welcome.' Lizzie pauses, staring around at us all from her precarious perch halfway up the steps. She lets the pause drag on just that little bit too long, until we're all collectively shifting our weight. 'We are now going up into the loft to start our work in earnest. Each of you will begin your quest tonight.

'Before coming up these steps, please ask yourself one last time if you are truly committed to changing your life. In this moment, right now, you can still walk away and return to your life the way it is.' She pauses again. 'If you stay, and climb these steps, things will start to change.'

I look at Doreen, who raises her eyebrows at me in amusement. I can't help but shake my head.

Geoff bends his head and murmurs in my ear, 'Run, Tori, run . . . save yourself!'

I swat playfully at his arm, but I can't help but feel a bit of a nervous twitch. There's a tiny part of me that wants to listen to him and hotfoot it straight back up the lane. What on earth am I about to let myself in for? But then I think about my empty little flat. Do I really want to go back to that right now?

A bell rings and my attention grudgingly shifts back to the stairs. Ted has joined Lizzie and they stand together, side by side, watching us all. Then Ted speaks up.

'Come on up and let's learn about how we can help each other fulfil our quests.'

We all shuffle towards the bottom of the steps, forming a queue in classic British fashion. I make sure that I'm somewhere near the middle. A thrill flares in my belly. Now that I've decided not to make a break for it, I can't help but feel curious as to what's about to happen next.

I inch forward as each person disappears through the dark, curtained doorway at the top of the steps.

'So, what do you reckon? Ready for this?' Doreen asks from behind me.

'Sure . . . It's not like anything awful can happen, is it?' I say with way more bravado that I'm actually feeling.

'Tori,' Ted smiles at me as I step forward. He is out of his scruffy jeans and bobbly jumper. Instead, he's wearing a pristine, white cheesecloth shirt over wide, white, floaty trousers. On his feet are little green velvet shoes and under his chin is fastened a heavy brown cloak which is pushed back over one shoulder. I smile at him, my lips twitching as I struggle to contain a giggle. He looks like an extra from *The Hobbit*.

'It is now time for you to commit yourself fully to this process and to surrender any guilt you feel for being here. Can you do this?'

'Sure,' I reply. Well, they certainly enjoy repeating

themselves. I'm still here, aren't I? If I was going to make a break for it, I'd already be halfway down the M4 by now. And I'm certainly not feeling guilty about being here . . . I might make sure Nat does when I get back online though!

'Step through,' says Ted.

I push the curtain aside, take a step and come to an abrupt stop. It's pitch-black in here. The back of my neck tingles. I stand still, waiting for my eyes to acclimatize, but nothing happens. I still can't see. My breath starts to come quicker as my heart rate goes into overdrive. Can I hear the sound of water, or is that my imagination? I start to turn my head, searching for any movement or chink of light.

'Come, turn to face me.'

I let out a squeak of fright as Lizzie's voice, soft as silk, sounds in my ear. I turn to it, trying to breathe quietly and stop my hands from shaking.

'You don't need to be afraid. You need to trust us. Trust us enough to let us guide your unplanned steps into dark places. We will always be there to guide you through to the other side if you get lost.'

I let out an impatient sigh. I can feel my momentary fear turn to anger. I try to shove my emotions back down inside me.

'Do you trust me?'

It's a direct and blunt question, and I'm not going to answer it. *No, I bloody don't.* This is a completely random stranger who I've only just met. I take a deep breath. Seems my inner bitch has come out to protect me again . . .

'You're right to be cautious. But I will not let you fall. I will not let you get lost. I am here to guide you through your troubles, not to guide you around them.

Do you trust me?'

I get the sinking feeling that I'm not going to get any further until I say something.

'Fine. Yes, I trust you,' I huff.

'Good. Please step out of your shoes.'

Not the bloody shoes again? These people are fixated. I use my heel to slip out of one oversized welly boot and then the other. Bending down, I grope around in the darkness to pick them up.

'You can leave them here. Do not be afraid. I am going to place a blindfold over your eyes and lead you through to the next step.'

Before I know what's happening, a strip of material is being tied over my eyes. She may be gentle, but I jump as she makes contact in the dark and stand rigid until she's finished. At least the blindfold takes away that unnatural darkness, but still, the sooner this bit's over, the better.

A warm hand takes one of mine and I jump again. I'm going to be a nervous wreck by the time this is over. A gentle pressure on my back and a tug on my hand coaxes me forward. I stumble as I take an uncertain step in the dark. I know that they can't let me get hurt, but there's an irrational part of my brain currently on high alert, telling me I'm going to fall down a big, dark hole any second now.

After an eternity of being led in what feels like circles, we stop.

'Your next guide is here.'

A new hand takes mine. It's large, rough-skinned and warm. This time there's no pressure on my back, just an insistent tug at my arm, and I follow, trying to catch the pace of this new person. Whoever it is is walking faster, and I have to concentrate on the pressure on my hand and nothing else to stop me from tripping. I start to relax into it in spite of myself. After all, I've not been led straight into a brick wall. Yet.

Finally, we come to a halt and the hand lets go of mine. I stand there expecting someone to take my blindfold off, but nothing happens. I'm just starting to get jittery again when two hands land on my shoulders and I give a little shriek. I'm sure I hear a snort of laughter from behind me, but my heart is beating so fast I have no idea if I imagined it or not. I feel a gentle pressure and realize that they want me to sit down. Without being able to see what I'm doing, I brace myself to drop all the way to the floor, but hit something squishy that feels like a giant marshmallow.

This could be the library definition of uncomfortable. I wait for someone to come and take my blindfold off, but nothing happens. I'm getting a bit fidgety on my marshmallow and shift my bottom slightly, but end up almost tumbling onto the floor.

Of course, there's nothing to stop me from taking the blindfold off myself, except for self-consciousness. At least like this I don't have to take any responsibility for what's going on.

'We're all here!' Ted's voice rings out.

I shift my bum again as my legs threaten to go to sleep on me, this time careful not to disappear off the edge.

'You might be wondering what's happening; what this is all about. You are here with us to challenge your comfort zones. What better way to start than by trusting a stranger to blindfold you and lead you into unknown territory? While you're here there will be moments when you will need help. Remember that you are each a part of this — you need to be able to trust us and each other.'

There's restless shuffling and the sounds of breathing all around me. Someone clears their throat.

'We will now come around and give you the gift of your eyes once again. Please don't speak yet. Just hold in your heart your experience so far and what it means to you.'

The restlessness increases. I close my eyes tightly underneath the blindfold. I'm not sure I really want to see what's going on around me. What if my inner cynic decides to come out and party?

There's a gentle touch on my shoulder, letting me know that someone's standing behind me. I hold my breath. They remove my blindfold and, to my surprise, brush my hair away from my face with gentle fingers. My eyes fly open and light seems to flood in after being in the dark for so long. It's not the harsh light from an electric bulb, but the soft flicker of candles set in dozens of glass jars around the room.

I look around me, wondering if I'm going to be able to figure out who just decided to play with my hair. Ted's to one side, then I notice Lizzie the other side of me with Moth. It could have been either of them. Or the guy over there who lent me his wellies earlier. Good. This is a good thing. If I don't know who it was, I can't feel awkward about it.

We're all sitting in a circle under the eaves of the old barn. Doreen grins at me, but Geoff isn't looking quite so happy. His eyes are darting around furiously, as if trying to catch someone out. So it's not just me who's a tad uncomfortable with the situation then . . .

Directly across the circle from me, one of the three Beardy Weirdies is sitting in the lotus position.

Despite having his blindfold removed before me, his eyes remain closed and he has a little smile playing on his lips. I have to forcibly stop my eyes from rolling. It's all well and good to give yourself a couple of seconds to suck up the ambiance, but this guy is clearly just making sure that everyone notices his superior state of enlightenment before he deigns to join the rest of us in the room. Bloody muppet.

There's a dark-haired guy next to him that I don't recognize. This must be the late arrival, and much to my amusement his shoulders are shaking with suppressed giggles. He catches my eye and his whole face is a picture of someone trying not to laugh out loud. I bite my own lip in response and he winks at me, shaking his head.

Maybe it's all the candles, but it suddenly feels rather warm in here. Thank goodness for the soft, low light, though, as the look he's giving is making me melt and blush at the same time.

8

Cracking the Nut

> 'As you work to forge new connections, starting friendships and finding your community, you're going to have to open up and reveal a bit about yourself. That first crack, the first glimpse of the soft and beautiful inside, is hard-won, but so worth it.'
>
> ©TheBeginnersGuideToLoneliness.com

'Now, let's get to know each other a bit; find out what brings us all here and what we each hope to get out of the experience,' says Lizzie, easing herself onto a wooden chair next to Ted. Her hair is now hanging long and loose down her back and she's wearing a simple white dress with a short grey cloak over her shoulders. I sit up and try to concentrate rather than eyeballing the newcomer, who still seems to be fighting a losing battle with laughter. He's threatening to sweep me along with him if I'm not careful.

'We know,' Ted joins in, 'that this might be extremely difficult for you. And that's fine. It's okay to figure things out as you go along. But try to state what you feel right now in this moment. All we ask is that you are open. This evening is all about creating bonds of trust with each other.'

I drop my eyes to the floor, and when I look up again the new guy waggles his eyebrows at me. The yellow smiley-face badge pinned to the front of his shirt glints in the candlelight. I smile at him, but hastily straighten my face and tune back into what Lizzie is now saying.

'These bonds are likely to outlast your stay here with us. This is a time for making new connections. Don't be afraid. Embrace the experience fully. So, friends, be open, be truthful and be brave. That is all we ask.'

'First, names.' This comes from the guy who lent me his wellies. 'Let's go around the circle. I want the name you go by among friends; we don't care about official tags here. I also want one word to tell us all how you feel right now. I'll start. I'm Russ, and I'm feeling calm.' He turns to Bay, who's flopped on a beanbag next to him.

'I'm Bay. I'm excited. Oh, and this is Dennis,' he adds, patting the dog next to him on the head. 'He's usually happy.'

'Hi, I'm Doreen. I'm . . . um . . . ' she picks at her thumbnail.

'It's okay,' Ted smiles at her. 'Whatever comes to you first!'

'Terrified!' she squeaks with a little smile.

'Sam. Lost.'

'Emma. Excited.'

'Than. Curious.' It's the newcomer, and there's a little smile on his face as he speaks. It might be just me, but I swear he managed to make those two words sound just the tiniest bit sarcastic.

'Geoff. Hungry.' A titter of appreciation runs around the circle. Ted smiles but Lizzie's face pulls tight into a little frown of disapproval, which is hastily hidden under her love-for-all-mankind look.

'Moth. Open.' She turns to me. Ah. Shit.

'Tori. Erm . . . empty?' *Empty? Where the hell did that come from?* Now they're going to think that I'm some kind of emotionless robot! Why am I worrying about what this lot think of me anyway? Of course it would be lovely to make a few friends, but let's face it, the reality is I'll probably never see any of them again after the three weeks are up. I've just got to remember that I'm here to check out this course and write a review for the blog. And if I'm going to manage that, I'd better start concentrating. While I've been obsessing and staring at the floor, I've managed to miss a bunch of names. Bugger.

* * *

'Brilliant,' Lizzie smiles at us all. She peers around the circle, taking her time. I cringe, realizing that I've probably just been caught daydreaming. 'You've all been guided through your initiation and shown that you're willing to trust us to help you reach your goals. You are ready. Know that no thought is wrong, that no action should be considered incorrect and no reaction invalid. Allow yourselves to question — that's fine — but never halt in your journey. Follow your instincts down whichever paths you need to explore, safe in the knowledge that we are here to support you.'

A buzz of excitement runs around the group like bad wiring. This is already exceeding the wildest dreams of most of them. I don't join in. I'm frightened. Truly, little-girl-style scared at the thought of becoming close to a group of people who I stand to lose in a couple of weeks. And as for sharing my issues with them, right now I'm struggling with the idea of even sharing my breakfast preferences.

'Now, let's hear from each of your tutors. Ted, why don't you start?'

Ted nods. 'Okay, so most of you already know a bit about me, but just to level the playing field, here it is again. The Farm is my home, along with my wonderful wife, Lizzie, and our daughter, Rowan. I have no doubt you'll all meet her soon if you haven't already.

'We started this retreat because it's never been more important to learn how to safeguard our well-being and manage our mental health.

'I'm really looking forward to working with you all. I'm a registered counsellor as well as a certified fire-walk instructor, so I'll be the one leading that session when we come to it.'

Ted sits down and I join in with the applause on autopilot, my brain busy freaking out over the words 'fire walk'. When I saw that bit in the guidebook, I thought it was a metaphor for dealing with the scary stuff, not a literal burn-the-soles-of-your-feet-off session. Before I can panic too much, however, someone else around the circle speaks.

'I'm Claire.'

Claire is one of those women you just can't put an age on. She's wearing loose black trousers with a flimsy white shirt, and I can't help but stare as I notice that, even in this light, I can see straight through it. It appears she doesn't believe in bras. I look away as soon as I realize what I'm doing and catch Doreen's eye. She winks at me and nods over at one of the Beardy Weirdies, whose mouth is hanging open. As Claire raises a hand to run her fingers through her thick, dark hair, I swear the concentration levels in the room ramp up.

'When you're dealing with deep-seated emotions

and working through your innermost desires and fears, these can work inwards unless they are fully expressed and let out of your body. In fact, many people find that the root of their issues is stored as muscle memory; your body remembers things that your mind has managed to lock away.

'So, every day I will be running some form of bodywork. I will lead you in yoga, Pilates, dance and meditation. I work closely with Russ, but as he's up next, I won't spoil his bit.'

Claire sits down and Russ gets to his feet. 'Thanks, Claire. I'm Russ, and I'll be your mindfulness instructor. As Claire said, the purposes of our sessions will often cross over. There's a lot of evidence to support the use of mindfulness in combating depression and isolation. Learning to be fully present in the moment, no matter what you're doing or where you are, ultimately makes you more comfortable and confident, as well as more connected within your relationships.'

I jump as something cold and wet nudges my arm. Dennis is pushing his nose under my hand, attempting to sidle his considerable bulk up onto the beanbag beside me. I can't help but smile at him, and shift over as quietly as I can to make room. He clambers up, turns around twice, swiping me both times with his tail, and plonks down with his head resting on my lap. I place my hand on top of his hot head. I look up and lock eyes with Bay. I don't know how long he's been watching me, but he smiles. I smile back and glance down at Dennis. Well, if I can get over this particular fear so quickly, maybe there's hope for me yet.

Lizzie is the last of the instructors to speak, and she does it from the comfort of her chair, clearly a little bit worn out by this point. As well as being a trained counsellor like Ted, Lizzie will be working closely with us in the third week to guide us on the practicalities of taking everything we've learned and applying it to our real lives. I can't help but think she's being a bit optimistic. I've no doubt that she'd be more than up to the task, but somehow I wouldn't be surprised if the baby appeared before she's had her chance to shepherd us all back into the big wide world.

As soon as she's finished speaking, there's another round of applause and everyone looks around expectantly. Ted stands up.

'So, you all know what's to come while you're here. There will be a lot of surprises, not laid on by us, but generated by each of you. You will get out of this experience as much as you put into it, so I urge you to put aside any reservations and fully commit.

'In a moment, I'm going to ask you all to present your wrists so that I can bind us all together.' He pauses to show us a coil of silver-grey cord that he's just pulled out of his pocket. 'This is to symbolize our commitment to ourselves and the group as a whole.'

Okay, so this is it, my last chance to back out. I look down at Dennis again, who's now quietly snoring in my lap. What's waiting for me if I walk away now? An empty flat, a lacklustre life and a shitload of bad memories. It's not as though they can force me to do anything I really don't want to do. I lift my hands off of the dog's head and present them in front of me, looking around at the rest of the group.

To my surprise, I'm one of the first to do it. All of the tutors have their arms outstretched, but it's not as though they have any choice in the matter, is it? Doreen and Geoff give each other a little nod and follow suit. Than thrusts his hands out and grins across the circle at me. I feel a blush rise from my toes and reach the roots of my hair in seconds. Is it my imagination or is he trying to woo me over to the naughty corner he appears to have singlehandedly started?

Very soon, everyone's hands are in the circle. Well, all but one pair. Chief Beardy Weirdy, lotus-position plonker himself, is now looking mildly green. Ted turns to him with a questioning look.

Beardy shakes his head. 'You can't bind me, man! You can't make me commit! I'm a free spirit, man!' He scrambles to his feet and bolts for the doorway. Ted dashes after him.

'Don't touch me, man! I'm a free spirit! I am one, not one of a group, man!' And with that he practically falls out of the door, with Ted in hot pursuit.

There's complete silence until Doreen breaks it with a nervous giggle, followed very quickly by an apologetic mumble. I'm starting to feel pretty uncomfortable with my arms outstretched.

'It's okay.' Claire gets to her feet and takes hold of the cord. 'Not everyone is ready, and it's a big undertaking.' She starts to work her way around the circle, pausing in front of each person to ask 'Sure?' and waiting for a reply before gently looping the cord around their wrists.

'Sure?'

She's standing right in front of me, looking straight into my eyes. I want to look away, but I can't. I feel Dennis raise his head from my lap to greet her. Great. Just in my moment of need my newfound friend is going to abandon me. I gaze at Claire. What the hell am I doing here? What am I doing full stop? What choice do I have?

'Sure,' I whisper. She smiles faintly as she loops the

cord around my wrists.

Claire has just completed the circle when Ted returns, looking a little bit pink around the eyes. He's alone. He takes the cord with a grateful nod and loops it around Claire's wrists and then his own.

'Friends' — Ted's voice wobbles slightly — 'we are all one. We have committed. This cord flows between us, symbolizing our connection. Feel and cherish this bond. Learn from each other, help each other and support each other. That way the circle will never be broken.'

I can't believe it . . . I've got an actual lump in my throat.

Whatever they've got going on here, it's very clever. There's a tiny, cynical part of me that wouldn't be surprised if the guy who just bailed on us is a ringer that they use every time just for effect, just to make the rest of us feel like we're being brave because, miraculously, that's how I'm feeling right now.

9

To Boldly Go

'It's all well and good looking at the big picture and knowing where you need to get to. But it's important not to worry about how many steps it will take to get there. Just breathe deep and take that first step.'

©TheBeginnersGuideToLoneliness.com

I wake up with a start and shoot bolt upright in my bed. *Where the hell am I?* Oh yeah, that's right. Canvas roof and a duo of snores coming from the other side of the yurt. Both master and dog are still dead to the world.

I slump back against my pillows. What time is it? I go to reach for my phone, my usual port of call first thing in the morning, but it's not there. Of course it's not. Bloody great. I lift my arm and check Bay's watch. Old-school, but at least it'll give me an idea of how long I've got left in bed. We're meeting at seven for a communal breakfast. That gives me . . . oh crap, a full two hours to hang around. Why on earth am I awake so early anyway? I usually struggle into a cold shower at about eight thirty, followed by a litre of tar-strength coffee to kickstart my brain.

For a start, it's already ridiculously light. Also, the birds are tweeting loudly enough to wake the dead . . . Maybe that's their plan? And it's worse than just hanging around for a couple of hours. I need the loo. Pretty desperate too.

I'm going to have to risk the inadequacies of the composting bog.

What a great way to start the day. I don't know what else I was expecting though. It's not like I can just turn the tap off for three weeks.

I scramble out from under my mound of bedding and get to my feet as quietly as possible. Maybe it's for the best that I'm awake before anyone else. At least this way I'm going to be able to check out the facilities without being spotted. As I shuffle a pair of trousers on over my pyjamas, one line of snoring comes to a halt. I look over at Bay's bed just in time to see Dennis open his eyes sleepily. He thumps his tail and lifts his head as soon as he sees that I'm on my feet. I shake my head desperately and point at the bed, hoping against hope that he'll go back to sleep before he manages to wake Bay up.

Dennis gets to his feet, tail wagging sheepishly. *Damn it!*

'No, Dennis, bed!' I whisper sharply. If it weren't for my mission, I'd be glad of the company, but the dog is not a welcome addition to this particular party.

Dennis pauses in his tracks. Then he turns and, with a scathing look over his shoulder, makes straight for my recently vacated bed and flops down onto the rumpled pile of blankets.

I roll my eyes. I know that I should chuck him off straight away, otherwise I'm going to lose ground in the turf war we've got going on, but I'm so grateful that I'm not going to have an escort to the toilet that I leave him to snooze. I'll just have to deal with that particular problem later.

Sliding my feet into my loaned wellies, I push the

flap of the yurt open. I'm just about to step out when a sound comes from behind me. *Now what?* But it's only Dennis snuggling down and starting to snore again.

I stride away from the yurt in the direction of the little hut, following the line of the hedge. I keep my bleary eyes on the ground, watching my step on the slippery grass in my oversized boots. There's dew on everything, so much in fact that I'm surprised the inside of the yurt didn't feel damp. There's a crash directly overhead and I jump and swear as a fat grey pigeon almost falls out of the tree above me.

'Idiot,' I grunt at it, heart hammering against my ribs. I watch as a second one joins it, and can't help but laugh at how it flies at the branch and hopes to stick in an act of faith, rather than trying to make any effort to land gracefully.

I've never really seen this time of day before. The light is silvery-blue and the sun's not quite up yet. The air is chilly and heavy with the dew that's half on the ground and half hanging in a low mist around me. I shiver as the dampness reaches the bare skin beneath my clothing, reminding me what I'm doing up at this godforsaken hour in the first place. I badly need to pee.

I stride forward, this time keeping my eyes up, half watching out for the little hut I'm making my way towards and half enjoying the novelty of feeling so alone. You never feel like this in London. Lonely, yes, but never this depth of silence. Perhaps that's the wrong word, considering the racket the birds are making. 'Stillness' is probably nearer the mark.

Just thinking about London brings everything I'm trying to escape rushing back. I shake my head impatiently, but it doesn't dislodge the familiar, icy feeling in my chest. I haven't always been lonely, so at least I know it's not something that comes from an in-built part of my character. Or, at least, it never used to be. I had friends. There was a large, sprawling group of us. We went through school together, and then through college. Of course, that was before Mum died. Before things between me and Markus ended. Before everything went so very wrong.

I swallow hard and, giving myself a mental shake, push it all to the back of my mind again. Now isn't the time or place to start opening that particular mental file.

I spot the small wooden hut in front of me and hurry towards it. There's a short ramp leading up to the raised doorway. Its base is surrounded by what look to be pieces of old paisley carpet like my grandmother used to have in her living room. One thing that really takes me by surprise is that it doesn't smell terrible. There's an odd, earthy, pine smell, but not the kind of sewer stench I'd expected. It doesn't make me feel any more comfortable about going up there, but not wanting to puke while I do it is a bonus.

Glancing around me, I check to see that the coast is clear. It doesn't matter how desperate I am right now; I can't do this with any kind of audience.

It's completely still, so I gingerly make my way up the wooden ramp, my hand white-knuckled on the railing. There's no way I want to be the one found outside the bog in a heap with a broken ankle.

The door is a simple, slatted thing and there's a little sign hanging from a nail in the frame that reads 'Vacant' in narrow, charred writing. I flip it over so that it reads 'Busy' and step inside. I jump as the door bangs shut behind me and hold my breath as I search for the lock. There isn't one. Damn it! There's no way I'm going to be able to do my business with just a 'Busy' sign for protection. I look around for something to wedge in front of the door. There isn't anything apart from a bucket of sawdust, and that wouldn't be enough to stop man nor beast. Typical.

I stand there for a second, torn. It's just gone five in the morning. The likelihood of anyone else turning up mid-pee is tiny.

I look down at the toilet with some fear. It's just a wooden plank with an old toilet seat attached to the top of it. Sitting down, I breathe a sigh of relief and look around me. There's a small slit in the planking to my right-hand side directly at eye level. I peer through it and am met with dancing, golden beams as the sun makes its way above the horizon and peeps through the trees on the other side of the field. The light dapples and flickers as a breeze catches the branches. This view has to be the best I've ever had while sitting on the throne. A draft rushes up from under the toilet seat. *Eww*.

I finally locate a slightly damp, rough roll of loo paper and send up a silent prayer of thanks, having vaguely expected a pile of dried leaves. I look around for some kind of flush, but of course there isn't anything. My eyes rest on the bucket of shavings. It has a sign attached to the side that I didn't notice before. It says 'Sprinkle me. Two cups should do.'

Reaching in, I use the tin mug to throw pine shavings down the recently vacated hole. And that's that. I feel strangely proud of myself.

There's a tap attached to a fence post at the bottom of the ramp and I wash my hands with a lump of yellow, gritty soap from a little saucer next to it.

I'm just starting a leisurely stroll back in the direction of the yurt when it occurs to me that this is the perfect time for a little look around down by the farmhouse. No one in their right mind will be awake at this time of the morning — apart from me of course.

I head down the hill, retracing the path I followed yesterday with Dennis and Bay.

The farmhouse looks dark and sleepy. There's no one here silly enough to let the birds and early morning light cause them to lose sleep. I head past the house to take a proper look around the courtyard we gathered in last night. The room we used for the evening's ceremony is only a small part of this complex. It's essentially a courtyard surrounded by various barns and rooms that, I'm guessing, used to be the cow sheds. Now they're being used for the far more lucrative job of farming people's souls. I shudder at the image and creep across the silent cobbles.

I try one of the doors. It's locked. Huh. Maybe not such a caring, sharing and trusting community after all! I peer through the small window set in the wooden framed door, but all I can see are benches and a few other bits of random furniture. Nothing that interesting in there, then.

I retrace my steps back out of the courtyard and wander across the small front garden of the farmhouse, before winding around to the back.

Oh. My. God.

Ted is in the back garden.

And there is a whole lot more of him on display than I saw last night.

I freeze, but that doesn't stop the blush from starting in my toes and washing up over me like a wave.

I go to run, but realize that Ted has his eyes closed. Thank goodness for small mercies.

I turn away and hurtle back around the corner before he has the chance to spot me.

I know it's lame, but that's more than enough snooping for one morning. And besides, I've learned something very valuable: do not, under any circumstances, go near the back lawn of the farmhouse early in the morning.

⋆ ⋆ ⋆

I arrive back at the yurt panting, having rushed back with my head down all the way. I flip open the flap without a moment's pause and am treated to my *second* full frontal of the morning.

Bay is standing right in front of me, stark bollock naked.

Unfortunately, this one doesn't have his eyes closed.

'Shit, sorry, I thought you were out!' Bay quickly grabs a blanket from his bed, fumbles and drops it before managing to secure it tightly around himself.

'I was. I'm back . . . I — '

'I'm so sorry!'

I stand and stare at him, the image of his naked body seared into my brain. Two naked men on my first morning is a little bit too much to handle.

'Don't you people believe in clothes?' I huff, trying to cover my pure, unadulterated embarrassment with bluster.

'I'm sorry, I'm not quite used to sharing — '

'Well, neither am I, especially with butt-naked men. So please put some clothes on.'

Dennis is cowering on my bed. I stride over to him.

'Dennis, OFF.'

He scuttles straight off the bed and over to Bay, who promptly bends down to scratch his ears, almost losing his blanket again.

'Hey, don't take my nakedness out on Dennis. It's not his fault.'

'Unless you also smell of dog, I'm taking it out on the right man.'

'Well, you're pretty hideous first thing in the morning, aren't you? Good thing I learned this early on.'

'You don't look that great yourself, you know,' I mutter.

Lies! All lies. He actually looks toned and tanned, and kind of cute in his rumpled, early morning state. But that's beside the point.

'I didn't mean how you look . . . I mean . . . well . . . *you*!' says Bay.

I do a great impression of a landed goldfish for a couple of seconds before shooting back: 'Okay, try being me. I've got a coffee habit and I haven't had a coffee. I'm not even allowed to get a coffee because it's on the banned list for some reason. I've seen two naked men, and there's a bloody great big dog in my bed! All this before six in the morning!'

Bay smiles at me. 'Well, turn away for a minute or you're going to get another eyeful.'

I groan and throw myself face down on my bed. *EWW!* It smells of warm dog. I fume silently into my pillow, listening to Bay rustling around on the other side of the yurt. Seriously, this guy takes longer to get dressed than anyone I've ever met.

'Are you done yet?' I mutter. It comes out slightly muffled by my pillow.

'Hang on,' he calls.

For goodness sake, how long does he expect me to stay like this? And what is that noise? What's he doing now? Having a complete strip wash while I suffocate in the aroma of dog?

'Oi!'

I get a nudge in my ribcage. Swinging around, I come face to face with Bay, who is now fully clothed and proffering a cup of something that smells suspiciously like coffee. 'For you. To help you get over the shock.'

'Oh. Thanks,' I grunt, taking the cup from him and sniffing it. He gets up and retrieves his own mug from the table.

'Hang on,' I say suspiciously. 'I thought we weren't meant to 'alter our pathways' with mind-enhancing caffeine? Don't tell me this is made from sheep poo?'

'Nope. Not sheep poo. You have the very fortunate luck of landing yourself in a tent with another hard-core caffeine addict. This is purest Columbian. Should set you up for the day!' he smiles at me. 'And I was on the course the year that convinced Ted and Lizzie to add coffee to the banned list . . . Turns out that having a bunch of people working through their issues while they're souped-up on enough coffee to keep an entire city running can be a pretty explosive mixture. They decided they'd be better off dealing with a bunch of caffeine-withdrawal headaches than vulnerable people at exploding point.'

I take a tentative sip and groan in ecstasy. *Coffee, my old friend!*

'Thank you for breaking the rules,' I say gratefully, and carefully transfer the cup to my other hand so that I can sit up.

'Pleasure's all mine,' smiles Bay, taking a sip from

his own cup. 'Can't leave a fellow addict to suffer now, can I? There's a price though . . . '

Oh great. Mind you, I'll happily pay just about anything right now for the few precious sips I've already had. I can feel myself becoming more human by the second.

'Give me the gossip!' Bay grins, watching me intently.

'What gossip? I only just got here.'

'Exactly. You were here when I went to sleep and gone when I woke up. And you've seen *two* naked men today. I've clearly got the dubious pleasure of being number two. Who else?' He waggles his eyebrows at me.

I shake my head. I've always suspected that men are worse gossips than women, but this is ridiculous. 'It was Ted. I went for a walk. He was naked in his garden.' I cringe at the memory.

Bay chuckles. 'That sounds about right. Damn, I thought there was some juicy gossip to be had, but Ted gets his kit off all the time. He likes to greet the day that way.'

'Can't he just put some boxers on before he pokes someone's eye out?'

'In his own back garden?'

'I was lost,' I say defensively.

'At five thirty in the morning?'

'I went to explore. I found the loo — got that sussed. Then I found Ted and Lizzie's back garden. Trust me, I don't much fancy revisiting either place.'

'Hey! I can understand you not wanting to get a second eyeful of Ted, but I'll not have you say a word against my shitter. I put blood, sweat and tears into building that.'

I laugh but stop abruptly, wondering if he's being serious. The usual rules of conversation simply don't seem to apply here. I bury my nose in my coffee again and inhale deeply.

'I'm surprised they didn't confiscate your grounds when you got here.'

'Oh, they did. They've been locked in the safe since I arrived. I should have learned by now!' he says with a smile. I don't know whether to take him seriously or not.

'Honest! These were sourced at a very high price by a very handy Rowan. And this was my last lot. Time to get her in again if you want anything?'

'Thanks, I'll think about it.' I don't fully trust Bay yet and I think I'd prefer to keep any smuggled bars of soap a secret for now. It's definitely time for me to leave my first note in the gatepost for Rowan. I could do with checking my emails and sending a quick message to the Warriors for starters.

'Just don't go accepting coffee from anyone else,' Bay says. 'It'll most likely be acorn coffee. Tastes about as good as Dennis smells!'

10

Courage Conquers Fear

'Find the thing that you're most scared of — you know, the one that haunts you — and find a way to face it head on. The courage it takes for you to face your biggest fear and conquer it will help you realize that you've got this. That courage came from you. You just saved yourself . . . and you can do it again and again.'

©TheBeginnersGuideToLoneliness.com

On my way back down towards the farmhouse, I pause to leave my letter for Rowan in the fence post. I check around me before wedging it firmly into the crack. I've decided there's no way I'm doing three weeks without chocolate or deodorant.

Hoping against hope that Ted has put some clothes on by now, I make my way around to the courtyard. I'm in luck. Everyone's gathered around a long wooden table that has been lifted into place since my early morning visit. On it there are jugs of juice, massive bowls of fruit, porridge and large jars of honey. I sigh inwardly. No chance of my customary Pop-Tart here, then. I smile at Lizzie, who's brandishing a huge jug of what looks like coffee. Oh, thank goodness for that — Bay was just kidding earlier. She offers me a cup and I nod gratefully, eyeballing my large mug greedily. Bay flops down onto the bench opposite me with an odd smile on his face.

I ignore him, pick up my mug and take a sip.

And stop.

Abruptly.

I. Must. Not. Spit. This. Out.

Swallow, Tori, swallow.

It's like scrapings of burned Marmite.

'Acorn coffee,' Bay smirks at me. 'Delicious!'

I grab an apple from the bowl nearby and take a bite, desperate to get rid of the awful flavour. Damn that man for being right. I turn my attention away from him and smile as Doreen heads towards me looking pale. In fact, she looks shattered, and her hair is about three times the size it was yesterday.

'Hey, how was your first night?'

Doreen gives me a wan smile. 'Dark. Dark and very, very quiet.'

'Same. Until five, when I was so rudely awakened by the birds,' I nod sympathetically.

'I wouldn't know. That's just about when I drifted off, I think. I need coffee . . . '

'Oh no you don't,' I mutter in a low voice. 'That's not coffee. It's burned acorns pretending to be coffee. It tastes like shite and has zero caffeine. Steer clear!'

'Oh.' Doreen pushes her hair back and rests her head on her hands. Her eyes instantly begin to droop.

I grab a mug, fill it full of juice and push it towards her.

* * *

It's not long before everyone has joined us at the table, though the level of chat is fairly low. Half of us seem to be experiencing caffeine-withdrawal symptoms already, making me feel like I've got a terrible, guilty secret. The other half are enjoying the Zen-like calm of the early morning.

I hate this half.

'Morning, everyone!' Ted smiles around at us. 'Good to see you all up and ready to go!' He catches my eye as he looks around the table and I blush and look away.

Crap. I wonder if I'm ever going to be able to get that image of him out of my head!

'Now,' says Ted, clapping his hands and making me jump, 'I'm aware that a lot of you aren't used to the early start. Your bodies will be adjusting, so it's a nice, easy session this morning. You're all off for your first wild swim in the river. It'll wake you up like nothing else and wash away the cobwebs.'

Easy session? I can hear my pulse loud in my ears and my breathing is getting faster. Too fast. I put my apple down and focus hard on the edge of the table. The thundering in my ears is getting louder, and for a couple of minutes I zone in and out, trying to get my breathing back under control. I soon realize that everyone's chattering again, excited by the fact that their time here is about to kick off properly.

'Love, are you okay? You've gone very pale!' Doreen is staring at me, worry on her face.

I just nod at her. This isn't anyone's problem but mine, and I'm not about to mess up Doreen's first morning as well as my own.

Pretty soon, breakfast is over and we're all set to reconvene in ten minutes with our swimming gear. Bay is quiet as we head back to the yurt, and I'm glad of the silence.

My heart rate is still erratic and prickles of panic are rushing down my arms and pulsing in my fingertips. As long as I don't have to set foot in that river, I'll be okay. I keep telling myself this over and over again but it's not making any difference. I can't even bear to be near a bloody river. Lies . . . they're the only way to go, and no one needs to be any the wiser.

'I can't swim,' I blurt as we push our way inside.

'I thought you looked worried when Ted announced it. Don't worry, there are plenty of people who don't get in on their first visit to the river. Most just paddle in up to their knees and that's plenty for them. Just do that,' says Bay.

I swallow. Sure. I can do that. Can't I? Of course I can't. Who am I kidding? Even the word 'river' makes me feel sick.

I drag my feet getting ready. I didn't bring a swimming costume, for obvious reasons, but with Bay's quiet eyes on me, I feel like such a cop-out that I fling an old T-shirt, pair of boxer-knickers and a towel into a canvas bag. Not that I'll be using them. The closest I'm going to get to that river is the bank — if I don't pass out through panic before then.

We rejoin the others and set off across the fields. The sun is just starting to climb higher in the sky, and for a second I relax as its warmth hits my face. I'd even enjoy listening to the excited chatter around me if it weren't for the ice block of pure fear in my stomach. This is a morning so far removed from what I'm used to. Where are the four grey walls of my quiet flat and the inbox full of nothing but spam? Yet another essay waiting to be finished, only to disappear into nothingness the moment I submit it? That's all a very long way away.

Right now, I'm stuck with a bunch of excitable nutters who want to solve their problems by jumping in a very cold river. It's not fair! It really isn't. I'd be very happy to bare my soul, chant away my evils and visualize my chakras being cleansed of all pollution. But jumping in a river is just not going to happen. It's not the fact that it's going to be cold that's the problem. I'm just as rough and tough as the Beardy Weirdies — at least the two that made it through the welcoming ceremony anyway. But I really can't do this. No chance. No way.

'Are you all right, Tori? You're very quiet!' It's Emma, looking pretty and fresh with a pink polka-dot bikini peeking out from under a voluminous white shirt. Why is it that happy, outgoing people think it's helpful to check quiet people are okay by calling them out on their silence?

'Sure. Just . . . you know?' I'm not sure what to say, and I realize that this is the first time we've spoken. We're such a small group it makes sense to chat to her and get to know her at some point, but right now doesn't quite feel like the ideal moment for small talk. Not when I'm about to have the mother of all meltdowns.

She looks at me expectantly and then, giving up on any more of an answer, carries on anyway. 'It's so exciting, isn't it? I just knew when I read about this place for the first time that it had to be our honeymoon. I mean, it's perfect, isn't it?'

'Uh, sure. I'm sure it'll be great . . . ' I'm not sure at all, but it's not like I can admit that, is it?

'And, of course, they've had celebrities here you know?' Emma drops her voice slightly as she says this, grinning at me like the excited teenager she probably still is. 'So I just knew it was going to be brilliant!'

'Wow, seriously? Real celebrities? Like who?' I try to match Emma's wide-eyed, secretive tone. If I can keep her going on this topic, maybe it'll stop her from noticing the pure, unadulterated terror that must be oozing from my pores.

'Well, it's just gossip, but apparently they've had a girl band member, a footballer and a chef with anger issues . . . I dunno exactly who, it just hinted at their professions in the piece I read. And I just knew that it would be perfect here!'

'Right,' I smile brightly. I've already noticed that Emma talks about things being perfect a lot. I overheard her last night, talking about how perfect the welcoming ceremony had been. I already feel a bit sorry for Sam, poor lad. From what I've seen of him so far, he spends his entire time listening while she goes on about the 'aesthetic' of her Instagram feed, how important it is that each photograph is perfect and bewailing the fact that she can't update it while she's here. He also seems to spend as much time as possible sneaking away from Emma, or looking sheepish as he's dragged back for yet another public love-in.

Finally, Russ rounds up our staggered group at the edge of the third field we've crossed. We're at the top of a steep hill that presumably leads down to the river's edge. I give a little shiver even though there's no breeze and the air is starting to warm up in the early morning sunshine.

Than ambles up and comes to a standstill between me and Emma. I turn to look at him, but my face can't seem to muster a smile. I'm pretty sure I must look like I'm headed to my death.

'Okay, folks, we're almost there,' says Russ. 'When

we get to the bottom of the hill, just head under the trees and you'll see the bit we're aiming for. It has hollowed out over the years into this fantastic natural pool. Perfect for everyone's first wild swim.'

The group shifts with excitement, bustling forward en masse a couple of inches. I, however, shuffle backwards a few feet. With a wry smile, undoubtedly thinking this is a bit of a game, Than copies me, giving me a wink.

'So let's get down there, get in and just enjoy it. This is one of those things that you won't understand the magic of until you've tried it. Trust me, as soon as you get in that water, you'll get it!' Russ grins around at us. 'And don't worry, I've been swimming here for years and have never had any problems. The water is beautifully clean and clear.'

The group starts to surge down the hill. Emma breaks into a run and I can hear her giggling as she navigates the steep slope. The others follow at a more leisurely pace, Bay and Russ striding together side by side. I don't budge and, for a second, I think I'm going to be the only one left at the top of the hill. After taking a couple of steps forward with the others, Than turns and looks at me with his eyebrows raised.

'Wanna get out of here?' he grins at me, and I'm instantly back in the naughty corner I found myself drawn to last night.

I nod.

'Come on then, quick, before they spot us.'

Before I've had a chance to think about it, he's grabbing my hand and towing me away, back through the gateway. We run hand in hand across the field, away from the rest of the group.

We don't stop until we reach the edges of the

orchard. I can just spot Doreen and Geoff's cabin in the distance between the neat rows of trees. The blossom smells amazing in the early morning air. As we come to a halt and lean on the wooden fence, I try to catch my breath.

'Thank God we escaped that embarrassment!' Than laughs. 'I didn't much fancy replacing caffeine with cold water as a new way of waking up!'

I smile awkwardly at him. 'Me neither.'

Than quirks an eyebrow at me. 'I thought you were going to puke there for a second, you know! I mean, I know the others are a bit much to take, but that was quite some reaction you were having . . .'

Damn it! Now I don't actually have to go through with the whole water torture thing, I want to enjoy my freedom. I definitely don't want to talk about it. That's almost as bad as having to get in the bloody river.

I duck under the bars of the fence and take a couple of steps into the little orchard. 'What are we going to do now?' I say. All well and good doing a bunk with a guy I don't know, but now what do I do with him?

'How about we find somewhere to sit down, wake up properly and enjoy . . .' — he pauses and rummages in the little rucksack he's carrying — '. . . some of this!' he cries, triumphantly waving a little purple packet at me.

No. Effing. Way. 'Chocolate? Seriously? How on earth did you manage to smuggle that in?' I gasp.

'I have my sources,' he winks at me again, and I can't help it — my insides squeeze a little at the cheeky look he's giving me. He's all dark, messy hair and early morning stubble. Let's just say that I've seen much worse sights.

'Rowan?' I ask, swiping the chocolate from his hands. Mmm, fruit and nut, my favourite.

'Yep. But don't you dare tell her I told you.'

'Blimey, you got in there fast! And don't worry about me blabbing,' I say, falling into step next to him as we make our way down a little avenue of trees, 'I've got the full price list back at the yurt!'

Than points to the remnants of a fallen tree, much older and larger than the part-grown ones now gracing this well-tended little haven. The grass has grown up around it so that it looks like an outdoor settee. We both head over and, slumping down side by side, rest our backs up against it.

I hand Than back the bar of chocolate and without a moment's hesitation he rips it open, snaps it in two and hands me half.

'So,' he says around a mouthful, 'what was all that about back there? Why the need to escape? Desperate to get away from Emma, the vacant wannabe influencer?' He nudges my leg with his knee. The feel of his warm leg against mine sends a wave of butterflies through me.

'Nah, more like I couldn't handle much more of the inane smile of Doreen the bored housewife,' I joke. Than grins at me, but I instantly feel sick with myself. Doreen and Geoff have been nothing but nice to me. 'Actually, it's just that I don't like water,' I say curtly. End of subject please.

He blinks at me. 'Well, no one would when it's cold and — '

'No. I *really* don't like water,' I say.

'What, *all* water?' he asks, and I can't help but notice a strange look on his face as I peep at him. What is it? Amusement? Disbelief?

'No. Running water.'

'So, rivers . . . '

I nod. I want to get off the subject.

'What is it about them?' he asks curiously.

'Everything,' I say. My mouth's gone dry and the chocolate feels like it's about to lodge in my throat.

'I didn't even know that was a thing, fear of running water.'

I spot that look again. I know what it is. It's scepticism.

'Well, it is,' I snap.

'Sorry, I didn't mean it like that!' he says.

'No, I'm sorry,' I sigh. 'I get . . . panicked. I usually manage to avoid it pretty well. This morning was just a bit too close. It makes me — '

'Anxious?' Than supplies.

'Oh yes. And that makes me bitchy!' I say.

'How bad is it?'

How do I answer that when I've barely admitted it to myself yet? I started off being frightened around rivers. Now I can't even bear to have a shower because the rushing sound can kick my anxiety off.

'Pretty bad,' I say. 'Put it like this, showers are out — I'm a bath girl all the way!'

Than shoots me a naughty look. 'Well, they're much better for the whole candlelit experience, aren't they?'

I blush. 'That's exactly what I always say.'

It feels strange to be sitting here with the sun on my face, stuffing myself with chocolate and admitting these things to someone face to face for the first time. I've told the Warriors online, and I've discussed it a lot with them, but that's not the same as having to say it out loud and deal with the questions and reactions that follow. I feel a warm ball of pride blossom somewhere inside me. This morning's session might not have been exactly what the powers-that-be had planned for me, but it's definitely doing me a lot of good.

'Thanks for rescuing me,' I smile at Than.

'You're welcome.'

My butterflies are now going completely nuts, but I'm not sure if it's Than or the tail end of my river-induced panic that's causing their over-excitement.

Than stands up and offers me his hand, pulling me up from my soft, grassy pillow.

'Next time, snacks are on you . . . and they'd better not be dried acorn cookies!'

'Okay, deal,' I say, holding on to his hand just a couple of seconds longer than is strictly necessary.

11

No Man is an Island

'Asking for help is a good thing. Seeking professional support and advice can help you recognize and break bad patterns, setting you on the path to making new, authentic relationships.'

©TheBeginnersGuideToLoneliness.com

'Well met, my friends,' says Lizzie, gliding into the centre of our circle. We've all piled into the small space that Lizzie has chosen for her classroom. It's dark, stuffy and womblike, especially given the low, red-tinged lighting. Taking her time to rotate slowly on her axis, Lizzie peers at each of us in turn.

This afternoon, she's wearing a long, Grecian-looking dress in flowing white cheesecloth. Its twisted straps snake over her shoulders in a halter, and swathes of extra material cover and frame her massive bump.

When her eyes land on me, I shift uncomfortably. It's like she knows what happened this morning. Maybe one of the others said something. There's a part of me that feels bad for disappearing, but another part that's still excited by what happened instead. Lizzie smiles at me and moves on. I wish I were back out under the apple blossom right now.

'Something that you might already be learning about your stay is that things happen here. Unexpected things. Small things. Momentous things. Not one of you will be able to ride out this process as a passenger or observer. Not every realization or awakening will feel positive at first and not all of them will make sense straight away.

'You will all face fears while you are here, and this is a safe place for you to do so. However, you need to listen to yourselves and to each other to make this process as productive as possible.'

I feel Than shift on his cushion next to me and I peep at him. He winks at me and nudges my shoulder with his. The room gets even hotter, and I feel my face flame. Why? Why do I have to blush so easily? Maybe it's my guilty conscience . . .

I managed to grab Rowan and use her phone for a couple of minutes at vast expense before this session kicked off. I wanted to let the Warriors know that I've had my phone confiscated so that they don't worry where I've disappeared to. I may have also just dropped a quick mention of Than and his cheeky smile while I was at it.

I look back up to find Lizzie's eyes fixed on Than. Poor guy. She's pretty scary when she wants to be.

'Something else you all need to understand is that you need to be present in order for this process to work for you. You need to actually *face* your fears, not keep turning away from them. You each need to take responsibility for yourself. You need to show up to each session, both physically and mentally. Be there and make every second count. It might not always be comfortable, but it will always take you one step closer towards your destination.'

Than shifts again, clearly uncomfortable. Lizzie nods once, finally looking away from him and moves slowly to sit in a chair at the far end of the small space.

'Right. Forgive me, I won't be able to get up if I

join you all down there on the cushions.'

A little laugh runs around the group, breaking the strange atmosphere for a moment.

'This afternoon will be a deceptively simple session, but I think you'll be surprised how much it will help you over the next few weeks. We all need to be able to ask for help openly and without any fear, and to do this we need to be able to trust each other fully.'

My eyes start to droop in the warmth and soft, dim light. If it wasn't for the fact that I'm sitting bolt upright, making sure that no millimetre of me comes into contact with Than, who is positively lounging on the cushion next to me, I think I'd drop off. I stifle a yawn, and hear Than snigger quietly. I shake myself. All that fresh air this morning and the adrenalin surge at my near miss with the river have left me exhausted.

'First things first. Please clear the cushions to the sides of the room,' says Lizzie, 'then pair up, and try to aim for someone who's not the obvious choice for you!' she adds, catching Doreen eyeballing me from across the room.

Than grabs my arm as we struggle to our feet. It feels a little bit like being back at primary school, as we giggle at our naughtiness and chuck our cushions onto the pile with abandon. Suddenly I'm wide awake again.

As we turn, grinning, back to the rest of the room, there's not much other movement going on. There's plenty of uncomfortable shuffling and eye-contact-avoidance though.

'Come on, it's not that hard, is it?' laughs Lizzie. 'Just aim for someone you don't know much about; someone you haven't spoken to yet.'

There's more muttering as everyone starts to make

awkward pairings around us. I know I'm getting disapproving looks from Lizzie right now, but if I refuse to look in her direction I can pretend they don't exist.

Before long, the whole room is paired off. Bay is with Emma, Moth has teamed up with Bob, one of the Beardy Weirdies, and Doreen is standing with the other Beardy Weirdy, whose name I still don't know.

'Good. Right, today we'll be facing some pretty ingrained stuff about ourselves. The thing is, if you're able to do this with a stranger, it should make it easier to open up to people who are close to you.'

Than turns to me and rolls his eyes. I clear my throat awkwardly. This sounds like the stuff we had to do at those interminable team-building days when I was working at the advertising agency. I used to hate every second — throwing myself backwards into the arms of someone who'd given me a bollocking the day before was never going to be fun.

But it turns out to be a very different experience with Than. We've been at it for a full ten minutes and we haven't stopped laughing the whole time. Things just feel so easy and simple between us, and I have to admit, that's quite scary in itself.

'Take a look at Bay's face!' he sniggers in my ear as he hauls me back up to my feet for the third time in a row. 'Do you think he's worried that Emma's going to drop him? Fluffy idiot!'

I sneak a peek over at the pair, and wince as Bay throws himself backwards into Emma's waiting arms. Miraculously, she manages to take his weight before he hits the floor, and I can't help but smile when I spot the look of relief on his face.

'Okay, my turn,' says Than, throwing himself backwards and grabbing my attention only just in time.

I like this feeling. It's like we're in our own little club, and the rest of them don't matter because we're having such a great time.

I instantly feel bad for letting this thought even cross my mind.

Once I've set Than back on his feet, I look around the room to see how everyone else is doing and watch as Beardy Weirdy catches Doreen. He doesn't seem to have the upper-body strength to set her back on her feet though, and both of them end up on the floor in a heap. I'm not surprised to see Doreen's in fits of giggles, but it looks like she's managed to unearth the little boy in the heart of the stoic hippy. He's laughing so hard that he's wiping tears from his eyes as Doreen punches him playfully on the elbow.

This signals the end of the serious part of this particular exercise, as their giggling is contagious and sweeps across the room, catching everyone unawares until we're all clutching at our sides, trying to avoid each other's eyes as we attempt to catch our collective breath.

I jump as Than flings an arm around my shoulder. The gesture feels too intimate in the moment, especially with everyone else around. I don't like it.

Doing my best to appear natural, I take a step away from Than and stretch, forcing him to drop his arm. When I catch his eye again, he smiles, completely relaxed. *Phew*.

I watch as Lizzie tries to regain some kind of control over the rest of the giggling group, and see that Bay is staring at us from the other side of the room. I'm not sure why, but I feel like I've been caught doing something wrong.

'Okay, guys, great work,' Lizzie slips back into her

chair, a little out of breath. 'You all look like you're working as a team. Can you feel the difference?'

There's a bit of nodding around the room. I hear Than tut next to me.

'Let's test this newfound teamwork out a bit, shall we?' she grins at us wickedly. For the next ten minutes, with Lizzie instructing us from her chair, she guides us into a circle, and then, on her command, has us all sit down so that each of us is sitting on the lap of the person behind us in one unbroken loop. I've got Moth sat on mine while I'm perched on Than's.

I can't stop grinning. This is a bonkers exercise, and totally dependent on us all working together and trusting the person behind us to support our weight. It only gets a little bit chaotic when Lizzie instructs us back to our feet. We're all a bit slow to react, meaning that some people try to stand before the rest, resulting in half of the group landing in a giggling mess on the floor. Then we all shift around the room and try it again. This time I'm sitting on Doreen's lap and Emma's sitting on mine.

'Next,' calls Lizzie, clapping her hands to get our attention after we've all struggled back to our feet again, 'I want you to tell your partner from earlier a secret. This should be something that you haven't shared with anyone else here yet. They will hold this secret for you and, in return, you'll hold their secret for them.'

Crap. There goes the nice, relaxed feeling, then. I don't want to tell Than a secret. I don't want to tell *any*one any secrets. That's why they're called secrets! I look sideways at Than and see that he's looking pretty wary too.

'Take a moment,' Lizzie's voice cuts in again. 'Think

about what you're going to share with each other. Make sure that it's something that will be equal in the exchange. It has to be worth trading, and something that you truly care about.'

'Come on,' I mutter to Than, 'let's find a bit of space.'

We drag one of the cushions out of the pile and head towards the back of the room, as far from the others as we can get. We sit facing each other in complete silence, looking anywhere but at each other.

'Imagine,' he says, and I jump after the long silence, 'just imagine if someone here admitted to an affair!' He looks at me, his eyes alight with mischief.

'Or murder!' I whisper back. 'But you couldn't tell anyone, because you promised, and they'd know that it was you who dobbed them in.'

We stare at each other in wide-eyed amusement for a second before I snort, a laugh escaping against my will. Than chuckles.

'Please focus on your own secrets for a moment and how you plan to share them!' Lizzie's voice cuts across the room, and I duck my head down.

'Oops. Rumbled!' laughs Than.

'So, who's going to start?' I ask.

'I don't mind . . . '

'Okay. I'll go . . . ' I take a deep breath, and I see his shoulders relax a bit, knowing he's been let off the hook for a few minutes. 'One of the reasons I'm here — something I'm trying to come to terms with — is that my mum passed away.'

Than nods in encouragement but doesn't say anything. My heart is starting to hammer. What am I going to tell him? How much? 'She . . . she died in a car accident.'

'I'm sorry.' Than puts his hand out, like he's going to take mine. I pull my hand away before he has the chance to make contact. Every ounce of me is focused on sharing my secret, and if he touches me, I'm scared I'm not going to be able to get the words out.

'It was raining and the roads were really messy. Apparently, the car hit a patch of water and skidded. There was a river right next to the road. The car flipped and landed on its roof in the water.'

'Tori . . . ' Than whispers. His hand is up to his mouth, his eyes wide.

'She drowned before anyone could get her out.' I take a deep breath. Is that it? Is that all I'm going to tell him? Maybe a little bit more. Maybe . . .

'There's something else. I told you when we skipped swimming earlier — '

'That you don't like running water?' he interrupts.

'Yes.'

'Well, now I can understand why.'

'Yeah.' I sigh, sit forward and hug my crossed legs like a little child. 'Well, it's a bit more than 'don't like'. I have severe potamophobia.'

'Pota . . . What's that?'

'Potamophobia. Fear of running water. Because of the accident.'

He looks non-plussed.

'You know how people with agoraphobia are terrified of open spaces and situations they feel they can't escape from? Some become housebound? My terror is running water.' I take a deep breath. My hands are starting to shake and my heartbeat is starting to race. Another deep breath. 'Rivers. Waterfalls. Showers because of the sound . . . That urgent, pounding water.' I stop abruptly. My mouth has gone dry. I feel a bit sick.

Than nods, but doesn't say anything. He's wide-eyed and expectant, like he's waiting for me to say something more.

I shrug. 'So that's it. That's me.'

'But . . . you didn't have it before the accident?' he asks.

'Nope.'

'But you . . . you weren't there when it happened?'

I shake my head. That's enough now. I can't think about it anymore. I definitely can't share any more.

'How are you dealing with it?' he asks.

'Every day. Small things,' I say evasively. That really is enough. 'Some days are worse, some days better.' I clear my throat. 'Anyway. Your turn.'

Than jumps, almost like I've scalded him. I surreptitiously wipe my palms on my trousers, and let out a long, slow breath. I did it. I told someone other than Nat, Hugh and Sue. It's the first time I've had to say it out loud and I didn't go to pieces. Probably because I haven't shared the worst part yet. The part that has stopped me from getting professional help before now. I just couldn't handle the idea of someone prising it out of me.

'Huh. I don't know where to start with mine,' mutters Than, and my attention snaps straight back into the room.

'Why don't you tell me a bit about how it makes you feel first?' I offer. He's looking shifty, like he might do a runner.

'I can do that. Scared. Guilty. Angry. That pretty much sums it up.'

Okay, that hasn't narrowed anything down. In fact, that could pretty much describe how I'm feeling too.

'My brother's ill,' he blurts out. For some reason it's not what I was expecting. 'He needs a new kidney and I'm the only option. He's asked me and I don't know what to do. I mean, obviously I do — I have to help him. But I'm scared.'

My jaw has dropped, and I quickly shut my mouth. I'd been expecting some kind of light-hearted admission, not a life-or-death situation.

'What if something goes wrong? What if I get ill? What if it doesn't help? And I'm angry. Why me? And then there's the guilt. This is my brother. I shouldn't be feeling like this, should I? I shouldn't be doubting this at all. I should be glad that I can help him. But I'm not. I've basically got no choice in the matter.'

'And there are no other options?' I ask as gently as I can.

'Nope. There are no other matches. This needs to happen yesterday and here I am, hanging out here, trying to get my head around everything, when I should be in a hospital saving my brother's life.'

It's my turn to lean forward. I go to take his hand, but I hesitate, knowing that I didn't want this just a minute ago. Than, however, grabs my hand like it's a lifeline.

'I'd be scared too. I think anyone would be,' I say.

'No. No, they wouldn't. You hear about people doing this all the time, and they're glad to do it. Not running away like I am.'

'You're not running away,' I say, looking at him steadily. 'You're here, aren't you? You're dealing with it in your own way.'

Than nods, squeezes my hand and stares fixedly at the floor. Finally he says, 'You won't tell this lot, will you?'

'Of course not. Isn't that the whole point?' I say.

'Thanks, Tori.' Than lets out a long sigh. 'He gave this to me, you know,' he fingers the yellow smiley badge still pinned to his top. 'He gave it to me when we were kids. I thought I'd wear it . . . to remind me why I'm here, who I'm here for.'

I nod and smile at him, feeling incredibly selfish for a second. Here I am, all me me me, and here he is, trying to find the courage to save his brother's life.

I'm still holding Than's hand. I don't pull away, but it seems like we've said everything we're going to say. I stare around the rest of the room. It's like there's been some kind of energy shift as everyone comes to the end of their confessions.

I'm not surprised to see that a couple of people have been in tears. Emma is sitting next to Bay, looking pale and withdrawn, and Bay looks decidedly wrong-footed. He looks up at me, and I turn away just as he catches my eye.

I smile back at Than and gradually ease my grip on his hand until I can reclaim mine. I want out, now. I've shared more than enough of myself for one day.

To my great relief, Lizzie seems to agree as she claps her hands to get our attention.

'Excellent, guys. Great to see these new bonds you've started to form. I want to remind you before you go that anything you've learned here today is confidential and not something to be chatted about idly around the campfire. Thank you.'

I'm on my feet and out of the door before the clapping has ended.

* * *

As soon as I'm outside, I start to feel better. The fresh air washes over me, and the images that have been haunting me in the claustrophobic little room dissolve in the sunshine.

I've never really talked much about the accident. Of course, I've told the Warriors most of the play-by-play facts, but typing them was a lot easier than saying them out loud. The real-life friends I had at the time tried to get me to talk about how I was feeling, but their support quickly turned into suggestions of 'rejoining the real world', urging me to go out, socialize and have some fun, because it was 'what Mum would have wanted'. They couldn't have been further from the truth. To add to the fun and games, in the middle of it all, my relationship with Markus imploded quite spectacularly, and as I continued to turn down every single invitation that came my way, they soon dried up.

I was left alone to struggle with the huge weight of grief and guilt about Mum, licking my wounds over Markus, little realizing that the biggest ball-ache to come out of it all would be this crushing, intense loneliness.

'Hey, how're you doing?'

It's Bay. I swing around to find him standing just behind me, and realize that he's probably been there for a while. I clear my throat and remind myself that he's not a mind-reader.

'Good.' Completely monosyllabic. Completely rude. Told you I was all talked out.

'Good session for you?' He sounds curious.

'Yeah,' I take a couple of steps away from him as if I'm about to head off back to the yurt, but then remember the look on his face at the end of the secrets exercise. 'How about you? You must have done it a few times before?'

'Once or twice,' he says, catching up with me. 'I've done Lizzie's sessions every time I've been here. Trust me, that's a lot of sessions.'

'So, do you tell the same secret over and over again?' A stock secret would be very handy, and not so hard to share after the first time, I guess.

'No. No, there's usually something new, or at least a new aspect of something I need to share that my partner draws out of me.'

'Emma draw anything interesting out?' I ask. I'm not sure I believe him, if I'm honest.

'That'd be telling, wouldn't it?'

His words might be flippant, but a troubled look crosses his face. So, that's a yes.

'What about you, Tori?'

'Like I said, it was good.'

'Which bit, the listening or the sharing?'

'Both. Surprising. But that's all I'm saying.'

Bay frowns and lifts a hand irritably to brush his hair back off his face. He looks uncomfortable, like there's something really bothering him.

Behind us, I can hear the rest of the group emerging from the classroom, a tide of eager chatter following them into the sunlit courtyard. Bay opens his mouth as if he's about to share something with me.

'Tori! Wait up!' Than's voice causes me to whirl around. As he jogs up next to me, I hastily plaster on a smile. Behind me, Bay lets out a huff and starts to walk away.

'What's up with him?' asks Than.

I shrug. My brain's full enough after that session without adding Bay's worries to the pile. 'No idea! Come on, let's go make a start on supper.'

12

Your Body, the Storyteller

'When you start your healing process, you can work on your head all you want, but the key to success lies in working with your whole body. Get it moving and unlock those stored emotions.'
©TheBeginnersGuideToLoneliness.com

'Hey, everyone!' Claire smiles around at us all.

It's our first yoga session this morning, and I'm desperately trying to send her telepathic messages, begging her not to torture me on my first time. I know bending and stretching is meant to be good for you, I'm just not sure how bendy and stretchy I feel right now.

I actually slept really well last night. After Lizzie's session, I have to admit my mind was reeling and I was dreading going back to the yurt and just lying there in the dark while my brain replayed everything we'd talked about in the session. As it turns out, volunteering to make a start on supper was the best thing I could have done. At first, I was worried that Than would want to carry on talking about what we'd been discussing in the session, but he was way more interested in messing around. After about five minutes Moth joined us, and we didn't get into anything heavier than speculating about how hard Claire's first yoga session was going to be.

The light conversation with everyone over dinner

meant that I didn't have to say much of anything, but with Than sitting on one side, giving me the occasional wink and nudge, and Moth nattering on about knitting on my other side, I felt warm and content in a way that I haven't for a long time. I wandered back to the yurt with Bay fairly early, leaving another shift of willing volunteers on washing-up duty. Bay was quiet too, and after the bare minimum of chat, and a last-minute cuddle with Dennis, I fell asleep before I'd even registered I was in bed.

'Right,' says Claire, 'before any of you start to worry, this session might be called 'yoga' on the timetable, but you can forget all about those showy-offy poses you've seen online. We're looking at gentle movement to get in touch with our bodies. A chance to find out where we might be tight and caught up, where the aches and pains are. The last thing we want to be doing is adding to them!'

I let out a long breath of relief. That sounds just about manageable. I'm sitting on my borrowed mat that smells like a hundred strangers' feet, surrounded by the rest of the group. I tried to get a spot at the back of the room, but everyone else had the same idea, and Geoff, Sam and Emma beat me to it. So I've set up as close to the side wall as possible, right in front of Emma, with Doreen by my side. I'm so grateful that she nabbed that spot before Than could. The last thing I need while I'm trying not to seize up is to be worrying what I look like. He's set up his mat directly in front of me instead.

'Now, some of you will be more flexible than others, but just do what feels good for you. The most important thing is that you don't compare yourself to anyone else — either in the room or out of it. This is all about your personal journey, and no two sessions will feel the same.'

Turns out, I love every second of it once I manage to forget about the others around me — which isn't that easy, as Doreen spends most of the session giggling from one gentle pose to the next. Her balance is appalling — even worse than mine. I know I'm meant to be fully engrossed in what I'm doing to the exclusion of everything else, but it's harder than it sounds when the person next to you periodically overbalances so badly that she hops onto your mat with you.

Than peeps over his shoulder at me a couple of times, but I'm too focused on what I'm doing to pay much attention to anything else. Every stretch and release, the curve of my spine and the feeling of my skin and muscles relaxing into the floor is new to me. I almost feel drunk with the sensations.

On the couple of occasions I look around the room while trying to get my balance back, it's Moth that really catches my eye. Claire wasn't joking when she said that some people might be more flexible than others. Moth takes this to the next level. She's moving like a dancer, graceful and full of energy. Her whole body seems to flow, and the positions she's getting herself into would be jaw-dropping for a twenty-year-old, let alone someone of her age. I make a mental note to ask her about it when I get the chance.

By the end of the session, I'm so relaxed that my entire body seems to be tingling. I'm not tired, just . . . *chilled.*

'I'm starving,' says Geoff from the back row as we all clap for Claire.

'You're always starving!' Doreen laughs as she rolls her mat up.

'It's all this exercise and fresh air we're getting!' he says. 'Swimming yesterday, yoga today. Walking back and forth to the cabin. I'm going to be like a rake by the time we get home.' He pats his stomach and Doreen chuckles.

I straighten up from rolling my mat and catch Than watching me, a smirk on his face.

'What?' I say, self-consciously.

'Enjoy that?' he asks.

I nod.

'It was brilliant, wasn't it?' says Doreen. 'Nice to have the chance to be able to join in without being out of my depth in the first couple of minutes.'

'I bet,' says Than.

Doreen just smiles at him, but I swear I hear a little growl from Geoff's direction. I turn to look at him but he's already making his way towards Bay, who's standing over by the door. It must have been my over-active imagination.

'Shall we go make a start on lunch then?' I ask the other two to break the tension that seems to have popped up out of nowhere. I don't want to lose my relaxed feeling so soon.

'We don't have to,' says Than indignantly. 'We did the food last night.'

'Yeah, but I enjoyed it,' I say.

'Okay, come on then. Let's go recreate the magic.' Than links arms with me and hauls me towards the door, away from Doreen and the others.

* * *

As it turns out, I do have fun getting the lunch ready with Than at the little outdoor cooking station. Beardy Weirdy joins us and then Moth rocks up again too.

'You know, we're going to have to watch out that we don't get lumbered with all the kitchen duties!' Than says as he passes a huge stack of plates over to Moth.

'Oh, I hope I do!' Moth laughs. 'You know, all the best parties happen in the kitchen . . . even an outdoor one like this.'

'Hear hear!' says Beardy as he tosses a green salad with gusto.

I grab a handful of cutlery and follow Moth to the table. 'You know, that's the first time I've ever done yoga,' I say.

'Did you like it?' she asks, straightening up and looking at me.

'I did — after I'd finished checking out what everyone else was up to, and worrying that I was getting it all wrong. I felt . . . well . . . like it gave my brain a chance to slow down for a bit.'

Moth smiles. 'That's wonderful, Tori! And don't worry about having a look around you, everyone does it. It's just human nature to be curious.'

'I suppose,' I say, feeling a little bit less awkward about the fact that I've clocked how bendy she is.

'You should see some of the classes I go to,' she says as she starts to arrange plates down the opposite side of the table. 'Some of the women spend more time looking over their shoulders than worrying about what they're doing with their own bodies. It's sad really.'

'I thought you must have done other classes!' I say, then realize that I've just outed myself for spying on her. 'I'm sorry, I promise I wasn't staring — I just couldn't help but notice how beautifully you move.'

Oh. My. God. That might just be the most awkward thing I've ever said to a stranger.

Moth, however, is beaming at me. 'That's such a lovely thing to say, thank you! I do love a good yoga class — it keeps me in touch with what's going on in my body. I used to dance a lot, but . . . but not so much now.' She trails off, looking a little bit wistful.

'What kind of dancing?' I ask.

'Argentinean tango.'

'Seriously?' I gasp, struggling to imagine this silver-haired seventy-something with her hand-knits in the middle of a smouldering tango.

'Oh yes. It was the second love of my life,' she smiles, 'after my husband. And it was something we loved to do together.'

'But you stopped?'

'I lost Fred three years ago,' she says, and calmly sets the last plate in its place.

My breath catches. 'Oh, Moth, I'm really sorry.'

She just shakes her head. 'Don't be. We had a wonderful life together. And I've been coming here twice a year ever since, so I've done a lot of work around my loss. But . . . I haven't been able to bring myself to dance with another partner. Not yet.'

'Oi, you two slackers!' Than appears, carrying the huge bowl of salad Beardy has prepared. 'Are you going to help or leave it all up to me?'

'My fault!' Moth smiles over at him. 'Let's get this lunch on the table.'

13

Challenge Your Comfort Zones

> 'To move forward and grow, we need to venture beyond our comfort zones. Yes, we are protected there, but we're also cut off from all sorts of wonderful experiences and opportunities.'
>
> ©TheBeginnersGuideToLoneliness.com

It's Ted's turn to try to tame us this afternoon, though I reckon he's got an easy session ahead of him, given how chilled we all are after the yoga class. It has turned into an absolutely gorgeous day, so, after lunch, we all troop through to the apple orchard and sit in a circle under the blossom.

'I hope you don't mind being outside,' Ted smiles around at us all, 'but when we're given a day as glorious as this, why waste it inside?'

I smile and lift my face to the blue sky, sucking in a lungful of fresh air. I'm not sure whether Claire slipped something into our bottles of water after yoga this morning, but I've not felt this relaxed in ages. Considering that we're about to have a session of group therapy with Ted, that's a bit of a miracle. This sort of thing would normally have me tense enough to snap. But right now, what's the point? I'm sitting comfortably in the long grass with Than on one side of me and Bay on the other.

'Okay, so everyone's here, that's great.' Ted beams. 'It's a simple session this afternoon. We're going to spend a bit of time getting to know each other better as a group, and then we're going to pair up to do some one-to-one sessions.'

Than nudges my elbow and grins at me. I smile back. I really want to get to know him better, but he doesn't take these sessions as seriously as the others, and after this morning went so surprisingly well, I'm quite keen to give this wellbeing thing a real shot.

'Now, don't go jumping ahead of yourselves, worrying about the second part,' says Ted, and I stiffen a bit. It's like these guys can read my mind sometimes. I look up at him, but he's not looking my way, so I don't think that particular comment was aimed at me.

'I know you did some partner work with Lizzie yesterday, sharing a secret. This afternoon is going to be about sharing one more thing, but this time, with the whole group. Remember, this needs to be about *you*. I want you to tell us about something that you feel holds you back in your day-today life. It can be anything.'

Suddenly, I'm not so relaxed. Share something with the whole group? Whatever I say, I'm not going to come out of it looking too great, am I? I sneak a quick, worried look around the circle and almost let out a laugh. Every single one of us, including old-hands Bay and Moth, are shifting uncomfortably. There's a lot of fiddling with nails and scratching of beards going on.

'Anyone want to go first?' Ted asks gently.

'Me.' It's Sam, looking rather surprised at the sound of his own voice.

'Well done, Sam,' Ted nods encouragingly at him. 'So, tell us something that you feel holds you back.'

Emma looks at her young husband with worried

eyes.

'Well, erm . . . I dunno if this is the kind of thing . . . if this is right . . . but, it's like, every day I'm worried that I'm not perfect.' Sam's eyes are on the ground, and he's ripping up handfuls of grass.

Worried he's not perfect? Who is? I feel Than nudge my arm, but I ignore his quiet invitation to mock the others like we did last time. I might not quite get what Sam has just said, but even I can see that it took balls for him to say it.

Ted's nodding at Sam, waiting for him to say something else, but when he doesn't, Ted asks, 'And how does this make you feel?'

Sam looks at him. 'Scared. Scared that I'm not good enough. That . . . that . . . maybe Emma might see that I'm not perfect for her . . . that I might lose everything.'

Emma's now got tears in her eyes and she's shaking her head.

'Well done, Sam. That's a big thing to share with the group. We will do more work on everything that comes up today, but for now, just stating these things and bringing them out into the sunlight is a big enough step. Emma, Sam, you'll get a chance to work together later, okay?'

They both nod, Sam's staring hard at his mounting pile of grass. Emma quickly wipes her eyes with the back of her hand.

'Who'd like to go next?'

'I will,' I say. Bay jumps a little next to me, obviously not expecting me to speak up so soon.

'Great, Tori . . . '

'There's something that really holds me back. I suffer from potamophobia . . . ' I pause, looking to Ted for assistance.

'And for the benefit of the rest of the group, are you able to explain what that is?'

'Oh, of course,' I say feeling a bit foolish. 'It's a fear of running water. Rivers . . . waterfalls . . . It's been getting steadily worse over the last two years. If I go out, I have to plan around avoiding rivers. I know it doesn't sound like a big deal but . . . well, it can cause me to have pretty bad panic attacks. Anyway, that's why I didn't make it down to the river for the first wild swim. I want to get over it, to face it . . . but . . . well . . . I'm sorry I bailed out without explaining why, but I'm just not ready.'

Ted nods at me. 'Thanks for sharing that with us, Tori. And it's important that you know — that you all know — working through issues takes time. It's not like skydiving, pushing yourself out of a plane and *bam*, you're there. It's all about tiny steps, little victories, allowing you to take control of the things that are holding you back. Sometimes even the act of acknowledging that they exist is a big enough step to take. Yes, we're here to take challenges and push ourselves, but we don't want to break while doing it.'

'I'm not brave.' Doreen's voice comes from the opposite side of the circle. 'There are things I wish I could do, or say or put in action . . . and I just can't make that first move.'

'And how does that make you feel?' asks Ted gently.

'Stuck. Like a big, fat, stupid, stuck coward,' Doreen growls.

I look at her in shock. She sounds so angry. Her face is white and set. I'm so surprised at Doreen's revelation. She seems so comfortable in her own skin. So confident. But what she's just said about herself is such a harsh image it almost feels like someone has torn the air out of our circle.

'Doreen,' says Ted calmly, 'is there anything else you want to add?'

Doreen shakes her head glumly.

'We're going to keep going until everyone has shared, but we're going to be working a lot on all of this, okay?'

Doreen nods once and sits staring at the grass. I want to rush over to her and wrap her in a hug, but maybe it's a good thing I can't — she looks like she could knock out a troll right now.

'Can I go?' asks Bay next to me.

Ted nods.

'I'm realizing that I'm too quick to judge people. Too quick to form an opinion of them based on the tiniest snapshot of what I've seen. I let this get in the way of getting to know who they really are. I let it colour things.' He huffs out an irritated breath. 'I used to think this was a good thing. I prided myself on being a good judge of character . . . but, actually, it's the opposite.'

'Thank you, Bay,' says Ted.

'I'll go,' says Than quickly. 'I do too much for people. Money, gifts. I forgive over and over. I lose myself in other people and forget that I'm important too.'

The back of my neck prickles as a breeze rustles the branches of the apple trees above us.

That was weird.

Set against the backdrop of what Bay just said, Than's issue sounds almost like a good thing. The complete opposite of what Bay just admitted to struggling with. Almost . . . like a brag. Than shifts his weight next to me and as Ted moves on to the next person, the sensation passes. Maybe I'm reading too much into everything.

I tune back in to hear Geoff finish talking about how he's struggling to remember to have a bit of fun after focusing too long on keeping their heads above water financially. I know how he feels on that one. Bob nearly has me in tears as he tells us about how much he misses his partner who passed away over a decade ago, and how no other guy comes near to matching up to him. Moth nods vigorously as Bob talks, clearly understanding every word and emotion that's crossing his face.

Finally, it's Beardy Weirdy's turn. 'Mine sounds ridiculous,' he rumbles in his low voice.

'Nothing you say is ridiculous,' says Ted, his voice comforting. 'It can be the simplest or the strangest things that can hold us back.'

Beardy nods. 'Well, I've been getting really bad panic attacks.'

I can't help but stare at Beardy. Really? Someone as grounded and weathered as him having panic attacks?

'And do you know what sparks them? What the trigger is?' asks Ted gently.

'Yes. That's the ridiculous bit.' Beardy takes a deep breath and looks around at us all, as if expecting someone to start laughing. 'It's . . . well, it's whenever I think about the environment . . . the destruction of the planet. If I catch something on the news, or come across an article. I start to think about it, and that thought joins a bunch of other worries, and then I start to feel helpless . . . I mean there's nothing any of us can do on our own is there? And then it just . . . it just . . . spirals.'

Beardy stops talking. His breath is coming in short,

sharp bursts. My heart goes out to him. His reaction is one of the least ridiculous things I've ever seen, probably because it's so familiar.

'Thank you for sharing,' says Ted. 'Thank you all for sharing. These are things we're going to be working on over the coming weeks. This is just the start. You've all taken a huge step today. It's important to be open so that we can act as each other's mirrors, reflecting back a different take on these issues and fears so that we can see them from new perspectives and start to understand them better.' Ted pauses to look around at us all.

'Right, everybody up!' Ted says, clapping loudly. Everyone jumps at the unexpected noise.

He bounds to his feet and a couple of the others follow his lead more slowly, shaking their heads and stretching as if they've just come out of a doze. I'm still sitting. I can't seem to shake the sense of heaviness that has fallen over me.

'Here, Tori!' Bay, who's already on his feet and looking about as perky as Ted, offers me his hand with a smile. I hesitate for just a second and then let him pull me to my feet. He misjudges it a bit and pulls so hard that I end up crashing into his chest. His spare arm wraps around me as we stagger back under the force of the impact.

'Thanks,' I laugh.

'No worries!'

For a second I'm caught up in his eyes, more hazel than green this afternoon in the soft light of the orchard.

'Tori, can you give me a hand? My leg's gone to sleep!'

Than's voice makes me quickly step away from

Bay. We both reach down to help him up between us, but Than grabs my arm and is on his feet without even acknowledging Bay's offer to help. Bay shrugs and walks away.

'Okay, gang, I think a quick game of catch is in order!' Ted calls excitedly.

'Catch?' Emma says, looking like she's missed something.

'Yep. No home bases and I'll start!'

Before anyone has quite figured out what's happening, Ted darts straight towards an unsuspecting Bob, pats him on the elbow and yells 'Tag!' before hotfooting it in the other direction.

For the next ten minutes, all kinds of chaos break loose as we dart around the orchard in the sunshine. Bob chases me three times around the same tree before turning back on himself and catching me at full tilt coming towards him. I catch Than, who's only a couple of paces away. He promptly chases Bay around the whole orchard, zigzagging in and out of the trees with the rest of us cheering, until he finally catches him. Bay promptly dashes straight at Doreen and catches her in a matter of seconds.

Emma lets out a high-pitched squeal as Doreen makes a heroic lunge for her, catching her on the arm, only to do an unexpected commando-roll into the grass as she completely fails to stop. Emma turns around to help her up, only to yell 'Tag' as Doreen reaches for her hand. We all dissolve into a round of giggles and the game comes to a rather unruly end.

'Excellent!' yells Ted. We all gather around him, breathing heavily and grinning. 'Just a quick reminder not to get stuck in our heads. It's important stuff we're talking about, but it's just as important to play in the sunshine, have fun together and be in the moment . . . '

I raise my eyebrows. Man, he's good. He does have a point — the whole time we were whizzing around the orchard, I didn't think about anything other than whether I was being chased or not.

'Can't believe I paid for this,' mutters Than beside me.

I elbow him in the ribs. I know he enjoyed that every bit as much as I did.

'Okay, we're going to pair off for the rest of the session and carry on from where we left off earlier.'

Than links his arm through mine. I glance at him and force a smile. It's not that I don't want to work with him again, but I'd really love the chance to get to know the others a bit too. Just hearing them talk earlier made me realize that I've hardly had the chance . . . or maybe I should say, I've hardly made the effort to get to know them yet.

'This time,' Ted continues, and I look back at him, fixed smile still on my face, 'I'm going to pair you up. It's human nature to gravitate towards the same people, but that's going to keep you in your comfort zones, and that's not what today is about. So . . . '

Ted runs through some quick pairings. Than ends up with Bay, while I, much to my delighted surprise, am partnered up with Doreen. When he's done, Ted goes through all the pairs very quickly, assigning the letter A or B to each partner.

'Okay, it's A's turn to talk today, and B, you are the set of ears, the listener and the questioner. This isn't about trying to catch your partner out; it's about listening and understanding their story. And I want all you As to tell your partner about one thing you want to address while you're here. It can be more about what you told us just now, or it can be something completely new.

'I'll be here in the orchard working with Emma and Sam, if any of you need to find me. I advise you all to stay out in the fresh air, but feel free to roam the place until you find somewhere you're both comfortable. You've got the rest of the afternoon, and we'll all meet up again to start preparing supper at six.'

14

Ban the Snooze Button

> 'When you start trying to change your life, it can all feel a bit scary. You're beginning to wake up, but it's too much at times. But don't hit the snooze button on your life. Get up, get dressed and find out what life has in store for you today!'
>
> ©TheBeginnersGuideToLoneliness.com

'I seriously can't believe that they let us two pair up,' laughs Doreen as we make our way out of the yard.

'Why not?' I ask. 'Hey, do you mind if we head up towards the woods instead of that way?'

'Of course not!' says Doreen. We make a quick change of direction and set off up the field past the yurt. 'Oh, the river's down that way, isn't it?'

I nod.

'Sorry, I didn't think.'

'Don't be sorry. I don't expect everyone else to have to remember my oddities! Anyway, why shouldn't they let us pair up?'

'Well, you'd think they'd be worried about us gossiping the whole session away!'

'Actually, I think that's what they're hoping for!' I laugh. 'At least in a controlled kind of way. I think they were aiming to pair people up who'd be comfortable together.'

'Well, in that case, I'm surprised you're not with Than.'

I blush at her blunt, forthright approach. 'Than?' I squeak.

'Well . . . yes! You've spent more time together than the rest of us have, I think.'

'Oh . . . I . . . ' I feel awkward all of a sudden. I mean, yes, I've chatted to Than, he tends to seek me out when we're all together, but I figure it's just because I'm the only one who knows what's going on for him at the moment. I don't think he's shared much with the others yet.

'Don't worry, love,' says Doreen. 'You know, it's not a crime to find a guy attractive and want to spend time with him.'

'Attractive?'

'Well, don't you?'

I can feel the heat rushing up from my feet. 'I . . . erm . . . '

'Wow, girl, slow down!' puffs Doreen. 'That game of catch almost killed me. I don't need you finishing me off!'

I've subconsciously picked up my pace and have started to route-march up the hill as if I'm trying to outrun Doreen's questions. 'Sorry,' I say, slowing down as she catches up.

'So, do you?' she prods.

'What?'

I know what, I'm just playing for time.

'Like Than? I mean . . . find him attractive . . . you know, *like* him?' She waggles her eyebrows at me.

I can't help but laugh. 'I guess,' I say. 'I mean, he's a good-looking guy. He's been really nice and I've enjoyed his company — '

'Wow, you sound like a maiden aunt!' Doreen laughs.

'Jeez, thanks very much.'

'Well, you do! Where are the butterflies and the sparks and the heart-pounding excitement?'

'The thing is, I'm not here for that. I'm not looking for someone else at the moment. I've got too much to do, too much I want to get my head around.'

'I hear you,' says Doreen softly at my side. 'Shame, though. I was looking forward to you providing me with all the juicy retreat gossip.'

'Well, sorry to disappoint!' I grin at her as we reach the top of the field. We both turn and lean our backs against the gate, gazing back down towards the yurt and over the farmhouse and yard.

'Love, it's not me you'll be disappointing,' says Doreen with a serious face.

I don't know what to say to that. Maybe there is a little flutter when I see Than and when we spend time together. I know there shouldn't be, but he does seem to understand me. It's like there's some kind of unspoken communication between us, like we've known each other for longer than the couple of days we've been here at The Farm.

'Sorry, Tori, I shouldn't have said anything,' Doreen says, patting my arm, her face a picture of concern.

'Oh, don't worry about that. I've got so much in my head, I just don't feel like I can trust my instincts on anything at the moment. Anyway, that's enough about me. This session's meant to be about you!' I say, unhooking the gate from the post and swinging it back so that we can make our way into the baby woodland beyond.

'Me?' squeaks Doreen, turning to help me heave the gate closed behind us.

'Yep.'

'I . . . You know, Tori, I don't think I'm ready,' she says.

I look at Doreen and see a cloud cross her usually sunny face.

'But you've had to put up with me wittering all the way up here. And anyway, you're group A and I'm group B. And group A gets their turn today.' I grin at her, trying to lift her out of whatever slump she's slipped into.

Doreen shakes her head at me.

'Don't you trust me?' I ask. I feel a tiny shard of hurt hit me in the chest.

'Oh, love, it's not that. I don't trust *myself* yet. You're so brave, sharing your phobia with the group . . . and I, I just can't. Not yet. Not even with you. And you'd be the first person I could tell.'

I swallow down a lump in my throat and grab Doreen's hand, giving it a squeeze. She looks at me, surprised.

'It's okay. I'll swap with you. But when you're ready, I'm here, okay?' I say.

Doreen squeezes my hand hard and sniffs. 'Okay.'

We wander through the young trees in silence for a while, my hand still in hers. The sun has come out now, and rather than feeling tense and uncomfortable, like I did when Ted told us about this session, I'm completely relaxed. I'm enjoying the warmth on my face, and the company of this lovely woman I'm coming to think of as a friend.

'So . . . ' prompts Doreen at last.

'So?' I say, stopping in a little clearing. There's thick grass in between the trees here. They haven't grown tall enough to cut out the light yet, and little wild flowers are dotted like bright jewels among the green. 'Shall we sit down?'

'Sure!' says Doreen. 'Two secs . . . ' She yanks a canvas tote bag that I hadn't even noticed she was carrying off her arm and draws out a red tartan blanket.

'Ooh, snazzy!'

'Well, it was in the cabin, and Bay mentioned last night that Ted tends to prefer to send us outside rather than working indoors, so I thought it might come in handy.'

'Good thinking,' I sigh as I sink down onto the blanket next to Doreen.

'So . . . ' she smiles at me.

'Ah. Back to that. Now what was it Ted said we were meant to do?'

'Tell me one of the reasons that you came here. It can be anything.'

I shrug. 'That's an easy one.'

'Is it?' Doreen gapes at me, surprised.

'Of course,' I say, settling down with my legs crossed. I know Claire said that the yoga session was a gentle one, but I can still feel a faint, delicious hum in my muscles that I'm not used to.

'I'm lonely,' I say, matter-of-factly. Why is it so easy to say that to Doreen?

'You are?' She looks a bit surprised.

'Yes. That's the big thing I'm here to . . . fix? Is that the right word?'

'But how are you lonely? You're so easy to talk to, so lovely,' says Doreen. 'I thought your reason for being here was the water thing . . . '

'I guess that's part of it,' I say. *Not the part I want to talk about right now, though.*

Doreen picks a long piece of grass from the edge of

the rug and starts to twist it around her finger like a ring. 'How long have you been feeling like that?' she asks.

I sigh. When did it start? When Mum died? That would be logical . . . but, if I'm honest, it was even before then. 'You know, I think it's been there since I was a kid in a way. I was always a part of a large group, but never had one close friend that really stuck. It was like that all the way through school and uni. I guess it really started to have an impact when I left work just over two years ago,' I say.

'I used to be a copywriter for a big advertising agency. I never really liked it much. The work was okay, but the whole office thing was exhausting. I felt like I had to put on a different persona just to fit in. Then there were the days when my anxiety would take over, and it was a real struggle just to face the commute, let alone deal with everyone when I actually reached the office. Anyway, in the end I plucked up the courage to go self-employed.'

'Wow, that was brave!' says Doreen.

'I guess so. But it meant I lost that connection with all those people I saw every day.'

'You didn't stay in touch with your friends from work?'

'They weren't really friends; just colleagues. And I was so busy trying to scrape enough income together that I let it slip. We'd never really socialized anyway, so as soon as I finished at the office that was that.'

'But what about your other friends? Surely you didn't only have your work colleagues?'

I shake my head and sigh. 'No, I had a big group of friends. Actually, we'd all been mates since secondary school. We managed to stay in touch through uni.'

'So what happened?'

'My fiancé, Markus, was part of the same group. We'd all been together for what felt like forever.'

'Sounds perfect,' Doreen sighs.

'It does, doesn't it? At least from the outside,' I huff. 'But then, when everything went wrong, it meant *everything* went wrong.'

'What happened?' Doreen asks, looking worried.

'Markus cheated on me.'

'He didn't!' Doreen looks horrified.

'Yep.'

'With one of your friends?'

I look at her, surprised. 'No. No, not with one of my friends. It was with a random barmaid.'

'Oh. Sorry.'

I shrug.

'So what did you do?'

'I split up with him.'

'As you would expect. That must have really hurt.'

'It did . . . but I had other stuff to worry about at the time.'

'So your friends sided with him?'

'No, not at first. They kept inviting me out, trying to help me over it with offers of girly nights out and shopping.'

'It didn't work?' asks Doreen gently.

'I didn't accept any of the invitations, and it didn't take long for them to dry up completely. And before I knew it, Markus was seeing this other girl and they were a part of the group . . . and I was out.' I let out a sigh and pick at one of my nails.

'I can understand you pulling back after it had just ended, but didn't you want to reconnect with your friends after a while? Surely they could see you were hurting and — '

I shake my head. 'I wasn't easy to be around. I do understand that.'

'I'm missing something here,' says Doreen, and my heart sinks. She's not stupid, this one, is she? 'If you've been friends with someone for that long, whether you're friends with her ex or not, you make sure she's okay. And no matter what she throws at you, you keep trying.'

'My mum had just died. They didn't know how to handle it.'

Doreen looks like I've just slapped her. 'Your mum? Oh, you poor lamb! So you're telling me you lost your mum and then Markus cheated on you — all in the same year?'

I shift my legs, stretching them out and then hugging them back to me. Now I've come this far, I may as well tell her. 'The same month,' I say.

'Son of a bitch!' Doreen spits, taking me by surprise. I look at her and can't help but smile at the thunderous expression on her face.

'You could say that,' I agree.

'And your friends were okay with what he'd done to you?'

'I wouldn't say that they were okay with it. Actually, I don't think many of them knew exactly what had happened. Markus had this interesting take on things — how I wasn't giving him enough attention and he'd been forced to look elsewhere. I was in shock, and to be honest, I was numb when I found out what he'd done. I just split up with him and then got on with wading through all the shitty practicalities that come with losing a parent. I got quite good at not feeling anything.'

'And your friends just abandoned you?'

'Like I said, they asked me out, they really tried. But I wasn't in the mood to be told that I needed to 'get over it', that a couple of drinks and a bit of fun was all I needed to feel better.'

'Of course not. I'm so sorry,' Doreen reaches over and pats my hand. I smile at her.

'So that's where it started. No work colleagues, no friends, no significant other.'

'And all that grief and anger and sadness to work through.'

I nod.

'What about your dad? Do you have any other family?'

I shake my head. 'Dad left when I was a baby. He's never been in my life and I don't know him. I don't have any brothers or sisters. Mum was an only kid too, so there aren't even any aunts or uncles in the sidelines either.'

'Do you need a hug?' Doreen asks me suddenly.

I grin at her. 'I'm okay,' I say.

'I don't understand how you haven't exploded?' she says.

'I went online. I had to talk to someone, so I joined this grief support group. That was just a couple of weeks after it all happened.'

'Oh, thank God!' said Doreen.

'Exactly what I said,' I laugh. 'I met my three best friends in that group. One night, I just felt like I was sinking under it all. I needed to talk to someone who was going through something similar. Anyway, this girl called Nat started to chat with me, and we got on really well. I swear she was my lifeline. I talked poor Nat's ear off in our private chat that week.'

'And the other two?'

'I met them about a week later in the same chat room.'

'And this was all two years ago?'

'Yep! I started to chat with Nat first, and then I invited the other two into our private chat when I met them . . . and we still talk every single day. I probably chat with Nat the most; she's always checking in with me. But we've all been able to support each other. Like when Hugh's brother passed away, we were all there for him.'

'But you still feel lonely, even with these three?'

'They are amazing, but we've never met in person, and no matter how much they mean to me, it's just not the same somehow.'

'You've never met?'

I shake my head. 'Nope, we chat every day online but we're spread all over the country. Sue has baby twins now, so she's pretty tied up. Hugh lives right up north. Nat and I have arranged to meet up a couple of times as she's not that far from me, but we've never quite managed to make it happen.'

Doreen blows out her cheeks, looking flummoxed. 'Well, now I see why you feel lonely. Two years is a hell of a long time.'

I nod. 'I'm at home in my flat all day. Of course, I meet people when I'm out shopping or whatever, but . . . London's quite impersonal, you know? Millions of people . . . but they're millions of strangers.'

I stop talking, hyper aware that I've just dumped all my rubbish on someone else who's here for help. She didn't need to hear all that. 'Doreen, I'm so sorry,' I say, slightly embarrassed.

'What for?'

'Offloading! That wasn't fair.'

'Erm . . . I think you'll find that's exactly what we're meant to be doing,' Doreen chuckles.

'I guess,' I sigh. I thought I'd feel better for telling someone, but actually, I just feel exhausted, like I could sleep for a week. I lie back on the blanket and watch a little white cloud scud across the sky. I can see Doreen, to the side of me, fiddling with another piece of grass.

'You get stuck,' I say, as if I'm answering a silent question. 'After a while, it's impossible to remember how to make new friends, how to meet people. Where to even start. And you have all this input, every day. Stuff happens, good, bad, big, small . . . life happens, and you have no one there to share it with.' I swallow hard. The backs of my eyes are prickling, and I blink once, twice, willing the tears to magically disappear. Instead they spill over my cheeks as Doreen quietly reaches over and takes my hand.

15

Trust Your Instincts

> 'It can be difficult to tell the difference between your gut instinct and anxiety. This can lead to people with anxiety disorders losing trust in themselves. The good news is, there are ways to learn to differentiate between the two, and doing so will help you to learn to trust yourself again.'
> ©TheBeginnersGuideToLoneliness.com

It's amazing what running around together in the sunshine can achieve. Despite the fact that this afternoon was emotionally exhausting, there's a lightness to our communal meal this evening. When Doreen and I trundled back from the woods in time to make a start on the evening meal, we found it already set out on the table. Russ and Claire had decided to use their afternoon off to prepare a feast for us.

I don't think garden salad, boiled eggs and fresh herby bread has ever tasted so delicious. Being out in the fresh air all day has made me hungry, and Doreen and I tuck in with relish. The others join us as they all start to rock up in their pairs. When Emma, Sam and Ted appear, the couple look a lot more relaxed than they did earlier, though strangely younger and more shy around each other. There's a huge part of me that really wants to ask Emma what happened in their session, but I know I'd hate it if anyone wanted me to tell them about my afternoon with Doreen. I can only imagine it would be worse, and doubly as private, between a couple and one of the counsellors. Instead, I smile at them both, and pat the place next to me on the bench for Emma to join me. She returns my smile, but before she's had a chance to make her way around the table, Than slumps into the spot instead.

'Hey!' he grins.

'Oh, hi,' I say, surprised. 'I think Emma was about to sit there.'

'There's plenty of room!' Than laughs, and Emma takes the seat the other side of him. 'See, no big deal.'

I smile back at him. Sure. No big deal. I suppose. Other than the fact that Doreen's words from earlier on are playing on a loop in my head. *Than . . . attractive . . . disappointing him*. I wonder if that's what everyone else thinks too. I hadn't really considered it before. Maybe that was naive of me. I take a peek at Than's face, trying to figure it out. Yes, he's definitely attractive. Dark hair, cropped fairly short. Clear skin. Almond-shaped blue eyes.

'You okay?' he asks, shooting me a sideways grin, clearly having caught me staring.

'Oh, uh . . . yeah,' I smile. 'Away with the fairies. I'm absolutely wiped!' I reach for my glass of water. 'Have a good afternoon?'

'Oh. Sure. I guess,' he says tightly. The smile has dropped from his face now and he fidgets a bit. Reaching for a piece of bread, he starts to break it up into tiny pieces, rolling each one into a sticky ball before dropping it onto his plate.

'You know, you should try a bite . . . that bread's heavenly!' I say, trying to lighten his sudden mood.

'Cheers!' says Russ from across the table. 'That's my speciality, that is!'

'You made it?' I ask, looking at him in surprise.

'With my own, not so fair, hands!' he says, cutting himself a thick slice and smothering it with honey.

'Honey and herbs? Really?' I say, scrunching my nose up.

'Don't judge until you've tried it!' he says, and to my great surprise, he picks up the slice and offers it across the table for me to take a bite. I only hesitate for a second and then sink my teeth into it.

'Oh. My. God.' I mutter through a mouthful of herby honey deliciousness.

'And that's what you call a foodgasm!' laughs Doreen, raising her glass of juice to me. I smack her arm as I continue to chew, and she and Russ both crease up. Next to me, Than lets out a huff and reaches out to fill his water glass.

'What's up?' I ask quietly under the cover of the rising volume of chatter as more people join us at the table.

'Would you be up for coming for a walk with me after dinner?' he asks.

'What about the washing-up?'

'I think we've done our fair share of kitchen duties for a couple of days.'

'I guess you're right,' I say, but still not liking the idea of leaving it all to the others.

'Course I'm right. And I could really do with a friend this evening.'

My heart squeezes in sympathy. That's one feeling I understand right at the core of me.

'Sure thing,' I say.

* * *

But my promise to spend some time with Than leaves me with a rather heavy feeling for the rest of the meal. You'd think we'd all be talked out after the session we've just had, but it's more like a cork has come out of a bottle. The whole group's chatting away and getting to know each other. There's a lovely sense of community, and I'd like nothing more than to take time over my meal and join in. But as soon as Than finishes eating, I can feel his impatience coming at me in waves as he waits for me to finish. In the end, I give up. I'm not even enjoying the food now that I've got someone watching me eat every mouthful and sighing every time I take another sip of my drink.

As we stand together and leave the others chatting, Doreen catches my eye and gives me a wink. I want to turn around and tell her it's not what she thinks, but Than chooses that moment to tuck my arm into his as we walk away from the group, and I see Doreen raise her eyebrows.

'So, where do you fancy going?' I ask lightly, resigning myself to the walk.

'If you don't mind, I'd really like to go back to my tent for a chat, if that's okay?'

'Oh . . . uh, sure . . . ' I say uncertainly.

'I would have suggested your place, as I guess you might be more comfortable there, but Bay could turn up any moment, and I don't fancy spending any more time with him today.'

I glance at him and see his jaw clench. *Uh oh!* I'm guessing that wasn't a particularly easy session for the two of them this afternoon then.

'It's okay!' I say. 'I haven't been up to the campsite since you've all arrived and set up. I'd love to see it now.'

'Cool!' says Than, and I feel him relax a bit.

'So, what's up?' I ask, as we swing the gate to the woodland closed behind us.

'Just . . . all the questions, you know? They want to get all this personal shit out of you and I can't see the point.'

'Well . . . haven't you found it's helping at all?' I ask gently. 'The bits that you've shared already, haven't they got you thinking?'

'I don't need any extra shit to think about, thanks!' he snaps.

'Oh. I didn't mean . . . '

'Sorry, Tori.' Than stops in his tracks. 'I'm sorry. I didn't mean to take it out on you. That's the last thing I want to do.'

'It's okay,' I shrug.

'No. It's not.' He sighs and runs a hand through his hair, leaving it sticking up here and there. 'Look, can we just hang out for a bit, gossip, have a laugh . . . not get into the heavy stuff? I think that'll do me more good than anything else they've thrown at us today.'

I look at him and can't help but smile. He looks like a little boy, with his dark hair all tufty, and his ever-present smiley-face badge slightly askew on the front of his top. 'Of course,' I say, 'sounds like a plan.'

There's a part of me that's now desperate to find out what Bay and Than discussed in their session. I didn't catch which one of them was due to do the talking, but from Than's reaction to the whole afternoon, I'm guessing it was him. Still, maybe he'll tell me a bit about it later once he's calmed down.

We're both pretty quiet as we walk the rest of the way to the campsite, but the atmosphere between us is now far more relaxed. It's a beautiful evening again.

The light is soft and the scent of blossom seems to be drifting up from the orchard below us. I take in a deep breath as we walk and let it out slowly. Who'd have thought I'd enjoy being here as much as I am? And on an evening stroll with a handsome guy, no less.

When we reach the campsite, it's pretty clear that there's no one else here. The fire pit is black and lifeless, and the four tent entrances are zipped up tight. They're arranged in a wide, loose circle around the fire, far enough away that there's no chance of a stray spark or bit of floating ash causing an issue.

Than beckons me over to an old-school green and orange affair that looks like it would be at home in an Enid Blyton book.

'This is me,' he says, unzipping the front.

It's a tiny space, especially compared with the yurt, which is basically a palace.

'You want to get a fire going and hang out here?' I ask hopefully.

Than shakes his head. 'Nah, let's stay in here for a bit. I'm totally knackered, and there's plenty of space for us both to crash out for a while.'

He crawls in, and I hesitate, a bit at a loss for words. Than heaves a pack from inside the tent and dumps it unceremoniously on the ground outside. Then, crawling back in, he straightens a sleeping bag out on one side of the tent and places a tartan blanket on the other side.

'There ya go,' he grins back over his shoulder. 'You've got your own blanket and everything.'

Resigning myself to saying goodbye to the beautiful, sunlit evening and hello to the cramped, stuffy inside of Than's tent, I kick off my Converse and crawl in after him.

'Here!' he says, passing one of his pillows to me.

'Ta.' I scoot around and sit in an awkward, cross-legged position as Than sprawls full length onto his sleeping bag. I tuck my ankles in even further, hoping that my socks don't stink after a day in my hot shoes. Uh oh, there's zero chance of that!

'Seriously, Tori, make yourself comfortable! You look like you're sitting on a pile of drawing pins!'

Well, it seems I can't beat him, so I may as well join him. And besides, it gives me an excuse to get my potentially stinky feet as far away from both our noses as possible. I stretch out full length next to Than, wiggling my feet under my blanket while I'm at it, and lean my head up on one hand.

'That's more like it!' he smiles approvingly, and brings his arms up behind his head.

Now I'm lying down, the epic tiredness from earlier sweeps over me and I force back a yawn.

'Boring you already?' Than says, turning his head to look at me.

'I'm sorry!' I laugh. 'Of course you're not. I'm just wiped out. It's all the fresh air, I think.'

'Yeah. That and all the questions,' Than grumbles, looking back up at the canvas roof again.

'Hey, we weren't going to talk about that, remember?' I tease, poking him in the side with my free hand.

Than squirms at my touch, and shifts over onto his side, mirroring me. Wow. Okay, flood of butterflies — where did they come from? Perhaps it's something to do with those blue eyes quite so close to mine. We're not touching, but it wouldn't take much for me to reach out and make contact again.

I try to breathe as slowly as possible, not wanting

him to sense what's running through my mind.

'So how was your afternoon?' Than asks quietly.

I raise my eyebrows, surprised. 'You sure you want to talk about this stuff?' I ask.

'As long as I don't have to talk about mine, then we're good,' he quirks a smile at me, and for a second I can't take my eyes off his mouth.

'Deal,' I say, my voice coming out huskily. I clear my throat. I settle my head back onto my pillow and turn on my back to face the canvas ceiling. 'Well, our session was good,' I say.

'It was Doreen's turn this time, wasn't it?' he asks.

'Yep, but . . . '

'What did she have to tell you, then?' he interrupts. 'What's a housewife like her really got to worry about?'

I swallow. Well, that's one way to kill a mood stone dead. My butterflies have just dive-bombed off the edge of a cliff. I had been about to tell him that we swapped, that I'd taken the turn to talk, but something makes me keep that to myself.

'That's not very fair,' I say as lightly as I can.

'But she's so insipid. You know she is.'

'I like Doreen,' I say. I really like her and I really don't like what's happening right now.

'Well, I suppose there's not much there to dislike.'

'Than!'

'Fine, fine.' He laughs. 'I'm sure she's lovely.' He says it in his arch sarcastic voice, and I bristle.

'She is lovely,' I say firmly.

'So what did the lovely Doreen have to say for herself?'

'You know I can't tell you that . . . ' I say. I sit up and hug my knees to me. Now I feel really bloody uncomfortable, and I'd quite like an excuse to go back to the others.

'Tori?' Than sits up beside me. 'I'm sorry, I was only messing around.'

I turn to look at him, and his face is sincere, his eyes searching mine. Maybe I'm overreacting, overthinking everything. I stare hard at the smiley badge on his chest, trying to get a handle on my feelings.

'Really, I didn't mean to upset you,' he says, and rests his hand briefly on my arm.

I shake my head and give him a small smile. 'It's okay. Sorry, Than. Maybe I'm just a bit tired.'

'So I'm forgiven?' he asks.

'Nothing to forgive,' I say, and with a sigh I slump back onto the pillow again.

Than lies back down next to me and, taking my hand, gives it a quick squeeze before letting go. 'Thanks for coming with me this evening.'

'That's okay,' I say, and close my eyes as another wave of weariness washes over me. We lie in silence for a couple of minutes.

'You know, I miss this . . . ' I say at last.

'What?' Than sounds alert, perplexed.

'Lying next to someone and just talking.'

Than laughs. 'What, you mean pillow talk?'

'I guess,' I say, slightly embarrassed.

'So no other half at home, then?'

'Not anymore. Actually, not for a couple of years now.'

'You still miss him?' Than asks.

I take a second to think about it. 'You know what? No . . . I don't miss him. It's like I said, I miss this. The talking. Being close to someone.'

Than turns back on his side to face me and I move to do the same.

'Well . . . just for the record, I'm always available for a bit of pillow talk.' He winks at me and I smile back.

I find myself hooked on his eyes again, and something in the atmosphere between us changes. I'm doing the slow, light breathing thing again, and the space between us feels like it's getting smaller. I can feel the warmth of his skin radiating out from him. Our faces are so close, I can see darker flecks in his eyes.

There's a crash outside the tent, followed by the sounds of two people laughing and chattering. There's another crash, and I spring away from Than as if someone's thrown a bucket of iced water over my head.

Through the tent's entrance, I just have the chance to spot Claire and Moth next to a pile of wood they've just gathered, before a brown and white blur hurtles straight at me, tail wagging nineteen to the dozen. It's Dennis, and he's insistent on a cuddle at the same time as trying to give my face a wash with his tongue.

I struggle to my knees, laughing and trying to keep my face slobber-free. But I give in and wrap my arms around the warm dog. For a second, all I can hear is his tail beating against my legs.

'Out, dog!' Than shouts, making me jump.

Dennis pulls away from me and eyeballs Than warily.

'Go on, out!' Than shouts again. Dennis looks from Than to me, and back again, clearly unused to being spoken to like this.

'It's okay, Than,' I say gently.

'No, it's not. Out!' Than barks at Dennis for a third time, and I feel the rumble of a growl come from Dennis.

'You're scaring him,' I say. 'It's okay, boy, come on.'

I go to lead Dennis out of the tent before he and Than get into a real argument.

As Dennis scuttles out in front of me, Than leans forward and, placing one hand on my shoulder, tries to draw me gently back towards him. I shake my head at him and scramble out after the dog.

16

Permission to Pause

'You've pushed your boundaries, opened yourself to new experiences and challenged your comfort zones over and over again. It's okay to give yourself permission to pause. You're not stopping in your incredible journey, just taking a moment to admire how far you've come.'
©TheBeginnersGuideToLoneliness.com

I spot the yurt in the distance and breathe a sigh of relief. As I pause for a second to catch my breath, Dennis sits down and leans his head against my leg. From the moment we got out of Than's tent, he has glued himself to me, acting like a large, furry shadow.

I only stopped for a couple of minutes to say hello to Claire and Moth, shoving my shoes back on while they did their best to hide their obvious surprise at the sight of me and Than emerging from his tent. We've probably just managed to provide tomorrow's juicy gossip. I cringe at the thought.

Claire mentioned that everyone was going to reconvene down at the main fire pit for the evening. Than was all for us both walking straight back down there together, but I managed to wriggle out of it. Thinking about it now, I might have been a tad too firm with him about coming back on my own. I used Dennis as my excuse, but really, I just needed a bit of space. That little chat was taking a turn I didn't feel particularly in control of, and the way he reacted to Dennis's innocent appearance turned my butterflies into something that felt uncomfortably close to panic. Anyway, I'm craving some peace and quiet to work it all out a bit.

As we head down the hill towards the yurt, Dennis's tail goes into overdrive, and he pulls ahead of me and scoots inside before I get there. I flip open the flap to find Bay lounging at full stretch on the sofa.

'Oh, hi!' I say. I don't know why I'm surprised to see him. I mean, he does live here too.

Bay lifts his head off the cushions and smiles at me.

'Hey, Tori. Sorry, let me budge up. I thought you were out for the evening.' He swings his feet down, making space for me at the other end of the little sofa. Bang goes my chance of a quiet hour to myself.

'I was,' I say, flopping down next to him and leaning over to scratch Dennis's ears. 'But I thought I'd better bring this monkey home before the argument between him and Than got any more serious!'

Bay raises his eyebrows. 'Argument? What did he do?'

'Oh, just growled at Than a bit.'

'I didn't mean Dennis.'

I shrug. 'Dennis bowled into Than's tent. We were in there talking and Than told Dennis to get out . . . a couple of times . . . and poor old Dennis didn't like it. No big deal.'

Bay frowns. 'Actually, it is a big deal. Dennis never growls.'

'Well, he was as good as gold once I got him out of the tent, and he stuck right by me all the way home . . . or at least he did until he caught your scent and hurtled in here like a daddy's boy!'

'Well, thanks for bringing him back,' says Bay. 'You

know, it sounds like he was trying to protect you.'

I laugh. 'Nah, he just wanted tickles and didn't like being told off.'

'Well, whatever. Thanks for making sure he was okay. And sorry he dragged you away from your, erm, talk . . . '

I feel my face start to redden. 'No probs. I wanted to head back here anyway.'

'Need a bit of space?' he asks, ruffling Dennis's ears.

I nod. 'It's quite intense here, isn't it?'

'Sometimes.'

'You okay?' I ask curiously, realizing that I've just interrupted his moment of peace. 'You weren't at dinner . . . '

'Yeah. I just needed some time to digest today's sessions.'

'You were with Than this afternoon, weren't you?' I say as lightly as possible.

'Yup.' Bay leans back against the sofa, looking wiped.

'Do you want me to make you a cuppa before I go?'

Bay shakes his head. 'Nah, I'm good, thanks. You back off up to the campsite?' he asks, looking pissed off for some reason.

'Nope, they've decided to have a fire down in the main pit. You fancy it?'

'I think I'll stay put, thanks. I'm not in the best of moods.'

'No, can't say I'm feeling that settled either . . . but I'm learning sometimes company is the answer to that.'

Bay smiles at me wearily. 'Look, there's something I wanted to say to you.'

I wait to see what he says next, but he goes quiet.

'What, Bay?' I laugh, eventually breaking the silence.

'This is between you and me . . . ' he blurts.

'Ah, come on, I'm all secreted out for one day!'

'I'll give you this one for free, as long as you keep it to yourself. But after what you've just said, I think I've got to say something.'

I shrug and don't reply. Half of me is now super-curious to see what's getting to him, and the other half is irritated that my moment of peace is turning into something far more complicated. I get to my feet and cross over to my case, intending to pull out a warmer jumper to wear down to the fire.

'Watch out for Than,' he says abruptly.

I stop in my tracks, dumbfounded, and swing back around to face him.

'What do you mean, watch out?'

'I mean, just be a bit careful, Tori.' He sits straighter on the sofa and twists to look at me. 'There's something about him that I'm not sure about.'

'You can't say that!' I squeak, indignation oozing out of me. 'I mean, we've all got stuff going on. That's why we're here. It's meant to be a safe space to share with each other!'

'I know. But something just isn't sitting right.'

I huff and go to defend Than further, but Bay cuts me off. 'I've seen a lot, and I mean a lot, of troubled souls coming through here. They're all looking for an answer to something. Trust me, some of the stuff that they're looking for help with is pretty horrific. And none of them — not one — has ever caused these alarm bells before.'

'And why exactly are you more worried about me than the rest of the group?'

'I'm not blind, Tori. I see how Than is with you.

He spent the whole opening ceremony staring at you. He's managed to completely separate you from the rest of the group on more than one occasion . . . like when you two skipped out on the wild swimming session, and it sounds like he managed to do it again this afternoon after dinner.'

'You're imagining things. I told everyone I was sorry about the swimming session.'

'I know . . . but why was he the one there to hold your hand? To encourage you to give in to your fears?' Bay shakes his head as if there's a fly irritating him. 'How can it be best for you to just avoid the things you need to work on?'

I shrug, and then go over to straighten my bed covers. I don't have to listen to this rubbish.

'Bay,' I say, trying to keep my voice steady, 'I did what was best for me. Than just happened to be there and noticed what was going on. For your information, I got a lot out of that session. Out of the whole day, actually.'

'Oh yeah,' he says, the sarcasm in his voice is so heavy that he sounds like a completely different person. 'I'm sure you got loads out of Lizzie's session, spending the whole time staring into his eyes.'

'Me? Staring at him? I . . . ' Damn and blast my bloody blush reflex. I can feel the heat radiating from my cheeks.

'I saw it, Tori,' Bay says again.

'Well, you don't need to worry about me. Besides, it looks like I'm going to have you and your bloody dog as a chaperone most of my waking life while I'm here, so there's no chance anything could happen even if I wanted it to, is there?'

'Nope,' Bay snaps. 'Not if I have anything to do

with it anyway.'

I shake my head in irritation. There is literally nothing I can say to make him believe that I'm not interested in Than . . . especially as, right now, I'm not one hundred per cent certain on that point either.

⋆ ⋆ ⋆

The fire turns out to be a blessing. For starters, it means I don't have to hang out in the yurt, silently fuming while pretending that what Bay said about Than didn't bug me. Because it really did. A lot. And that's the other good thing about tonight. I'm not on my own with Than either. Because no matter how pissed off I am with Bay, his words of warning have lodged somewhere very deep down in my anxiety-prone brain. Between that and the weird turn things took up at the campsite earlier, I suddenly feel a little bit uncomfortable around Than.

I could curse Bay for making me feel like this, because Than is back to being his usual friendly self. But now I can't help but notice how he's . . . I don't know . . . he's zoning in on me a bit. Every time I look up, he's watching me. Whenever there's a spot available next to me on one of the straw bales around the fire, he seems to be there, ready to fill it. But the whole group is here this evening. The only glaring exception is Bay, and that's fine by me because at least it means I'm not going to constantly be on edge, worrying about what he imagines he can see between the two of us.

'Hey!'

I turn to find Doreen sitting next to me.

'Glad you made it back for the fire,' she grins. 'I

was wondering if you and a certain someone might be a bit too busy to join us!'

And there I was, thinking I'd managed to escape that particular smoking gun.

'He just wanted a chat . . . ' I mutter. Urgh, is everyone watching and wondering if there's something going on?

'Mm hmm . . . ' She leans closer and whispers, 'Well, can't say I'd blame you if you did more than just chat!'

'Shhh!' I wince, peeping back over my shoulder at Than, who's sitting the other side of me. I can only hope he's too busy chatting with Bob to have heard anything.

'Nothing happened,' I hiss, and Doreen's perm seems to deflate a little bit with disappointment.

'Really?' she begs. 'Not even a tiny snippet of juicy gossip?'

I laugh and shake my head. I could tell her about what I think *almost* happened, the butterflies . . . but frankly, I think we're getting enough unwanted attention at the moment without fanning the flames.

'So, how are you doing?' I ask, trying to deflect the conversation away from the tangle I'm in.

'Oh, fine, you know. Geoff reckons he already feels twenty years younger, what with the yoga and the swimming.' She smiles and looks wistfully across the fire to where her husband is deep in conversation with Sam. She wipes a stray tear from her cheek so quickly it's obvious that she's hoping I won't notice.

'You okay?' I ask, shuffling around to face her properly.

Doreen nods and sniffs. 'You know I said I couldn't talk to you earlier?'

I nod.

'Can I tell you now?' she whispers.

'Of course!' I say.

'It's just so strange, being here together. I've wanted to be able to spend more time with Geoff for ages . . . and now we're here, I'm scared that we've both changed too much for it to work.'

I pat Doreen's arm ineffectually, and watch Ted haul another large log onto the fire. 'But you're getting the chance to get to know each other again?'

'Well, yes. I've been caring for my mother for ages. Geoff's a sweetheart, and has been so supportive, but having Mum living with us and being a full-time carer while Geoff has held everything together financially has put a lot of pressure on our marriage.'

'You said your mum is in a home now?' I ask, struggling to remember what she'd said at that first meeting in the farmhouse.

'Yes. Social Services finally decided that it would be best for her.'

'I'm so sorry,' I say.

'That's the problem,' Doreen laughs, but I can hear that it's thick with unshed tears, 'I'm not. I feel so guilty saying this, but it's the biggest relief. It's hard enough when your own mother doesn't recognize you, but she was becoming more and more difficult to care for. She got really violent at times. You must think I'm so horrible . . . '

Doreen starts to cry in earnest. I shuffle right over to the edge of my straw bale and put an arm around her shoulders. 'I don't think anything of the sort,' I say quietly. I remember the horrible comment I made to Than when we skived off from the swim, and what he said about Doreen earlier, and a part of me cringes.

'Thanks, Tori!' Doreen snuffles, pulling back and wiping her face. 'I just . . . I'm just so scared that me and Geoff won't find that thing between us again, you know?' she says. 'He's my best friend and he knows me better than anyone else in the world . . . but . . . that's not enough, is it?'

I shrug. 'Sorry, not my area of expertise.'

She smiles at me, her lips trembling. 'Oh, don't you go worrying about that. You're sharing your tent with one guy who can't take his eyes off you,' she leans in a bit closer, 'and sharing a bale with another one.'

I roll my eyes at her and she nudges me in the ribs.

'I'll leave that kind of thing up to you!' I say. 'Sharing with Bay is like a cross between sharing with a mean older brother and a strict head teacher.'

'We'll see,' she says, gazing longingly across the fire at Geoff.

* * *

By the time I head back to the yurt, it's ridiculously late. It was just me, Than, Doreen, Geoff and Beardy Weirdy left, so I figured I'd make a break for it before there was any chance of being left alone with Than. If I'm being totally honest, I might have timed my rather abrupt departure when he and Geoff were deep in conversation to avoid any chance of him offering to walk me back. Let's face it, appearing this late with Than in tow wouldn't be the best way to keep the peace with Bay.

I feel a little thrill of pride when I spot the yurt in front of me, happy that I've managed to find my way back on my own in the dark.

I slip off my boots and sneak in through the entrance

flap to be greeted by two rounds of loud snoring. I breathe a soft sigh of relief. There'll be no first degree nor the need for any more awkward conversation tonight. That'll just have to keep until morning.

17

Extraordinarily Ordinary

> 'Stop looking for those big changes that scare you. Stop waiting for the lightning bolt that will change your life in one strike. Instead, open yourself up and look around you every day for the opportunities to make an ordinary moment extraordinary.'
>
> ©TheBeginnersGuideToLoneliness.com

Turns out, I'm not going to have to make awkward conversation with Bay this morning after all. Based on the racket the birds are still making outside, it's not that late, but when I peer over at Bay's side of the yurt I'm met with an empty bed. My own, however, appears to have gained an extra body. I try to wiggle my feet, but they've been trapped by a large, snoozing mound of Dennis.

'Hey, boy!' I say, reaching down and just managing to tickle the top of his head. My hand gets a thorough slobbering in response and then Dennis wriggles himself up so that his head is almost on the pillow next to mine. 'Reckon your dad's going to be in a better mood today?'

Dennis licks my nose, and I splutter. Nice. Ah well, at least someone's glad to see me. If I'm completely honest with myself, I'm a bit gutted that Bay isn't here. There's a part of me that really wants to apologize for yesterday. He caught me off guard, when

I was completely knackered, and now, with a bit of perspective, I know he was only trying to look out for me, and I wasn't exactly grateful. At all. Ah well, I'm sure I'll get the chance to say something later.

Today is Russ's first mindfulness session with us, and, according to the handbook, it includes a body-work aspect of its own, so we don't have Claire's usual session on top of it. I realize that I'm actually a little bit gutted about this. I enjoyed starting yesterday off with the yoga . . . I just hope Russ has something similar up his sleeve.

I'm not sure what I think of this whole 'mindfulness' thing anyway. It feels a bit like a buzz word — all style, no substance. I can't help but feel a tiny bit sceptical.

* * *

When Dennis and I reach the breakfast table, it seems the rest of the group have similar reservations.

'What do you think?' Geoff asks, slumping onto the bench next to me and yawning widely. 'This session going to be any good, or can I head home and grab forty winks?'

'I haven't got a clue,' I say, stuffing my face with porridge before it goes cold and congeals into cement in my bowl.

'Ah, come on, don't give us that!' says Sam from across the table. 'You know Bay's involved in helping Russ with today's session. He must have told you about it at some point, what with you two living together . . .'

'What do you mean he's helping Russ? He's here for the retreat like the rest of us . . .' I say, looking surprised.

'Oh, it's something to do with the garden,' says Beardy Weirdy. 'Bay designed it for them and does a bit of work on it a couple of times a year when he comes down for the retreats. At least, that's what he told me. He's a bit of an unofficial volunteer here, really.'

'Well, he's not told me anything about it,' I say, feeling a bit wrong-footed. I'm just realizing that I've not taken much interest in getting to know Bay.

'Well, I reckon today's going to be complete crap.' Than's voice cuts across the table. There's something about the way he says it that makes me bristle.

Doreen catches my eye and raises her eyebrows at me. I shrug. 'I'm looking forward to it,' I say.

We're gossiping around the edge of the vegetable patch when Russ's voice makes us all jump.

'Welcome to your first mindfulness session.' He makes his way quietly to the front of the group and turns to face us. 'So, what is mindfulness? It's a practice, a meditation, a manner of truly living in the world, moment by moment, without following our thoughts down the rabbit holes that take us away from the reality that surrounds us.'

He's already lost me. Ironic really. I shift from foot to foot as Russ waffles on and catch myself staring at Bay. He's next to Russ, and the sunlight on his hair is making tiny, golden lights appear and disappear as he tilts his head this way and that. My attention finally snaps back as Russ says, 'Mindfulness can stop you chasing thoughts that lead to your fears and encourage anxiety. When you're fully in the moment, you don't worry about the past and you're not anxious about the future. You're just reacting to this moment right now.'

Well, that makes a bit more sense. I guess.

'We'll be coming back here to the garden a little later on to discuss the session and work on some jobs that Bay's got lined up, but first I want to take you all on a walk.'

A murmur of dissent runs around the group, and I catch Geoff's whisper of 'Not another bloody walk.'

'I've done this walk several times with you all in mind. It passes through some really important energy points on the land,' Russ continues.

'Christ, energy points? What is this — how to be a gullible hippy using twenty simple clichés?' says Than, smirking and giving my arm a nudge.

I look at my feet. Despite what was going through my head yesterday in his tent, this morning I don't want to be a part of Than's club. It's not just Bay's warnings last night that have put me on edge . . . I can't quite put my finger on it, but there's something in the way that Than treats the others too. I noticed it around the fire last night, and then again at breakfast. I've got a feeling it's been there all along, but I've been too overwhelmed by his attention to notice.

'I have certain points on the walk where you will each be dropped off,' Russ continues. 'From there, I want you to wander at will for a couple of minutes until you feel compelled to wait and watch and listen. Use all of your senses to really be there, in that moment.'

'What are we watching and listening for?' asks Emma, sounding both excited and confused.

'For whatever comes to you. Open your hearts. Try to stay in the moment. Don't let your minds wander, but trust your senses.'

'How long for?' asks Doreen.

'For as long as it takes, and then we'll meet back

here. Bay, I'll start with you. I'd like you to remain in the garden and complete your session from here. This is familiar territory for you, but I wonder how much of it you truly see and experience as you work on the garden?'

Bay nods, and sits down on the edge of one of the raised beds.

'Okay, let's go. And I want silence please. Open your ears and your hearts.'

* * *

There's a definite sense of mutiny in the air as we traipse out of the garden, through the little paddock and towards the young woodland on the other side of the valley.

Than is the first to be dropped off, and as we march solemnly past him, I catch his eye. He winks at me and does a huge fake yawn.

About ten minutes later, after both Emma and Moth have been left at separate spots, Russ says, 'Okay, Tori, this is you. Stay within about two minutes' walk of here. Good luck.'

No one meets my eye as I stand stock still and watch them trudge away. I feel quite strange, staring at their departing backs. Well, there's nothing for it but to explore my little parcel of countryside and hunt out somewhere comfortable to sit.

It's a lovely spot. I turn a slow three sixty degrees to get my bearings. I'd been so intent on watching the feet of the others ahead of me on the way here that I hadn't noticed how far up the side of the valley we've climbed. Stretching out in front of me is the patchwork of fields on the valley floor, with the farmhouse nestled in the distance, snug as a bug in its blanket of greenery. I can see the willow beds that Ted pointed out on our first trip to find our various campsites. As a light breeze blows down the valley, the slender trees throw up the undersides of their leaves, turning the patch of green into rustling silver.

I'm now at the corner of a large stretch of young woodland. The trees are small enough that they've still got little plastic guards protecting their trunks. Around the edges of this baby woodland, as far as I can see, runs a border of enormous, full grown trees. They must have formed the boundary when this was just a field. Some of them are so big that I wouldn't be able to get my arms around them if I hugged them — which, of course, I'm not about to do. I'm just not a tree-hugging kind of person. Still, they're bloody enormous trees.

I walk a little way along the bank and notice that there's the remains of a wire fence, and here and there strands of barbed wire have scarred the oaks. In some cases it runs through the centre of the tree, and in others the wire is looped right around the trunk. Clearly, in the past, some farmer has saved on fence posts by nailing the wire directly to the trees.

I come to a halt next to one that has been ringed completely. The tree has tried to grow around the wire and the wood almost looks like it has spilled over the top. It's been completely strangled. The tree is dead, and I can see that some of the others are going to follow it very soon.

I sit down heavily on the bank, my heart beating fast. What's wrong with me? They're just trees. At some point they saved a farmer all the extra work of putting in fence posts. But sitting here now, I can see how short-sighted that was. Sure, it might have saved him the extra work and cash back then, but what about now? He has condemned these beautiful trees to a slow death.

God, this is a depressing place to sit. I struggle back to my feet, deciding that I've already had enough, and start to retrace my steps back towards the farm. I'll go back to the yurt for a while.

As I reach the edge of the woodland, the wind starts to pick up. The large oaks groan and strain in the sudden gust, but the young trees just sway gently, protected by their dying rear guard.

A bank of stormy-looking clouds is marching across the sky towards me like they're looking for a fight, and the wind picks up another notch. That's it, I'm out of here. I'm starting to freak myself out. Rather than opening the gate, I climb it and jump down the other side.

I break into a run and the wind seems to chase me down the hill, catching and whipping my hair up behind me. I'm hurtling back towards the field where the yurt is nestled as fast as my feet can carry me. The mayhem of the wind is echoed in the frantic beating of my heart. I feel like a child again, trying to outstrip some unknown terror as I run, my breath coming hard and fast. At last, I spot the yurt.

I'm just metres away from the flap when it happens. The skies open and the feel of giant raindrops on my skin brings me to an abrupt halt. It's something I usually avoid at all costs, but right now, in the middle of this field, it has caught me by surprise. I'm frozen in place.

As if someone is cranking up an invisible dial, the rain gets harder and heavier, the warm drops pound against my head and soak into my hair. My heart is still hammering from the run, but for the first time in a long time, I'm getting drenched by falling rain and I'm not afraid. The smell of damp grass and earth rises up to greet me. I open my arms wide and, raising my face up to the sky, I start to laugh.

'Are you insane?'

I jump and peer through the deluge towards the voice coming from the yurt.

It's Bay, standing just inside, laughing at me.

'What are you doing here?!' I call.

'Hiding from the rain!'

'Come out! It's beautiful,' I yell. In response, whoever's controlling the rain dial turns it to maximum. Bay shakes his head, still laughing. I march straight towards him and, grabbing the front of his shirt, I drag him, barefoot, out into the rain until we're both standing, laughing at each other as we're pummelled by the downpour.

Bay reaches forward and gently pushes a sodden strand of hair off my face. Suddenly we're not laughing anymore. We just stand, staring at each other. My hand is still holding the front of his shirt and my breath is still coming too fast, but I'm not so sure that's because of the running anymore. I'm staring into Bay's green eyes, and all of the movement I felt in my soul as I pelted down the field comes to a halt as I lose myself in his gaze.

The rain stops just as abruptly as it started, and the silence that follows breaks the spell between us.

'I — ' Bay says.

'We'd better — ' I say at exactly the same time.

'Sure,' he says, turning away from me and striding back into the yurt. I take a deep breath and follow more slowly. In a completely useless move, I try to wipe my hands dry on my sodden jeans.

As I struggle through the dripping entrance flap, I see that Bay has already stripped off his wet shirt and is stepping into a pair of dry trousers.

I go straight over to my bed and, with my back to Bay, strip off my top. I don't dare turn around for fear he might be watching me . . . or is it hope? What just happened out there in the rain?

I tug on a pair of dry jeans and top with some difficulty and then turn back to Bay. He's now sitting quite calmly on the little settee, flipping through a book on herbs as if nothing unusual has happened. Which, of course, it hasn't. Not really. So why do I feel disappointed?

I go and sit next to him.

'So . . . did you get bored?' he asks, looking at me steadily.

'Bored? No. No, not bored. Completely freaked out may be nearer the mark,' I say.

Bay nods. 'I saw you come belting down the field.'

'Well, yes.' I don't really want to talk about this yet. I'll save it for later, I think. 'What are you doing here, anyway? I thought you were being mindful in the garden?' I smile at him.

'I was . . . until I spotted a big black bank of cloud heading my way. So I thought I'd avoid a drenching. Or I would have, if it wasn't for you. Anyway, I don't get it . . . You have a fear of water and there you are, enjoying the rain?'

I think about this for a second. 'My phobia is really specific. Rivers, waterfalls . . . running bodies of water. Rain's different somehow. It's tiny drops.'

'So is a shower,' Bay counters, trying to understand.

I shiver and rub my arms. 'A shower is more intense. It thunders at you, straight on your head and on your face . . . and there's that pounding noise.' I pause and take a deep breath. 'I mean, I do usually avoid getting caught out in the rain, but that's more about wanting to avoid any chance of having a panic attack, if I can help it. It's not about fear of the rain itself. Does that make any sense?'

Bay nods slowly. 'You get scared of having a panic attack, so that starts to make you afraid of even more things?'

I nod. Nailed it in one. It starts to control more and more of your life. But that's enough of that subject for me for a while . . .

'Bay, look, I wanted to say sorry about yesterday.'

'Why?' He looks surprised at my sudden change of subject.

'For the way I reacted, I guess. I know you were just trying to look out for me.'

Bay shakes his head and sighs. 'It's me who should apologize. I'm sorry, that was probably not the most sensitive way I could have said what I did. I was . . . I am worried, and I didn't think it was fair not to give you a heads-up.'

'Truce?' I say. He nods and then chucks a towel straight at my head.

'You might need this. You're still dripping all over my cushions!'

18

Busy Hands Calm the Monkey Mind

'Your mind is a tree; its branches are your thoughts. Imagine your consciousness is a monkey swinging through these branches. It grabs hold of one thought, only to swing to another. It's rushing, excitable, frantic.

'Simple, repetitive work that keeps your hands busy can become a tool to help calm your monkey mind.'

©TheBeginnersGuideToLoneliness.com

Even though we hang out in the yurt for twenty minutes before heading back down to the garden together, Bay and I get there way before most of the others. I'm guessing they've all had to go in search of a dry set of clothes after a good, mindful drenching. Doreen's there though, so as Bay makes his way over to join Russ, I go and sit next to her underneath the overhanging roof of the little tool shelter.

'How was it for you?' I ask.

'Well . . . uh . . . I listened to the land,' she says, avoiding my eye, 'and, well . . . I went for a bit of a walk. And it was really weird because I walked straight into Geoff.'

'Really?' I raise my eyebrows, wondering what's coming next. They barely seemed to be talking last night.

'Well, you could say that, rather than listening to

the land, it had to listen to us instead,' she says, looking uncomfortable.

'Oh no. You had a fight? Are you okay?' I ask. Poor Doreen, she's so desperate to reconnect with Geoff.

'No, no . . . not a fight! Completely the opposite,' she pulls a horrified face at me.

My jaw drops. 'You *didn't*?'

'It was like we couldn't bear any space between us, and we just . . . kind of . . . melted into each other . . . ' She turns the most epic shade of beetroot I've ever witnessed.

I'm not sure I really want to hear the rest of the story if I'm honest, but I am intrigued. 'You weren't worried that someone might hear you?' I say.

'Didn't even consider it. It was like everything bad and all of the rubbish times we've been through just disappeared.'

She looks at me, and pure happiness is shining from her face.

'I'm so happy for you!' I say.

'Well, this is all meant to be about new experiences, isn't it?' says Doreen with a giggle. 'And I've never done it up against a tree before!'

Argh. There it is. Too much information.

She takes in the horrified expression on my face and laughs. 'What, didn't think we were past it, did you?!'

I shake my head, as much to dislodge the unwelcome image she's conjured as to answer her question.

'Well,' I say finally, 'this makes my tiny bit of gossip feel rather insignificant.'

'Ooh, gossip! Play fair now, Tori!' Doreen's eyes have the light of mischief in them, and she looks about twenty years younger.

'Well, you know that rainstorm?' I start.

'Don't I just? In fact, I blame that for . . . sorry, you carry on!'

'Well, I was caught out in it. I got all freaked out by the wind, and then the rain came and I sort of stopped in my tracks. And just stood in the rain. And I loved how it felt,' I say.

'Nope. You were right. Your piece of gossip is crap,' Doreen says, her face falling. 'Oh and there's something else you should know,' she leans in close to my ear, 'they're turning you into a hippy!' she whispers.

I dig her in the ribs with my elbow. 'I wasn't at the good part yet,' I mutter.

'Oh, thank heavens for that. So, what else happened?'

'Bay turned up.' I swallow. Now I'm telling someone about it, the moment feels really precious, like I want to hug it close and savour it for a bit longer. But there's no hope of that. Doreen's eyes have gone wide.

'When you say 'turned up' . . . ?'

'I saw him watching me from the yurt and dragged him out into the rain.'

'This place is definitely doing you good,' Doreen nods approvingly. 'Go on, what happened next?'

'Just this moment, you know? This look? And then he brushed a strand of hair off my face and it was like you said, all the space between us seemed to disappear.'

'You *didn't*?!'

'No, we didn't. Not if you mean like what you guys got up to — '

I'm interrupted by the sound of someone clearing their throat. We both look up guiltily to find that the rest of the group has rocked up while we've been chatting, and Bay is staring at us from his position up in front with Russ. They've clearly both been waiting for us all to calm down and shut up so that they can start this part of the session, but it looks like Doreen and I have managed to outstrip even chilled Russ's patience quota.

Oh God. What if Bay just heard everything I said? I feel the now familiar blush hit my cheeks again.

'Doreen, where's Geoff? Is he okay?' asks Russ gently.

'Oh, yes. He's . . . okay. Just tired. Really tired. He needed a rest. This morning took it out of him,' Doreen widens her eyes, trying to look as innocent as possible.

Russ nods. I can't help letting out a little snort of laughter.

'Tired? I bet he is!' I mutter.

Doreen chuckles and settles back comfortably against the side of the shed to let the session unfold around her.

'This morning's session was all about the senses,' says Russ, addressing the whole group. 'What you saw, heard, felt . . . maybe even smelled and tasted. It was about staying in the moment and witnessing what was happening without letting random thoughts distract you. The key to the second part of the session is getting you all grounded again.'

'Already done that bit,' Doreen whispers in my ear, and I have to bite my lip.

'We've all done plenty of sitting and talking, so this afternoon is going to be about work. Getting our hands dirty and doing something useful.'

'Great!'

It's Than. He's come to stand right next to us,

slouching against the tool shed, legs crossed, arms crossed and, as I peep up at him, a truly pissed-off expression on his face.

'There's actually no better way to practise mindfulness than by doing something practical to help keep your attention rooted in the moment,' Russ continues. 'You'll find that it's incredibly balancing too.'

'So we're not going to talk about this morning's session?' Emma asks.

'Oh, we will, but we'll do it as we work. Over to you, Bay. What have you got lined up for us?'

'Well, there's always plenty to do in the garden, but especially at this time of the year. Lots of weeding,' he gestures around at the raised beds, 'and there are some tomato plants that I want planted in the bed at the back of the tool shed. We should be safe from the frosts by now, but the shed will give them a little bit of extra shelter and the warmth of the tin in the sun will create a microclimate for them.'

Microclimate? He's lost me. I pick a blade of grass and start twisting it around my fingers absently. As I watch Bay talk, I think about his fingers gently brushing the hair off my face in the rain.

'Tori?'

I jump at the sound of my name, and everyone looks around at me. It's Doreen's turn to dig me in the ribs this time.

'Um, yes?' I say guiltily.

'We were just going through jobs. Are you happy to do some weeding? We need to get the beds cleared for the courgettes to go in soon.'

'Of course. Yep. Fine!' I say. *Must learn not to daydream in public.* Mindfulness — stay in the moment . . . May need a bit more practice at that.

I feel Doreen shaking with silent giggles next to me as Bay turns to Beardy Weirdy to see if he's happy to lead the tomato crew.

'Oi!' I whisper in her ear.

'You should see your face,' she laughs. 'Thinking of a certain moment in the rain by any chance? All very *Four Weddings*!'

'Shhh!' I say. I don't like the way Than's looking at me. I could really do without having to tell him about what happened with Bay. I've got a sneaking suspicion that he wouldn't be quite as enthusiastic as Doreen.

⋆ ⋆ ⋆

Russ was right; I find the weeding incredibly therapeutic. Bay has designed the garden so that most of it is set out in raised beds. Huge wooden railway sleepers piled on top of each other form the edges and bring the level of the soil up by a good couple of feet. I'm perched comfortably on one of them, pulling greenery out of the wet earth to my heart's content, Bay having told us before we started that there is nothing that needs saving in this patch.

Than, Doreen and Emma are all dotted around the same bed, and we've been listening to Emma describe a tiny patch of grass she'd decided to focus on this morning. She tells us about every single little critter she'd spotted in about a square metre, and I can't help but smile at how different her experience was to mine.

Bay joins us part way through Emma's description and becomes so entranced by what she's saying, he's barely touched a single weed.

'Oi, slacker!' I laugh, tapping his empty bucket as

Emma finishes her story.

Bay grins at me. 'Sorry. It's just so amazing. I've done this exercise so many times, and I've literally never heard anything like that before.'

Emma beams at him.

'It's like you discovered a whole universe in that patch of grass!' he smiles at her.

Emma nods enthusiastically. 'That's exactly it. I was there for ages, and I just kept noticing more and more.'

'And that's why this work is just so incredible. We all learn to look at the world differently through each other's eyes,' says Russ, wandering over to see how we're getting on.

I smile at his earnest tone.

'What about you, Doreen?' asks Russ. 'How did you find this morning's exercise?'

Doreen's suddenly weeding with such concentration you'd think she's performing heart surgery.

'Care to share?' I ask, grinning at her.

'It was good,' she mutters. 'Lots of connection with the land and stuff.' She clears her throat.

'Any details . . . ?' I'm laughing now. Bay catches my eye and raises an eyebrow.

'Nope. No details. It felt . . . private,' mutters Doreen.

'Fair enough. Sometimes it's too close to the bone to share,' nods Russ.

At the word 'bone', I promptly dissolve into a fit of giggles, and Doreen joins me. I almost manage to sober up at the sight of the bemused look on Russ's face, but a snort from Doreen sets me off again and we just keep getting worse. In fact, it's not long before Emma joins the hysteria, tears pouring down her face even though she's got no idea why she's laughing.

We're practically unable to breathe by this point.

I've just about managed to calm down, with the occasional hiccup of mirth, when I catch Bay's eye again and notice that he's completely given up on trying to keep a straight face too. Even Russ is grinning as he shakes his head in despair and heads off to check on the tomato crew. Clearly we all needed to let off a bit of steam after this morning.

The only person who seems to be immune is Than. As I look around me, taking deep, steadying breaths, I notice his face, and there's only one word to describe it: grim.

I sober up immediately. Maybe today's been too much for him to even think about smiling.

Bay looks up at him too. 'How about you, Than? What did you get from this morning?'

'I didn't,' Than rips up a handful of weeds and lobs them into his bucket as if they're a hand grenade. He straightens his back and glares at Bay.

'Care to elaborate?' Bay asks.

I glance back at him. The mirth of just a couple of seconds ago has been replaced by barely suppressed irritation.

'How can I?' bites Than. 'I sat in a field. I got bored. It was cold, wet and windy. I came back. The end.' Than stares at Bay as if daring him to contradict him.

'So you didn't bother with Russ's exercise?' Bay prompts mildly.

Next to me, Doreen has gone back to weeding with intense concentration.

'If it had been a proper exercise,' says Than, voice full of heavy sarcasm, 'I would have bothered.'

'Obviously you didn't engage in it with an open mind.'

'How open-minded do you have to be to make up some crock-of-bullshit answer after sitting in a field, freezing your naggers off for a morning?' Than's on his feet now.

'Maybe it just wasn't the exercise for you.' Bay is tight-lipped, and I can see that he's struggling to keep a lid on his own rising anger.

'Yeah, maybe,' says Than, shrugging. 'Look, I'm going back to my tent. Like Geoff, I'm a bit *tired*.' He does scare quotes around the last word with his fingers before turning his back on us.

'Should I go after him?' I ask, not because I particularly want to, but because it feels like maybe someone should.

Bay shakes his head, an even darker expression on his face. I see him swallow.

'Let him go,' he says in a tight voice. 'He needs a bit of time to calm down. Someone can check on him later to see if he wants to join us for the hot tub this evening if he's up for it.'

* * *

By the end of the afternoon, I'm aching all over. In spite of the fact that I've discovered muscles in places I didn't even know existed, I feel amazing, just like I did after the yoga session. Under Bay's instruction, and with Russ's ongoing input about staying mindful and grounded as we worked, we ended up weeding four massive beds. There's only one left to finish, and that's just because the weeds are way too well established to yank out by hand. The others have managed to plant out the tomatoes around the back of the shed as well as filling two little greenhouses.

We're all just about ready to drop, so I can't believe it when Bay says he still wants to do a bit more work after dinner if anyone wants to join him. Apparently the potatoes need hoeing up in the evening because the leaves point upwards then. Who knew?

I stare straight ahead, not wanting to catch his eye. As much as I'd love to help him out, I don't think my poor back will take much more.

'I know,' says Doreen, and for a second I think she's about to volunteer, 'I'll send Geoff down to help. He's skived for long enough. Time for him to earn his place in the hot tub tonight!'

19

Avoiding the Friendship Monoculture

> 'There are three friendship scenarios that can lead to a monoculture; the 'best friend as only friend', the 'romantic partner as best friend' and the 'all my friends are in the same group' set-up. Should something cause any of these friendships to end, you could find yourself isolated far too easily. As in nature, friendships benefit from bio-diversity.'
>
> ©TheBeginnersGuideToLoneliness.com

When I arrive at the hot tub, it seems that Doreen has been as bad as her word. Both Bay and Geoff are missing from the party, and I'm guessing they're hard at work hoeing up the potatoes. I would feel bad for them, but right now I'm too achy and anxious to do much about it. In fact, the aching seems to have doubled since we stopped work, and there's a part of me that is desperate to get into some hot water and soak myself. Unfortunately, that part is having to put up quite a fight with the anxious part of my brain, which is really starting to kick in. I know it's not running water, but there are so many of us that I'm not going to have much control over the situation should panic start to creep in.

I dump my bag and go to help the others shift wood from under a tarpaulin. There's a solar-heated water tank, but a little wood-fired boiler helps to top up the warm water. I can't seem to stop worrying about Than. He's not here yet and I'm starting to feel like I should have followed him earlier. Actually, I'm wondering if he was kind of expecting me to.

'Why the long face?' Doreen asks, rescuing me from one of the two large logs I'm trying to heave over to Beardy Weirdy and Bob, who're taking it in turns to wield an axe and chop the bigger bits down to size.

'I'm fine,' I say, 'just a bit worried about Than.'

'Ah, he'll be all right. Different things set us off, don't they? Anyway, I think Geoff was planning to go up to see him after they finish off in the garden.'

My shoulders sag with relief. Geoff. If anyone can talk Than down, it'll be lovely, calm Geoff.

'So, you ready for this?' I ask, as we both potter back towards the tub.

'Oh, yes! How can pulling a few weeds up leave you hurting quite so much?' Doreen asks with a laugh.

As soon as the tub's full of warm water, everyone piles in. As if by magic, Claire, Russ and Bay appear to join in the fun.

I turn just in time to see a white bum dash past me. Beardy Weirdy, keen to be first into the water, has dumped his clothes and leaps stark bollock naked into the tub. This seems to be the sign everyone has been waiting for. Before my eyes, trousers are being dropped, T-shirts cast aside with abandon and boxers are lying in the grass wherever I look.

My heart is hammering, but it's not the water that's causing it this time. I just caught a glimpse of Bay's surprisingly tanned behind as he slipped into the water. My case of butterflies has levelled up and I now feel like I've got a flock of pigeons in my belly.

To my great relief, not everyone is baring all. Doreen

is in her bra and pants, and grins as Claire and Russ shift up to make room for her.

The tub is packed like a tin of sardines. We're about to cook up a large vat of hippy soup and the water is already turning an interesting browny-beige colour. Actually, that might not be a bad thing — at least it'll cover everyone up!

I changed into my boxer briefs earlier and left my bra back at the yurt, so I just take off my jeans, fold them carefully and leave my T-shirt on.

'Come on, Tori!' Claire calls. 'Hop in while it's nice and clean . . . kinda,' she laughs.

I head over to the side where she and Doreen are lounging on a submerged ledge. I sit on the edge and dangle my legs over the side. There. That's far enough. I can handle this without any trouble, as long as no one makes any sudden movements.

'You not coming in?' asks Doreen, looking up at me.

'I'm good here for a bit.' I smile at her.

'We can make room if I sit on Bob's lap!' says Claire, winking at Bob.

'Nah, I'm good thanks,' I say. I'm starting to relax. There's no pressure here. Just a bunch of people trying to be nice to me. I look over to find Bay watching me. 'Like I said, I'm not good with water. Running water mostly, but I'm a bit weird with all water to be honest. It's just one of my oddities,' I laugh, trying to make light of it. An oddity that pretty much controls my life at times, but we don't need to go into that bit right now. I don't want this evening to turn into another therapy-fest just because of my issues.

'Oh, wow,' says Beardy Weirdy. 'This is a big step for you, then?'

I shrug. 'I'm okay.' Time to change the subject. 'You know, this is awful, but I still haven't caught your name.'

'It's Messa,' he grins at me. 'Nice to meet you!'

Everyone's in full chat mode now. There's lots of talk about the garden and how well we did with the work today. I act as main fire stoker, and every now and then hop up to add more wood to keep the water warm. The others keep offering to take turns, but I've laid claim to the role. For one thing, it stops it being strange that I'm still perched on the side of the tub, and for another, it means I don't have to see a naked butt streak past me every twenty minutes.

I feel a bit bad when Geoff turns up with Than in tow. I've been having such a good time that I'd actually forgotten they were still missing from the group.

Geoff promptly strips down to his boxers and squeezes into the water between Claire and Doreen, throwing his arm around his wife.

'Oi, you two,' laughs Sam, 'not in the hot tub!' This causes much sniggering, and Doreen does her beetroot impression again.

Than makes his way around the tub, takes off his shoes, rolls up his trousers and joins me on the edge. 'Hey,' he says with a smile.

'All right?' I ask quietly as the others noisily continue to rib Geoff for his late appearance.

'Yeah fine,' he huffs. 'It's just . . . '

'SNAKE!'

The scream comes from Emma. Everyone stares at her.

'In the water!' She's scrabbling backwards out of the tub. Both Than and I draw our feet quickly out of the water. Doreen's busy making a swift getaway too, and even Messa is retreating as fast as his little white backside will allow. There's general uproar, squealing and a lot of laughter from Bay, who hasn't budged.

'Seriously, Bay, get out!' shouts Bob from a safe distance.

'No need!' he chuckles. 'I just saw it over there next to Geoff!'

It's Geoff's turn to scramble up the side and sit dripping on the edge.

'Tori, chuck me a stick,' says Bay, calm as a cucumber.

I dash to the pile, grab the longest one I can find and chuck it across the water to Bay.

'Perfect. I should be able to get it with that!' he grins, aiming it at the water like a spear.

As one, the whole group seems to take a step back. What does this guy think he's doing? Now he's the only one left in the tub. We're all standing around, dripping, watching open-mouthed.

With a quick thrust, Bay plunges the stick into the water, then brings the point up slowly into the air. I don't understand why he's laughing, or why Claire and Russ are laughing — and now Geoff too.

'Got it! You might be wanting this . . . ' And with a flick, Bay sends the snake flying through the air straight towards Messa. He lets out the most unearthly squeal, slips on the grass and falls, todger akimbo, in a heap with the dead snake on top of him. He hurriedly flicks it off of him, and then, sitting up slowly, stares at it.

He turns to Bay, whose lips are quivering. 'Bastard!' he says mildly, and, picking up the 'snake', lobs it back at Bay.

Bay catches it, wraps it around his neck and pretends to be sinking under the water, only to surface again, laughing his head off with it dangling from his fingertips.

A lone dreadlock. Clearly one of Messa's.

* * *

It takes ages for the laughter to die down. Just when it looks like it's about to stop, someone yells 'Snake!' and off we all go again. Even Than is chuckling along next to me as we take it in turns to feed the fire.

When Bay finally declares he's calling it a night to make a bit more room in the tub, he starts a kind of mass exodus, and within twenty minutes it's just me, Than and Messa left.

'You coming in now it's quieter?' Messa asks me, gazing up at the sky.

'Erm . . . maybe.'

'I'll chuck some more wood on the fire,' says Than, and heads over to the depleted pile.

'It's not just you facing your fears tonight, you know,' says Messa quietly. 'What Bay doesn't know is that I'm absolutely terrified of snakes!'

'Oh my God!'

He shrugs. 'I survived,' he smiles at me. 'Might have a bit of a bruise on the arse tomorrow, but hey, at least Bay saved my dreadlock.'

I nod. 'You know, I might get in for a few minutes before heading off. Could do with it after all that weeding!'

Messa grins. 'Atta girl.'

As Than comes back over, he slips off his jeans and tee and hops into the tub in his pants. I quickly avert my eyes until he's sitting on the bench opposite me.

'Right!' says Messa. 'That's quite enough excitement

for me for one night. My roll mat's calling.'

'Night!' I say, and close my eyes quickly as he hauls himself out of the tub. I just don't need to see that again.

When I open my eyes, he's wandering away with a towel around his waist, one hand raised in farewell. All of a sudden, I'm very aware that I'm alone with Than.

'You okay?' he asks.

I nod.

'Sure?'

'I will be if you stop asking me that and talk to me about something else,' I snap.

He gives me a hurt look.

'Sorry, sorry. Inner anxiety bitch surfaces again.' He doesn't need to know that it's not anxiety about the water this time. We sit in silence for a minute.

'Anyway,' I say, 'it's my turn. Are you okay? After earlier? I couldn't really ask you properly with everyone else here.'

Than shrugs. 'I'm fine. I just had to get away before the urge to smash Bay's smug face became too much.'

'Oh.' I don't really know what to say, but I find myself wishing I'd left with everyone else.

'Look, Tori, you need to be careful around him,' he says.

I shake my head. Not again! What is it with these two?

'Than, Bay's a good guy.'

He shakes his head at me, looking angry.

'He is,' I say. 'Earlier, in the garden, he was . . . '

'Don't tell me he was trying to help,' Than growls.

'Well, he was,' I say, 'just like they all are in their own, weird ways.'

'Trust me, that's not what he was doing. And anyway, he's all over you like a rash. I mean, living with you, watching you, joking around just to get your attention.'

I laugh. 'Bay had no choice in the matter when it came to sharing the yurt. I was dumped on him because I booked last minute.'

'So did I, and I'm not staying there,' he says sulkily.

'Because you opted for camping.' I'm starting to feel cross.

'But you can't deny that he watches you.'

'Look, this is ridiculous,' I say. 'Just because you don't like him, don't expect me to feel the same way, because I don't.'

Than holds his hands up. 'Fine, fine!' He sounds huffy again, and I sigh.

'I think I'm going to head back.' I start to get to my feet, but Than jumps up and grabs one of my hands.

'Don't,' he says urgently. 'Don't go. I'm sorry.'

I look at him, shake my head and sit back down again. He sits next to me. 'Really, I'm sorry. It's not fair to take it out on you. You're still the only person I've trusted enough to tell about my brother,' he sighs.

I settle back onto the bench. Poor guy, he's got so much to deal with. I just wish he'd share it with the others, especially the instructors. Let's face it, they're definitely better equipped to deal with the fallout than I am.

'It's okay,' I say.

Before I know what's happening, he's leant forward. His face is right in front of mine. Oh my God, he's going in for a kiss. I whip my head sideways and his lips catch me on the corner of the mouth.

'Than, no,' I say, pushing him away as gently as I

can.

'Why?' he says, his voice hoarse.

'Because I don't want . . . this,' I say, pointing back and forth between us. I can feel the first stirrings of panic. Time to get out of here, I think. 'This isn't the place. I'm not here for . . . this.'

'But we — '

'We're friends,' I say, standing up and quickly climbing over the side. 'That's it. Friends.'

'But you — '

'Nothing, Than. I've done nothing. Look, let's just forget it. I'm tired, I'm going to bed.'

'I'm sorry, Tori. I'll walk you back,' he says, getting to his feet.

'No. Thank you. I'm fine.'

I grab my towel, wrap it around me and bundle my clothes up off of the floor. Then I turn back to see him, still standing in the tub, watching me.

'We'll talk tomorrow, okay?' I say.

He just shrugs, so I turn and walk as quickly as I can back towards the farmyard.

Oh God, how did that just go so wrong? My first thought is to get straight back to the yurt, but I realize that I need my friends. My *real* friends. I need the Warriors, which means I need to find Rowan.

Despite everyone having headed back to their various camps, it's not dark yet. I make my way towards the farmhouse, hoping to bump into her.

As if by magic, I spot Rowan heading towards me as soon as I get into the yard.

'Rowan!' I say.

'Ye–s,' she grins at me, seeing a sale in the offing.

'I need to use your phone for a couple of minutes.'

She whips it out of her back pocket. 'Call, text or

internet?'

'Internet, please,' I say.

'Knock yourself out. You know the price!'

I nod. 'Mind if I take it around to the fire pit for a minute, just so I can sit down?'

'I wouldn't. That's where Mum and Dad are hanging out. Come down to the barn with me for a sec, I've got to get some feed for the chickens anyway, and there's a bench in there.'

'Thanks!' I smile at her and pull the towel tighter round me.

'You know,' she says as we walk down the yard, 'it might be a good idea for you to put that jumper on. Don't want you catching a chill!'

As soon as I'm ensconced on a little wooden bench which is sandwiched between an old chest freezer full of chicken food and a pile of straw bales, I follow her advice and pull my jumper on over my wet T-shirt. I really don't much fancy nursing a cold here on top of everything else.

Grabbing a scoop of feed, Rowan leaves me to it. I log into the chatroom and send a bunch of messages as quickly as I can.

WriterTori: Hey, guys. Still alive. Really miss you all. Need to offload – am being charged by the millisecond though so have to be quick . . . Than, that guy I told you about before, he just tried to kiss me. Totally out of the blue. It made me feel awful. I don't think I feel like that about him. Thought for a sec I might, but I think I was just excited to have someone on my side, someone who wanted to spend time with me. I just abandoned him in the hot tub. Feel really bad. Tomorrow is going to be awkward! What do I do? Give me advice? Pretty please.

WriterTori: There's something else too. There is someone I might actually like . . . like that. Completely unexpected, and also awkward as it's Bay, the guy I'm sharing the yurt with. We had this moment earlier in the rain, and it made me see him properly for the first time. But we're living together . . . I think Than hates him and . . . GAH! I need to talk to you. Why aren't you online? Hellooooo?

WriterTori: Damn. Gotta go. This message has just cost me about a gazillion pounds. I love you guys. Thanks for listening.

'You done?' comes Rowan's voice as she wanders back into the barn, empty feed scoop in hand.

'Yep. Give me a sec to log off.' I do so quickly and then erase the site from the phone's history. Don't know why, I just always do.

'That'll be six quid, please.'

'I don't have any cash on me,' I say.

'No probs . . . just log on to PayPal. Make sure you add an extra fifty pence though — transaction fee.'

I roll my eyes. This girl's going to go far.

20

Let Your Lion Loose

'For those who suffer with anxiety, it's natural to avoid confrontation, but there are moments when we have to let our lion loose. When a situation demands it, it can often be the right move to let that roar out.'
©TheBeginnersGuideToLoneliness.com

I've never been so glad to see my bed in my life. Bay is already snuggled up on the sofa under a blanket. I'm so tempted to flop down next to him, but I'm still wearing a semi-dry jumper over very wet clothes, so I drag my feet over to my bed and start to get changed into something warm. I feel strangely shy around him after what I've just told the Warriors.

'Bay . . . can I borrow a thick jumper?' I ask, cringing as my voice comes out all breathy.

'Sure.' He goes to his pack and then throws a chunky, woolly sweater to me. 'I left you something next to your notebook too,' he says, pointing at my little makeshift bedside table.

I look over and there's a travel mug. I pop the lid off and take a sniff. Hot chocolate. It's official. I'm smitten. Just a moment ago, I felt incredibly lost and lonely and, without even trying, Bay's managed to hit upon the one thing that's guaranteed to cheer me up.

'You're a saint,' I sigh, sitting on my bed and cradling the warm drink.

'Hope it's still hot? You were a bit longer than I thought you'd be.'

'Mmm,' I mumble.

'What's up?'

'Mmm?'

'Difficult evening? Was it the water? You did really well.'

'I got in,' I say. I feel a bit like a six-year-old showing off my swimming badge for the first time.

'Good for you!'

'Thanks. And it wasn't that.'

'Oh?'

'It was . . . people.'

'Bit of group dynamics come out to bite you?'

'Erm, something like that.'

'Well, if you need to talk . . . I'm always here, you know.'

I smile at him. 'Thanks, Bay. I'm okay. I think I just need my bed.' There's no way I can tell him about Than. I mean, that's a sure route to 'I told you so' if ever there was one, and right now I could really do without that.

'Not surprised. That'll be the fresh air, gardening and running around like a lunatic in the rain,' he laughs.

I feel a weight land on my feet and look down to see Dennis slinking up next to me for a hug. I snuggle back into the pillows, hot drink in one hand and my other arm wrapped around Dennis's warm body. He leans his whole weight against me, head lolling on my shoulder. It's possibly the best cuddle I could have asked for right now.

'Well, looks like whatever's bothering you, Dennis knows you need some love,' says Bay. 'You'd better be careful or you'll end up sharing that bed again!'

* * *

I wake up the following morning next to a large, snoring mound of dog, and can't help but smile. Bay's words to me last night before I drifted off to sleep seem to have come true. He must have covered me up with the blankets and taken the cup out of my hand, as I've got absolutely no recollection of doing either.

'Morning, sleepyhead,' Bay grins over at me as he bounds into the yurt carrying the kettle. 'Coffee?'

'I'd love one,' I yawn, 'but I owe you some treats, you know. All this pampering with coffee and hot chocolate.'

'Ah, I'm sure we'll figure it out,' he says, busy pouring the hot water into his cafetière. 'You look better for a good sleep.'

'I *feel* better. Thanks for last night. I felt a bit weirded out, you know?'

'I do. And it's fine, that's what friends are for.'

Friends. That word should have my little heart jumping with joy. Instead it has curled up in disappointment. *Uh oh*.

Still, I force a smile and take the hot cup of coffee out of his hands as if it's life-saving nectar.

'Warned you that would happen,' he says, nodding down at the still snoozing dog.

'I don't mind,' I say, hyper aware of my change of tune since I got here. 'That was the best night's sleep I've had in ages.'

'No nightmares,' Bay says matter-of-factly.

'No. How did you know?'

'You didn't do your usual whimpering along with the dawn chorus.'

Oh. My. God. 'I'm so sorry. I didn't realize I'd been

disturbing you!' I say.

'Don't worry about it. I'm awake on and off all night.

'You looking forward to Claire's session this morning?' I ask just to change the subject.

'Ah, actually I'm going to miss this one. I promised Ted I'd help out again. We need to do some bits in the garden and get some of the outdoor work finished before the baby comes. He's having to do more with the course than usual as Lizzie's had to slow down, and he's starting to fret that he's going to get behind.'

'But . . . surely it's not good for you to miss a session?'

Bay shrugs. 'I've done it plenty of times before. And besides, this is a part of the deal. I get to come here and benefit from the retreat and in return I make sure I do as much as I can to help on the gardens and anything else they need a hand with while I'm here. They've done so much for me over the years, it's the very least I can do.'

'Pfft, but another day in the garden?' I say, trying to hide my sudden disappointment that Bay's not going to be around today. 'I'm tired just thinking about it.'

'Ah, you get used to it,' he grins at me.

* * *

There's a big part of me that really wants to skip breakfast this morning. Because I'm a wuss, and the thought of facing Than after what happened last night in the hot tub makes me squirm. But then, that would make me a coward, and I don't want to make any bigger deal out of this than it needs to be. With any luck, he'll have shrugged it off.

Bay comes down to breakfast with me, and Dennis trots along between us. I'm grateful for the company, as it stops me disappearing into my own head and chasing my worries around in circles.

As it happens, all the worrying is completely in vain anyway. Than is nowhere to be seen. It actually turns out to be a really joyful meal. Everyone else is here, and the party atmosphere from last night seems to have spilled over into the morning. We're all just starting to tuck in to breakfast when Sam screams 'snake' and we all fall about laughing. The look of complete confusion on Ted and Lizzie's faces just makes matters worse, and my sides start to ache. Messa takes it all in his stride as the tale is told again. I get the feeling that this little anecdote is going to become a bit of a legend here at The Farm.

* * *

We're all still giggling and chatting as we head off to get started on Claire's session. As she is one of the gang from last night, there's a general sense that this morning's going to be a lot of fun. My heart is light as I follow the others up the stairs into the loft space where we had our welcoming ceremony.

'Okay, gang, pull up the cushions for a minute while I explain what we're doing today.'

Like a horde of eager toddlers, we surge over to the pile of cushions. I grab the end of one just as Emma grabs the other end. I give it an almighty tug, managing to snatch it from her and promptly beat her over the head with it. She snatches up another one, and before I know what's happening I'm begging for mercy, laughing so hard I can barely breathe as she pummels me over and over again with the supersized pillow. It's far from a fair fight, though, as Doreen and Moth have both taken their own cushions and have leapt into the fray, all three now focusing on obtaining my surrender.

We end up in a tangled, squashy heap of cushions and limbs, all four of us laughing and trying to extricate ourselves from the pile.

'All right, you lot, get your behinds over here so that we can start!' calls Claire, who sounds like she'd actually quite like to join in.

I sit up only to be met by the look on Than's face as he walks through the door. The smile drops from my lips the moment I catch sight of his expression. I know I sound like a complete drama queen, but he is looking nothing short of thunderous.

I quickly look away and drag my cushion over to join the others in the circle, plonking myself down between Messa and Doreen. Suddenly I'm not quite so excited about this session anymore. Than sits down across from me and I feel like he barely takes his eyes off me, though I guess it's likely that my anxiety-prone brain is just imagining the waves of hostility he's sending my way.

'Okay, so we're all here. Great!' says Claire. 'Lizzie usually takes this session, but as you know, she's asked me to step in for her this once. Today is going to be all about vocalizing. Now, I know that sounds a bit vague and fluffy, but it's actually something incredibly powerful. We are all here to deal with things. Emotional blocks, fears and barriers. We've started to share what they are with each other, but what we haven't worked on is saying, out loud, how these things make us feel.'

Doreen shifts uncomfortably next to me, but this

might just be down to the fact that these cushions are really not that supportive.

'I hope we're now at a point where we all feel that we can place our trust in this group. You have all come to know each other, shared experiences and, from what I saw last night and this morning, have developed a lovely, playful bond. So, it's time.' She jumps to her feet in one yoga-honed movement and indicates for the rest of us to join her. We do, much slower and with a lot more groaning involved, which sends another giggle around the room.

Or, at least, it makes most of us smile. Than is still stony-faced.

Urgh, is he going to keep this up for the whole day?

I fold my arms protectively across my chest and look back to Claire. Actually, I don't much fancy sharing anything today. Not with the group. Well, not with *one* of the group. How can one person affect the whole dynamic so quickly?

'First things first, I want you all to scream.'

'Scream?' says Emma.

'Scream. As loud as you can!'

'Snake!' squeaks Moth.

Claire grins at her. 'Exactly, but maybe more like this: *SSSNNNNNNAAAAAKKKKKKEEEEEE!*' Claire screams the word using every last ounce of breath. The strength and pitch of her voice is awesome. My teeth get that feeling in them like I've just bitten into ice cream, and I wouldn't be surprised right now if the windows of the barn started to shatter. When she's done, we break into a spontaneous round of applause and she takes a tiny bow. 'Now you!' she says. 'On three . . .'

As she counts us in, I suck in a breath, but when

it comes to screaming, I let it whoosh out of me with no sound attached. I'm too caught up in listening to the insane cacophony around me. I catch Than's eye again and feel a bit like I've been punched. His arms are crossed, and he is still glaring at me, his mouth firmly closed.

'Okay, great!' says Claire. 'But there's even more in there. Some of you are still holding back, and I know I was completely missing a couple of you just then . . . '

I could kiss her for not naming and shaming.

'Everyone close your eyes and choose your own words to scream. No one's going to know what you're saying. It'll all mix into one big noise.'

When I close my eyes, I can still see Than's glaring face. Right . . .

'Three, two, one . . . '

'PISS! OFF!' I scream. Over and over and over, until the words lose all sense and shape. Until my breath runs out.

I open my eyes and suck in another deep breath.

That. Felt. Amazing.

My fngertips are tingling and I feel properly, fully awake. I look over at Claire and she nods back at me, a big smile on her face.

'You know how many things your voices can do, how many emotions they can convey. It's my belief that when we feel an excess of emotion, it can get caught up in our chests. If we don't let it out somehow, this can just keep building.'

Claire could be describing one of my panic attacks. I'm so accustomed to the feeling of the build-up in my chest and not knowing how to get control of it before it leads to a meltdown.

'Of course, it's not just the scream sound we can

use to let it out. In a way, you had all started working on this session before we even reached this room. Can anyone tell me how?'

'The laughter!' says Messa.

'Exactly that. The release of the joyful emotions you are all experiencing here together. So what other common ways do we express emotion by voice?'

'Anger,' says Geoff.

'Right,' says Claire, 'but how does that tend to sound when vocalized at its absolute peak?'

'Shouting. And sometimes screaming, I guess,' he replies.

'So let's look at shouting next. Describe how shouting makes you feel . . . '

'Mean?' says Doreen.

'Maybe after the fact, but what about in the moment?' prompts Claire.

Doreen looks confused.

'Forceful?' I say. I'm imagining words flying out of my mouth towards a target.

'Yes,' says Claire. 'Forceful, powerful.'

'And out of control . . . ' says Emma, frowning.

'Shouting can certainly stem from feeling out of control, or let out so many emotions that it can lead you in that direction, yes,' agrees Claire. 'But let's focus on the power behind it. Take a minute to think of the main issue you want to deal with while you're here, and what element about that makes you feel angry. It could be a particular person, situation or anything about it. What do you want to take control of?'

We all look around nervously at each other.

'Okay, I think we need to move for a minute. Take a walk around the space and think about what you want to shout at.'

I move off, grateful to escape the beam of everyone's nervous energy. You can feel it in the room now; it has shifted away from self-consciousness to fear — fear that Claire is about to start taking us near the bits that really matter.

I scoot around the corner of the room and walk in a diagonal path to the other end, head down, avoiding eye contact. What am I angry about? That I lost my mother? That her death weighs me down with guilt every single day? That I'm still grieving for someone I struggled to even like and who had come to hate me in return? I swallow. That she's still managing to ruin my life even now she's gone? My heart rate's climbing and the sound of running water is creeping into my mind.

I come to an abrupt halt near the centre of the room, bend over for a second and place my hands on my knees.

'Okay, Tori?' Claire asks quietly.

I don't answer. I just take a deep breath in and let it out slowly as I stand up. The roaring water calms back down to a trickle.

'Tori?' Claire prompts gently.

I nod. 'I'm okay.' I spot Than leaning against the opposite wall watching us.

'Okay, everyone, when you're ready,' Claire calls, 'I want us all in a line, facing the wall,' she points to the far end of the room.

Than pushes away from the side and comes to stand next to Claire. As the others join us, the sense of fear builds. Most faces are pale and set. Doreen is chewing her lip. Geoff is looking petrified.

'Now remember, this is a safe space. There is no

judgement here.'

Doreen stands next to me and her hand slips into mine. I give it a gentle squeeze.

'Who wants to go first?'

Before anyone can move, before there's even a second to think, Geoff bellows at the wall, 'I want my wife back!'

I feel Doreen go stiff beside me. I squeeze her hand again, but this time there's no response.

'Okay, guys, don't leave Geoff hanging, who's next?'

'I never told you I loved you.' Bob's the next to hurl his voice across the room.

'None of you really know me!' Emma yells. I've never heard her voice so strong and so loud.

'I'm not ready for this!' Sam follows her.

My heart rate is going insane. I have to get this out.

'I'm sick of feeling guilty!' The words rush through my throat, feeling like they're tearing their way out, leaving me raw, hurting and shaking.

Then Doreen's yelling, and Moth, and Messa.

'Than?' Claire prompts.

I glance across at him. He is shaking his head.

'Just yell at the wall. It doesn't matter what comes out,' she says.

Than takes a step forward out of the line. He looks like he's gearing up, and my heart goes out to him. I think he's got so good at keeping a lid on how he's feeling, it must be nearly impossible to let it out.

'Than?' Claire gently prompts again.

I watch him take in a deep breath. Then he swivels towards us and stares straight at me. In a voice that's more shocking than any of our shouts, he whispers.

'You're a fucking liar.'

21

Control the Controllables

> 'It is not possible for anyone to completely control their environment. This desire for control, coupled with its inherent impossibility, can lead to anxiety. By refusing to spend energy worrying about aspects we have no influence over, life becomes ours for the taking.'
> ©TheBeginnersGuideToLoneliness.com

There is complete silence for a couple of seconds. It's like everyone is watching this bullet travel towards me in slow motion.

I catch the blow straight to the chest and stumble back a couple of paces.

'What the hell?' comes Doreen's voice.

Muttering breaks out along the line and everyone breaks ranks, crowding around me.

'Okay, everyone, settle down,' says Claire.

But I don't want to settle down. What the fuck was that? I push my way past the concerned faces grouped around me and take a step towards Than. 'What is your problem?'

'Tori . . . ' Claire says warningly.

'I can't take any more of this bullshit,' Than gestures around at everyone. '*Oh, look at my problem . . .* ' he says, doing a whiny child's voice.

'Than — ' Claire tries to intervene, but I interrupt her.

'Don't you dare question anyone else's feelings just because you don't understand them,' I say.

'You of all people have the nerve to say that? You're a hypocrite. You know it and I know it.'

I can feel white-hot anger pulsing out of him, and there's no doubt it's directed straight at me.

'What are you saying?'

'I'm forbidden to tell anyone, remember? And even I have too much integrity to blab a secret to the group.'

'Okay, Than, that's enough.' Claire's voice cuts across him. He's now glaring at her, and I can see his chest rising and falling, his anger still building. 'This is not about Tori or any of the rest of the group. Please don't mistakenly direct your anger and fear at them.'

Than turns back to me and I feel the full weight of accusation hit me. 'My *fear*?' he hisses. 'Seems that even if *I* can keep a secret, you can't. Tell lover boy and everyone else everything about me, did you? Well fuck you, Tori.' He turns on his heel and heads straight out of the room.

For a second, there's complete silence.

'Break time, I think,' says Claire. 'Can I suggest that you all head back to your separate camps for a while? Go home, decompress and we'll get together again later.'

She starts to usher everyone out of the door. We're all a bit slow to respond. I think everyone's in shock. I know I am. My legs feel like jelly and navigating my way down the outside steps is quite tricky.

When I get to the bottom, Geoff, Doreen, Messa and Emma are already waiting for me, but Claire beats them to it.

'Tori, walk with me for a minute,' she says, giving me no choice but to send a longing look back towards the others as I follow her. It's pretty clear they're not going to take up Claire's suggestion of separate camps.

She leads me towards the farmhouse but then, to my surprise, lets us in through the side gate and ushers me through to Lizzie and Ted's private back garden. They're both there drinking tea in the sunshine. Ted looks hot and sweaty and must have only just got back from his session in the garden with Bay.

They both look surprised to see us.

'Hi. Sorry to interrupt. Ted, you might need to bring that one-to-one session we discussed last night forward?'

This means absolutely nothing to me, but it clearly does to the other two. They both look solemn and Ted gets to his feet straight away.

'I'll just change out of this stuff,' he says, pulling at the neck of his sweat-soaked T-shirt and hurrying inside.

'Tori, have a seat and wait for me a sec?' Claire says. 'Lizzie, can I borrow you for a mo?'

Lizzie nods and looks surprised, but gets to her feet with difficulty and follows Claire inside the house, rubbing her back as she goes.

I sit on one of the garden benches against the back wall of the house and stare at a bed of early roses, their buds just about ready to flower fully. It's quiet here and incredibly beautiful, so why do I feel like I'm sitting outside the head teacher's office, waiting to be told off?

I don't get it. Is Than really so cross about the fact that I didn't want to kiss him that he decided to give me a public flailing?

I sigh. I feel like shit. That session was proving to be hard enough as it was without all his crap coming my way too. It feels like he's trying to punish me for something. Maybe just knowing about his issues is enough to make him resent me.

'Tori, Claire's asked me to spend a bit of time with you, if you're up for it?'

I look up in surprise. It's Lizzie. I notice she's still clutching her back, and seems to have quite a lot of trouble manoeuvring herself back into her seat.

'Oh, okay,' I say. She looks exhausted and far too hot. I guess that's the reality of being ready to pop at any moment, but still, I feel guilty for disturbing her downtime. 'Would you be more comfortable inside?' I ask in concern, watching as she gently rubs her stomach.

'No, no, not at all. Can't have you disrupting your progress by going in there,' she says. 'So, Claire briefly explained what just happened in the session. Are you okay?'

'Yes, fine,' I reply automatically, then instantly change my mind. 'Well, no.'

Lizzie nods but doesn't say anything.

'I felt really awkward when I came here,' I say, 'a different person.'

'A little less than a week ago?' Lizzie asks gently, placing no weight on the words.

'Yes,' I say, surprised. I thought Lizzie of all people would be pleased to hear that. 'A lot has happened and I've learned a lot.'

'Of course. But you're not a different person. Don't worry, it's a mistake that's easily made.' She winces slightly and shifts her weight in the chair, trying to get comfy.

'So you're saying the changes aren't real?' I'm feeling the prickle of tears. Maybe it's not just Than who thinks I'm a liar.

'The changes are real, but you're not a different person. We provide experiences that help you learn about yourself. But the things you learn were already a part of you when you arrived here. So no, you're not a different person, you're a person that just happens to recognize more pieces of who you truly are.'

I nod. I think that makes sense but I'm not sure how it really fits with what just happened with Than.

'Did Claire tell you about Than?' I ask.

'Than's behaviour? Yes. It sounds like it stems from a deep, personal fear. He has yet to open up and allow this experience to help him — unlike you, who are already benefiting from it.'

'But this was personal!' I say.

'Yes. About as personal as it can get. You two became very close, very quickly . . . '

'Oh, you noticed . . . '

'You don't run a place like this for twenty years and miss out on much of the hot gossip,' Lizzie laughs, before clutching her bump again.

'Can I get you some water or anything?' I ask, concerned.

She waves me away. 'You and Than were partners in crime for a couple of days, and then you started to discover things about yourself.'

'It was hard not to be drawn to him. He just seemed to really understand me, almost better than I understood myself, you know?'

'But then you started to make other friends here, and I think he's missing having you all to himself.'

'Hm. Given his behaviour in the hot tub last night, I'm not sure it's just my other *friends* he's worrying about.'

Now Lizzie looks truly concerned. 'What happened?'

'He tried to kiss me,' I say, looking at my feet. I feel incredibly awkward. I didn't mean for that to come out.

'And you didn't want that?'

'No. And I told him that,' I say. I need Lizzie to understand the whole picture though. 'It's flattering to have a good-looking guy interested, of course it is. But any feelings I thought I might be experiencing for him . . . I think they were actually just this massive sense of relief. Someone actually wanting to spend time with me.'

'What happened after you turned him down last night?'

'I left.'

'So this morning's little performance could be all that angry rejection coming out?'

'I guess so. But it felt like it was about more than that, somehow,' I say. 'I just didn't think last night was that big a deal. It was awkward, but I thought he'd get over it.'

Lizzie gets up slowly and paces along the slate path, walking over to the flower bed and back.

'Can I ask you a personal question?'

'Of course,' I say.

'Claire said he accused you of telling something to 'Lover Boy'. Did he mean Bay?'

Here comes that bloody blush again. 'Yes. I think so,' I mutter.

'Are you and Bay . . . ?'

'No, we're not.' I don't feel the need to mention the moment in the rain. After all, that was probably just me getting thoroughly carried away. 'Than was saying stuff about Bay last night, before he kissed me. Trying to warn me away from him.'

'He was?'

'Mind you, Bay warned me about Than a couple of days ago too, so I can hardly hold it against him, can I?'

'Oh God!' Lizzie gasps.

Have I just landed Bay in it? I look up at her in surprise, expecting to be questioned some more. Instead, Lizzie is looking down at a pool of water surrounding her feet, darkening the slates.

'What the . . . '

'Erm, I think my water just broke.'

'*What?!*'

'It's fine, don't panic.'

'Okay. Okay. I'll go and get Ted!' I say.

'No. No, he's gone over to Than.'

'Okay, I'll go and get Claire?'

'She's gone for a walk in the woods. Let's not worry, I've got plenty of time to call the midwife. Then when she's here we can sort out getting Ted back! I don't understand, I've not had any contractions yet . . . '

'Is that normal?'

'No, with Rowan I had contractions for hours before this happened.'

'Rowan. Let me call Rowan . . . '

'She's out somewhere!'

'There must be *someone* around?'

'Okay, Tori, deep breaths,' laughs Lizzie.

'Hey, isn't that meant to be my line?'

Suddenly, all the drama from this morning, my worries about Than and what Bay might think, just don't matter.

'Let's call that midwife and go from there,' I say.

'Good pl — '

The 'aaaaannn' part of her last word comes out as a shriek as she clasps her stomach and bends forward, clearly in pain. I'm guessing that this is one of those missing contractions, and it's going on way longer than I would have guessed.

Lizzie starts to pant, and I rush to her side, gingerly putting a hand on her back. Finally she straightens up and takes several deep breaths to steady herself.

'Sorry, sorry!' she says. 'Look, I'll go in and make the call and get changed. I'll be back . . . ' Still holding her stomach, Lizzie disappears through the door.

I don't know what to do. I nip back through the gate to have a quick look around the yard, but typically there's no one to be seen. I can hear the vague murmuring of Lizzie on the telephone inside. I really need Ted. Or Doreen. Or maybe some professionals here right about now!

'TORI!' The yell of pain from inside the house brings me back to reality, and I rush straight back through to the garden.

'TORI!!'

Okay, if Lizzie's calling me from inside the house, this has got to classify as one of those dire emergencies they mentioned when we first arrived. I head straight through the back door and into the kitchen. Lizzie's on her hands and knees on the floor, and the old phone handset is dangling from its cord.

'What happened?'

I rush to her and go to help her up, but she shakes her head, breathing hard.

'It's okay,' I whisper, 'you're okay.'

'This. Is. Too. Fast!' she breathes.

I rub her back ineffectually until she breathes easier again.

‘Let me help you up,’ I say.

‘No. I’ll stay here.’

‘Okay. First things first. Midwife?’ I catch up the dangling phone and put it to my ear. There’s no one there, just a dial tone.

‘She’s on her way. She’s just finished a visit to someone else. May be a while though.’

‘Shit,’ I say, without thinking.

‘My thoughts exactly!’

‘Look, let’s get you comfy. I’ll grab some pillows and stuff?’

‘Our bedroom’s upstairs. End of the hall then to the right.’

I leg it straight up the stairs and along the hallway, not caring that I sound like a one-woman herd of elephants as I rush to gather things and get back to Lizzie. I don’t want to leave her alone for too long.

I don’t even take a moment to marvel at their epic, canopied four-poster bed. I just bundle two pillows under one arm, grab a massive bath sheet off a pile on a chair in the corner and, as an afterthought, snag a big, fluffy dressing gown from the back of the door. I hurry back down to the kitchen, dump the whole lot unceremoniously onto the floor and then take the pillows over to Lizzie.

‘You’re an angel!’ she smiles. We place one behind her back so that she can lean more comfortably up against the edge of the old dresser. ‘I’ll move in a minute.’

‘There’s no . . . ’

I was going to say that there was no rush, but Lizzie’s straining forward again. I crouch down next to her and hold her hand, which she promptly crushes in a vice-like grip.

'Tori, I feel like I need to push!'

'What? Already? But the midwife's not here yet!'

She moans.

'Breathe!' I say. *That's what they all say in films, isn't it?* Lizzie instantly starts doing some weird breathing pattern. Okay, this is ridiculous.

'Phew. Okay. It's easing off . . . '

'Lizzie, I think I need to call an ambulance,' I say.

'No, we'll be fine. The midwife's on her way.'

'But . . . '

'Tori! What the hell?' Rowan's face appears, pale and worried-looking. 'What was that noise? I heard it from outside . . . '

'That would be your mum,' I say.

'The baby's coming, love!' Lizzie says.

'But . . . where's Dad?'

'He's talking to Than, I'm guessing over at the campsite?' I say.

'Do you want me to run and get him?'

'Please!' I nod.

Rowan dashes off, but before I get the chance to say anything else to Lizzie, she's scooted around so that she's on all fours and is groaning again. Right, I don't care what she says, this isn't normal. I'm calling an ambulance.

I pick up the phone and dial 999.

'Emergency, which service do you require? Fire, police or ambulance?'

'Ambulance, please,' I say, my heart hammering. There's a click on the line. I must be being transferred.

'Ambulance service. What's your emergency?'

'My friend. She's gone into labour and there's no one else here. We've called the midwife but things have ramped up rather suddenly. She just said she wants to push!'

Lizzie promptly gives a bellow of pain.

The operator quickly takes my details, Lizzie's name, The Farm's address and a contact number, which I read off the body of the phone on the wall.

'Has her water broken?'

'Yes. And she's having really awful contractions.'

'How far apart?'

'Um . . . I don't know . . . maybe every three to five minutes.'

'Okay, and how long are the contractions?'

'Well, one started just before we connected and it's only just easing.'

'It sounds like the baby is going to be there very soon. An ambulance is on its way to you. I need you to keep me on the phone while you wait for the midwife or ambulance to arrive.'

'Okay. Can I put you on speaker?'

'Please do.'

I click a button on the old-fashioned set on the wall and cross my fingers that it's going to work. 'Hello, can you still hear me?'

'Yes. I'm still here,' comes the woman's calm voice. At least I'm not on my own anymore. 'Hi, Lizzie, I'm Georgia. I'm just going to talk to you while you're waiting for some help to arrive, okay.'

'M'kay,' Lizzie pants.

'Are you somewhere safe?'

'She's on the kitchen floor on all fours.'

'Lizzie, it sounds like the baby is going to be there soon. Now, Tori, I need you to look around for me. Is there enough space around your friend for the midwife and paramedics to be able to help when they arrive?'

'Yes, plenty,' I say.

'Okay, good. And is she comfortable?'

'I am,' says Lizzie. 'I . . . oooohhhh!'

Another contraction starts and I can barely hear Georgia's tinny voice over the handset, but I can hear she's counting.

'I need to push!' yells Lizzie again.

'Lizzie, blow out three short breaths. Did you do that pattern in your classes?'

Lizzie nods. I'm glad this makes any sense to her, because it's Greek to me. She starts a strange panting rhythm over and over.

'Tori, I need you to get some towels, and if you can find a bucket or washing-up bowl to have on hand, and some bin liners?'

I quickly get to my feet. I've already got the towel from upstairs. I locate the bin liners and a plastic tub in the cupboard under the kitchen sink and place them on the floor near Lizzie.

I lay the towel on the floor for her as she sits back down, prop the other cushion behind her back, then fetch the dressing gown from where I dumped it and hold it out to her. She just cuddles it to her.

'Lizzie, love?!' Ted flies in through the back door with Rowan at his heels. They're both completely out of breath and must have run all the way back from the campsite.

'Ted?' Lizzie pants.

'Who's arrived, Tori?' Georgia's voice comes from the phone.

'It's Ted, the baby's dad,' I say.

'Who's that?' says Ted, catching hold of Lizzie's hand and peering around, bewildered.

'It's Georgia, the 999 operator, on speakerphone,' I say. 'She's going to stay on the line with us until the midwife or ambulance arrives.'

'Ambulance?' says Rowan, looking freaked.

'The baby's coming very quickly, Rowan,' I say.

'Nothing to worry about,' comes Georgia's calm voice.

The scream that comes from Lizzie rather contradicts what Georgia's saying. Rowan goes pale so I get up and go over to her.

'Can you help me?'

She nods.

'Find me as many clean towels as possible.'

'Small or large?'

'Both. And then put a full kettle on to boil.'

'Why the kettle?'

'They always do it in films,' I say.

Rowan dashes off upstairs.

'Knock knock!' calls a woman's voice from the back door.

'Hello?' I rush over and spot a kindly face peering around the open door.

'Hi, I'm Val, Lizzie's midwife.'

'Oh, thank God!' I say, breathing a sigh of relief. 'She's over there. And we've got Georgia on the phone. I was on my own with Lizzie and she kept wanting to push, so I called 999.'

'Okay. Good. Can you get me towels?'

'Already on their way,' I say, and hurry off to check on Rowan and leave the people who actually know what they're doing to get on with it.

After delivering the towels into a kitchen that seems to be full of the sound of pain, I check if Val needs anything else, and when she shakes her head, I beat a hasty retreat with Rowan at my side. I was aiming for the back garden, but the wailing from inside the house is still way too loud. 'Fancy coming back to the yurt with me?' I say.

'Shouldn't we be doing something?' Rowan asks, looking desperate.

'We've done our bit,' I smile at her. 'Your mum and the baby are in safe hands now. Thanks so much for helping!'

Rowan shrugs, looking scared.

As we traipse down the yard, an ambulance appears at the bottom of the track. Rowan runs to open the gate for them and, pointing them in the direction of the house, tells them to go straight round to the back door.

* * *

Bay's sitting outside when we get to the yurt.

'Tori, you okay? I heard — '

I shake my head quickly to cut him off and say, 'Lizzie's gone into labour. Looks like the baby's nearly here!'

'What? But . . . *what?*'

'I was with her when it kicked off,' I say, pointing Rowan into one of the wooden chairs around the cold fire pit. 'We left her with Ted and the midwife, and the ambulance guys arrived just as we were headed over here.'

'Ambulance?' he says, looking worried.

'Well, we weren't sure how long the midwife was going to be, and I needed help, so I called 999,' I say a tad defensively. 'She'll be okay,' I add gently, turning to Rowan.

‘I thought you got more warning than that,’ she says. ‘I heard that Val person say the baby’s coming really soon!’

I nod. ‘Well, seems your little brother or sister is in a hurry.’ I sit on the bench next to her.

‘I’m going to have a brother or sister,’ Rowan says in amazement, and then buries her face in my shoulder and starts to cry. I pause for just a moment and then put my arm around her.

22

Sometimes 'No' Is Enough

''No' is an important word. Anxiety can make us feel like we're not allowed to use it. So, instead, we go against our instincts simply because saying 'yes' is just more comfortable. Learning to say 'no' again can be a powerful game-changer. And you don't need to use excuses to justify it. Sometimes 'no' is enough.'

©TheBeginnersGuideToLoneliness.com

Val comes to find us about an hour after Rowan and I beat our retreat. After calming Rowan down, Bay and I decided that we'd light a fire and settle in for the afternoon, assuming that things might take a while to work themselves out. As it is, we've only just got the wood together, the fire going and the kettle on before our visitor arrives.

'Your mum and dad asked me to come and tell you that it's a girl. You've got a beautiful baby sister,' Val says kindly to Rowan.

Rowan starts cheering, I promptly burst into tears and Bay leaps to his feet and starts doing a little dance next to the fire, unable to keep his bum on the chair.

Val grins at us. 'They've all gone in the ambulance to the hospital. The baby came so fast that Lizzie needs a few stitches, and that's best done there. They'll be able to check baby over too.'

'But she's okay?' Rowan asks, looking worried.

'Yes, they'll both be fine after a little bit of TLC,' Val reassures her gently.

'Was that normal? How fast everything happened, I mean?' asks Rowan.

'It's unusual, but it does happen to about one woman in every two hundred.'

'Trust Mum to be different!' Rowan says with pride.

'Tea, Val?' Bay asks, grabbing the kettle.

'Don't mind if I do!' she says, and sinks gratefully onto one of the benches.

* * *

Supper tonight has turned into one great big celebration, and it's like the difficult session we all shared this morning happened in another lifetime. Of course, Ted and Lizzie are missing as they're still at the hospital, and Bay has taken Rowan in the Land Rover to meet her baby sister.

Everyone wants to hear the story, and I repeat it several times. They're treating me like some kind of hero, but in reality, all I did was use the phone. Even so, I feel so bloody proud and grateful. There's a healthy new baby in the world, and I got to play a tiny part in that.

'Can I talk to you?' Than asks, coming over to me at the little outdoor kitchen as I'm refilling my cup of elderflower bubbly.

'Erm. Okay,' I say. I'm suddenly aware of eyes following us. I glance over to the table to find Claire watching us. She raises an eyebrow, and I give her a little nod. I hope she understands this as code for 'I'm okay, no need for rescue.' She's plainly still on alert after this morning's fiasco.

'Look,' says Than, 'I wanted to say sorry.'

'Because you really are sorry, or because Ted told you to?' I ask, my voice flat.

'Come on, Tori! Because I want to. I wanted to come straight back up those stairs the minute I left the session, but I was in such a state, I wasn't thinking straight.'

'Why did you do it? I don't know what I'm meant to have done wrong,' I say quietly. Maybe I should just accept the apology, but I'm genuinely curious, and there's something about today's turn of events that makes me feel like I'm allowed to ask.

Than shrugs. 'I'm not sure.' He doesn't meet my eye, and I can't read the look on his face. 'But I'm really sorry for what I did. I guess I've got a lot more to work out than I realized.'

'I've only ever been on your side, Than. What you did this morning was really shitty. I do understand that you've got a lot to deal with — ' I look at him, and he goes to say something, but I cut him off with my hand raised. 'I do, I get it. But we're all vulnerable; that's why we're here. We're all working through something. But . . . that doesn't give any of us the right to behave like you did this morning.' I peter off. I know what I want to say, but it feels so alien to speak my mind that it's coming out a bit jumbled.

'Last night was difficult for me and, I don't know . . . I just . . . ' Than lets out a huge sigh. 'Look, it was a mistake.'

I shrug. This just isn't important anymore. 'Okay, let's just move on,' I say. 'Bubbly?' I ask, offering him a cup.

Than takes it, takes a sip and looks at the ground. I can't help but do an inward sigh. I was enjoying this evening, but now I feel like I have some kind of responsibility to pull Than out of the slump he's in.

'Would you like to come for a walk?' Than asks, looking up at me.

I want to grind my teeth a little bit when I spot a hint of his usual smile is back in place. I may have said we could 'move on', but I'm not a complete sap. I know that there was more to this morning's outburst than Than struggling with what happened — or *didn't* happen last night.

'Thanks, Than, but I want to stay here and celebrate with everyone,' I say, keeping my voice as light as possible.

'I could just use a friend right now. Someone who knows what I'm dealing with,' he says, and the wobble that's suddenly back in his voice is clearly designed to undo my resolve.

I shake my head. 'I can't tonight. I'm tired and a bit wobbly myself after everything. Why don't you ask if Russ or Claire have a bit of time free?'

Than makes a snorting sound, and my irritation towards him turns into full-blown annoyance.

'They just won't get it like you do,' says Than, and now he sounds like a stroppy teen.

'Well, it's their job, so I'd say they'd be a better bet than me this evening!' I say. I want to rejoin the group. Now. I've had enough of whatever game he's playing.

'But . . . we have things we need to talk about . . . ' he pouts.

'No, Than, we don't. You've apologized. We're good. Now I'm going back to the others. Come with me if you want.'

'But last night . . . '

I let out a sigh of frustration and turn to face him

properly. 'I said everything I needed to last night.'

'You said we could talk,' he shoots back at me mutinously.

Something inside me snaps. 'I said that so I could get away from you! I've really enjoyed your company, getting to know you, hanging out a bit. But I've got stuff of my own to deal with, and I've got to focus on that.'

'But, Tori . . . '

I hear him, but I've already turned my back and am headed over towards the others, back towards the celebrations and the food. When I've squeezed myself onto one of the benches in between Sam and Messa, I glance back over to where we'd been standing.

Than has gone.

* * *

It should have been the perfect evening, but my second standoff of the day with Than has put a decided dampener on my spirits. When Rowan, Bay and Ted appear back from the hospital with the news that Lizzie and the baby are doing well, I feel the tiredness truly catch up with me. Now all I want is to head back to the yurt, get into bed and let my head start to digest some of the insanity that has happened today. Before I do, I decide to take my own advice and seek out Claire.

She greets me with a huge hug.

'You doing okay, Tori? I saw Than catch up with you earlier.'

'I'm okay,' I say quietly. I don't really want to go into anything with the others around. 'I didn't get much chance to speak with Lizzie before everything kicked off . . . '

'You want to chat now?' she asks, and I could hug her again for not making me ask.

'You sure that would be okay?' I say.

'Of course! Did you want to talk here, or . . . ?'

'I was thinking of heading back to the yurt soon. I'm wiped.'

'I bet! How about I come with you? We can walk and talk . . . '

'That would be perfect.'

I say my goodnights to everyone and enjoy another full round of hugs. When I get to Ted, he holds me close for a long time. Anyone would think I'd single-handedly delivered his baby the way he's thanking me.

Bay's the last to wrap his arms around me, and as I soak in the warmth of his body and snuggle my face against his soft, worn jumper, my head quietens down. Just for a moment, I stop worrying about everything.

'You gonna be okay to head back to the yurt on your own?' he asks gently as I step back from him. 'Only, I need to eat and then I'll help the others clear this lot up.'

I nod and breathe a sigh of relief, knowing that Claire and I are going to be able to chat for a while without being disturbed.

⋆ ⋆ ⋆

To begin with, I'm a bit halting as I start talking to Claire, but her easy manner and friendliness mean that before we've even crossed into the first field, I'm opening up to her about Than in a way that I haven't with anyone else. I tell her about the weird sense of attraction I felt at first, which I'm now pretty sure was just relief that someone liked me after I'd been on my own for so long. I tell her how he's been seeking me out for advice and support, and that although I've been happy to listen, I know it's way beyond my ability to help. I tell her about Bay's warning, and I tell her about Than trying to kiss me in the hot tub.

'And then there was this morning's outburst,' says Claire quietly.

'Yup.'

'So what happened this evening?'

'He said sorry about this morning and then wanted to talk about the almost-kiss. And he wanted me to go with him so that he could talk privately about his 'stuff'.' I sigh. 'Thing is, last time he 'wanted to talk', he didn't actually want to talk at all.'

'What happened that time?' Claire asks curiously.

'We just went back to his tent and hung out for a bit. He wanted to gossip and just chill out and . . . yeah. To be honest, I think if you and Moth hadn't arrived, and Dennis hadn't bowled into the tent, he would probably have tried to kiss me then.'

Claire nods. 'It's not unusual for strong feelings to come out when you're at a place like this, you know. I've seen it before. It's happened to me at retreats I've been to.'

'It has?' I ask in surprise.

'Of course! You're there, opening up and clearing all these blocks. And there's this huge release of energy. I've made some of my dearest friends at places like this.'

I nod. It's actually a relief to be told that these relationships are real, even if they start in the weirdest of ways. And I'm not thinking about whatever has happened between me and Than. I'm thinking of the others. Doreen and Geoff. Messa and Moth. Sam, Emma and Bob. Even Bay. I've already started to dread losing these guys when the course is over. But why should I? This bunch of nutty buggers are becoming my friends. And I don't have to live without them after we're done here.

'Tori, I think there are a couple of suggestions I'd like to make, if you're willing to hear them?' Claire says as we come in sight of the yurt.

'Of course. Please!' I say, turning to smile at her.

'Okay, number one: enjoy the group. From what I've seen, Than has monopolized you quite a bit. But you stand to gain more from being a part of the whole group. You've got the weekend ahead of you — spend time with the others. It'll then be up to Than whether he joins in too, or whether he continues to separate himself.'

I nod. That's exactly what I've been wanting to do anyway, I realize. My instinct has been telling me to be with the others more.

'The second thing I want you to do,' Claire takes my hand and turns to look at me, 'is to trust your instincts. If something feels right, and good, deep down in your core, then you're probably right. And if something feels wrong, or awkward, or out of place, trust that feeling.'

I nearly laugh out loud. 'I think you're a mind-reader,' I say as I pull Claire into a hug and thank her for clearing my head.

23

One Step Forwards . . .

'It's not always going to be plain sailing. Sometimes it can feel like we take one step forwards, only to stumble back by two. But the key thing is to keep moving forwards. Keep taking those steps and you will make the connections you're looking for.'

©TheBeginnersGuideToLoneliness.com

It turns out the baby's birth and everything else that happened on Friday has had more of an effect on me than I could have imagined. I know, it's not like I was there for the actual delivery or anything, but I feel like a different person somehow. If I'm honest, it might not just be the baby's arrival that has changed me. Standing up for myself to Than and asking Claire for help might have something to do with it too. I've had the weekend for everything to sink in, and I feel bolder. Braver. Like I can take on a challenge.

Funnily enough, this morning has presented me with the perfect opportunity. The rest of the group have decided to start the week off with another wild swim. And, after everything that's happened, I'm ready to face my very worst fear. I mean, it's not like I'm about to give birth on a kitchen floor, is it?!

'So, you're coming with us this morning?' Bay grins across the yurt at me as I stuff a towel determinedly into a cloth bag. 'Not going to skive off?'

I laugh. 'I'm coming for the walk at least,' I say. 'For me, even getting near that river is a big step.'

'I know. Can I ask, what is it about rivers, exactly?'

I pause, hugging my bag to my chest. *How much do I tell him?*

'I'm sorry, you don't have to answer that if you don't want to,' he says quickly.

'Well . . . ' Maybe it's a good plan to fill him in a bit. 'There was an accident two years ago . . . involving a river. And since then I've had this phobia.'

He blinks at me. 'So this is the perfect way for you to face it, then. You'll be with the rest of us. You'll be completely safe.'

'I wish it was that rational. Even the sound of a river can set me off. I don't think I'll be able to get into that water — ' My voice has started to tremble.

'Hey, you haven't even seen it yet,' he says, his voice gentle.

'I don't need to. It's a river.' I thought I was up for a challenge . . .

'Okay, come for the walk. Check it out, take it slow . . . and if nothing else you get to laugh at the rest of us freezing our backsides off, right?'

* * *

I'm the last one to make it to the bottom of the hill, and as I stoop to navigate my way under the low-hanging branches of the trees near the river's edge, I can already hear squeals and laughter. Unfortunately, I can also hear the river. My stomach lurches and I shiver. It takes all my determination to reach the small, shingle beach where a couple of the others are standing, gazing at the water.

Objectively, I can see that it's a beautiful place. A large, deep pool has formed where the rapids meet a steep cliff. Here the river becomes so slow and lazy that it merely trickles out of the other side. The cliff itself has several small trees growing out of its rough face. On our side of the river, the shingle beach leads right to the water's edge.

The pool is so clear that you can see all the way to the bottom, apart from the deepest parts where it just turns into an inky blackness. The thundering of the river as it hits the cliff is deafeningly hypnotic, and it's taking every ounce of will power I can muster not to turn tail and run. The shards of sunlight that filter down through the leaves bathe the whole area in a strange, greenish light. I shiver again, trying to calm my breathing and slow my heart rate down.

'Take your time,' says Bay, 'you're doing great.'

I nod. I can't get a word out. I'm battling an image of a car sinking into the pool. I shake my head and focus on what's really in front of me.

Russ, Emma, Sam and Geoff are already in the water, splashing wildly and laughing. The others are all on the beach, peeling off clothes and shedding their shoes.

'Come on, guys, it's beautiful!' Geoff shouts, brushing his slicked down hair out of his eyes and grinning at us from the water.

'Idiot,' mutters Doreen, coming to stand by my side. 'He's always been like this with water.'

We stand quietly together for a moment, watching as Than marches into the pool. He makes his way straight past the others and starts swimming steadily further out into the deep water.

'Get your bum in here, Mrs McVey, or I'm coming

to get you!' Geoff growls to his wife in mock serious tones. He takes a couple of strokes forwards as if he's going to make good on his promise, and Doreen squeals, making me jump.

'Don't you dare, you naughty man. Give me a second!' She shrugs off the enormous jumper she's wearing and tosses it further up the beach. Stepping as daintily out of her wellies as she can, she strips down to a violently pink one-piece. Very slowly, Doreen picks her way over the slate and down towards the water's edge.

I watch, half in admiration, half with a growing sense of horror. Part of me wants to run after her, to pull her back, away from the water. This is a brave woman. I should be taking notes.

She reaches the water's edge and comes to a grinding halt.

'Come on, love, or I swear I'm coming out to get you!' laughs Geoff, beckoning to Doreen.

'I'm not sure.' Doreen dips a toe in. 'Bloody hell, it's freezing!'

'Watch out . . . I'm coming in!' The cry comes from behind me, and just as I turn to see who it is, Bay streaks past and does an almighty belly flop right into the middle of the pool, sending up a massive tidal wave that laps right up over Doreen's knees and splashes her so badly that the water drips off her hair and runs down her face.

Bay comes up gasping and rubbing his eyes while the others laugh at him, shaking their heads like a pack of dogs.

'Oh, sod it!' mutters Doreen. She turns her back on the pool, reverses into the water until it reaches the middle of her thighs, locks her body straight and, with a shriek, falls backwards into the water.

Everyone claps and cheers as she surfaces, spluttering and gasping.

'That's my girl!' shouts Geoff.

Doreen splashes an armful of water at him.

'Hey, Tori, you coming in or what?' Geoff calls.

All the sounds of splashing have had me frozen to the spot in fear, fighting a rising tide of panic, but at the sound of Geoff's voice I automatically take a couple of steps backwards, away from the water.

'Thanks, I'm fine,' I choke. 'I'm just going to watch for a bit!'

No. *No no no*. I'm having enough trouble being this close to the water and not legging it as it is. But then I think about Lizzie giving birth on the kitchen floor. And about sticking up for myself.

I take a deep breath.

I did come here for a challenge.

I take another deep breath.

I take a couple of steps forwards again. And then a couple more, getting closer to the water. My heart's pounding, but I take another deep breath in and let it out slowly.

'Come in, Tori, you'll like it!' shouts Than as he rejoins the group after exploring the further edges of the pool.

'No. Thanks.' I gasp the words out. *I'm fine. I'm safe.*

'It's mandatory to the course you know!' he laughs.

'No.' I can feel the anger starting to rise and mingle with my fear.

'At least come in for a paddle?'

'No, Than.' My breath is coming quicker. This is ridiculous. Why can't he just leave me alone?

'Let her take her own time,' I hear Bay mutter to Than.

I bristle. I'm grateful, but I'm not a charity case. I feel my resolve stiffen. I can do this.

I bend down and start taking my boots and socks off. I fight to roll my trousers up, my shaking fingers making it difficult. I take a tentative step towards the water's edge, struggling to keep my balance on the loose stones underfoot.

Breathe in. Slowly out.

See. It's fine. It's just water. I'm fine.

Fuck. I wince as the soles of my feet make contact with the damp shingle at the water's edge. I'm not in the river yet but that's far enough. My whole vision is filling with water. I let out the breath that I hadn't even realized I'd been holding. I can do this. I can . . .

I catch Bay's eye. He's watching me with a smile on his face. He gives me an almost imperceptible nod. I nod back curtly. See. I'm no one's charity case. I'm . . .

I gasp and choke as a torrent of water hits me in the face. I shake my head, trying to clear it from my eyes only to be hit by another wave. This time I scream and fail my arms, and as I do, my feet start to slip on the stones beneath me. I'm hit again and again. I'm aware of the others shouting, but I can't make sense of what's happening.

'No! No, no, NO! STOP!' I hear a voice screaming. It's mine, but it seems to be coming from a long way away, from the other side of the humming buzz that has started in my brain and is taking over any sense I have left.

Another wave hits me. The buzzing starts to drown me and I feel my feet slip as the stones beneath me shift.

The shouting and screaming have disappeared. All I can hear is the buzzing in my head and each breath heaving into my lungs as if I'm sucking the air in through a bathroom sponge. And then I'm back in the middle of my worst nightmare. There's water all around me. And screaming. I can see fingers clawing at the windows of a drowning car, scrabbling to be released. She's desperate to get out of there. And then the fingers go limp, and I'm screaming and screaming for my mother.

24

The Voices in Your Head

'What kind of voice do you use when you talk to yourself? So often it is cruel and mocking. You would never talk to a friend that way, so why do it to yourself? It's time to show yourself some kindness.'

©TheBeginnersGuideToLoneliness.com

When I come to, I'm lying on the shingle beach a couple of feet away from the river's edge. Two things instantly make me want to crawl under a duvet and hide. Number one: my head is being cradled in someone's lap. Number two: I'm sobbing. Really going for it. A full-blown, howling snot-fest. As soon as I realize this, I gulp several times and try to calm down, but it's no use. It's like hiccups — completely out of my hands.

'Shh, shh. It's okay, you're okay.'

It's a man's voice. Gentle hands stroke the wet hair away from my face.

'Is your head okay? Did you hit it?'

'Put her in the recovery position.'

'Give her Rescue Remedy!'

'Is she hurt?'

'Is she cut?'

'Did she slip?'

'Okay, back off everyone!'

I recognize this last voice as Doreen's and I struggle to sit up and wipe the heavy tears away from my face at the same time. A hand supports the middle of my back. I turn to see who it is, and Bay's worried eyes stare back at me.

'Are you okay? Are you hurt?' he asks gently.

'No . . . no, I don't think so. What happened?'

'You got splashed. *Than* splashed you . . . I tried to stop him . . . '

'Drama queen,' I hear Than mutter.

'Shut up,' Bay growls.

I struggle to my feet, not quite trusting my shaking legs to hold me up. Bay quickly stands up and reaches out again to steady me, but I shake him off and move towards Than, who's scowling at me.

'What the fuck did you think you were doing?' I hiss at him, as I feel every ounce of shock and fear turn into cold anger.

'Having a laugh. I didn't think you were going to spaz out on us, did I?'

'*Spaz out?*' I spit, advancing on him. 'You know I'm scared of water. I told you about my phobia! You know more than anyone else here.'

'Yeah yeah, you're terrified I'm sure!'

'Okay, guys, let's have a group hug and let this go!' chirrups a nervous-sounding Emma from somewhere behind me.

'I'm not having a fucking group hug. Listen to me, you prick, do you know what I see when I'm near water and I lose control?'

'Jaws?' Than tries to laugh it off, and looks around for support, but only gets disbelieving stares from the others. 'Get over it,' he huffs.

'I see my mother's fingers clawing at the window of her sinking car. My mother, desperate to get out, bleeding and terrified. My mother, drowning.' I can't help it; I start to sob again.

Than glares at me and the others have gone completely quiet. I see Doreen wipe her eyes. Bay steps forward to place his hand on my shoulder. I shrug him off again.

'Maybe I am a drama queen, but I think I've got a pretty good reason. If you don't, then fuck you.' I grab my boots, ram them onto my feet and trudge back up the shingle bank and away from the paralyzed group behind me.

As soon as I step out from under the canopy of trees and feel the sunlight on my face, my body relaxes, my shoulders slump and my sobs ease into a free flow of salty tears. I actually don't mind the tears now that I'm away from the others. I know from bitter experience that if I try to hold them in, they'll only catch up with me later.

I stride away from the sound of voices behind me and go in search of a little bit of peace and privacy where I can get back in control of my feelings. I need to get my armour back in place.

I'm already regretting my outburst. I didn't want everyone to find out like that — or at all, really. Mind you, it's not like I had much choice in the matter.

It doesn't take long for the crying and shaking to start to calm, but all that means is that I'm now aware that my arm is throbbing. I look down at my hand and see that there's blood dripping from my fingertips. *Oh. Shit.*

Coming to a halt at the top of the hill, I twist this way and that, trying to get a good look at where the blood is coming from. There's a messy gash that runs down the back of my forearm. It looks pretty filthy too. Damn. All I want right now is a bit of peace and quiet, but I'll have to get someone to help me clean this up, whether I want to or not.

I stand still just a moment or two longer and look back down the hill to where the others are emerging from under the trees, their swim cut short by the drama. I spot Bay striking out in my direction. Thankfully it's just him; the others seem to be staying put. I really don't want to talk about it yet, so I take a couple of steps towards the field gate.

'Tori, wait! Please!' Bay calls, speeding up in spite of the hill.

'Why?'

'You're in shock. You're hurt. You can't go off on your own.'

'Right. Well. Right.' I hang my head. All of a sudden, I'm absolutely knackered.

'It's not your fault, you know?'

Great. Someone else telling me it's not my fault. Does he really think I've not tried to tell myself that before? I shrug. The tears have started again. I can feel them snaking down my cheeks, hot and heavy. I wipe my face with the back of my hand.

'Shit, Tori, you're covered in blood!' Bay gasps.

I examine my hand and realize that I've probably just managed to smear blood across my face.

'Don't worry, it's just my arm,' I sigh.

'Don't worry?'

'I mean, it's not my head or anything serious.'

'Show me,' says Bay, taking a step closer. I get the sense he's been holding back until now for fear of spooking me, like a wild deer or something. But the sight of the blood seems to have galvanized him into action. I twist my arm around to show him.

He peers closely at it. 'It doesn't look too deep, but

it does need cleaning properly.'

I know this. Really I do. But right now, I don't want to go anywhere near the rest of the group. 'I might just go for a bit of a walk to calm down,' I say.

'Sorry, Tori, but you really need to come back with us. You're hurt and in shock, and that cut needs attention.'

'I think I've had enough attention already, thanks.'

'Tori, you have to — '

'I don't have to do anything! I didn't have to get in that river, and I don't have to come with you.' I glare at Bay. My arm is now full-on throbbing. I know that I'm behaving like a child, but embarrassment is now mingling with the shock of what just happened, and right now, Bay is the only available target.

All I really want to do is hide under a fluffy duvet with a strong drink at the ready, followed by some serious comfort TV, but there's no chance of any of that.

'Fine,' Bay sighs. 'Look, tell you what, give me a second to let the others know what's happening, and I'll walk you back to the yurt so that you can have a rest somewhere safe. No need for you to talk to the others yet. Deal?'

I feel like arguing, but I have zero energy left, and if I'm honest I'm starting to feel a little bit fuzzy around the edges. I don't particularly like the idea of being called a drama queen again because I fainted in the middle of a field like some drippy Jane Austen heroine.

'Okay, deal,' I say quietly.

As I watch Bay pelt back down the hill towards the others, I feel all my bravery and my desire for a new challenge dissolve. Reality is crashing over me. I'm broke, my only friends are people I've never met, I live in a damp, unappealing broom cupboard and the only man I've ever loved broke my heart in the worst way possible.

And here I am, at the culmination of it all, standing in a field with blood dripping down my arm, recovering from a panic attack and a dead faint.

* * *

As soon as Bay gets back, we start to walk quietly in the direction of the yurt. I hold my arm, doing my best to wrap it in a bit of clean T-shirt. The sense of relief when I spot the yurt is insane. All I want to do now is lie down and let the shock, which is slowly making my body feel like a heavy piece of putty, subside. I need to get some sleep and then I'll feel a lot better. After that, I'll decide how best to pay that bloody arsehole back.

'Okay, you chill out here for a while and I'll go in search of a first-aid kit. I'll be back in a bit, okay?' Bay says, his voice gentle.

I nod and duck into the yurt, grateful to be on my own for a few minutes. I yank my boots off and, after peeling off the rest of my damp clothing, I put on some fresh, loose trousers, wincing at the dark bruises that are already starting to bloom on my legs. The blood has pretty much stopped seeping out of the cut now, but I can see a whole bunch of dark flecks stuck in it. I'll have to clean that properly, but right now, all I want to do is get warm and dry. I pull on the jumper I borrowed from Bay the other night, careful to wrap my arm in the T-shirt again to stop any blood staining it, and then I climb under my blankets.

* * *

The water is closing in on me and there's nowhere to go. The fabric-lined ceiling above me is getting closer and closer and there are only inches of air left. My fingers are raw and bleeding, but I won't stop clawing at the windows. I grab the door handle and still it won't give. The air gap is almost gone. I gasp a few more lungfuls and press as hard as I can against the window. It won't budge. My vision is filled with my mother's unconscious face, eyes gazing lifelessly through the murky water, hair floating in a halo about her head like possessed seaweed. I suck in my last breath and scream, trying to wake her up. And then it's gone, the air gap has closed.

I thrash wildly, holding my breath, but my lungs are about to burst. I open my mouth to scream again, but the in-breath just pulls in water. It streams up my nose and clogs my throat. I scream and scream but no noise comes out; there's just tightness in my chest as my lungs fill. I am drowning and no one can hear my silent cries.

Then there are arms around me, lifting me, saving me. They're pulling me upwards through the water towards the light, but I'm still screaming. Can't they see my mum is still down there? She's stuck. Unconscious. Drowning.

'Help her!' This time the cry isn't silent. It shoots through the air and tears at the fabric of my dream, waking me up. But the hands are still there, holding on to mine.

'Tori, it's all right. You're okay, you're safe.' It's a man's voice. I'm sobbing so hard I can't see. I can barely hear.

'Tori, calm down.'

'Bay?' I squeak through the tears.

'Yes, it's me. You've been asleep for hours, you know.'

I know. I can tell from the stiffness in my neck and the layers of fear that have built up inside me. I've been living that dream over and over again without the relief of waking in between.

'Tori, you need to get that arm cleaned up. And you probably need something to eat too.'

'No, no, I don't. I just need to rest. I'll be fine,' I mutter.

'No.' This time there's no arguing with Bay's tone. 'Tori, you need a rest from your nightmares. You've been tossing and turning for ages. Look, I brought you something.' He gestures over towards the centre of the yurt.

I sit up to see what he's talking about, pushing back my tangled hair and trying to unglue the strands from my damp face.

In the middle of the space is an old, metal bathtub, filled with steaming water. The air is sweet and herby.

'A bath?'

'As near as it gets. I wasn't sure about the water after . . . but you said running water?'

'Running water,' I nod, and shudder. 'Water that's fast moving . . . that's rising or . . . or comes up at me . . . unexpected.' Damn, I've started to shiver in earnest at the memory of the face full of water earlier and the torrent of images it triggered. I shake my head to try to clear it.

'So a bath is . . . ?' Bay checks.

'Perfect. Thank you,' I force a smile. 'How on earth did you fill it?'

Bay shrugs. 'It did take a few trips, but I thought it might help. Even if you can't get in, you can soak your arm and use it to wash.'

I spot a couple of buckets next to the bath, still steaming. It must have taken him ages, lugging the water up here.

'What's the smell?' I wrinkle my nose. It's not unpleasant . . . just . . . *clean.*

'Oh, just a bit of lavender and tea tree oil. It might sting a bit, but it'll help clean that cut of yours, and the lavender will help with the bruising too.'

'I don't think I'll bruise. It was nothing really.'

'Well, it won't do you any harm, anyway . . . ' I see Bay looking at my arm on top of the bedcover where my sleeve has ridden up. There's already the hint of a blue-black bruise on show. 'Anyway, it'll help you relax.' Bay looks down, and suddenly seems awkward. 'I'll go. I'll be off for at least a couple of hours, so just take your time.'

'Right. Um . . . thanks. It's really kind of you.'

'I'll get Doreen to look in on you in about an hour — just to check you're okay. Right. I'll go then.'

'Bay?'

'Yeah?' His voice is low. He clears his throat, looking fidgety. I shift uncomfortably too. I'm still not very good at asking for help from people in real life.

'Do you . . . could you . . . could you help me clean my arm? There are bits in it, and I don't think I'll be able to get at them properly.' Cue a huge blush from me.

Why? I've only asked for some first-aid help . . . but after he's spent a large portion of his day trudging backwards and forwards to fill a bath for me, it somehow feels far more intimate.

'Of course!' he says, sounding relieved for some reason. 'Claire gave me a first-aid kit earlier. Come over here.' Bay helps me to my feet and gets me to perch on a stool near the entrance flap so that he's got more light.

He rummages through the little first-aid kit, pulling on a pair of gloves and handing me a couple of wrapped antiseptic wipes to hold. Finally, he pulls out a triangle sling bandage. 'Needs must!' he grins at me, dips it into the bath water, wrings it out and wads it up into a little pad.

'Okay, this is going to sting a bit . . .' He gently takes my arm in his hand.

I draw in a sharp breath as Bay swabs at the newly dried edges of my cut. I feel the sting of the cloth with every little movement he makes. He works in silence for a few minutes, but pauses briefly every time I give a squeak of discomfort.

'Okay, that looks good,' he says finally.

I stop biting my lip and heave a sigh of relief. That was worse than I expected, especially as he's had to remove the little dark bits of dirt and slate out of it too.

'Thank you — I think!'

'No problem.' He smiles at me and peels off the gloves that are so incongruous in this setting.

'And thanks again for the bath. I'll just . . .' I'm eyeing the hot water.

'Sure, sure. I'll get out of your way.' He scrambles to his feet. 'You're going to be fine, you know.' He gives me a tiny smile, and before I know what's happening, he leans over and plants a gentle kiss on my forehead before disappearing out of the yurt.

I'm left sitting on my stool, mouth slightly open in

surprise, wondering what the hell just happened. Did Bay just kiss me? No. Not really. That was him just trying to make me feel better, wasn't it? That was just the weird, slightly lowered boundaries that are normal around this place. It didn't mean anything.

The question is, why am I struggling to catch my breath again? This time, it's not through terror, but something far more . . . exciting?

I shake my head again in an attempt to clear the cotton wool clouds that are drifting around my brain. I must still be in shock from earlier, that's all it is. Right. Bath.

After sticking my head out of the entrance flap to double check that the coast is clear, I place a huge towel on a clothes rack and position it in front of the bath. There. Now, if anyone does happen to peek in, they won't get an eyeful.

I sigh as I sink into the water, careful not to splash myself. The warmth starts to soothe the aches and I feel the last traces of my nightmare melt away. All that remains now is the image of a pair of strong, gentle hands, and the feel of a warm kiss on my forehead.

* * *

'Knock knock! Are you decent?' Doreen's voice calls from outside.

'Come on in!' I call. After lounging around in my bath for what felt like an eternity, the water cooled so much I had to get out.

I feel so much better, like someone has washed the inside of my head for me too. I feel like I'm free of something; it's hard to describe it, but I'm calm. My arm feels loads better too. It's stopped throbbing, but that's probably because it's not full of little bits of stone anymore.

'How're you feeling?' Doreen's face appears. 'Wow! This place is gorgeous!' She sniffs. 'What's that smell?'

I smile back at her. 'That'd be my bath.'

'Bath?' Doreen moves into the space and eyes the metal tub. 'You lucky mare . . . Though I don't fancy having to haul all that water up here!'

I feel myself start to blush again. 'Erm . . . Bay did it. He thought it'd make me feel better.'

'Ooh, get you and your special treatment!' Doreen smiles and winks. I shift my weight uncomfortably. Hmm . . . maybe not the best thing for everyone to know about. 'You won't tell anyone, will you?'

'Course not!' she says reassuringly. 'Anyway, I was just kidding. You must have needed it after that fall. Are you okay?'

A finger of fear creeps back into my mind. Am I going to have to talk everything through with Doreen? And then the others too? I really can't face analyzing it all.

'I'm fine,' I reply tightly.

'So, you're ready for the next ordeal, then!' says Doreen as she bounces around the yurt, picking things up, examining them and replacing them.

I shiver. Nope. I'm not ready for anything.

'No one really expects you to turn up, you know. I think they're all half-expecting you to disappear on us.'

I pull a face. Right now, I just want to hide out here. I can't face seeing the others yet. Maybe they're right; maybe I should bow out and head home.

'You know,' she says gently, 'if you get on with things and have some new experiences, after a while, no one's going to give much weight to what happened this morning.'

'Yeah. I know you're right.' I say. 'Anyway, I don't fancy becoming the legend of the panicking water-girl.'

'Well then, what could be better than Ted's fire walk the day after tomorrow? It'll give you a day to recover . . . But I'm not going to be able to do it if you're not there to cheer me on, you know. Say you'll come!'

'Okay, I'll be there,' I say decidedly. 'I can't let you have all the fun, can I?'

25

Fall in Love with the Journey

> 'Everything about our society is set up to make us focus on outcomes; it's all about the destination, not the journey. But it's time to fall in love with the little steps that take us somewhere. Let us not forget to look around us and enjoy the view as we travel.'
>
> ©TheBeginnersGuideToLoneliness.com

How am I not *completely* freaking out right now? I'm about to help build a fire. Doesn't sound too bad, does it, a nice little bonfire? How about if I add that we're all expected to walk over the bloody thing? See, I should be freaking out!

But I'm not; I'm strangely calm about this part of the course. Cool as a cucumber. Because there's no doubt about the fact that it's going to bloody hurt and at least one of us is going to get seriously injured. It's the law of the universe. Do something stupid and you're going to get burned.

If I'm honest, I'm feeling so totally miserable right now, I'm not sure I care much. I'm still in hermit mode after everything that happened at the river. I don't really want to engage with the others, and I especially don't want to talk to Than. I managed to avoid all of them apart from Bay and Doreen yesterday. Claire came up to the yurt to try to talk things through with me, but I couldn't, and my policy for today is blanking the whole thing out. I just want to get it over and done with so that I can go back to the yurt and hide out with Dennis.

'Okay, gang! In a few hours you will all have completed at least one fire walk!' Ted shouts. He's so excited he sounds like he's almost ready to burst. 'How do you all feel about that?'

He looks around at us eagerly, but rather than the rousing chorus of cheers he was clearly expecting, all he gets are a few nervous smiles, blank nods and even a groan here and there — mainly from Doreen's direction. I just stay quiet.

Ted's face falls briefly. 'So, you're nervous? That's good.' He rallies, smiling around at us all. 'That's completely natural. If you were facing something this dangerous without a hint of fear or apprehension in your heart, I would have to call you a foolhardy idiot.' He looks at each of us in turn. 'The purpose of this fire walk is to stare fear in the face. Fear of failure, fear of pain, fear of the untried and fear of the unknown. But it's not just about staring it in the face, it's about embracing it, tangoing with it and ultimately learning that you can always overcome it.

'The fire will help you learn that life's not always about taking the long route around your troubles. Sometimes, you need to walk straight at them to reach the other side.'

I roll my eyes before I can catch myself, but it doesn't matter, everyone else's eyes are glued to Ted. I sigh. I'm not so sure that scorching the living daylights out of my feet will turn out to have all these magical, life-affirming properties.

I fidget.

No, I'm not looking forward to this, but I really,

really want to get it over and done with. The sooner we start, the sooner it will be over. Then I can take up a nice comfy bed in the nearest casualty department. Maybe I'll even get the chance to visit Lizzie and the baby while I'm at it.

* * *

Hours later, I'm exhausted from gathering wood from the nearby coppice and hauling load after load over to the fire. The afternoon has been full of the random, lively chatter of the others, but I've kept pretty quiet. After what happened at the river, I don't feel much like small talk. Most of my spare energy has been taken up with avoiding Than. Wherever he is is where I don't want to be. I've worked mainly with Bay, as he seems to understand my need to stay silent. Being with Bay also has the added bonus that Than is even less likely to try to talk to me.

As the flames start to settle, so does the conversation. We're all grouped around the fire, staring at the glowing mound of embers in front of us.

I feel a hand in mine and look sideways to find Doreen at my side. I smile at her, but don't receive one in return. She's pale and quivering.

'All right?' I ask quietly, just as Ted begins to rake the glowing embers flat, sending a cloud of sparks dancing and snapping over our heads.

Doreen shakes her head, lip wobbling. 'Not sure,' she mutters.

'I don't think anyone is,' I reply, giving her hand a squeeze. There's no point in comforting her beyond letting her know she's not alone. Right now, I think we're all shitting our pants.

'Okay, everyone,' calls Ted in a clear voice, 'you need to listen to me. I know that this is going to sound very obvious, but you need to take this in. This is a fire. You built it, and you've seen it burning. Now, I know that it's down to embers, but they're still burning at around 1,200 degrees Fahrenheit. What we are about to do needs concentration and respect. For each other, for yourselves and for the process. It is safe if you follow my lead. If you don't, this is dangerous. If you aren't happy to follow my lead, please head back to your camps now. This isn't the time for games. There is zero tolerance here for mucking about.' Ted pauses and looks around at all of us again.

No one budges an inch, but I can sense Doreen's breathing picking up a notch or two. I'm still strangely calm. After everything that's already happened, this just isn't pushing my buttons. I glance across the fire at Than. He's standing as stiff as a gatepost, arms folded, looking mutinous as the light from the embers glints off his smiley-face badge.

'Okay then. I'll take your silence as commitment. What happens next is this: we have a damp mat here at the start of the walk. There is another one at the other side. There are tubs of water here, here and here.' He indicates at various points around the fire. 'You start from where I am, and walk straight across to where Bay's standing, in a straight, steady line.'

'How?' Bob asks, his voice completely f at.

'Just concentrate. Know that you can do this. Know that it is not going to hurt you. And know that it will make you stronger. This is not an experience that can be explained more fully to someone who hasn't tried it yet. I'm sorry.'

Bob nods, turning his eyes back to the glowing

embers.

'There are, of course, some rules. Make sure that your trousers are rolled high up above your knees. If they won't do this, I suggest that you remove them. You can control your own bodies, but you can't control how your flares are feeling!'

A titter runs around the group, and it's like gas being freed from a can of Coke as the tension releases a little bit.

'The second rule is, don't run. There's no need. It means more pressure on your feet, less concentration and flicking burning embers around, so just don't.'

A few people nod. I'm starting to breathe faster. Am I really going to do this? I guess so.

'All right, here we go. Watch me first just so that you can see that it can be done safely.'

Ted steps onto the damp matting just in front of the bed of embers. He paces side to side for a few seconds, staring straight out ahead of him. I take a deep breath in and hold it. This is insane. Every cell in my body wants to shout at him to stop. To wait. To step away from the fire.

Ted strides forward. He doesn't rush or hang around. He simply paces in a steady rhythm, seven strides over the embers and onto the matting at the other side. I let my breath out in a rush as he paces side to side on the damp mat, dousing any coals that have stuck to the bottom of his feet.

We all start cheering simultaneously as Ted turns to face us with a grin, arms outstretched like he's trying to hug us all at once.

'Any questions?'

'Does it hurt?' Emma asks.

'No, no, it doesn't hurt. You can feel the heat as you

walk, but it's not uncomfortable; like walking across hot sand . . . or maybe eggshells. Just be sure to pace at the end to clear your feet while you're still focusing. We're all going to try to walk at least once today, but there's no rush. Take your time and decide when's best for you.' He smiles around at us all. 'So, who's ready?'

Everything goes unnaturally quiet, and for a moment all I can hear is the spitting fire. All eyes have dropped to look at the embers.

Even if you paid me a million quid right now, I wouldn't feel ready to do this.

Let's face it, I'm never going to be ready.

And I need the loo.

It's the nerves, I know, but I can't stop fidgeting. The base of my spine is tingling and my top lip is stinging with sweat.

'I'll do it!' I say. I ignore both the surprised murmuring and the sounds of encouragement from around me. Doreen squeezes my hand and lets go abruptly, as if I might drag her with me if she's not careful. I walk over to Ted and feel the rough, damp matting cooling the soles of my feet.

'Well done, Tori,' Ted smiles at me. I nod, bend down and with a bit of a fight between my shaking hands and the stiff denim, manage to roll my jeans up securely above my knees. Bay was right when he said I'd bruise — and now they're on full display to the world.

'Ready?' asks Ted gently from beside me.

Am I ready?

I stare at the embers glowing in front of me. I can feel the heat coming at me in waves. There are encouraging shouts from around the fire, though I'm not sure who they're coming from. All I can focus on are the miniature flames licking up from the embers here and there. There's a big cheer to my left, and I glance over to see Doreen grinning at me. Next to her stands Than. He's got a strange, blank expression on his face, but I haven't got time to worry about him now. Someone has started a slow clap for me.

'Focus now, Tori,' says Ted at my side.

I pause, holding my breath for a moment, staring at the fire.

Can I do this?

My mum's face appears in my mind. I let the image float away.

Can I do this?

Than's taunts at the river start to ring in my ears. I let them go. All I can hear now is the slow clap. Everything else has disappeared.

I focus on the beat and step out.

The embers spark around me and I can feel the heat rising from below. I take a step, and then another.

Clap. Clap. Clap.

I'm doing this. I can't believe I'm actually doing this! The embers are pricking the soles of my feet, but I'm calm and completely focused on what I'm doing and where I'm going.

Clap. Clap. Clap.

I take a step, and then another.

Now I'm standing on a cold, wet mat, pacing side to side, cooling the soles of my feet. And then other sounds creep back in: a roaring that is neither coming from my head nor the fire behind me. It's my friends cheering for me. The clapping beat has gone from slow and steady to mad and cheerful.

Bay's chanting my name, jumping up and down like

a six-year-old, a huge grin lighting up his entire face.

And I run.

I run back to the group and into their waiting arms, receiving kisses and hugs from each of them, including Ted, who's beaming from ear to ear.

When we finally settle down, the atmosphere becomes serious and respectful again, but this time you can't feel the fearful tension that was there before. One of us has managed to come through this and shown the others that it's possible. I can't stop grinning, and I feel like I've left every ounce of my uncomfortable, nervous energy in the fire. Now it's my turn to cheer the others on.

Sam goes next, and then Emma. Messa approaches the mat and stands there for several long minutes before setting out, but he does manage it. It's as he's pacing across the coals that I look around the group to see how many more of us are left to go. Than's missing. He's gone, nowhere to be seen among the cheering, elated faces.

I turn to ask Doreen if she knows what's happened to him, but she's looking pale and sweaty. Before I get a word out, she steps forward and heads for the mat with a determined, if slightly wobbly, stride. I instantly forget about Than as I feel my nerves surge in support for my friend. I want to reach out to her, give her a hug and show her I'm here for her.

I watch as she has a couple of quiet words with Ted and then steps onto the mat. The others start to cheer and shout encouragement.

To my right, Bay starts a slow clap. I glance up at him and smile. It was his clap that carried me over those coals.

It's time to do the same thing for Doreen. I join in.

As Doreen steps forward, she seems to pause as the first cloud of sparks rises up around her. I feel my mouth grow dry, but she paces forwards, matching the beat of our claps, and before I know what's happened, she's already on the other side.

My cheers join the others' as we all erupt with happiness. Another one of our clan has made it through the test. Doreen just stands on the cool, damp mat with a look of complete confusion on her face. As I watch, it slowly warms to a delighted smile, and she flies towards us. We engulf her in a tangled mass of arms and cheering.

We can do this — together.

26

Behind the Anger

> 'It's completely natural to be angry about your loneliness. Whatever the root cause, you can feel let down by the world and want to lash out. But in order to heal, you need to look at what's behind the anger. Your anger is a reaction, not a trigger. Look for the cause and you can work on healing it.'
>
> ©TheBeginnersGuideToLoneliness.com

I peel away from Doreen, letting the rest of the group take their turns to smother her in hugs and kisses, and look around again in search of Than. He's the last of the group left to do the walk, and as things start to quieten down again, he's rather conspicuous in his absence.

'Ted,' I mutter, coming to stand next to him, 'did you see where Than went? Is he okay?' 'He left,' sighs Ted, his smile dropping briefly. 'Happens sometimes.'

'When?' I ask in surprise.

'Just after you'd started your walk. He headed back towards the campsite I think.' Ted smiles kindly at me. 'Don't worry, he'll be fine. Sometimes this step just comes too soon for some people. You did brilliantly. Really well done!' He clasps my shoulder, and I can see pride in his eyes. It brings a lump to my throat.

'Thanks, Ted.' I smile back at him, but I can't help but feel like the air has been let out of me a little bit. I know that whatever bond Than and I had is well and truly broken after everything that's happened, but the fact that he didn't even bother to wait until I'd finished my fire walk feels a bit like someone jamming a knitting needle into my heart. It makes it personal.

'Tori, get over here!' calls Bay, holding out an arm and beckoning me into the tangle of celebrating bodies. I jog over to them, but it's with a much heavier heart than just a couple of minutes ago.

* * *

I can't get comfortable in my bed. No matter how much I snuggle down, I just can't relax. It's a warm night, and I've kicked my duvet off and retrieved it twice already. I don't really need it, but I feel vulnerable lying here uncovered, wearing just my pyjamas.

I left everyone celebrating their success around the communal fire pit and came back to the yurt early. What I really wanted to do was go in search of Than. He didn't turn up for supper and was nowhere to be seen around the fire pit either. I don't know why, after everything he's done, but I just wanted to check that he's okay . . . or maybe I just wanted to pick a fight and ask him exactly what his problem is. Either way, common sense prevailed, and I came back here instead. Whatever he's going through right now, I've learned enough over the past few days to know that I'm not the one to help him unravel it. Doesn't make it any easier to stay put though.

Dennis reappeared about half an hour ago, and after a cursory lick of my hand and a quick snuffle around for any dog biscuits I might have hidden on my person, he turned tail, jumped up onto Bay's pillows and has been loudly snoring ever since.

I jump as the flap flips open and Bay appears. He grins over at me as soon as he sees I'm still awake, and it dawns on me that I've been waiting for him. That's why I haven't been able to get to sleep. He's the perfect person to pump for information about Than.

'Hey!' I swallow. *Hmm, how to approach this . . .*

'Hi. Nice job today leading the charge. Dennis, OFF!' He strides over to his bed and attempts to nudge the snoozing dog off his pillows. Dennis is not having any of it though, and after a quick wag of his tail promptly rolls onto his back in a full stretch and falls back to sleep. 'Honestly, hound,' laughs Bay, rubbing his belly affectionately.

'So, uh . . . did Than turn up in the end?' Damn. Not exactly casual.

'No,' Bay says shortly, the laughter disappearing from his face in an instant. 'Why are you so worried, anyway? I thought you were keeping your distance?'

'Yeah, that's true,' I say. Bay doesn't need to know that I've been lying here, repeatedly talking myself out of going in search of Than. 'I'm just a bit worried after he took off like that. He's working through some pretty serious stuff.'

Bay rolls his eyes. 'Aren't we all?'

'So, you really haven't seen him?'

Bay gives me a completely unreadable look, so I stick my tongue out at him.

'What was that for?'

'Being a loser. I know you know what's happened . . . Why won't you just tell me?'

Bay hesitates, and then sighs. 'Fine, fine. I'll tell you. He left just as you started your walk. Then, when we got back, Ted went to find him to talk things through and he'd gone.'

'What do you mean, 'gone'?'

'Gone. Left. Vamoosed. All his stuff, his tent. Everything.'

'He just left?'

'Yup. And probably a good thing for him, after some of the crap he's been up to. I was so close to having a word with Ted to get him kicked out anyway, especially after that stunt he pulled on you down at the river.'

'You know, I don't need you to babysit me. I can look after myself.'

'Trust me, I know that. I'm more than aware that you're capable of making your own mistakes.'

'What's that supposed to mean?' I glare at him.

'That I know that you can look after yourself, no matter what's thrown at you . . . even if it's your own fault that it's being thrown in the first place.'

'That's so much better, thanks for clarifying,' I mutter. My chest feels tight and my eyes are prickling. I know I was spoiling for a fight with Than, but I didn't expect to have one with Bay instead.

'Look, the guy's a total shit.'

'He is not a shit,' I growl at Bay, making myself jump. Dennis sits bolt upright and stares at me.

'Tori! Why the hell are you still defending him? He was awful to you.'

'That's my problem.'

'Yes, it is, but that makes it everyone's problem while you're here.'

'You want me to go too?' I get up off the bed and stand staring at him. That hurt. Bay is my friend, or I thought he was. I thought . . . I thought there was something between us; that we meant something to each other. Maybe I got it all wrong.

'Of course I don't want you to go,' Bay says, running a hand roughly through his hair. 'I just don't want you to waste any more energy on an idiot.'

'Well, like I said, just let me worry about myself, will you?'

'For once, will you stop thinking about yourself and try looking at it from my . . . from someone else's perspective?' The hard lines on Bay's face are so unlike him that I take an involuntary step backwards. 'Friends look out for each other, whether it's *needed* or not. That's what real friends do. Can you get your head around that?'

I turn away from him, swallowing repeatedly, desperate to stop the tears from falling. I try to ignore the human thunderstorm behind me. Maybe Bay's right. I don't know how to have friends, how to *be* a friend. Which means my mother was right, and Markus was right.

I deserve to be alone.

I heave in a deep breath and suddenly need to put as much space as possible between me and Bay, me and this stupid, pointless fight. I turn and, as the tears start to fall, I leave the yurt.

* * *

By the next morning, I've calmed down. I slept surprisingly well on the thin strip of hard floor at the foot of Geoff and Doreen's bed, padded out with their spare blankets and one of Geoff's old sweaters as a pillow.

After the fight with Bay, I stomped back down to the fire pit, hoping to find Doreen. As it turned out, only Messa, Moth and Bob were left nattering around the flames. As lovely as they are, a lecture on which particular planetary alignment was causing my upset or how taking up knitting would help wasn't the kind of sympathy I was after, so I beat a hasty retreat. After a dark and rather winding walk, I finally ended up at Doreen and Geoff's cabin door.

If I need to take lessons on how to be a friend, I know who I'll be taking them from. I might have interrupted their evening by turning up snot-nosed and tear-stained, but Geoff and Doreen couldn't have been kinder to me. We talked for hours. Doreen gently helped me to see that maybe, just maybe, I was defending a version of Than that I hoped existed, rather than the real version; the one who was publicly cruel, snide and downright mean.

And Geoff? Well, Geoff was the biggest eye-opener of the evening. I was mid rant about Bay when he interrupted and gently but firmly told me to give the guy a break. He pointed out that it couldn't have been easy for him to watch as I stood up for a guy who was trying to break me. Of course I argued, but Geoff was having none of it.

As I settled down to sleep, all talked out, I had to admit to myself that maybe Geoff did have a point. Bay was on my side. He had been the good guy in all this. And to have that thrown back in his face had to hurt. I drifted off to sleep with one thought in my mind — Bay was right; I did have a lot to learn. But maybe I was finally ready to admit it and start trying.

* * *

This morning, it's time for yoga again, and I'm thankful it's not a more chatty kind of a session. As soon as we reach the studio, I set up my mat and am ready to get started before Claire even arrives. I'm nervous to see Bay after our argument, but I'm excited too.

So a small part of me wilts when he doesn't turn up. I'd forgotten that he was due to be helping Ted out again this morning. The group feels strangely small with both him and Than missing. As Claire makes a start and I let my mind sink into the movements, I realize that, despite what happened last night, I'm way more relaxed this morning than I have been in a while. It takes a moment or two for me to realize that this is because Than isn't here, and I'm not waiting for today's dose of drama to hit.

Come lunchtime, however, my newfound sense of calm has deserted me, and my brain's up to its usual tricks, hopping all over the place from problem to problem. I'm trying to listen to a story Bob's telling the group, but I've missed most of it as I'm too busy staring over his shoulder, planning how I'm going to apologize to Bay when he finally turns up.

'You okay?' Emma asks me quietly.

I snap back to the present and stare at her uncomprehendingly.

'You've been staring at Bob's ear for the last ten minutes and you haven't eaten anything. Are you missing Than?'

I shake my head. 'No . . . no . . . '

'No, you're not okay, or no, you're not missing him?' Emma smiles at me.

'Erm, both?' I say with an apologetic grin. 'Sorry, Em, I'm not very with it.'

'Brain too full,' she says. It's not a question, just a

simple, understanding statement.

'Exactly!' I say, relieved she knows what I mean.

'I get that. This place throws up so many questions and changes, I think there are these moments where you just have to slow down and let it all sink in, you know?'

I nod at her. 'You know, I really don't miss Than,' I say, just to make sure she understands.

'No, I bet. Not after what he was like with you.'

'Well, he was going through a lot,' I say like a stuck record.

'So what? That's no excuse.'

For some reason, hearing it from Emma makes it sink in. No, there really isn't an excuse for treating anyone like that, is there?

'Anyway,' she says to me, 'I find when my brain does what yours is doing, I head off and follow some of Russ's mindfulness tips.'

'You do?' I ask, surprised.

She nods. 'Does wonders for clearing the fog. I can't tell you how many times I've gone for a walk and just found a patch of grass to stare at,' she laughs.

* * *

The garden is quiet. I've left the others at the lunch table, tucking in and swapping stories. I've decided to take Emma's advice while we're still on our break. Everything is looking lovely in the early afternoon sunshine.

I wander over to the potato patch and admire the long ridges where Geoff and Bay worked together last week to hoe them up. The dark leaves have already re-emerged in tufts from the tops of the ridges. I take in a deep breath and let it out slowly, letting my shoulders drop. The beds that we weeded last week are now dotted with sturdy little plants. They must be the courgettes that Bay had planned. The bed nearest the compost heap is still half full of weeds, the ones that needed a fork to lift them as they'd taken hold a bit too strongly for weeding by hand.

I grab a bucket and hand fork from the little tool shed, perch on the railway sleepers and start methodically working away at the weeds.

* * *

'Hi, Tori!'

Bay's voice makes me jump. I've become so engrossed in clearing my little patch, I've lost track of time, and by the angry complaints coming from my back, I've been sitting in one position for far too long.

I stand up slowly and stretch as Bay makes his way over to me.

'Wow! That's quite some job you've done. Thanks.' Bay grins, inspecting the now pristine patch in front of us.

Now that he's here, I don't know what to say. Emma was right though; I had to consciously keep my head clear for the first five minutes of weeding, bringing my attention back to what I was doing and the feel of yanking each clump of weeds out from the earth . . . but it didn't take long until it completely absorbed me, and it's been a blessed relief from worrying in circles.

'Hi!' I say at last, realizing that Bay is just standing there, staring at me. I've just remembered what I was worrying about in the first place. 'Bay, I wanted to apologize . . . for last night.'

Bay cocks his head. 'So you did some gardening for me?' His smile almost looks shy.

'Well, uh . . . no . . . that was actually me trying to calm my head down a little bit.'

'Oh. Did it work?' he asks.

I nod. 'But I do still want to say sorry.'

'What for?' he asks curiously.

'For reacting like I did. Again.'

Bay nods. 'Well, for the record, help with the weeding is always an acceptable apology,' he laughs.

I smile at him in relief.

'Anyway, I'm sorry too. What I wanted to say, well, it kind of came out wrong. I didn't mean to upset you. Actually, that's the last thing I wanted to do. It's just, you're good at being a friend to other people, and I hate to see you not accepting that friendship in return.'

Damn. This doesn't feel like it's going to be a case of easypeasy, gloss it over forgive-and-forget. Bang goes my sense of calm for the second time today.

I let out a sigh and sit back down on the side of the raised bed. Bay sits next to me.

'Talk to me, Tori. Why'd you disappear on me last night, other than because I was being a bit of a knob?'

I let out a chuckle and shake my head. 'We were both being knobs, if it helps.' I look at him and see that he's just waiting, just being my friend. There's no ulterior motive here. 'Look, I've been on my own for a very long two years. Probably longer if I'm being honest.'

'What do you mean, on your own? As in, single?'

I clear my throat. 'Well, yes, that. I spilt up with my ex, Markus, just after Mum died in the accident. We were both part of this huge group of friends. We'd all been close since school, you know?'

Bay nods, but stays quiet, waiting for me to carry on.

'After we split up, our friends did try to make me socialize, but I was so cut up about the accident. I was numb and completely confused. The last thing I wanted to do was party — and their sympathy had a really short shelf life. Anyway, it didn't take long for the invitations to dry up, and basically, Markus ended up inheriting our friends in the break-up.'

I feel a bit foolish saying all this out loud, but if Bay really wants to understand what last night was about, this is where it came from.

'But you must have had other friends, work colleagues, family who stuck by you?' Bay asks quietly.

I shake my head, feeling the usual sense of shame, as if it's somehow my fault that I ended up so isolated. 'Nope. I'm self-employed, work from home and am an only child. Suddenly my life was quiet and pretty empty.'

'Shit, that must have been tough.'

I nod and shrug at the same time. Tough. Nearly impossible. 'I think it would have eventually broken me if it hadn't been for a couple of friends I made online. They helped.'

I stop again, but Bay's still quiet.

'Anyway,' I say as the silence starts to feel uncomfortable, 'that's why I disappeared on you last night. You made me face something I've been trying to hide from — that I don't know how to be a friend anymore.'

'That's bullshit,' Bay says, and he turns to face me full on. 'You've supported every single person here when they've needed it. You know how to be a friend — '

'But when you said — '

'I'm sorry for the way things came out last night. What I meant was, perhaps you struggle to accept friendship in return. And after what you've just told me, I'm not surprised that you might be a little bit . . .'

'Rusty?' I laugh.

''Hesitant' was what I had in mind, but I think they both work,' Bay says a little sadly. 'Anyway, I'm sorry that it all came out in the way it did. I was angry and, well . . .'

'What?' I ask curiously.

'Jealous, Tori. I was jealous.'

'Of me?' I say, confused.

'No, not you. Than and you. And the way that, no matter what he threw at you, you still stuck up for him.'

I stare at him, mouth open.

'Sorry. Maybe I shouldn't have said that,' says Bay, looking a bit sheepish.

I close my mouth and shake my head. 'Actually, it's fine. After talking to Geoff and Doreen last night, I think I know where you were coming from. They've helped me see that the version of Than I've been busy defending is nothing but a figment of my imagination.'

'For what it's worth, I'm really sorry I was right about him,' says Bay, digging his heel into the mud.

'No, you're not,' I smile, giving him a nudge with my elbow.

Bay grins at me. 'Okay. Maybe not.'

27

Issue Deep Dive

> 'Working through issues is never easy. When you first seek external support you will experience breakthroughs — but you're not done! Now is the time for an issue deep dive. Don't cheat and use this moment as an excuse to stall in your progress — keep pushing through.'
>
> ©TheBeginnersGuideToLoneliness.com

'I'm so sorry I'm late!' I puff as I rush into the little, light attic space that Ted uses for his one-to-one counselling sessions.

'No problem.' Ted looks up from a book on his desk and smiles at me. 'Oh, by the way, I take it Bay managed to catch up with you yesterday lunchtime?'

'Bay?' I ask, surprised. I drop into the seat at the little coffee table in the middle of the room as Ted turns to join me.

'Between you and me, he was extremely anxious that he might have upset you, so when you weren't at lunch, I suggested he went to look for you.'

I look at him, surprised. I thought counsellors were usually more woolly than this rather direct approach.

'Yes, he found me. I was doing some weeding.'

'Good for you! I find the garden's a good place for sorting your head out.'

'I . . . well . . . Bay and I had an argument the night before.'

Ted just nods.

'About Than,' I continue. 'Well, that's where it started, but it became more about friendship, and, well . . . how to give it and how to receive it.'

'And when you say you argued . . . ?' Ted nudges me.

'It was my fault,' I say quickly. 'I was defending Than, and Bay got annoyed.'

'It's hard to see someone we care about being treated badly.'

'I don't really care about Than . . . '

'I didn't mean him. I meant Bay seeing the way you were being treated.'

Oh. I didn't see that coming. I don't know what to say, so I plough on.

'Anyway, we both got a bit . . . cross . . . heated . . . you know? And I thought Bay was saying that I didn't know how to be a friend.'

'And when he found you, did you discuss it?' Ted asks gently.

I nod. 'That's not what he meant. He . . . well, he said that he couldn't stand that I seemed not to be able to accept friendship even though I could give it.'

'And what do you think?'

I look at my hands in my lap and pick at the skin around my nail. 'It's not the first time someone has said that I'm a crap friend,' I mutter, thinking of my mum and Markus again.

'But that's not what he was saying, is it?' says Ted.

'No. It's not. But . . . I mean . . . I've been on my own for so long now, maybe that's the case. My only friends are online and . . . well . . . yeah, I'm lonely, and I've enjoyed having people around while I've been here. But it's not real, is it? When I go back to my life, this isn't real?'

'Everything you do in life is real. Every experience changes us, shapes us and will impact on how we think and what we do in the future. So yes, I'd say this is very real. And only you can decide how much it will affect your day-to-day life when you leave here. It might be just a memory — a happy one, I hope. Or it might have a profound effect on every moment of your life from here on out. Or it could land somewhere in between.'

I swallow as the words lodge in my mind and take root. These friendships, the things I'm learning here . . . I'm the one who decides how important they are to me.

'Now, I'd like to touch on how you're doing with your phobia. Sharing it with the group was a huge step. Have you talked it through with anyone since your visit to the river?'

I feel like I've just swallowed an ice cube. I shake my head. 'I've been focusing more on the loneliness and where that's coming from,' I say.

'And it sounds like that's bringing you some great insights and understanding. But I think it might be important for you to remember that one issue doesn't sit separately from the other. They're interlinked; both a part of you.'

'Okay . . . ' I say. I don't like where this is going. I've become comfortable with the idea of talking about being lonely. Sounds strange, but after writing about it on the blog for so long and discussing it openly here several times now, I've got the talking points all mapped out. Quitting my job. Losing Markus and my friends. Grief making me pull back. It's like a safe little list I can work through.

'You mentioned that your fear of water is linked to your mother's death?' Ted asks gently.

'Mentioned' is a very polite way of describing how I screamed this at Than after the disastrous swimming session.

'Yes. She drowned in a car accident,' I say tightly.

'And you weren't involved in the accident?' he prompts.

I shake my head. My hands have started to sweat and I rub them on my trousers. I don't want to tell him. I can't tell him. I couldn't bear to see the look on his face if he knew that it was all my fault.

'Tori,' Ted says, looking at me steadily, 'I think, this week, it would be good for you to use the sessions to talk more about your phobia. Have you sought professional support before? Did your doctor ever refer you to a grief counsellor after your mother passed?'

I shake my head again. 'I just . . . no. I've not been to the doctor . . . or anyone. I just . . . deal with it,' I mutter.

'I'm afraid your body's way of dealing with your grief is via this phobia and your panic attacks,' says Ted seriously.

I swallow. 'I just want to focus on the loneliness. Tackle one thing at a time.'

Ted leans forward in his chair, placing his elbows on his knees. He peers at me intently.

'Sometimes prolonged isolation is a defence mechanism, you know. Your subconscious thinks it's protecting you by keeping you away from other people. You keep yourself stuck there because you're afraid of anyone coming too close, and finding out too much. Essentially, without working through it you will keep sabotaging your new connections.'

I feel a bit sick. Actually, very sick. I swallow hard. Ted pours me a glass of water from a jug on the table and pushes it towards me without a word.

I take a sip. 'But I've admitted I'm lonely and I want to do something about it,' I say shakily.

'You have,' smiles Ted. 'Now all you've got to do is believe that you deserve these new friendships. You've got to start letting people near the scary bits.'

I nod, although my lips are quivering. I feel pretty close to tears.

'But surely . . . I don't have to share everything with everyone. I don't want to be *that* person.'

Ted laughs. 'No. You don't. It's not so much about 'having to share'; it's more about not feeling the need to hide. It's about coming to terms with who you are and where you've come from.

'Loneliness isn't always about a lack of people. It can be about a lack of communication and connection. And that disconnect? That's the bit you need to work on.'

By the time I'm headed back towards the yurt, my heart is in my shoes. I thought I'd feel better after Ted's session, but it's the opposite. I thought I was doing really well, that I was sharing with the others and forming bonds. But Ted's right. There's something that's holding me back. I know exactly what it is. The problem is, I know that if I share it, it's not going to be this miraculous, healing moment. It's just going to mean that I'll be back to square one, because no one is going to want to know me after they find out what I've done.

* * *

I'm so thankful to find the yurt empty when I get there, and I fling myself down onto my bed and let out an almighty groan into my pillow. Why couldn't I be reviewing a spa instead? And not the 'back to earth' kind. Oh no, I want the kind with hot water jets, Jacuzzis and fluffy towels. If only my blog was all lifestyle and interiors, I could be comfortably wrapped in some seaweed and sipping bubbles right now. Instead, I'm tired to my very core.

I sigh and flip over on my blankets to find Bay staring down at me with a very strange look.

'Did you just mutter something about a Jacuzzi?' he grins.

'What? No, of course not!!'

'Sounded like it to me!' he laughs.

I rub my face and sigh again.

'Hey, are you okay?' The laughter disappears and is quickly replaced by a look of concern.

'I guess. Just . . . well . . . knackered.'

'Tough session with Ted?' he asks, dropping down to sit at the end of my bed.

I sit up and face him, cross-legged, and nod.

'Want to talk about it?'

I shake my head.

'Sure?'

I shake my head again.

'Well, if you do, I'm here. Anyway, you'll probably feel a bit better after dinner with everyone. I always find that food gets me grounded again after a difficult day.'

'I don't think I can face food with everyone,' I say. 'I just need a bit of time here. Just quiet.'

'You want me to disappear for a bit?' he asks gently.

'No, no! I didn't mean you,' I say quickly, because

I really didn't. 'I just . . . there's something different about the whole group. It can be quite a lot to take, you know?'

Bay nods.

'Where's Dennis, by the way?' I ask, realizing I could do with a cuddle.

'He's gone to spend the night with Claire in her tent. I think she was in need of a bit of company.'

'Oh,' I say surprised. 'Is she okay?'

'She's fine,' Bay nods, getting to his feet and crossing over to his side of the yurt. 'Just in need of the therapy mutt.'

I smile. It's true. Sometimes Dennis is the best medicine going.

'So,' says Bay, 'if you're not going to join everyone for dinner, what do you fancy? I'm assuming you haven't got any food lined up?'

'How far do you reckon the nearest bacon sandwich is?' I ask hopefully.

'I'd say about ten miles that way,' he says, pointing over his shoulder.

'Balls,' I say, my heart slipping another notch. 'I could kill for a bacon sandwich right now.'

'Don't shoot!' Bay laughs, holding up his hands. 'Look, I've got a plan. How about I head down and rustle us up a picnic? I'll let them know we're okay, and bring our dinner back here so we can have a quiet evening?'

'That sounds amazing,' I smile at him gratefully. 'Is there anything I can do to help?'

'Just chill out till I come back with the picnic,' says Bay, disappearing out of the yurt at high speed.

Two minutes ago I was at full-blown get-me-out-of-here overwhelm. Two minutes chatting with Bay and I've got a smile on my face and everything magically feels that little bit better.

* * *

While Bay's gone, I tidy all our bits and pieces off the little round table in front of the sofa so that we've got somewhere to sit and eat. Then I change into my pyjama bottoms and a soft T-shirt and, curling up on one side of the sofa, I make a valiant effort not to drift off to sleep before he comes back.

The delicious smell of herbs and hot tomato reaches me before Bay's even back inside the yurt.

'Sorry I took so long!' he says, bustling in through the flap and plonking a wicker basket onto the table in front of me.

I stretch in an attempt to wake up properly. 'To be honest, I think I nodded off!'

Bay chuckles. 'Well, I hope you're in the mood for pasta? I knocked up a quick herby tomato sauce. I cooked up a vat of it so that there's enough for the others too.'

'Sounds perfect,' I say. I lean over and lift plates and cutlery out of the basket and set them down for us.

Bay then takes a tub of hot pasta and divvies it out between us before pouring a deep red sauce over each portion. Then he lifts half a loaf out of the basket too. Heaven.

'Not quite a bacon sandwich, but I did my best,' he smiles.

We eat in silence, and when I've finished mopping up the last of the sauce from my plate with my bread, I sit back with a contented sigh.

'Better?'

I nod. 'Thank you so much.'

'It's amazing what food and a bit of peace and quiet can do,' he says, placing his own plate carefully down on the table, and leaning back on the sofa.

We sit quietly for a few minutes, but the companionable silence we've just eaten in seems to be morphing into something different. You could cut and layer this silence onto a piece of toast, it's that thick.

'You okay?' he asks, his voice sounding strained.

I nod. I can't get Ted's words out of my head. This isn't real. This friendship I have with Bay can't be real because I'm hiding something. I need to trust him. But . . . I can't bear to lose him, and that's what would happen if he knew.

'Tori, what is it?' he asks quietly.

I can feel my tears building, and that deep, aching pain at the thought of losing all of my friends here. Bay reaches over and covers my hand briefly with his.

'There's so much you don't know about me,' I say, my voice thick.

Bay smiles. 'I should hope so too.'

'But talking to Ted today . . . I need to open up, I guess.' Bay nods, looking thoughtful. 'You know, there's plenty about me that you don't know too.'

There's a look on his face that I don't recognize. Is that nerves? Whatever it is can't possibly be as bad as what I'm keeping secret.

'For example, you don't know much about my work yet.'

'Okay,' I smile.

'Well, I'm pretty good at it,' he says.

'I bet!' I say. I've seen the gardens here. I can see how much he loves what he does, even if it doesn't exactly make him a go-getting high-flier.

'There's more to it than you think . . .'

'I'm sure there is.'

I'm not sure where he's going with this, but I'm too tired to get into anything serious right now.

'Tell me something I don't know about you,' he prompts.

'I'm tired,' I sigh.

'I already guessed that,' he chuckles.

'Can we do this another time?' I ask, sounding a bit like a moody toddler.

The food has managed to offset my extreme drowsiness for a couple of minutes, but the longer we sit here, cocooned on the sofa, the more my eyelids are drooping. I don't quite know how I manage it, but my head dips to rest on Bay's shoulder.

Bay shifts a little next to me, and I feel his arm reach around my shoulders, pulling me gently towards him. I let out a sigh. I know this is the point where I should really sit up and move away, but I don't want to. Instead, I reach across and take his free hand in mine, lacing my fingers through his.

His intake of breath is like a question mark hovering between us.

The question is, what do I want?

All I want, right now, is this. I want to thank him again for the food. For the company. For the friendship. But this is the point where my exhaustion finally body-snatches me, and my eyes drift closed.

* * *

I wake up with a start, then snuggle back into the arms wrapped around me and bury myself deeper into the soft mound of blankets.

Hang on. *Arms? Whose* arms? Where on earth am I?!

My head is resting on someone. *Bay*. I'm snuggled up in Bay's arms, my face against his chest, and I'm pretty sure that that's his hand resting against my hip. It feels so bloody lovely, I can't help the pang of regret as I start to wiggle away as slowly and quietly as I can. Gently, inch by inch, I try to put as much space as possible between us, which is a lot harder than it sounds on this tiny sofa. Every movement makes me less comfortable, and I sigh. Why couldn't I have just pretended to still be asleep and stayed put?

Bay's eyes open. He stretches and sleepily comes to as I fidget away from him. He breathes in deeply and tightens one arm around me, undoing all my good work by bringing us face to face.

I hold my breath, my heart hammering as I wait to see if he'll just drop back off to sleep. But his eyes are focused on mine, and I can see he's just figured out where he is and with whom. I shiver. I can feel every hair on the back of my neck stand to attention as Bay holds my gaze. Very slowly, not blinking, his face comes closer to mine, until he's so close, his breath is tickling my skin. So close that we're almost touching. I hold my breath again, waiting for him to cover that last tiny distance between us . . . but he doesn't. He is completely still, his eyes locked on mine.

Slowly, very slowly, I close the gap between us until my lips gently touch his. And then I'm still, just letting this new touch flood through my whole body. Seconds. Minutes. Maybe an eternity. My whole world is focused in on the tiny contact that feels like the most important, most amazing thing ever.

We shift at exactly the same moment, and the kiss deepens. Our lips move over each other's. My hands fight through the layers of blanket and slide up under his soft, moth-eaten T-shirt to rest against his skin. He cups my face and kisses me harder.

28

Wish, Dream, Act

> 'When we're caught in the vortex of grief, loneliness or anxiety, we can lose sight of our dreams. Simple survival can feel like a super-human effort.
>
> 'But, as we begin to heal, it's important to start making wishes again, to dream new dreams and then — act.'
>
> ©TheBeginnersGuideToLoneliness.com

Bacon. It has to be the best smell in the world to wake up to. The salty aroma reaches me before I've even opened my eyes. I yawn and stretch luxuriously.

'Morning, sleepyhead,' Bay smiles at me as I struggle to sit up. 'I come bearing gifts,' he waves a grease-covered white paper bag under my nose and my taste buds cry out in longing.

All I want to do right now is hide in a slightly darkened cupboard and figure out what happened last night. I mean, I know what happened: we kissed on the sofa, and eventually tumbled off in a giggling heap onto the floor, then we kissed in Bay's bed — for most of the night. It was wonderful, like being a teenager again. But what does it mean? I'm not quite so clear on that part.

I want to retreat, but there's not much chance of that given that I'm still in his bed, and he's just plonked himself down right next to me. I surreptitiously try to wipe away any traces of dribble and eye-snot and quickly figure out what I'm wearing. T-shirt and PJ bottoms are still firmly in place. I'm decent. At least that's something!

'How? How on earth . . . I mean? Where?' I wave the paper bag at him, bacon fumes wafting deliciously in its wake.

'I borrowed Frank and went on a clandestine bacon bap mission.'

'For me? Just like that?'

'Okay, so I might be making it sound riskier than it was. I promised Ted I'd do a grocery shop to help them out a bit — I just snuck in a quick stop for a bacon sandwich on the way back! Anyway, you said you wanted one.' He laughs, peeling the paper off his own sandwich and taking a huge bite.

I can't take my eyes off him. I feel a hot blush start at my toes and sweep right up through my body. I mean, I knew he had beautiful eyes and a nice bum and . . . and . . . *Gah!*

'You've not turned veggie on me since last night, have you?' asks Bay, one eyebrow raised.

'No, no, of course not!' I say, ripping into the paper bag. 'Bay, I . . . we . . . do you . . . last night . . . ' I'm not really sure what I'm trying to ask him. I just need to know what he thinks about us, about last night.

'What, Tori?' he asks.

I swallow. I seem to have lost the power of speech.

'Last night? Last night was . . . ' he pauses, and this huge smile spreads over his face. He doesn't need to finish the sentence for me to know exactly what he thinks about last night, and a flood of warmth spreads through my chest.

He clears his throat. 'What about you?' he asks

gruffly.

I stay quiet and look down at my sandwich. What about me? I'm excited and terrified and happy and I can't wait to kiss him again. But that's not what I say.

'What about Than?' I say quietly.

'What?' Bay looks like I've slapped him. 'Are you serious? You want to talk about him? Now? After everything . . . ?'

'No! No, that's not what I mean!' I feel a dead weight in my stomach. Nope. Not what I mean at all.

'Then what, Tori? Because now's not a brilliant time to drop another guy's name, especially not that little f— '

'I mean,' I cut across him, 'I mean, what if everyone thinks that I've just hopped straight from him to you?'

Bay sighs. 'But there was no 'him and you', was there?' he says, his voice gentle again. 'As long as we know the truth and we're happy, what does it matter what anyone else thinks? Not that they would anyway!'

I shrug. Of course they'll think it.

'If you're going to take anything away from this place, Tori, you need to stop worrying about what other people think of you. It's your life. You can live it exactly the way you want to.'

I swallow. And then nod.

'So. What's the answer, then?' he prompts.

'Last night was . . . ' I pause and smile. 'I want to find out what this is,' I say, pointing at him and then back to me.

'Well then,' says Bay, 'what's so bad about people knowing that?'

'Nothing,' I shake my head, 'but there are things you don't know about me — '

Bay laughs. 'And there's loads of stuff that I want to share with you too. We've got all the time in the world to get to know everything about each other.' He leans forward and gently kisses my cheek.

'Guys!' Rowan's voice outside makes us jump apart. 'Knock knock!'

'Don't tell me you haven't paid up for something?' Bay mutters, jumping up from the bed and heading towards the yurt entrance.

'Not guilty,' I reply under my breath as I roll off the other side and quickly straighten my pyjamas.

'Thank God you're here,' says Rowan as she bursts in. 'All hell's broken loose!'

Bay looks worried. 'Is Lizzie okay? And the baby? What's happened?'

I move to stand next to him. I can feel the waves of worry coming off him, so I reach over and take his hand, which he grasps out of instinct.

Rowan raises her eyebrows, a smirk on her face. 'Looks like you two've been having fun.'

'Rowan!' I squeak in horror, though I can't help a smile escaping. 'Tell us what's happened. Is everyone okay?'

'Oh, sure,' she says. 'Everyone else is fine. It's you we're worried about.'

'Why?' Bay asks, clearly as confused as I am, though the relief is evident in his voice.

'There was this piece written —' Rowan reaches into her back jeans pocket and draws out a folded printout.

'Knock knock?'

This time it's Ted's voice, and Bay lets go of my hand and heads out to greet him. I follow closely, wondering what the hell is going on.

Ted claps Bay on the shoulder then turns to Rowan. 'Back to the house. Now!'

'Oh, come on, Dad, they don't know anything. I was just going to fill them in — '

'Now, Rowan!'

I wince at the sharp edge to Ted's voice and realize that whatever this is, it must be fairly serious to cause this level of reaction.

'Tori,' he turns to me and smiles faintly, 'you need to come up to the house. We need to talk.'

I feel a chill wash over me. What on earth is this all about? I look up at Bay and he takes my hand again. 'I'll come too,' he says.

'Actually,' says Ted, raising an eyebrow at our clasped hands, 'I need you to do me a favour, if you don't mind? Could you go and find Russ and ask him to come down to the farmhouse? I need to talk to him and Claire before this morning's session. I'd go find him, but I really need to speak with Tori first.'

'Of course,' says Bay. 'You'll be okay?' he looks at me.

'Yep, you go. I'll catch you later.' I smile at him and he squeezes my hand and walks away.

* * *

There, on the screen of Ted's iPad, is a photograph of me. My face is tear-streaked and grimy, hair dripping, T-shirt soaked. This must have been taken during my disastrous trip to the river. Questions ping into my head: how? And by who? And what the hell am I doing on the Reflect Online gossip site?!

I can't take this in. After getting dressed, Ted led me down to the private back garden of the farmhouse and brought his iPad out. He gently explained that a piece about The Farm had been posted — a piece that was mostly about me. Then he handed me the tablet so that I could see for myself, but so far, the shock of the photographs has completely consumed me, and I've not actually read any of the accompanying words.

'I know this must be a huge shock,' says Ted. 'We wanted to let you know that this was out there as soon as possible, but remember, you're completely safe here with us.'

I don't say anything but keep scrolling down. There are more photographs of me here at The Farm: there's one of me at the fire walk, one of me being comforted by Doreen and Geoff, one of me and Messa sat side by side in the hot tub. And one of me and Bay in the rain, my hand wrapped in his T-shirt as he pushes a strand of hair out of my face.

I gasp and place the tablet down on the table.

'Tori, I think it's best if you read the whole thing, so that you're prepared,' Ted prompts gently.

I nod and pick it back up reluctantly. There seems to be acres and acres of text, and for a moment I can't focus as tears of shock blur my vision. Then sentences start to jump out at me . . .

'*. . . at best, deadly dull, at worst bordering on the cultish . . .*'

'*. . . a haven for drama queens like thirty-three-year-old Tori Williamson . . .*'

'*. . . hunting for the affection of any man to ease her sense of loneliness and guilt surrounding the death of her mother . . .*'

'*. . . her life empty after losing her fiancé, Markus, to another woman . . .*'

Who would want to do this to me? I rub my eyes

and stare closer at the screen, zooming in on the name and tiny author's photograph at the end of the article.

Dark hair. Handsome face. It's Than.

Or, as it says in the byline: Nathan Jones.

Okay. Deep breath — read from the start.

'. . . *a dangerous combination of vulnerable and predatory* . . .'

'. . . *a messed-up fraud* . . . *self-absorbed and cruel to others, including her so-called closest friend at the retreat, Doreen McVey* . . .'

'. . . *I can reveal the identity of the anonymous author of popular blog The Beginner's Guide To Loneliness* . . .'

Oh. My. God. He's outed me. The one thing I would never, ever tell anyone.

But how did he even know? How did he get all those photos? It doesn't make any sense. And he's written what I said about Doreen. I didn't even mean it; I was just caught up in my fear of the river and desperate to make him change the subject.

I bury my head in my hands.

'Tori?' says Ted gently. 'Are you okay?'

'How can I be?' I ask. My voice is low and f at. Something inside me feels like it has broken. 'How did he get those photos?' I say. It's probably the smallest detail, but right now, I can't face the more serious questions.

'I've been thinking about that,' Ted sighs. 'He handed over a mobile when he arrived, but when he left, he left without it. He must have had a second one, or some other camera.'

I look at the photos again and shake my head. 'No. He would never have been able to hide using a phone in some of these. Anyone would have seen if he'd had one at the fire walk. And we'd have seen him at it in this one of the hot tub too. And look how close I am in this one,' I say, scrolling to a close-up of me, lying back against a pillow. It's me in Than's tent. I close my eyes and picture that evening.

'Well, he must have had a hidden camera or something, then,' says Ted sadly. 'In his clothing, or a pocket . . . '

Hidden camera. 'Or that badge he was always wearing?' I say, thinking of the yellow smiley badge he told me his brother had given him.

'Could be,' sighs Ted. 'The sad thing is, that means he planned this from the start.'

That makes me feel sick. Than has taken everything I shared with him, every little detail, and twisted it to paint me as some kind of monster. He's used some of the most private, painful details about my life and turned them into cheap entertainment to feed the trolls.

I feel like I've been thumped in the chest, and my breathing is suddenly coming too fast. *Oh God, not this again*. I take a couple of long, steady breaths. I feel Ted's hand rest gently on my shoulder. Everything's going to be okay. *Breathe in. Deal with the issue in front of me*.

'I'm so sorry,' I sigh.

'*Sorry?* What for?' asks Ted, surprised.

'This,' I say, pointing at the tablet.

'Did you *ask* Than to follow you around, take photographs of you and pretend to be someone he wasn't?'

'No, but — '

'Did you *ask* him to share your secrets with the world?'

I look into Ted's eyes. 'No.'

'Well then, nothing to apologize for.'

I take another deep breath and try to take everything in as Ted watches me. I need to read that article again. My mind is racing. What I don't get is how Than even knew about some of the stuff. I must have shared way more than I realized while my guard was down.

'What am I going to do?' I say it out loud, not really expecting Ted to have any kind of answer. 'How am I going to find out why he did this? *How* he did this? How am I going to deal with the blog and everything else?'

'Well,' says Ted, 'I'd suggest starting with the bits that you're in control of right now. You're not directly contactable and you're not online while you're here with us, so you've got some space to work out what you're going to do.'

I nod. 'Thank you,' I say shakily.

'If you want my advice, I think you need to start by talking to Doreen. You two have become really close, and there are some pretty horrible quotes in that piece about her. No doubt made up, but even so . . . '

I nod. I wish they *were* made up, but Than is too clever for that. I said those words; he's just managed to twist them out of context and make them sound ten times worse.

'Tori, I'm sure you understand that we're going to need to share this article with the whole group. The photographs include nearly everyone here, and it's our duty to make sure that they are aware and to support them through this, if they need it.'

'Of course,' I say.

'I asked Claire to head over and fill Doreen in while I spoke to you. As it mentions her by her full name, we had to tell her and Geoff before the rest of the group.'

My heart is pounding. I can't bear the thought of

Doreen having to hear this. The things I said about her, the fact that I hid who I really am.

'I'd like to suggest you and Doreen head off on a one-to-one together. Find some space and peace and quiet and talk this through.'

I swallow hard. I know he's right, but my heart feels like it's going to break at the thought of losing my friend. Perhaps all my friends. 'Thanks, Ted. For everything,' I say, quietly.

He pats my shoulder. The sense of comfort from this friendly little gesture brings tears to my eyes.

'Dad!' Rowan's voice calls from the back door. 'Dad? Phone for you!'

'Can you take a message?' He shouts.

'It's Mel. She said it's urgent!'

'Sorry, Tori,' Ted says, hastily getting to his feet. 'I have to take this. Claire should be here with Doreen any moment, then you two can head off. Claire and Russ will be speaking with the rest of the group a bit later on. There's going to be plenty of time to talk this all through and work it out, okay?'

I nod, but I'm not sure he catches it as he rushes indoors to take his call.

29

Allow Joy

> 'Happiness, hurting and healing can happen at the same time. Just because you're grieving, or feeling lonely, suffering from anxiety or stress, doesn't mean that moments of pure happiness can't co-exist in your day-to-day life. It's so important to allow yourself to feel that joy.'
>
> ©TheBeginnersGuideToLoneliness.com

My heart sinks at the sight of the grim expression on Doreen's face as she rounds the corner into the garden.

'Hi!' I leap to my feet and try to smile at her, but it feels unnatural. My eyes are stinging. I wish I'd got a bit more sleep last night.

'Claire said we should go for a walk. Somewhere quiet. To talk,' Doreen says. There's not a hint of her usual smile. She looks so worried, it feels like my heart might break.

I nod glumly. 'Ted said the same. You up for it?'

'Okay,' she agrees, quietly.

I can't stand seeing Doreen like this. It's so . . . unnatural. She's usually so warm and funny and bubbly, not this pale, scared person. But as much as I want to blame this all on Than, I can't. This is my fault. I said those things about her.

Mum and Markus were both right. I don't deserve friends. And this — this absolute fucking disaster has proved it once and for all. I want to crawl back to my flat and hide. But I can't. I have to try to fix this. The least I can do, right now, is apologize and explain everything to Doreen. She deserves that.

'Doreen, I'm so sorry.'

'Come on,' she says, and, taking my hand, she leads me out of the garden.

I can feel the tears prickling and threatening to spill over, but I can't give in to them, not yet. This isn't about me.

We head out of the farmyard and follow the same route that Russ took us on for our first mindfulness session — up the side of the valley and away from The Farm. I trudge alongside her and we walk in tense silence for what feels like hours, but is actually probably only about five minutes. The words — the need to apologize and explain everything — are bubbling up inside of me so insistently I feel like I'm about to burst.

'Doreen, I — ' I start.

'Are you okay?' Doreen says at exactly the same time.

We come to an abrupt halt and turn to stare at each other. My hand is still firmly clasped in hers.

'Sorry,' I say.

'No, no, you go . . . ' she shakes her head.

I look into her face and feel the tears well in my eyes again. I try to will them back, but no luck this time. They spill down my cheeks. I let out a sigh that comes out more like a sob, and sink down into the long grass at the side of the path and rub my face hard.

I feel a soft arm around my shoulder. Doreen is next to me in the grass. I look at her and try to smile, but I can't keep my bottom lip from quivering as more tears spill down my cheeks.

'Hey. Hey . . . ' Seeing my tears, she scoops me into her arms and rocks me back and forth like a baby as I give in and soak the shoulder of her jumper.

'I'm so, so sorry,' I sob into her neck.

'What?' says Doreen, pulling away from me gently so she can see my mess of a face.

'I'm sorry for what that piece said. About you.' I shudder, trying to get control of my tears and gulping in air. I feel her stiffen slightly, but she doesn't pull away.

'Don't be silly. I'm sure what he wrote was complete rubbish. He was clearly putting words in your mouth.' She goes to stroke my hair away from my face, but I pull back from her a little.

'I said those things,' I sniffle. 'I was a mess when I got here. You were so kind and I just didn't know what to do with that, with your optimism and openness.'

'But, Tori, you said I was dull . . . a bored, insipid housewife . . . '

'I know, and I really didn't mean what I said. I was just being a bitch. Lashing out, and you were the most obvious target. It was during that first swimming session when we skived off? I was just desperate to get Than on side, trying to get him off the subject of why I'd legged it from the river . . . trying to make him like me. I did say it, but if it helps, I hated myself the second the words left my mouth.'

Doreen stares at me and sits back. She looks pale and thoughtful. 'It's okay,' she says quietly, staring at her feet for a couple of seconds. 'On the first day here, I told Geoff I thought you were a spoiled little brat with no life.' She grimaces. 'Lucky for me, he's not the type to publish what I said online.'

I shake my head. 'Well, you're pretty much spot on about me. Or, you were. You've been one of my closest friends here, which basically means my closest friend full stop. And now . . . now I can't imagine my life without you in it.' I swallow hard as the tears threaten to reappear.

'You're not so bad either, apart from your terrible choice in confidantes!' She smiles at me and pulls me in for a hug.

'I have to say, you're an amazing writer,' says Doreen after we've sat quietly next to each other for several minutes, just watching the sky and the clouds and letting things settle. 'I can't believe you're the one behind Beginner's Guide. Geoff and I read it religiously! I mean, I'd noticed that there were similarities in your past, but I never for a second imagined that it would actually *be* you!'

My heart flutters and I feel a tingling rush of panic course through me. 'I can't believe he told everyone who I am.'

Doreen pats my arm. 'It really is a terrible betrayal to go public with such an important secret — especially one you told him here.'

'That's just it. I didn't tell him,' I say. There's a slight growl to my voice as my panic veers dangerously in the direction of anger.

'Oh. Goodness,' says Doreen, looking surprised. 'I just assumed that you'd shared it with him in one of the sessions.'

I shake my head. 'Nope.'

'Well, he must have done some serious digging.'

I can't take it in. I can't even begin to figure out how he knows. Right now, I'm more worried about what it means. Everyone will know everything. Everything

I've written on my blog is so personal. All my fears and hopes, tied to my research. The reality of living like I do. How low it has taken me. My heart is racing and a river starts to pound in my head.

I close my eyes, but all I can see is the caption under the photograph of me and Bay in the rain. *Tori Williamson, the blogger behind The Beginner's Guide to Loneliness: not so lonely after all.*

I want to be sick.

'Tori? Love?' Doreen's voice is worried, but I can't look at her right now. But then her hands are in mine. 'Look at me.'

I shake my head, eyes still firmly closed.

'Look at me, Tori.'

I do as she asks.

'Don't be frightened of letting people know how amazing you are. Your writing is so powerful. I bet you can't even begin to imagine the number of people you've helped by being so honest, by sharing everything with them.'

'But you don't know everything,' I say, my voice shaky.

'I know some awful things have happened in your life. And I know how brave you are. That's what people will learn about you from reading your site. Nothing more or less.'

'So, tell me,' she says after a couple of minutes, 'where were you at dinnertime last night? Both you and Bay were missing.'

'Oh . . . ' I'm grateful to think about something aside from Than and that stupid article for a moment. 'I had a one-to-one session with Ted yesterday afternoon, and by the time we were finished, I was absolutely wiped. And . . . well, I just couldn't face chatting with everyone over food.'

'I can understand that,' says Doreen, peering at me, 'but why was Bay missing as well?'

I can't stop a smile from creeping onto my face. 'Erm . . . well, he got us dinner and brought it back to the yurt.'

'*Aaand . . .?*'

'And we ended up kissing.'

Doreen squeals and claps her hands excitedly. 'Tori, this is so exciting!' she says, grabbing my hands. 'So you and Bay are . . .?'

'I'm looking forward to finding out what we are.'

Doreen sighs and swipes at her eyes.

'Don't be such a sap,' I laugh.

'I can't help it. I'm a sucker for happy endings.'

'Well, you'd better hold that thought for a sec. I need to go and find Bay. I'm not sure whether he'll have seen the article yet, but you're not the only one with shit written about you.'

* * *

'Tori! Tori! I've got to talk to you!'

As soon as we reach the farmyard, Rowan skids to a halt in front of us and clutches her ribs, bending over double. Apparently she doesn't do much cardio in among the wheeling and dealing.

'Me first!' I say before she can recover. 'Have you seen Bay? I really need to talk to him.'

Rowan just holds one index finger out to me, indicating to give her a second.

I smirk at Doreen and cross my arms until Rowan finally straightens up and gasps out, 'He's gone.'

'What do you mean 'gone'?' says Doreen, raising

her eyebrows in surprise.

'He grabbed Dennis and headed off not long after you guys left for your walk.'

'Oh.' I feel completely wrong-footed. This isn't how this bit is supposed to go. 'When's he back?'

'He's not coming back.'

'What? Don't be silly. Where'd he go? I have to talk to him!'

'London. Something to do with work. He borrowed Frank.'

'Work?' I feel like someone has stuck a pin in me and I'm slowly deflating.

'I don't know. Some kind of emergency. Anyway, forget about that for a minute — this is serious.' Rowan throws a quick look over her shoulder and rummages in her jeans pockets, pulling out the same wodge of computer printouts she was waving at me earlier. 'It's about Than.'

Rowan looks uncharacteristically worried, and my heart swells with warmth for this clever little cookie — even if she has pretty much emptied my bank account single-handedly since I arrived.

'Don't worry, Rowan, I know about the article. Your dad told me everything.'

'No, that's not — ' Rowan shakes her head impatiently but is interrupted by Ted bellowing her name from the farmhouse.

Before she's had a chance to say anything else, he's come into view and looks decidedly less fluffy than usual.

'Rowan Myrtle Mullins, get back up to that house this instant. I told you not to bother Tori. Go and get ready. We're off to see your mum and little sister in ten minutes!'

Rowan tuts and looks sulky. 'But, Dad, I — '

'Now, Rowan.'

'Here.' Rowan thrusts the wad of paper at me. 'You need *all* the facts. Make sure you read it *all*.'

'Thanks, Rowan,' I smile at her. 'I've read it all, but thanks.'

'No, you might've missed bits in the shock.' She looks at me, eyes wide, before retreating back to the house.

'What was all that about?' asks Doreen, watching them go.

'I don't know . . . Maybe she was hoping to get a nice little payout for the printout!' I laugh. 'Anyway, right now I'm more worried about Bay. I don't get it. Why'd he just disappear?'

'Maybe something really did come up for him.'

'Something that meant he couldn't wait around for an extra ten minutes to talk to me? Especially after last night. It's got to have something to do with this,' I say, waving the printout pages crossly.

'Bay's got to finish off the course, hasn't he? And he's got to return Frank . . . I'm sure he'll be back soon.'

'I guess you're right.' I shrug and kick at the ground. 'Shame Ted turned up right at that second though. With Bay gone, I could have done with asking Rowan for some coffee. I'm dying for a cup.'

'Tell you what,' Doreen says, linking her arm through mine, 'let's head back to my place. Geoff will be desperate to catch up with you and know you're okay. I've even got some teabags — proper PG Tips and everything.'

30

The Mirrors You Can't Avoid

'Friends are the mirrors we can't avoid. We might be able to hide certain things from ourselves, but good friends will always find a way to reflect them back at us. Go ahead and take a look.'
©TheBeginnersGuideToLoneliness.com

As I sink onto the little settee inside Doreen and Geoff's cabin, I feel completely knackered. It's probably not even midday yet, but today has already been one of the weirdest days of my life so far, and that's saying something. There are so many thoughts whizzing around in my head, I'm not sure which one to grab hold of and examine first.

'So. You two worked everything out, then?' Geoff asks lightly as he plops onto a wooden chair opposite and hands me a mug of strong tea.

'Oh, yes,' laughs Doreen, settling herself down next to me. 'I'm a bored, twittering housewife and she's a spoiled little brat.'

I snort into my mug and Geoff grins at us. 'Oh good. At least that clears that up.'

'Point is,' I say, 'we all say stupid stuff we don't mean at times.'

'Oh, I meant it,' Doreen smirks, and I dig her in the ribs with my elbow.

'So, you're okay, Tori?' Geoff asks.

'Not really. I don't know where to start with all this.

I think I'd feel better if Bay hadn't buggered off on me too.'

'What's this?' Geoff raises his eyebrows.

'Bay's gone to London, apparently. Some kind of emergency,' says Doreen, quickly filling him in while I sip my tea.

'When did he say he'd be back, Tori?'

'He didn't,' I say. 'He'd already left when we got back from our walk. Rowan told us.'

'Ah. Well . . . I'm sure he'll be back before you know it.'

'Question is, why didn't he wait and tell me himself?'

'Well, if it was an emergency, maybe he couldn't wait.'

'Not even for half an hour? I don't know . . . Something's off. I don't even know if he's seen Than's article.'

'He will have,' says Geoff. 'When Claire was here earlier, she said that they were going to have to share it with the whole group. There's no way that Ted would have let Bay leave without filling him in.'

'You're right,' I sigh. 'I just hope it wasn't something to do with the article that made him leave so suddenly . . . or maybe it was because of what happened last night.'

'What happened?' Geoff asks curiously.

'They had a moment!' Doreen says, waggling her eyebrows. 'And there's no way it would have anything to do with that, I'm sure.'

'A moment, eh?' Geoff smiles at me. 'So that's what the kids are calling it these days . . . '

'Well, I almost managed to screw it up by mentioning Than at a critical moment . . . *Shit,* I hope it wasn't that.' My brain is throwing worry after worry at me and I can't keep up.

'Tori, Bay's a really straightforward guy,' says Geoff, taking a sip of tea. 'If everything felt right, then it was right, so don't worry about things that you're only imagining. It'll all work out, you'll see. But on the subject of Than — *Nathan* — whatever we're calling him now, what are you going to do?'

My heart sinks even further.

'If I'm honest, I don't know.' I shrug helplessly. 'You know, this is my biggest fear come true.'

'What's that?'

'The whole world finding out.'

'What? That you're an amazing writer?' asks Geoff. 'Because you are, by the way!'

I shake my head. I have to do this. This is exactly what Ted was talking about — I've got to communicate the things that scare me the most. 'No. That I'm guilty . . . for my mother's death.'

Doreen looks at me with her eyes wide. 'Tori, that was an accident. I've read your posts and you told us about it that day at the river. A car accident. Horrific, but not your fault.'

'It was,' I say.

'But, love, you weren't even there.'

'No. And that's what makes it my fault. I should have been driving that day.'

My breath is coming hard and fast, but this isn't the usual sensation of panic returning. This is something else. Like a dam inside of me has burst.

'Tell us,' she says steadily. 'If you want to talk about it, we're here for you.'

Geoff nods. I take a deep breath.

'Mum and I had a very strained relationship. She

had a drinking problem. No matter what I did to try to help her . . . it was never enough. It had come to the point where she only called when she was drunk. She called when she needed help — whether it was money, or when she got in trouble with the police, or wanted me to act as her unpaid taxi. And I'd had enough. I loved her, of course I did, she was my mum, but she was so difficult to deal with. I know . . . I *know* that it was an illness, and I did try to be there for her. But sometimes, she was just awful.'

Doreen and Geoff are both listening intently, but neither try to comfort me nor interrupt, and I'm grateful. Now I've started, I'm not sure I can stop.

'She was emotionally abusive. I guess that's what you'd call it. She was like that when I was a kid, but it just got worse as the drinking got worse. On the night of the accident, I'd had enough. I was up to my eyeballs in work, trying to keep myself afloat, trying to keep Markus happy, and I just couldn't face bailing her out of whatever shite she'd landed herself in again.

When I saw her name flash up on my mobile, for the first time ever, I just ignored the call.'

'Oh, Tori,' Doreen says gently as I pause for breath, for a beat of calm before I have to say the worst part out loud.

'Because of me . . . because I was so *selfish* . . . my mum got behind the wheel when she was so far over the limit it was a miracle she was even conscious. I wasn't there for her when she needed me. I ignored her call. I'm responsible for her death, and I have to live with that guilt every single day for the rest of my life.'

Now that I've finished, I can't look at them. I stare

hard at my hands, trying to keep my breathing steady. Then I feel the warm weight of a comforting hand on my shoulder. I look up to find Geoff smiling gently down at me. Doreen takes my hand from the other side, and I look at her. Her eyes are pink from the tears that have snuck down her cheeks while I've been talking.

My biggest fear is out there, and the world hasn't ended.

'What can I do?' I ask, my voice breaking.

'Talk about it,' says Geoff. 'Talk to us. Talk to Ted and Lizzie. You're in the perfect place. Work through it. You're surrounded by friends.'

Doreen nods.

'I always thought that . . . well . . . that this means that I don't deserve friends,' I say, my voice coming out low and husky.

'Well, we're not going anywhere,' Doreen says quietly.

I smile shakily at them. 'Thank you.'

Geoff shakes his head as if to ward off my thanks and Doreen squeezes my hand and shrugs. 'What are friends for?'

'You know, I can't believe you told Than about your blog,' Geoff says, sitting back down. 'You've always been so clear on there that you wanted to remain anonymous.'

'She didn't tell him!' says Doreen, raising her eyebrows at her husband.

'Oh,' says Geoff, looking confused. 'Then how did he . . . ?'

'No idea,' I sigh. 'The only people I've ever told were the Warriors — the three people I'm friends with online. It was actually one of them, Nat, who encouraged me to start the blog.'

'Well then, he must have contacted them somehow. One of them must have let it slip,' says Geoff.

'Do you think? How would he have even known to contact them?'

'You two were very close, briefly,' says Doreen. She looks at me quizzically.

'We were. Sometimes it was like he understood me without me having to say anything . . . ' I trail off.

'Maybe you mentioned the group at some point and he went from there?' asks Geoff.

I shudder. Maybe I did. 'But even if he did that, and somehow managed to get hold of them, I know those three. They just wouldn't have told him.'

'Have you still got that printout of the article Rowan gave you?' Doreen asks. 'Maybe there's something we missed?'

I yank the pages out of my pocket and hand them over to Doreen.

'*Rowan*,' I say. It's a light-bulb moment that brings me absolutely no relief. 'I promised to let the Warriors know how it was going here, so I paid her to let me use her phone to get online and send them a couple of quick messages.'

'You don't think Rowan . . . ?' Geoff looks shocked.

I shake my head. 'No, not her, but maybe I left it logged in. It's a possibility, isn't it?'

Doreen stops reading the article and stares at me. 'And Than somehow found it, you mean?'

'It's a possibility, I guess,' says Geoff.

'I need to talk to Rowan, now!' I get to my feet, but Doreen grabs my arm.

'She'll be on her way to the hospital by now.'

I give an impatient huff, but flop back down onto the sofa. Doreen's right.

'Tori!' Doreen squeaks, making both me and Geoff jump. 'What's that group of yours called again?' she asks me, wide-eyed.

'What, the online one? The Warriors. I know it's a bit naff but — '

'Look!' says Doreen, thrusting a couple of pages under my nose.

I take them on autopilot, bracing myself for something I missed earlier, but this is something completely different. It takes me a couple of moments to figure out what I'm looking at.

'I don't believe this!' I gasp as it sinks in.

'What? What is it?' asks Geoff, leaning forward in his chair and looking ready to snatch the pages out of my hands.

'It's . . . it's our conversation. The Warriors chatroom, I mean!' I say.

'But why would Rowan give this to you?' asks Doreen, looking as nonplussed as I feel.

I rifle through the pages of conversation. It's all the most recent stuff over the past month or so. I peer at the last page, and the very last entry from me is the one where I told them that Than had tried to kiss me, and how I was feeling about Bay. Then there are a couple of replies to my message from Hugh and Sue, telling me to enjoy a bit of holiday romance while I can get it, and generally joking around about my supposed love triangle. Then they start tagging Nat as she'd gone quiet. Right at the bottom, in pink biro, is scrawled one word, underlined three times.

Catfish.

31

An Attitude of Gratitude

'It's all too easy to focus on how difficult life can be. The problem with these negatives is that they can spiral out of control. The solution is very simple: making conscious gratitude a part of your daily life will help you reframe your day. Don't know where to start? Find just one thing, right now, that you're truly grateful for.'
©TheBeginnersGuideToLoneliness.com

Someone hammers on the door of the cabin, making us all jump. 'There you are!' says Rowan as soon as I answer the door. 'I've been looking for you everywhere!' 'What are you doing here? I thought you were at the hospital?' I say.

Rowan shrugs. 'They rang to say Mum and the baby can come home, so I said I'd wait here so that there was more room in the car.' She swaggers into the cabin and plonks herself in my vacated seat. 'Well? Did you find my note?'

'Note?'

'On the printouts. Tell me you read them!'

'Oh, I read them. Rowan, how did you get those printouts? Did I leave myself logged in or . . . ?'

'You? Are you kidding? You clear your browser history every time you're finished!' Rowan laughs. She catches my eye, sees that I'm not joining in with the joke and continues hastily: 'It was Than. Than left himself logged in.'

My mind is reeling. This isn't making any sense.

'I think he's a catfish, Tori!'

'Slow down and explain,' says Doreen gently to Rowan.

'Catfish! Oh come on, surely . . . '

Geoff and Doreen look perplexed.

'A catfish is someone who pretends to be someone else online, to get people to like them, or to trust them, or get information from them . . . from you, Tori!'

'Okay, but I'd never met Than before I came here,' I say.

Rowan rolls her eyes. 'But you'd met Nat, or 'Nathalie33',' Rowan says, watching me intently.

'Nat's one of my best friends.'

Geoff has his hand over his mouth and Doreen is looking back and forth between me and Rowan like she's watching a game of ping-pong.

'Nat. Than. *Nathan* — Tori, they're all the same person. Look, I can prove it.' Rowan quickly grabs her phone out of her coat pocket and swipes it open. 'I left it logged in. He's logged in as Nathalie33. He is Nathalie33.'

I take the phone from her and peer at the familiar chat screen. The only difference is the avatar in the bottom left corner isn't my own face; it's a little silver quill pen on a black background. Nat's avatar.

'I can't believe this,' I say faintly.

'Dad was ranting on about Than's article, and how he wasn't who he said he was. So I went online to read it. Then I thought maybe there might be something in my history. I mean, he paid me quite a few times to go online. I had all these different tabs open. I spotted this one and didn't think anything of it until I saw your username. That's what got my attention, because you're always so careful about closing everything down. So I had a bit of a closer look and saw that it wasn't you logged in, but someone called Nathalie33. And there's no one called Nathalie here, and so I just put two and two together.'

I'm watching her with my mouth open. 'Two and two?!' I say.

'That it must have been him. If I'd known what he was doing, I swear I would have warned you!'

'But it doesn't make any sense. I've been friends with Nat online for years! She's the one who convinced me to come here.'

Rowan shrugs. 'Most people do it to lure their victims into some kind of relationship.'

I shudder at the word 'victim'. 'So why pretend to be a woman?'

'So you'd trust her . . . I mean him,' says Geoff, looking horrified. 'He must have wanted to meet you, so convinced you to come here and then booked his place after you'd confirmed. I mean, it's the perfect way to meet up with you without blowing his cover.'

'At least you know how he got all those details about you,' says Doreen, looking shocked.

The hairs on the back of my neck are prickling again. I feel like I'm being watched. This is horrible. One of my best friends isn't even real.

'Can I ask you something?' Rowan says slowly. 'Have you ever met the other two you talk to on there?'

'Hugh and Sue? No. None of us have ever met up.'

'If you've never met, how do we know that they aren't in on it too?'

'Oh God, don't say that!' I say.

'But I'm right though, aren't I?' Rowan asks, looking

between Geoff and Doreen for backup. 'They could be anyone . . . or they could all be the same person.'

I think for a moment. No, that doesn't feel right. 'They've always been really genuine on there. Sue's shared photos of her kids with us, and holiday snaps. I email her separately sometimes too as she proof-reads some of my work for me.'

'What about the other guy?' Geoff asks.

'Hugh? Actually, I've voice chatted with him a few times, as he gets bored on long drives, and he knows I'm around during the day.'

'Okay,' Rowan says slowly. 'And it never seemed weird to you that Nat never did this?'

'I never thought about it. We message on there. We message privately sometimes too, and that's always been . . . well, just normal.'

'I still think it would be a good idea to check the other two out. You thought Nat was genuine until about five minutes ago,' she says, looking a bit worried.

'How on earth am I going to do that?' I ask. This is so much worse than I could have ever imagined.

'We've got time to come up with something,' says Doreen calmly.

Rowan blows air into her cheeks then lets it out in a great huff.

I lean forward and rub my face. This is too much to get my head around. Nathan, Than, Nat — they're all the same person. For whatever reason, she, I mean *he*, orchestrated it so that we were both here at the same time. Then he befriended me, tried to kiss me, and when I turned him down, he just . . . imploded.

Now he's disappeared and gone public with details about me that were never meant to be shared. Even though I'm starting to see that it's not going to ruin my life, it's definitely going to change it.

There's still something that isn't adding up though. Why lure me in and try to start something between us with that kiss if he was just going to completely change direction and betray me?

'Hang on a minute!' I squeak.

'What?' Rowan jumps.

'I know why he was so randomly shitty in Claire's session! That was the morning after I . . . ' I clear my throat, trying to swallow down the embarrassment. 'After I sent a message to the group about liking Bay and not Than. After Than had tried to kiss me. He must have seen it.'

Rowan nods. 'Probably. He did ask to check his emails in the mornings a couple of times before the sessions kicked off.'

'He wasn't checking his emails. I bet you anything that was him logging on here to check if I'd sent anything to the group!'

'Probably hoping for a juicy update about himself,' says Doreen, looking mildly sick.

'And instead he got to hear that he was turning into a bit of an irritating pain in the bum and that you had the hots for Bay,' says Rowan.

'I never said that!' I snap.

'Okay, you never used the actual words, but your feelings were pretty clear.'

'Well, at least that explains why he had that massive blowup in Claire's session,' says Doreen.

'It's almost like he was trying to punish you,' says Geoff.

Rowan's eyes grow wide and I can see that this is starting to freak her out.

'He was always trying to get me onside,' I say, 'like we were in some kind of private little club. I wonder if any of the stuff he shared with me was even true . . . ' I say. I don't know if he told anyone else about his brother, and I'm certainly not going to share it, but the fact that he might have made up something so serious makes my skin crawl.

'Well, he certainly wanted you all to himself, didn't he?' says Doreen. 'Looks like he reacted pretty badly when things didn't go his way!'

'Thank God I didn't go there,' I sigh. 'So, what do we do now?'

Doreen, Geoff and I instinctively turn to Rowan.

'You know, I think it's time to remind you that I'm only thirteen. Time to bring in more adults.'

'You've got a point!' I say. 'When are your mum and dad due back?'

She looks uncharacteristically worried for a second. 'You're going to tell them, aren't you?'

'I need all the help I can get to work this mess out.'

Rowan nods but still looks worried.

'What's up?' asks Doreen.

'They're going to find out about my business.'

'Ah. Of course,' says Geoff. 'I'm sure we can figure something out.'

Rowan looks at him hopefully.

'I've got it!' I say. 'Okay . . . it's not going to get you completely off the hook, but it might mean you don't get busted.'

'I'm listening!' she says, raising one eyebrow.

'Well, we're going to have to tell them that it was your phone we were accessing the internet on . . . '

Rowan's face falls.

'*But* we tell them that I convinced you to lend me

your phone so I could check in with my friends. Just so they knew I was safe. No mention of money; you just did it out of the goodness of your heart.' I raise an eyebrow at the very thought of Rowan doing this, and she smirks.

'What about Than?'

'Your parents know how close we were. We'll say I told him, so he asked to borrow it too. Simple.'

'It might work . . . ' she says.

'Of course it will!' Doreen chips in. 'They've got no reason to doubt Tori, and it's not like Than is around to dispute it. The only other people who know are me and Geoff, and it's not like we're about to dob you in!'

'I'll still get in trouble for lending Tori my phone. After all, it's my fault all this happened. If he hadn't got onto the chat, you guys wouldn't have blown up and he wouldn't have written that article.'

'Listen to me, Rowan. None of this is your fault. He'd already targeted me, for whatever reason. Without you, we wouldn't have worked any of this out. Who knows what might have happened! We don't know why he did what he did or what he was planning, but it's definitely better that we know about it.'

'Mum and Dad won't see it like that,' she mutters and, much to my surprise, her lip wobbles.

'I'll make sure they do. Look, I know it's a lot to ask,' I say, turning to Geoff and Doreen, 'but would you guys mind helping us explain everything to Ted and Lizzie when they get back?'

'Of course!' says Doreen at once.

'Absolutely,' agrees Geoff.

'Thanks. Because it's not just a case of explaining it, but figuring out what needs to happen next. I wish Bay was here.'

'I'm sure he would too, if he knew the full story,' says Geoff.

'I'm dreading having to see everyone else,' I say.

'Well, I'm sure they'll all be right behind you,' says Doreen.

I nod, feeling a little glow of love for the group of oddballs that I'm now lucky enough to call friends. Every single one of them, from Emma and her insane enthusiasm to lovely Messa, giver of hugs and wearer of the finest beard I've ever met.

I just hope they will still think of me as a friend after all of this.

32

The Four Faces of Loneliness

> 'Loneliness has four faces: social, situational, emotional and chronic. No matter which of these you struggle with, it's important to tear off the protective mask you wear to fool the rest of the world and take a long look at the face underneath.'
>
> ©TheBeginnersGuideToLoneliness.com

I don't know how she does it, but Lizzie still manages to look like a goddess as she emerges from Ted's rusty little Micra bearing the sleeping baby in her carry seat.

Rowan, Geoff, Doreen and I all rush towards them, and we're suddenly one huge tangle of arms and happy tears and hugs and congratulations.

'It's so good to be back,' Lizzie smiles as Rowan finally pulls back from her mother.

'How're you feeling?' I ask. We've all come to the conclusion that there is no way we should burden Lizzie with the news the moment she's back.

'Great!' she replies. 'Tired. Sore. But, just look at her!' she beams down at her brand new daughter who is, miraculously, still asleep. 'But never mind me, how are you all? Ted's been filling me in. Tori, how are you holding up? Sounds like we've got a lot to talk about!'

I catch Rowan's look and Doreen stops in her tracks. Hm. Maybe our plan of letting Lizzie and Ted rest a while before dropping the next bombshell on them isn't quite going to work out as we planned.

'Oh, I'm fine,' I say with a smile. Maybe I can gloss over it until later.

'What's that?' Lizzie says, stopping to look at me properly, popping the carry seat down on the grass for a moment. 'Freaked out. Insecure. Neurotic and Emotional?'

'Mum!' gasps Rowan.

I shrug. 'Yep, that pretty much nails it.' I laugh.

'Well, if we're sharing,' says Doreen, 'I'm afraid there's quite a lot more that we need to catch you and Ted up on, when you've had a bit of a rest.'

'Rest? I've been in bed for days. Other than having a baby, I've been bored senseless. Rowan, help me get these things indoors and then put the kettle on. Sounds like it's time for tea and cake.'

My heart leaps at the mention of another cup of tea — actually I'd kill for a cup of Bay's coffee. Just the thought of Bay makes my heart twist painfully. I mustn't think about him. I can't go there. Not yet. Not with so many other things I need to figure out first.

⋆ ⋆ ⋆

It's about half an hour before we're all sitting around the long dining table in the courtyard. Between them, Rowan and Ted have managed to heft a high-backed armchair outside and have dragged it up to the head of the table for Lizzie. She's now ensconced as comfortably as possible, supported by many cushions, and is busy feeding the little one while the rest of us squabble over the homemade biscuits that Doreen just produced, having nipped back over to the cabin to get them. The tea, however, is the usual brew of hedge clippings, so I opt for some mint in hot water instead.

The rest of the group are nowhere to be seen, and Ted tells us that they've all gone off on a walk with Russ and Claire so that they can share Than's article with everyone at the same time.

'Do you want to start?' I ask Rowan, who's been sitting next to her mother and baby sister, uncommonly quiet.

Rowan looks up at me with a startled expression on her face and shakes her head.

'What've you done, Rowan?' Lizzie asks, looking serious.

'Nothing. She's . . . well, actually, she's pretty much saved me from something quite nasty,' I say, not quite knowing where to start. Doreen and Geoff both nod their agreement and I relax a little bit. 'It's about Than. Nathan.'

'Is it about that article?' asks Ted sharply.

'No, no, this is something else. Something worse, in a way. At least, worse for me.'

Rowan looks up at me, glances at her mum and then her dad, and rolls her eyes. 'Oh for God's sake, this is going to take hours if I leave it to you!' she huffs. 'That Nathan bloke has been *friends* with Tori online for years, by pretending to be a woman.'

'Huh?' Lizzie looks completely confused and I almost let out a laugh when I see the expression on Ted's face. I jump in quickly before Rowan manages to drop herself in it in her impatience to tell the story.

I tell them about the Warriors and our friendship. I navigate carefully around how I talked Rowan into letting me contact them a couple of times. And then how Rowan discovered what Than had been up to and how desperate she was to warn me.

'Rowan! I can't believe this,' Ted says. He looks angry, and shocked, and just a little bit proud.

'Look, it wasn't Rowan's fault, and as soon as she figured out that there was something off about the whole thing, she wanted to put it right.'

Rowan smiles at me.

'But still. Why didn't you tell me?' Ted demands.

'You had enough to worry about. I guess I didn't really think Tori would be in any real danger while she was with us and had no access to the internet. I told her as soon as I could.'

'Catfish?' says Lizzie, as if tasting the new term on her tongue.

'Apparently,' I say with a shrug.

'But I just don't understand what he hoped to gain from meeting up with Tori here?'

'Nothing good,' Rowan says with a dark look. 'You should see the horrible stuff it says about some of these cases online.'

I shudder. I don't want to think about it.

Geoff spots my mounting discomfort and jumps in. 'Look, I don't think it's going to help to talk about that now. Thanks to Rowan, we know what's going on. Now we need to help Tori decide what to do next.'

'Do you mean pressing charges or something?' asks Ted.

I shake my head quickly. There's no way I want to go down that route. What would be the point?

'What I'm worried about now,' says Doreen, who's been pretty quiet so far, 'is your other two friends on there.'

'What about them?' I ask. I'm not sure how I feel.

I defended them to Rowan earlier, and there's no way I believe that they could all be the same person, like Rowan suggested, but do they really not know about any of this?

'Doreen's right,' says Ted. 'They're both pretty vulnerable, not knowing that 'Nat' is a fraud. Whether they've seen that article yet or not, I think it's important that you warn them. After all, Than still has access to the chatroom. He doesn't know his cover's blown, does he?'

Lizzie nods. 'Actually, that's a really good point.'

'But what if they already know something about all this?' Rowan asks. 'I know you said earlier that you thought they were cool, but what if they're in on it?'

'Are you able to send them personal messages on there that don't appear for the whole group?' asks Geoff.

I nod.

'Well, if Rowan will lend you her phone again, why don't you send them both a private message and just ask if they've heard from 'Nat'? You know he's not been posting on the public bit, but he might have been talking to them privately.'

'That's a good idea,' nods Lizzie, hoisting the baby onto her shoulder and patting her back. 'Then, when they get back to you, you can decide whether to tell them everything.'

I nod slowly. 'I guess so.' I can hardly admit that, right now, the last thing I want to do is put my trust in another two people I've never met.

Doreen smiles at me gently. 'Tori, just because Than has completely messed up his relationship with you from the start, don't let that ruin what you've got with the other two.'

'That's just it,' I say. 'I've realized that they're not my friends. How can they be when I've never even met them? They could be anybody.' My bottom lip quivers and I bury my nose in my mug to hide the fact that, right at this moment, even though I'm surrounded by people who want to help me, I feel lonelier than I ever have before.

33

Journey Through, Not Around

'When faced with a tough situation, you've got two choices: find a way around it, or journey through it. No matter how hard it may seem, the journey through is the one that will work out better in the long run. Every time you avoid an issue, it finds a way to come back again and again.'
©TheBeginnersGuideToLoneliness.com

Rowan hands me her phone to contact Sue and Hugh. Even though I'd much rather scuttle off and work out these messages in private, I sit at the table with the others and log in to my account. I can see that they've been busy gossiping about some new Netflix show in the general chat, but there's nothing new from Nat.

'Okay, here goes,' I say as I pull up a chat with Sue first. I quickly send her a message to say hello and ask if she's heard from Nat recently. I keep it short and simple, and once I've done that I send an almost identical message to Hugh. 'Done.' I go to hand the phone back to Rowan but she shakes her head.

'Keep it on you. Hopefully they'll reply quickly and then we can move straight to phase two.'

I nod and leave the phone on the table in front of me so I can see any new notifications as they pop up.

'Good,' says Ted, clearly pleased that something practical is being done. 'Now, I think you must try to get a bit of rest this evening, Tori. I know that's going to be hard, but you've had one shock after another today.'

With that, I'm reminded of the other question I wanted to ask them. I feel a blush rising on my cheeks. 'Actually, there was something else, if you don't mind?'

I decide to skip straight over the sticky parts. 'Did you show Bay the article before he left?' I ask Ted. 'He'd already disappeared by the time I got back from my walk with Doreen. Rowan told us he'd gone to London, but I don't get why he'd go without talking to me?'

Ted shifts in his chair and Lizzie looks at him. Geoff and Doreen are listening intently. This is shit. I know that it's something awful and Ted just can't bring himself to tell me.

'Look, Tori . . . I did share the article with him before he left. He needed to know about it — especially as there are photographs of him,' says Ted. 'But that had nothing to do with him leaving so suddenly. He had a personal emergency. I'm sure he would have stayed to speak to you and say goodbye if it hadn't been so urgent.'

I can't believe he didn't think I was important enough to wait just an hour or so . . .

'Where did he go?' I ask.

'London,' replied Ted, not catching my eye.

'What for?'

'I'm sorry, Tori,' Lizzie breaks in gently. 'We can't tell you that. It wouldn't be fair to Bay.'

'Look, he's hoping to get back before the end of the course. You can discuss it then.'

'Can't I give him a quick call — '

'We can't give you his number, Tori. Sorry.' Ted looks sheepish, but I can tell he's not going to budge on this.

I slump my head into my hands. I feel completely defeated. I thought Bay and I had something special starting between us.

I'm just beginning to feel the spirals of panic taking hold when Rowan's phone lights up next to me. I grab it and scroll down.

'It's Sue. She hasn't heard anything from Nat,' I say flatly.

'That's one down, then,' says Ted.

'Should I go ahead and tell her, do you think?'

'I'd wait,' says Rowan. 'See what the other guy says and, if it's the same, you can tell them both at the same time.'

I nod wearily. This feels like game-playing and I've had enough. All I want to do is go back to the yurt, have a cup of coffee with Bay and cuddle up with Dennis. But, of course, both of those things are now impossible.

The phone lights up again. It's Hugh with the same news as Sue. No sign of Nat, but not to worry, as she said she was going to be having a busy few weeks. Well, he's got that bit right at least.

'That's both of them,' I say.

'Go on, Tori, tell them. Then at least you know you don't have to worry about them both being used against you somehow,' says Doreen.

I nod again. I'm starting to feel a bit like the Churchill nodding dog.

'Rowan, do you mind if I take your phone for ten minutes? I feel like I need to do this on my own.'

'Sure,' Rowan shrugs.

'Thanks.' I struggle up from the bench and Doreen goes to follow me.

I smile at my friend. I know she's worried, but right now I just need some time on my own to send these messages and grieve for this part of my life that has meant so much to me. 'I'll be back in a few minutes, Doreen. Just want to clear my head and get this right.'

'Okay. We'll be here if you need us,' she replies, sitting back down.

I walk away from the courtyard. As soon as I turn the corner and know for sure that the sympathetic gaze of the little group is no longer on my back, I relax a little bit.

I wander for a while, then find myself heading towards the garden and the vegetable patch.

When I get there, just the sight of the neat beds in the evening light calms my heart a little. This bit was real. No matter what's happened since, the time I spent with Bay here in the garden was real.

I sit down on the wooden railway sleepers and take a few deep breaths, staring around at the garden. Now it's time to deal with something that isn't real. I pull up the chat on Rowan's phone and stare hard at it.

I decide that I can only face doing this once, and as they're bound to ask the same questions, I start a new room and invite just the two of them to join it. They both accept and are there within seconds.

* * *

I'm crying by the time I've finished explaining. Not because of having to tell them about what's happened, nor their shocked, disbelieving and then angry responses, but because it feels like I'm killing something special. Something very dear and innocent.

Both of them have asked what they can do to help,

but I've told them that there really isn't anything and that I'll try to pop into this new chat to say hello when things settle down a bit. But in my heart, I know it can never be like it was before. For one thing, Nat won't be there. I know she was fictional, but I feel like I've lost someone I love. And let's face it, I'm never going to be able to trust the others in the same way again. I'm always going to triple-guess everything I post.

As neither of them have seen it yet, I drop the link to Than's article and then slip the phone into my pocket. I can't bring myself to wait for their reactions.

In a daze, I wipe my face on my sleeve, then stand and stretch. Time for that early night Ted suggested. I head back down to the courtyard and wave away offers of more tea.

'Thanks for the phone. All done,' I say, handing it back to Rowan.

'What did they say?' she asks curiously.

'I think they're in shock. They hadn't seen the piece Than wrote, so I gave them that link too.'

'Bet they were pissed off!' says Rowan.

'Yup. You could say that.'

'You did the right thing,' says Geoff.

'I know. And now the other right thing is an early night. I'm shattered.'

'Aren't you going to wait to speak to them again after they've read it?' asks Doreen, a look of surprise on her face.

I shake my head. 'I've told them everything they need to know.'

'But . . . but don't they want to help?'

'Yes, but let's face it, there's nothing anyone can do.'

'Go on, Tori,' says Ted, taking pity on me, 'head

back to the yurt and get some rest. We'll talk more tomorrow.'

I nod gratefully.

'We'll walk you back, shall we?' says Geoff.

'Thanks, but I'm fine,' I smile at him. 'I'm going to go straight to bed, so I won't be much company.'

He continues to look worried, so I say, 'Would you and Doreen perhaps swing by on your way down for breakfast tomorrow?'

He smiles back at me. 'Of course.'

* * *

I had thought getting back to the yurt would make me feel better, but I was wrong. When I unzip the flap, shuffle out of my boots and let myself in, I'm struck by how bloody quiet it is. And not in a good way.

Before, when I popped back, nine times out of ten I'd be greeted by either Bay, Dennis or both. And even when they weren't around, there was always the chance of them appearing at any moment. The space is still beautiful, but without those two, it no longer feels like home.

The thought hits me in the stomach. Of course, this isn't 'home' anyway. Very soon I'll be back in my empty f at and, now that I don't have the Warriors to gossip with, my even emptier life. This place was meant to help me work things out, not make them worse. Yes, I've figured out a lot, but right now I'd much prefer to return to my state of not-so-blissful ignorance.

I throw my pyjamas on and sink onto my bed. Turning my back on Bay's side of the yurt, I wrap myself in my blankets and close my eyes.

I mustn't think about Bay. I mustn't think about Than.

I just want to sleep.

* * *

'Give her a poke!' Rowan's voice drifts into my dreams, and I feel myself surfacing. I don't open my eyes straight away. I was having such a nice dream.

'Don't be mean,' Doreen's voice says softly. 'Tori?' she croons, sounding like she's trying to wake a baby.

'Wakey wakey!' Rowan bellows. I'm pretty sure I hear a snort of laughter from Geoff.

I smile into my pillow and open my eyes. 'You lot should form a comedy act,' I say, sitting up and rubbing my eyes.

'Sorry, love, you weren't awake when we stopped by before breakfast, so we brought some back up for you, but *someone* insisted on coming too,' Doreen nods at Rowan.

'Like I'm going to miss this!' she says.

I shake my head, throw my blankets off and swing my legs around to sit on the side of my bed.

'We've got a surprise for you!' Rowan announces, eyes sparkling.

I look from her excited face to Geoff's beaming one and then back to Doreen's rather more worried expression.

'What?' I ask suspiciously.

'Now don't get mad — ' says Doreen.

'Mad?' I say faintly. I'm completely lost. What on earth are these three up to?

'She's READY!' Rowan yells.

To my amazement, the flap of the yurt flips open

and two people enter. One woman I vaguely recognize, with her long blond hair in a side plait, and then there's a middle-aged guy who has something of a Matt Lucas air about him.

'Erm, hi?' I say.

'Tori, it's us!' says the man, watching the look of complete confusion on my face.

I know that voice. *Wait . . .*

'*Hugh?!*' I gasp.

Matt Lucas, who is obviously not Matt Lucas, nods, a huge grin on his face.

'Which means . . . ' I continue.

'Yep. That's Sue!' Rowan fills in for me eagerly.

The blond woman is staring at me with tears in her eyes. I stand up slowly, staring from one to the other. Then, I have no idea how it happens, but we're in a tangle of arms as the three of us hug each other so tightly that I swear there's going to be at least one cracked rib by the time we're done.

When we eventually pull away from each other, we still don't let go completely. Hugh has an arm around my shoulders and Sue is holding my hand.

I beam at them in turn. 'How? Why?'

'That would be our fault,' said Geoff from behind me.

I twist around to look at him, still holding on to my friends. 'I don't understand.'

'What's new?' laughs Rowan.

'Oi!' says Doreen sharply.

'Tori doesn't mind, do you?' Rowan grins at me.

I shake my head. Right now, I don't think I mind anything much.

34

Be Open, Be Honest, Be You

> 'Shall I tell you a secret? You're pretty great. Your story is important. When we have suffered loneliness, for whatever reason, it can be incredibly difficult to open up to other people again. But that, right there, is the path that leads through to the other side. Show the true you, share your wonderful self openly, and encourage others to do the same.'
>
> ©TheBeginnersGuideToLoneliness.com

'It was actually Geoff's idea,' says Doreen, after we've all trooped outside to sit on the wooden benches around the unlit fire pit.

'I don't know,' Geoff looks uncharacteristically bashful. 'I just thought it was such a shame that that idiot had made you wary of two people who are clearly so important to you.'

'Yeah, so when I saw you'd left yourself logged in last night, I said maybe we should talk to them,' says Rowan.

'We were both frantic after reading that article,' says Sue.

I can't get enough of her voice. It's as though she's bringing to life all the lines we've typed to each other over the years.

'We tried to get you on group voice, we both sent you messages in the new room and privately, but you weren't answering.'

'Of course, once Rowan had spotted you'd left yourself logged in, we could see all of this,' continues Doreen.

'So I said,' cuts in Rowan, 'let's message them and tell them you're all right.'

'And you just messaged them as me?' I ask, surprised.

'Course not. I asked Dad if it was okay first. He agreed. Well, of course, it came out under your name, but I told them straight away that it was me, and that you were okay-ish, and that we were looking after you and that you'd gone to bed.'

Sue nods. 'I just wanted to know that you were okay. I swear, if I'd had a shock like that, I don't know what state I'd have been in. And it's so scary to think that Nat — I mean this Nathan person — basically set out to meet you without you even knowing anything about it.' She gives an exaggerated shudder. 'Anyway, both of us wanted to do something. We wanted to come and be with you. Even if it was just for company while you dealt with the shock.'

My heart feels like it's slowly being pieced back together. All of these people doing all of this because they were worried about me. Because they care about me.

'So Rowan asked them both to stay logged in and she'd see what she could do,' says Doreen.

'And Dad said to invite them here!'

'And you just came?' I ask, open-mouthed, staring between Sue and Hugh.

'Well, I was relaying everything to my hubby as it was happening,' says Sue. 'He was so worried about you, and said that he'd look after the twins if there was any chance I could come and support you. There was one issue though — our car is in the garage so I had no transport.'

'So I went and fetched her!' laughs Hugh. 'As soon as Rowan invited us, I started throwing things in a bag. Then when Sue said she could come too but had no transport, that was an easy fix; I just detoured to collect her on my way down. I stayed at Sue's last night and then we set off mega-early this morning.'

I shake my head trying to take it all in. Sue and Hugh are really here. They've spent hours driving here just because they knew how much I needed them.

'I — I can't believe you'd do that for me,' I say. 'Thank you.'

'Anytime,' says Hugh matter-of-factly.

'Now where's this Bay character? I'm dying to meet him,' says Sue.

The change in the atmosphere is almost comical. Geoff busies himself with his shoelaces, Doreen pulls a tragic face as if someone has died and Rowan starts to fidget.

'What did I say?' says Sue, looking around at the others.

I sigh. 'Bay's gone.'

'*Gone?* What do you mean, 'gone'?'

'He had to rush off to London yesterday.'

'That's a shame, I'd like to meet the man that's finally swept you off your feet.' Hugh grins.

'How long's he gone for?' Sue adds.

'I'm not sure . . . ' I say.

'Didn't he tell you?' says Sue in surprise.

'He didn't say anything, not even goodbye. He disappeared while Doreen and I were off on a walk.'

'You're kidding me!' says Sue, eyes wide.

'Nope. Just gathered up his dog and left.'
'But why?'
'Supposedly some kind of urgent work thing came up, but . . . well . . . I can't help but think it's more likely to do with this bloody article.'
'I'm sure that's not true,' says Sue gently.
'And Ted did say he was hoping to be back before the end of the course, didn't he?' says Geoff.
'Apparently he's going to try,' I say, 'but it's not definite. His 'urgent business' might keep him tied up.'
'To be fair to Bay, it might,' pipes up Rowan, looking a bit cross. 'He is kinda famous you know.'
'Famous?' Sue says. 'Tori, you didn't tell us that.'
'Because he's not. Rowan's having you on!' I say.
'Am not! He is . . . in the world of gardens anyway. And I know it's crap he didn't wait to talk to you before he went Tori, but he's a good guy,' she finishes, looking a bit uncomfortable.
I watch Rowan as she stares at the ground and focuses on digging her heel into the mud. She's right. Bay is a good guy. Here's me, expecting him to take it on trust that I'm not the monster Than has made me out to be, while busily thinking the worst of him rather than trusting him. But after everything that's happened, I'm not sure I'm up for giving anyone the benefit of the doubt right now.
'So have you called him, Tori?' asks Hugh.
I shake my head.
'Why not?'
'One, I don't have his number. Two, I don't have a phone. Three, I'm not really sure what I'd say.'
'But hang on,' says Hugh, 'isn't our Rowan here the queen of information?'

Rowan looks up from her muddy boots and I can practically see her ego swelling with the knowledge that her reputation has reached beyond the boundaries of The Farm.

'Exactly! Can't you tell me where he's gone? Or at least start with something simpler, like his full name?'

Rowan's jaw drops. 'You're not telling me you did whatever you did with him and you don't even know his name?!'

'We only kissed, thank you very much!' I can feel myself going red, and the fact that both of the guys start to laugh isn't helping.

Rowan rolls her eyes. 'Okay, I can give you his name, but it'll cost you.'

'It'll have to be PayPal again,' I sigh.

'Don't worry about that!' says Hugh. He whips out his wallet and hands Rowan a ten-pound note. Her eyes go wide, but she quickly recovers.

'Okay, that's a start,' she says with a shrug. 'Bay's surname is Anderson. He's actually called Bailey Anderson, and his business is called . . .'

'Anderson, Simpson and Green!' squeals Sue.

We all turn to stare at her.

'What?' she says. 'Don't tell me you haven't heard of them! They do the gardens of the rich and the famous. I mean, Bailey Anderson's practically royalty . . . he's like a gardening god!'

'But . . . but he's just Bay!' I say.

Oh great, another person in my life who's been busy pretending to be someone else.

I can't believe this. Is no one going to turn out to be who they say they are?

'See!' says Rowan, pointing at Sue. 'That reaction is exactly why Bay prefers to keep a low profile when he's here. Of course, plenty of people recognize him, but he does his best not to make a big deal out of it.'

'Now we know his name, we don't need Ted to find out his number,' Hugh says as he whips out his own phone and within seconds has pulled up the Anderson, Simpson and Green website. It's going to be that easy to call him. But now that I can, I'm not sure I want to.

'Wait. I need food and I need to let everything sink in a bit first. Anyway, it's Sunday. If I'm going to call, I'm not going to be able to do it until tomorrow when their office is open.'

* * *

As it turns out, I needn't have worried for a second about how the rest of the group were going to react to Than's article. As they arrive to find Sue, Hugh and I setting the dinner table after a whole day spent together exploring the countryside around The Farm, I am engulfed by hugs and offers of support. They are all on my side, and all desperate to make sure I know it. Emma gushes about my writing, while Messa and Bob both offer to be there to talk any time I need them, day or night. Moth presents me with a beautiful knitted hairband in the hope that it might cheer me up, and even quiet Sam throws his arm around my shoulders and tells me how brave I am.

Supper is a ridiculously happy affair, and for a while I'm able to forget everything that's happened and just enjoy the amazing company. Ted and Lizzie are still celebrating being back at home with Rowan and the baby, and their joy overflows in their welcome to the new arrivals too.

In among all their plotting and planning, Rowan, Doreen and Geoff have arranged for Hugh and Sue to stay in the yurt with me tonight. Ted tells me it's the most practical option as the little settee pulls out into a bed. In my heart, though, I know they've planned this so that I don't have to spend another night on my own, and I'm deeply grateful.

We all help tidy up after the meal. Lizzie disappears off to bed early, and Ted follows soon after with strict instructions to Rowan not to stay up too late, which she roundly ignores. She's actually pretty indignant when the rest of us decide to head back to our respective camps soon after, but, as I explain, she's not missing out on anything as we're all headed straight to bed anyway.

By the time we're all snuggled up in our beds — Hugh has taken Bay's, and Sue's on the sofa as she's so tiny — my head is whirring again. So much has happened, I'm still trying to process it all. The issue that I keep coming back to, however, is Bay. Why did he leave without talking to me? Will he come back? Should I phone him?

'You okay, Tori?' asks Hugh.

'I am thanks to you two,' I sigh. 'Thank you so much for being here with me.'

'It's fun! An unexpected adventure. And anyway, you'd have done exactly the same for us!' says Sue.

I think about this, and realize that she's right. Hugh, Sue and, until yesterday, the fictional Nat are three people that I would have done almost anything for.

It's a wonderful feeling when I realize that, since I've been here, several new people have joined that list. And right at the top is Bay.

'You know I can't just call Bay, right?' I say into the

dark.

'Why not?' asks Hugh, surprised. 'You've got the number, and you can use my phone. No one else needs to know.'

'It's not that,' I say. 'I need to see him. It's got to be face to face.'

'Oh.' Hugh goes quiet.

'Well, he might come back in time,' says Sue in a soothing voice.

'I need to go back to London. As soon as possible,' I say, surprising myself. 'Do you reckon you could give me a lift down to Carmarthen tomorrow? I can catch the train from there — '

'Nope,' says Hugh. 'Think we're going to let you escape our clutches that quickly?'

'But — ' I start.

'I'll drive you to London. You up for another road trip, Sue?'

'Oooh, yes!' she squeals. 'I've got a few days to play with so — '

'Guys, you don't need to do that.'

'Oh yes we do!' says Hugh.

'Absolutely. I need to know how it's going to work out with you and your sex-god gardener!'

'What about your course, though? You won't get to finish it,' says Hugh.

'I think I've got quite a lot to write about already. And anyway, if everything goes to plan, perhaps I'll get the chance to come back in time to finish it off.'

'So what are we going to do tomorrow? Say good-bye to everyone and then head off after breakfast?' asks Sue.

My heart clenches at the thought of saying good-bye to Geoff and Doreen earlier than I have to. But I have to see Bay, I just have to. 'I don't think so. We're going to have to make a break for it early, otherwise I'm not sure that Ted and Lizzie will let us escape.'

'When you say early . . . '

'Ted's usually up at 5.30am.'

'With a newborn baby in the house you might find either of them up at any hour,' says Hugh.

'Good point. We need a distraction.'

'The car is parked up at the top of the lane, so it's just going to be a case of sneaking past the house,' says Hugh.

'How about Rowan?' asks Sue. 'She could be a lookout for us.'

'How on earth are we going to ask her now?'

'I've got her number,' says Hugh. 'I took it so that I could let her know when we would be arriving.'

'Perfect,' I say. 'Oh, and ask her to break my stuff out of the safe while she's at it.'

35

Survive vs Thrive

> 'Are you surviving or are you thriving? What's the difference? Surviving is an incredible achievement. You are pulling together the resources that you need to stay afloat. Surviving through some of the toughest times in life feels like a badge of honour.
>
> 'But thriving? Thriving means tapping into your potential. It's about joy and abundance. It's about growth.'
>
> ©TheBeginnersGuideToLoneliness.com

I feel kind of bad as we scuttle down the yard towards the lane at ridiculous o'clock the next morning. I should be saying goodbye to everyone, thanking them for basically changing my whole life.

I can't think like that now, though, otherwise I'll be crying again, and a tearful mess at five forty in the morning is not a good start.

Instead, I comfort myself with the thought that, if everything pans out, I'll be back soon enough to finish off the course.

'Thanks so much for everything,' I whisper as Rowan hands me the little bag with my shoes, phone and other bits and pieces from the safe.

'You owe me!' she yawns. She looks so much younger when she's all crumpled from sleep and sans make-up.

'I've already sent you twenty quid!' I say.

'You still owe me! Dad's going to do his nut when he knows you've done a runner.'

'Let us know what happens, won't you?' says Hugh.

'Sure.' Rowan yawns again, turning back towards her bed with a wave over her shoulder.

'You know, I think Ted's going to be more worried about his safe-breaking daughter than you disappearing after Bay,' Sue chuckles quietly. 'Come on, guys, let's get going.'

* * *

The journey feels like a breeze compared to the public transport marathon from hell it took to get me there. The best thing is, we don't stop talking until we reach the outskirts of the city. I may have only physically met these two yesterday, but there's no doubt that our friendship is real.

It might feel like we've talked about everything under the sun, but there are two subjects we've carefully been avoiding: Bay and Nat.

Gah, I've got to stop calling him Nat or Than in my head.

Nathan. Catfishing, bullshitting Nathan.

'Guys, what am I going to do about Nathan?' I finally ask when there's a lull in the conversation. 'I know what I said about not pressing charges, but it doesn't feel right to just let him get away with what he's done.'

'If it were me, I'd want to get even,' says Sue over her shoulder, peering at me in the back seat.

'You know,' says Hugh, not taking his eyes off the busy road, 'I think it's about more than that. This is someone who's successfully befriended the three of us while posing as someone else. For whatever reason, it looks like he has become completely obsessed with you, Tori, and when he didn't get what he wanted, he turned nasty.'

'Actually, if you think about it, how he behaved towards you at the retreat kind of mirrored what he was like in the chat,' says Sue. 'Nat swooped in and isolated you from the main chat almost as soon as you'd joined, and I don't think she — he — ever forgave me and Hugh for crashing your private group.'

I raise my eyebrows. Hindsight is a wonderful thing. I can see now that Sue's right.

'But how does that mirror what he was doing at The Farm?' I ask, confused.

'From what you said, he started to get all stroppy when he saw you were making friends with the others,' says Sue.

'Yeah. I mean, he was definitely jealous of your friendship with Doreen,' says Hugh. 'And it sounds like he tried to isolate you as often as he could, and acted out when his plans didn't work.'

'Well, he got the ultimate revenge, didn't he?' I say, shivering.

'No. No, he didn't,' Sue says, her voice firm. 'The only way he will have done that is if you let him undo all the amazing things you've achieved while you've been at The Farm.'

I nod. 'So, do you think I should go to the police?'

'Not if you don't want to go down that route,' says Hugh, thoughtfully, 'but I do think that, as he has gone public about his time with you, you'd be well within your rights to do the same to him.'

'Out him?'

'Yes. And while you're at it, raise some awareness.'

Sue's nodding in agreement. 'We're three relatively sensible adults — '

'Speak for yourself,' I laugh.

'What I mean is,' she continues, 'if he's doing it, there must be others targeting kids and vulnerable people who rely on the internet as their main source of interaction.'

'More people like me . . .' I say, realizing that's probably what had drawn him to me in the first place — the fact that I'm deeply vulnerable. Desperate. A fuck-up. No, let's rephrase that. The fact that, until very recently, I was a fuck-up. Now . . . now I'm more of a work-in-progress.

'Well, yes,' says Hugh. 'I mean, what's to stop him from doing it again?'

'Nothing,' I say. 'But even if I do write about this, he might do it again anyway.'

'You haven't got any control over what he does, but you have got complete control of how you respond to him.'

I sit back and think about this. By outing me as the blogger behind The Beginner's Guide to Loneliness, he's forced me to take ownership and go public with my most intimate thoughts. I mean, they were already out there, but their connection to me wasn't. It should have been my choice, and he's taken that away from me.

'You're right!' I say. 'I need to respond publicly, and it has to be on my blog.'

'Perfect idea,' says Hugh enthusiastically. 'I mean, after all the extra exposure from Nathan's piece, your readership is bound to be even higher than usual now. May as well take what he's caused and use it to get your own back!'

I hadn't even thought about what this drama might have done to the site itself. Sure, most of the new readers will probably be visiting out of morbid curiosity, hoping to find out more about this man-addicted slut-bag that Nathan's presented, but then, surely, that makes them the perfect audience to reach out to with my reply.

* * *

Getting back to my flat is a bit of an eye-opener. Of course, I've invited Sue and Hugh to stay. It's not going to be the most comfortable visit — Sue's going to have to share my double bed and Hugh will take the sofa — but it's not that that's bothering me. It's the fact that this place could be anyone's. It's an anonymous, colourless space with absolutely no personality or warmth. I can't even compare it to a hotel room, because at least hotels attempt to make you feel comfortable.

I dump my bag in the corner of the living room and turn to see both Hugh and Sue looking around with something close to dismay on both their faces.

'I'll completely understand if you'd prefer to stay in a hotel,' I say quickly. 'I know it's a bit — '

'No, it's great!' says Sue, her voice too bright.

'Yeah. We want to be with you, Tori!' says Hugh.

'Well . . . thanks.' I say.

'I like what you've done with the place,' he says.

I snort. I can't help it.

Hugh's lips are twitching, and Sue clearly doesn't know whether she should join in or keep up the polite facade.

'It's just a bit . . . '

'Bare?' I say.

'No . . . just . . . I'd never know you were the person living here. You've got so much energy and personality; you're so full of ideas and creativity and this place is . . . '

'Crap,' I finish for her.

'I didn't say that!' she says, looking worried.

'No, but I did. Thing is, it's taken this break for me to be able to see it properly. Seems like I really did keep myself for 'online only',' I sigh.

'But look how much has happened in such a short time. Just shows how fast things can change!' says Hugh.

I think he's trying to be encouraging, but I want to point out that having my privacy violated online, followed by Bay disappearing on me, weren't quite the changes I'd been hoping for. I keep my mouth shut. The flat is depressing enough, without me adding to it.

'Look, I know it's a bit shit. You guys sure you're still up for staying here?'

Both of them nod.

'Okay.' I take a deep breath and look around at the familiar bare walls, plain carpet and minimal furniture. 'I can't believe I was so worried about not scraping the rent together. Let's face it, not being able to stay in this place isn't exactly a big deal, is it?!'

'You thinking of maybe moving after your adventure?' asks Hugh.

'Not maybe. Definitely. I can write from anywhere, and this place doesn't fit the new me. The *real* me.'

* * *

The rest of the morning disappears in a haze as we struggle to combat the after-effects of our early morning dash from Wales. After an emergency supplies run to the local Tesco Express, we nurse ourselves with coffee and bacon sandwiches.

The question of what exactly I'm going to do about Bay, now that we've travelled across the country for me to see him, is looming large. Although neither of the other two have mentioned it, I know they're waiting for me to bring it up.

I really should get on and call that number on Bay's website, but there's something holding me back.

Our level of gossip has died right down with the wave of sleepiness that engulfs us after our lunch. I'm slumped in the armchair and the other two are on the sofa. Sue has slipped her shoes off and is sitting with her feet cosily tucked up under her bum. Hugh has his arms behind his head, legs outstretched in front of him and his eyes are almost closed.

'Right!' I say, practically leaping to my feet.

The other two jump.

'Sorry, sorry!' I laugh.

''Right' what?' asks Hugh, watching as I start to pace the room. Exactly two and a half strides one way. Turn. Two point five strides the other.

'I know what I need to do,' I say triumphantly.

'Call Bay?' asks Sue.

'Nope. I really want to, but first, I need to write that blog post.'

'You do? First?' asks Hugh surprised.

'Yep. Close that particular chapter of crap and draw a line under it. Whatever happens next with Bay, I don't want it to have anything to do with the whole Nathan Jones mess.'

'And if it doesn't work out between you?'

'Then it was something really lovely while it lasted, and I still don't want it to get mixed up in my head with Nathan's shite.'

'Great. Okay, so . . . ' Hugh's at a loss. He's great when there's something practical to help with, but I can see he's wondering what to do until he's given his next superman mission.

'Look . . . this is going to be incredibly boring for you two while I obsess over getting every word right,' I say. What I really want to ask is if they'd mind buggering off and doing a spot of sightseeing for a couple of hours. That way, I'd know my guests were enjoying themselves while I'd get the peace and quiet I need to get the job done.

'Ooh . . . do you mean we can go sightseeing without looking like we're being really rude?' Sue grins. It seems she's a mind-reader.

'If you'd like to? Or just chill out, or — '

'I'd like to go sightseeing!' says Hugh, suddenly looking wide awake. 'Of course, it won't be the same without you, but maybe we'll get to hang out together when you're done, Tori?'

'Sounds like a plan,' I grin at them, loving how excited they are.

'EEEK! This is amazing! Unexpected me-time and the whole London experience too?' Sue is on her feet, hopping up and down while yanking clothes out of her bag. 'Tori, can I use your bathroom to get ready?' she asks.

'Of course!'

While Sue's changing, I dig out a Tube map for Hugh and arrange to meet up with them this evening at the Italian restaurant just around the corner.

The minute the door closes behind them, I rush through to my tiny office and fire up my laptop. I log into my blog and let out a gasp. Hugh was right. The number of page hits since Nathan's article went live has been insane. I feel a little bit sick all of a sudden. All those people reading what I've written. All those people knowing so much about me . . .

Use it. That's all I can do. Use this platform to tell them what really happened. And anyway, there's nothing on here I should be ashamed of. There's some incredibly tough stuff, things I wish I'd never had to deal with. But this isn't an ideal world, and these things *did* happen to me. And if they happened to me, I'm certain they've happened to other people too.

There are hundreds of comments waiting for approval, but, for now, I need to get straight to the task in hand.

Dear Readers.

A big hello to all you lovely regulars, and welcome to all the new faces too.

As I'm sure most of you already know, I've recently been on a retreat to The Farm in west Wales. I'll be back next week to share more about the incredible, life-changing work they do there. But, rather a lot has happened while I've been away and, right now, that's what I need to talk to you about.

As you will have seen, the big secret is out and I am no longer able to remain anonymous. My name is Tori Williamson, I am 33 years old and currently live in London. If you don't know what on earth I'm talking about and why I've just so casually revealed my closely guarded secret, you need to have a read of this article by Nathan Jones before we go any further. Go on . . . follow the link . . . I'll wait.

I paste in the link to Nathan's piece and take a deep breath. Here goes.

> The first thing you need to know about Nathan Jones is that we have been friends online for two years. The second thing you need to know is that I didn't know him as Nathan. I knew him as a thirty-one-year-old female called Nathalie. Nathalie was one of my best friends, and was, in fact, the one who encouraged me to start up this blog in the first place. Unfortunately, Nathalie was completely fictional — an alias used by Nathan Jones to gain my trust and friendship.

By the time I've finished writing about the chatroom, 'Nathalie' encouraging me to go on the retreat, 'Than' befriending me and trying to initiate a physical relationship, and then Nathan sharing my identity along with my innermost secrets with the world, I'm shaking. But I've come this far, and I've got one more thing to say about him.

> The questions I keep asking myself, over and over again, are: why did he target me in the first place? Why, after two years, did this catfish finally decide to meet me? And what was he hoping to achieve? I guess I'll never know the answers. The

one thing I do know for sure is that a lot of his motivation for this final betrayal seems to have been revenge. What for? For rejecting him. For saying no. And for being romantically interested in someone else.

Nathan Jones tried to paint me as a deranged man-eater. When I got to The Farm, I was incredibly lonely — as my faithful readers will already know, and as you will have gathered from the title of this blog. With all his knowledge of me gathered over a long 'friendship', it didn't take much for Nathan to create a closeness between us. But at the same time I was learning how to make friends and to value the amazing people I was surrounded by. I was also opening my heart up for the first time in several years.

The lead photograph shows me with a fellow participant, my friend Bay. This is not an image capturing a fling between an impressionable man-eater (me) and an opportunistic retreater (Bay) as Nathan Jones would have you believe. It's a photograph that shows a joyful moment shared between friends — the moment when a little piece of me fell back into place, and I started to see possibilities all around.

I broke The Farm rules by accessing the internet while I was there. I logged into a chatroom I share with my three best friends and told them about this amazing moment. I also shared the fact that 'Than's' advances were unwelcome.

> 'Than' left The Farm soon afterwards, but not before his behaviour towards me became aggressive and erratic, and he used my triggers to expose my severe potamophobia to the whole group.
>
> Thankfully, he neglected to sign out of the chatroom while using the borrowed device, and this is how we discovered the depth of his deception.

There. Done. I take a deep breath and get on with the rest of the article, drawing attention to the dangers of catfishing and just how dark the outcomes to this kind of story can be.

When I'm finished, I read it back through several times. There's still something missing. I head out into my tiny kitchen to make a cup of tea, but before I get as far as pouring the water on the teabag, I've got it. I head back to my computer and type one final bit.

> This has been a truly frightening experience in many ways, and I lost one of my best friends when I discovered that 'Nathalie' doesn't really exist. But I find that I am grateful that you now know who's behind these words and this blog. Perhaps I was wrong to remain anonymous for so long. This is my journey, and I look forward to continuing to share it with you.
>
> Big love,
> Tori
> x

I stand up and stare at the screen for a moment. 'Fuck you, Nathan!' I say, sticking two fingers up at the screen. I reach over and click POST.

36

Real, Not Perfect

'The most powerful gift you can give yourself is acceptance. It's time to accept all of your facets — the dark as well as the light; your past as well as your dreams for the future. Accept the real version of yourself and forget about the pointless struggle for perfection.'

©TheBeginnersGuideToLoneliness.com

My taxi swings to an abrupt halt in front of a glass-fronted building with a carved wooden 'Anderson, Simpson and Green' sign adorning the front.

Okay, so this isn't a small, boutique kind of a company, then? Holy crap, this place is huge!

I pull open the vast slab of a door and find myself in the reception area, suddenly very aware of my scruffy clothes in the polished surroundings. Staring upwards, my mouth falls open and I come to a complete standstill.

The space is light and airy with the highest ceiling I've ever seen. The far wall appears to be made of living plants, the greens of which create a double-room-height pattern of a giant leaf. As I move closer, I notice that the delicate yellow and orange highlights are made up of tiny flowers, giving the appearance that it's being touched by late evening sunshine.

'Can I help you?'

The words cut across my awestruck staring, and

I look around. There's a girl smiling at me from behind a curved, wooden desk. It looks like the thing has grown straight up out of the floor and is a living, breathing part of the building.

'Oh, hi,' I say, returning her smile quickly. 'Sorry about that, it's just . . . '

'I know, right?' the girl laughs. 'Don't worry, it happens all the time. Gorgeous, isn't it?'

'Uh huh!' I nod, looking back at the living wall.

'This place was their first work as a team, and it's the best bit of advertising they could have ever given their new company, if you ask me!' she laughs.

I nod. And swallow. Okay, so that's the small talk done — now how am I going to approach this?

'Is Bay here?' I blurt.

There we go, that's one way. Desperate and just a little bit scary . . .

On second thought, I should probably have asked for Bailey.

'I'm guessing this is a social call rather than business?' the girl asks politely.

'Why?' I ask sharply. Has Bay told this girl to watch out for me? Maybe she's got a mugshot behind that vast desk somewhere and is, even now, gearing up to warn him to get into hiding.

'The nickname!' she smiles. 'Always a dead giveaway.'

'Oh. Oh, of course.' I shift my weight awkwardly. I'm feeling really out of place. Maybe I shouldn't have come.

'Is Mr Anderson expecting you, Miss . . . ?'

'Tori, my name's Tori Williamson. No, he isn't. I was just hoping to catch him.'

'He's not here at the moment; he's on site.'

I nod, unsure what to say next. Maybe there really has been some kind of an emergency after all. *Note to self: entire world does not revolve around you, Tori!*

'He shouldn't be too long; he's due to pop back for some paperwork. Would you like to wait?'

'Oh . . . okay. If that's all right?'

'Of course! I'm Mel by the way. If you need anything, just let me know.'

* * *

Half an hour later, I've skim-read every single brochure in the plush reception area, and I feel like I've learned about this whole other side of Bay. The side of him that is Bailey. Bailey couldn't be any further from the easy-going, warm guy I thought I'd come to know. This Bailey bloke is an award-winning landscape gardener who part-owns this globally renowned company. Together, he, Simpson and Green have become the city's leaders in ecologically sound landscaping and design for the super-rich.

I swallow down something that feels strangely like disappointment. This is definitely not the man I thought I knew. This is someone who's all about the money. He's a stranger and, what's worse, he's lied to me about who he is. Just like Nathan did.

Coming to a decision, I get to my feet, brush down my crumpled trousers and push my hair away from my face. What am I doing here, chasing after some guy who fed me a lie and then did a runner? I need to go home. I need to go and find my friends.

'Hi, Mel? I think I'm going to head off. I'll catch up with Bay later,' I fib.

'Oh, okay,' she says, looking worried. 'I've just heard

from him. He should be here in about ten minutes. I told him you were waiting.'

'He's coming? Now?' My voice comes out a bit faint.

'He was going to fit in another meeting first, but as soon as he heard you were here, he cancelled it. I'm really sorry, you should have said that it was so important! I would have called him straight away.' She wrings her hands nervously, evidently used to dealing with clients on a short fuse.

'Don't worry,' I say. 'Like I said, he wasn't even expecting me!'

'So you'll stay?' she asks, and I can hear the anxiety in her voice.

'Of course,' I smile at her, though inside I'm feeling anything but cheerful. But I may as well get this over and done with now, then I can crawl back to the others and lick my wounds.

'Come with me. He said for you to wait in his office until he arrives.'

* * *

I follow Mel down a hallway where the light seems to be funnelled in through tubes set in the high ceiling. The latticework of bare, warm wood that snakes over my head makes it feel like I'm walking under an avenue of vast trees.

'Here we are,' says Mel, pushing open a door to our left.

The room beyond is arched, the ceiling running from a high point just off centre all the way down to the floor on both sides. There's something about this beautiful office that makes me feel like I'm back in the yurt. I smile for a moment as I allow myself to imagine that the Bay I know is real, that my version of him is a part of this high-flier.

Natural light floods in through a huge window at the far end of the room and there are plants everywhere. In among the trailing leaves I spot a group of photographs, and I make my way over to look at them.

There he is: Bay at The Farm, just outside the yurt; Bay chopping wood; Dennis on his bed; Dennis trying to lick the camera.

I suck in a sharp breath: Bay — with his arm around a woman. A tall, immaculately beautiful woman.

'Have you been to The Farm?'

I jump. I'd forgotten about Mel still standing behind me. I nod.

'Oh, wow. I really want to go. Mr Anderson said he'll make sure that I can attend the course next year. I'm so excited. It's such an amazing opportunity . . . Hey, are you okay? You've gone very pale!'

'Mel . . . who's this?' I ask, gesturing to the woman in the photograph.

Mel comes to join me in front of the pictures.

'Oh, that's Imogene. Don't you know her?'

'No. I've only just met Bay. At The Farm . . . '

'Cool! So no, you wouldn't have met her, then. She never goes down there with him. Imogene is Bay's wife.'

* * *

I stare at Mel.

'I'll just go and get you a glass of water. Maybe you're a bit hot . . . ' Mel hurries to the door and throws a worried look back at me.

'Tell Bay I'm leaving,' I say, rubbing at my eyes.

'Tell him yourself!' comes a gruff reply.

My head snaps up and I see Bay closing the door behind him as Mel disappears on the other side.

No, not Bay. This is Bailey.

I barely recognize him in his smart chinos, white shirt and expensive-looking shoes. His hair has been swept back and his scruffy stubble is gone. It's only the gleam of concern in his eyes that marks him as the same man I shared the yurt with.

Before I can say anything, there's a scuffing at my feet and a large, panting head plops onto my lap. Dennis is staring up at me, his grin tempting me to smile back, and his manically wagging tail reassuring me that there's someone in this room who's happy to see me. I ruffle his ears. I want to cry.

'Tori, how are you here?' says Bay, still standing by the door. '*Why* are you here?'

'You're *married*?' I ask, completely ignoring his questions.

'No, I'm not,' he replies.

'Come on!' I growl, causing Dennis to whip his head out of my lap. He slinks back to Bay's side. 'That's the most pointless lie in the history of mankind.'

'I'm not lying. I'm not married.'

'Sure. Who's this, then?' I snap, standing up and slapping the photograph of the happy couple. 'Your fucking herbalist?!'

Bay winces. 'No. That was my wife. Now my ex-wife. I wanted to tell you but — '

'How come Mel said she's your wife, Bay?' I interrupt, a dogged determination coming over me. For once, won't someone just tell me the damned truth? 'I don't get it. You lie about this place. You lie about your *wife*?'

'I didn't lie, Tori. Mel, as lovely as she is, is an employee. I have my reasons for being careful how much I share about myself — '

'Oh, *reasons*? Wow. Great speech,' I fume. I'm so angry, I've started to revert to toddler mode. I need to leave. 'Excuse me,' I snap, trying to push past him to get to the door.

'Tori, what the hell? Where's the Tori I know disappeared to?'

'That's a bit bloody rich coming from the award-winning, married businessman,' I say.

'I'm not married. The divorce has been finalized. And this place? This place is the reason I got divorced. It's already wrecked things for me once, I didn't want it to happen a second time.'

I take a step back, and all of the fight feels like it's draining out of me. 'I don't get it. I just can't believe you didn't tell me.'

'Look, it's simple. Four years ago, I married a woman I loved. She just happened to be way more interested in my career than in me. It was all about the money. She was always pushing me to take on more projects here — things that didn't gel with our vision — just because they'd pay well. Every single time I did something for love rather than money, she'd throw a hissy fit, telling me that I was wasting my training, that I was endangering our future, the future of our children — '

'You have *children*?' I gasp.

'No, our unborn children. Unthought-of children. Anyway, she didn't want me to be happy, she just wanted me to be rich.'

'But why didn't you tell me? I'm not her.'

'I know that. But you know what it's like. If you're bitten once, you're slower to trust again.'

My thoughts fly straight to Markus, and then to Than. And how I've just behaved with Bay. He might have a point.

'I'm sorry, Tori,' he sighs.

'But you're not the man I've spent the last few weeks with. You're Bailey Anderson,' I say, gesturing from his tidy hair to his shiny shoes.

'Yes, I am . . . I'm also the person you got to know at The Farm. You can't just remove one part of me. I'm a mixture of all of the above and more!'

'But . . . you disappeared without even talking to me!'

'No offence, Tori, but you were kind of busy at the time. You'd disappeared off to sort things out with Doreen when Ted came to tell me that I'd had a phone call. I had no idea where you'd headed off to, nor how long you'd be. Than had landed all this crap on your plate with no warning, and I wanted to be there for you — to help you work through it all. But I was needed here urgently. Greg, one of my partners, fell and broke his leg. He hit his head too. Luckily nothing too serious, but he has concussion. He's right in the middle of a huge partnership — one of the show gardens at the Chelsea Flower Show. The whole firm's reputation is at stake, so I had to step in the minute I could. I left you a note — '

'Bullshit!' I say.

'I did. In the yurt. On your pillow. Didn't you get it?'

I shake my head, not sure whether to believe this or not.

'No wonder you're pissed off . . . you thought I just left without saying anything?'

I nod. If there really is a note, does it change anything? I don't know. Right now, I just don't know.

'Tori, you know me. I would never — '

'But I don't know you, do I?' I say, looking panicked.

We're interrupted by the sound of his phone ringing. We stare at each other, and I wonder if he's just going to ignore it.

'That's you . . . ' he says with a small smile.

Shit. Of course it is. I've got so used to not having a phone on me, I didn't even think about the bloody thing in my pocket. I rummage around, pull it out and, with an apologetic
look at Bay, answer it.

'Tori! You HAVE to check your emails.'

'Rowan?'

'Check. Your. Emails.'

'Can I call you back in about five minutes? I'm just finishing doing something.'

'Fine — say hi to Bay for me?'

'How do you know . . . ?'

'I'm assuming that's who you're finishing doing,' she snorts, and then rings off.

'Rowan says hi,' I say faintly.

Bay smiles. 'Look — '

'I can't do this, Bay,' I interrupt. 'Not now. I need to go. I need to think. I'm sorry. I'll call you?'

Bay looks surprised, but I don't give him the chance to answer. I push past him, and with a quick look back at Dennis, I leave his beautiful office behind me as fast as I can.

37

Discover Your Superpower

'We've all got a superpower — a gift that we can give to the world. When we're facing loneliness, grief and trauma, it becomes impossible for us to use our superpower, because each day simply becomes about surviving.

'As you begin to heal, start looking for your superpower. It will be there — and the more you use it to help others, the swifter your healing will be.'

©TheBeginnersGuideToLoneliness.com

I find a little park about two streets away from Bay's office and hurry through the wrought-iron gates. I'm on the hunt for a park bench; somewhere quiet to call Rowan back. I need her to do something for me.

Spotting a path, I follow it and end up in a small but perfectly formed rose garden. I sink gratefully onto a wooden bench and gaze around me for a few seconds, trying to catch my breath. I don't know what to think about everything that just happened with Bay. I almost don't want to think about it all, but really, what did I learn that's so terrible? If I'm honest, the thing that's bothering me most is the ex-wife and the fact that he hadn't told me about her. But should I really hold that against him? There are plenty of things I haven't told him about yet.

Well, there's one thing I do need to know. I pull out

my phone and redial Rowan's number.

'Did you see it?!' she squeals by way of greeting.

'See what?'

'The email?! Catch up!'

'Oh. No . . . '

'Seriously, Tori!'

'Wait, Rowan. There's something I've got to ask you first, something important . . . a favour.'

'Another one?' she whines. 'You do know the last favour I did for you got me grounded, right?'

'What?'

'Yep. Getting your stuff out of the safe and hiding the fact that you were doing a runner. As I predicted, Dad did his nut.'

'Oh no, Rowan, I'm so sorry. How long for?'

'Ah, don't worry about it. Neither him nor Mum actually know what grounding is supposed to mean. I think they've already forgotten about it,' she laughs. 'Anyway, I blamed as much of it as I could on Sue and Hugh. Tell them it's all their fault for me, will you?!'

I laugh. 'It'll have to wait till we meet up for dinner later. They're off sightseeing.'

'Oh. You guys going anywhere special?' she asks, lightly.

'Nah, just the little restaurant around the corner from my f at.'

There's a brief pause.

'So, what's this new favour, then?' asks Rowan.

'It's about Bay . . . '

'Of course it is,' she says sarcastically.

I pick at the flaking paint on the arm of the bench. 'Look, he said he left a letter for me on my pillow in the yurt before he left, but I never got it.'

'And . . . '

'And . . . could you go and see if you can find it for me?'

'On your pillow?'

'Well obviously it won't be there now. The three of us stayed in there last night, didn't we? But maybe it blew off onto the floor or something?'

'Okay, okay. I can't right now. I'm watching the baby while Mum and Dad have a rest, but I'll text you later when I've looked?'

'You're my hero,' I say thankfully.

'I know.'

It's not ideal. I'm not going to be able to focus on anything until I know for sure.

'Right . . . about this email?' I say. 'Actually, how do you know what emails I'm getting? You've not hacked me or something, have you?' I laugh a little nervously. Somehow, I wouldn't put it past her.

'Course not,' she says, sounding offended. 'I answered the house phone earlier and it was someone asking for you.'

'Me?'

'Yeah, there have been quite a few since that knob told everyone who you are. Mostly journalists asking for interviews. Mum and Dad have been fielding them and just writing the contacts down so they can give them to you.'

'Oh,' I say, my heart skipping in fear.

'Look, I didn't tell them about this one. I thought it might be too important to wait till you got back.'

'Right . . . '

'It was this woman from a publisher. She said she'd emailed you via your blog, but she was worried you wouldn't pick it up because you'd be snowed under, so she was calling us on the off-chance she could speak to you directly.'

'Someone from a publisher?'

'Yeah. When I said you weren't available, she asked if I could make sure that you knew she was trying to reach you, and she hoped to talk to you soon. Look, can't you just check your emails yourself and read what she's got to say?'

'I'm not anywhere near my computer . . .'

'You stayed with us for too long . . . your brain is fried. Let me put this in words you might understand: Turn. On. Your. Bloody. Mobile. Data. Her name's Sarah . . . erm, hang on . . . Sarah Mack.'

And with that, Rowan hangs up.

I shake my head and can't help but smile as I faff around with my phone and open my emails.

It takes me ages to find the one she's talking about. There are hundreds of new messages. I cringe as I scroll through dozens, all with subjects along the lines of 'interview request'. Then I spot it. Sarah Mack. The subject line reads 'The Beginner's Guide to Loneliness: Book Proposal.'

Holy sainted granny pants.

Dear Tori,

I've had the pleasure, following the recent publicity, of discovering your blog The Beginner's Guide to Loneliness. Your writing is nothing short of exquisite, fresh and honest. Having binge-read all of your posts, I had to get in touch.

I am the Commissioning Editor for Farthing, a publishing imprint focusing on mental health and wellness titles. I would love to discuss the opportunity of turning your blog into a book.

Give me a call when you get back to London, and if it's something that you might be interested in, we can arrange a meeting to discuss the idea further.

Please can I also just take this opportunity to congratulate you on your article this morning in response to Nathan Jones. I feel that you have touched on a topic that needs to be under the spotlight, and I'm so sorry to hear that you have been the victim of this behaviour. I do hope you are receiving the support you need.

I look forward to hearing from you soon,

Kind regards,

Sarah Mack,

Commissioning Editor, Farthing Press

Farthing Press? They're huge! I read the email through a couple more times, let out an excited squeal, then quickly shoot a text to Rowan containing just two words: 'Holy. Shit.'

I take a deep breath, reopen the email and call the number in the signature strip.

* * *

'Sorry I'm late!' I gasp, plopping down into my chair opposite the other two.

Hugh grins at me and Sue waves a chunk of focaccia dipped in copious amounts of oil and balsamic vinegar at me.

'S'okay!' she says with her mouth full. 'We may have started without you though!'

'Wine?' asks Hugh, waggling a bottle of red at me.

I nod enthusiastically as I struggle out of my coat

and tuck my bag under my chair so that no one goes arse over tit — lesson learned from bitter, mortifying experience.

Hugh pushes a large glass towards me and I take a grateful sip.

'So, what's up?' asks Sue. 'You look completely freaked! Is it the thought of having to face Bay tomorrow?'

I shake my head. Where to start . . .

'Well, I'm going to begin the evening with a toast now that we're all here,' says Hugh, unwittingly coming to my rescue. 'To old friends.'

Sue and I clink our glasses with his.

'And to your flippin' fantastic blog post,' says Sue, raising her glass again.

'How on earth have you already seen that?' I say.

'Oh come on,' says Hugh, 'she gave you all of half an hour after we left the f at and then kept refreshing your site on her phone until you posted.'

'You're kidding me?' I laugh. 'You were meant to be out enjoying yourselves and seeing the sights!'

'We were. The sights were just interrupted every five minutes for a quick blog check!' says Sue. 'I couldn't relax till I knew you'd finished. Must have been really hard.'

I nod. 'Not the easiest thing I've ever written, but definitely cathartic.' I smile to myself as the image of sticking two fingers up at my computer pops into my head.

'But where've you been since? I mean, I know you probably needed a bit of time to recover and everything, but that was hours ago. I was convinced you'd give us a call and come and join us, but you didn't . . . We were about to send out a search party,' she says.

'It's been a busy day. And I have some news.'

'Actually, we've got a bit of news for you too,' says Hugh, trying to flag down a waiter at the same time.

I catch Sue shooting a worried look at him. 'What? It can't be that bad,' I say, thinking of everything we've dealt with over the past twenty-four hours.

'Not bad for us, but definitely bad for Nathan,' Hugh mutters.

At the mention of his name, I stiffen.

'Turns out he's married,' says Sue.

Married? Why is everyone suddenly *married*? That is the very last thing I was expecting.

'How do you know?'

'A news site has already picked up on your post and done a bit of digging of their own.'

'Oh God, his poor wife!'

I don't know how I feel about this. Despite my little outburst in private, I didn't post my response for revenge. I posted it to warn other people of the dangers of this kind of behaviour, and in doing so I've unwittingly managed to warn his own wife.

'It's not for you to worry about, Tori,' says Hugh quietly.

I nod. This isn't happening to a friend. This is happening to a stranger who wormed his way into my life and then proceeded to do his best to ruin it. Nathan needs help, and somewhere deep down — right now, it's still *very* deep — I hope he finds it.

'Tell us your news, Tori!' says Sue excitedly.

'First, let's order,' I say, as a waiter appears at Hugh's elbow.

* * *

'Come on then, spill,' says Hugh as the waiter finally disappears with a rather full pad.

'Okay, so, big news, or *bigger* news first?' I ask.

'Is any of it to do with Bay?' asks Sue. 'Because that's the news I want first.'

'Okay. You've opted for 'big' news first. I've already seen him. I went to his office earlier.'

'And?' Hugh prompts impatiently.

'And discovered that he's married.'

'*WHAT!?*' explodes Hugh, making Sue and I jump.

'Okay . . . I should have said '*was* married'.'

'Didn't you know?' asks Sue.

'No. I didn't. And it was a shitty surprise. But, in fairness, I think he was going to tell me — we just hadn't quite got to that bit yet.'

'Ah. Awkward,' says Hugh sympathetically.

'Yep,' I agree.

'What about abandoning you without saying anything?' he asks.

'He said he left me a letter.'

'Really?'

'Yep. Said he left it on my pillow before he went.'

'But . . . you didn't get it?'

'Nope. I called Rowan and asked her if she'd go and hunt for it for me.'

'A letter . . . how romantic,' Sue sighs.

'If that is the case, surely it'll change things a bit?' asks Hugh.

'Hmm,' I say sceptically, 'rather depends on what it says.'

'So did you hear back from Rowan yet?' Sue prompts excitedly.

I shake my head. 'Last I heard she was baby wrangling, so goodness knows when she'll get the chance to go and look. We didn't spot anything, so there's no guarantees she'll find it, even if it is there!'

'But what about Bay? This afternoon?' prompts Hugh.

'Yeah, did you kiss and make up?' says Sue.

'Hardly.' I feel cold dread slide into my stomach. *What if we never do . . . ?*

'Why, what happened?'

'I just . . . I needed some time to think about things. As soon as I saw him, I realized that I needed to digest the fact that there's this whole side to him that he didn't tell me about. The business. The ex-wife. He's not the person I thought he was.'

'So when are you seeing him again?' asks Sue.

'I'm not. I just, well, I just . . . kind of left. Rowan called and I used that as an excuse to get the hell out of there.'

'Poor you, that sounds horrible.'

'It was.' I pick up a piece of bread and start to tear it into tiny chunks. 'In my head I think I had some kind of happy ever after planned out where it would all turn out to be a huge misunderstanding, and we'd fall into each other's arms. Instead it turns out that we're just two adults with a bunch of baggage, wondering if we can trust each other.'

There's silence around the table. The other two are staring at me like I'm the most depressing thing they've ever seen. I give myself a little shake, sweep the bread chunks into my hand and tip them onto a side plate.

'Anyway,' I say, 'enough of the big news. Who wants to hear the *bigger* news?!' I can't help but let a little smile creep onto my face.

'This better be happy news. You've nearly put me

off my food,' says Hugh, sitting back in his seat.

'Oh, this is good news. Actually, this is *amazing* news.'

'Out with it then.'

'Well, I told you Rowan called?'

'Uh huh?'

'A publisher's interested in turning my blog into a book!' I blurt, jumping straight to the end of my story.

'Okay, WHAT?!' Sue is frozen, glass halfway to her lips.

'Um . . .' says Hugh, 'rewind please.'

'Well,' I say, 'turns out Nathan's article has massively upped the visitors to my blog. Most of them are complete rubberneckers and just there to read about yours-truly-the-fuck-up. But, some of those new readers, well, it looks like they liked what they read.'

'Of course they did, your blog is amazing!' says Sue loyally.

'Well, one of my new visitors was Sarah Mack, Commissioning Editor at Farthing Press. She emailed me to invite me to a meeting. Then, just to make sure she reached me, she called The Farm. That's what Rowan was calling about. Can you believe it?!'

'And you just went? Just like that?!' asked Hugh, eyes wide.

'Well, it was just a coffee so we could meet — the real meeting will be in a couple of weeks — but I thought I may as well, as I had a free afternoon,' I grin.

'Oh my God!' Sue is threatening to go ultrasonic now, and I look around me, slightly embarrassed.

'Shhh! I'm meant to keep it quiet until everything's signed and sealed!' I laugh.

'Sorry . . . sorry. But WOW, Tori!'

'I can't believe it,' I say, and a wave of happiness floods through me. This is happening. 'Telling you two makes it feel real, somehow!'

'Well, that's you sorted, then, isn't it?!' says Hugh. 'Just think, you were busy melting down about work and money, and now you're going to be a published author!'

'Yeah, hopefully, and I guess I've got Nat — I mean *Nathan* — to thank for it. If he hadn't told the world who I was, Sarah might never have discovered my blog.' I'm not sure how I feel about this, to be honest. I don't particularly want to owe him anything.

'No,' says Sue, and I'm surprised at how determined she sounds. 'You only have yourself to thank. You put in all those hours of work. Thousands of people already loved your posts, so it was only a matter of time before a publisher saw your potential.'

'Sue's right. And if they do give you a book deal, you'll be able to put the money towards a new place,' says Hugh.

I grin at him as another wave of excitement washes through me.

'What sort of thing do you fancy? Flat? House? Romantic cottage?' asks Sue. I swear she's ready to pull up PrimeLocation as we eat and start searching for my new home straight away.

'I don't know yet,' I say honestly. 'But I'm finally ready to give myself the permission to find out.'

38

Integration and Return

> 'There will come a moment when you realize that you are no longer 'struggling' with loneliness. It might still be there on occasion, but when you've put in the work to accept yourself for the perfectly imperfect person you are, those occasions will no longer feel so threatening. You will always be in the company of one of your best friends – you.'
>
> ©TheBeginnersGuideToLoneliness.com

By the time I've filled them in on all the gossip from my unexpected meeting, we've worked our way through two bottles of wine, three courses each and are just settling down to coffees. I'm starting to flag. I'm bloody exhausted. I'm just considering talking the other two into heading back to the flat for an early night when my phone starts to ring. I flip it over and see Rowan's name f ashing up.

'Hey, Rowan!' I say, answering it before the ringing manages to bug the entire room. I hate answering phones in public places. Maybe I should go outside . . .

'Tori, it's Doreen.'

It's so wonderful to hear my friend's voice, but I instantly start to panic.

'What's happened?' I ask sharply. Sue and Hugh stop gossiping and look at me with concerned expressions.

'Nice to speak to you too!' laughs Doreen.

'Sorry, sorry . . . it's just — '

'I know, you were expecting Rowan. Everything's fine. Well, other than the fact that Rowan's grounded!' She laughs again.

'I know, she told me earlier,' I say faintly.

'Yes, well. That was before Ted went online to read your post and decided to look up 'how to ground a teenager' while he was at it.'

'Uh-oh!'

'Exactly. He confiscated her phone and gave it to me for safe-keeping, just in case you tried to make contact.'

'Wait, hang on . . . Ted gave you a phone? Is the world coming to an end?'

'No, we're just in the re-integration week, and he and Lizzie have decided that my friendship with you is an important part of mine!' she says. 'Plus, I don't think they liked the idea of it disturbing the baby.'

'Well, at least this explains why Rowan was taking so long to call me back,' I say.

'Yup. She managed to let Geoff know about your little mission earlier while she was helping him lay the table. Hope you don't mind, but we went and had a look for you instead.'

'Course I don't mind!' I say. 'Find anything?'

'Yes. A little white envelope with your name on it. Must have blown off your bed. It was mostly wedged under one of the rugs.'

So Bay was telling the truth. He didn't just disappear on me.

'What does it say?' I breathe.

'I don't know,' she says. 'We didn't want to open it without speaking to you first.'

Sue and Hugh are now riveted, like if they concentrate hard enough, they'll be able to catch both sides of the conversation. I smile at them and point to the door. Sue looks gutted, but Hugh nods.

'Give me two secs, Doreen. I'm just going to head outside.'

I stand on slightly wobbly legs. I think it's the nerves rather than the glasses of wine that hit me and make me stagger. I make my way towards the front of the restaurant and head out into the cool evening air.

'You still there?' I say at a more normal volume as I wander down the street away from the buzz of the restaurant.

'Yep! You okay?'

'Yeah. Just had to get out of the restaurant for a second. I've abandoned Hugh and Sue over coffee,' I say.

'So, do you want me to read it to you?' asks Doreen.

'If you don't mind?' I say. Frankly I think that's quite restrained considering I want to reach through the phone somehow and rip the thing out of her hands.

I hold my breath while I hear paper tearing and much crinkling.

'Okay . . . ' And she starts to read.

Dear Tori,

The outside world has come and bitten us both at the same time. I haven't told you much about my work yet, but I own a landscape and design company with two friends. We work with all sorts of insane people. I've just received a call to tell me that my partner Greg has been in an accident. He's hit his head and broken his leg. I don't know how bad he is yet, but I've got to head straight to London to take over a project for him. I don't want to rush off, but he's working on a garden at the Chelsea Flower Show and the deadline is nuts. I really want to see you before I go, but I've got no idea where you've gone or how long you're going to be.

Ted just showed me Than's article. I hope you're okay. I know everyone will look after you and I'll be back as soon as I can. I really, really want to be back before the course finishes.

There's so much for us to talk about and to share, and I can't wait for all of it. Last night was amazing. I'm a slow, cautious kind of person when it comes to my heart, and I'll tell you all about that when we see each other next. But for now, know that you're a very special person. I love spending time with you and I can't wait till I see you again.

Just remember how strong you are.

Bay

x

Doreen goes quiet, and I swear I can hear her sniffing.

I can't bring myself to say anything. There. That's the Bay I know. On that piece of paper that my friend is busy crying all over. And the best thing is, on that piece of paper is the proof that he wasn't keeping any kind of secret from me. There were no lies either. We just hadn't got round to that bit of the conversation yet.

'You still there?' comes Geoff's voice down the phone.

'I'm here!' I say, smiling to hear his voice. 'Is Doreen okay?'

'Ah she's fine, great big softy. But you could have been waiting for an age for her to compose herself!' he laughs. 'You okay, love?'

'Okay? Very okay. I've got loads to tell you both when I see you,' I say, making the snap decision that I want to share my news in person when I get back to The Farm. Because all of a sudden, I know that's where I need to go next.

'You're coming back? That's brilliant!' I can see his beaming face in my mind's eye, and hear a squeak of excitement from Doreen in the background. I turn and head back towards the restaurant.

'Look, I'd better go. I'll see you soon, okay? And Geoff? Thank you!'

'Wait! Tori! There's something else we should tell you!' comes Geoff's voice, and it sounds urgent.

'Go for it!' I say, coming to a halt outside the restaurant and peering through the windows for a glimpse of my friends at the back.

'There was another reason for Rowan getting grounded. She — '

'Oh. My. God!' I breathe.

'What? You okay?'

'Don't tell me,' I say, 'she gave Bay the details of where I'm having dinner, didn't she?'

'How on earth did you know that?'

Because I've just managed to spot Hugh and Sue at our table. And Bay is sitting in my chair.

'Gotta go!' I squeak. I hang up on Geoff and push straight into the restaurant.

What on earth am I going to say?

I stare at the little group and start walking towards them. I feel like a zombie, weaving between the tables and other diners. The poor, bemused waiting staff have to duck out of my way as I can't take my eyes off of Bay, laughing with my friends.

I manage to make it most of the way before Bay, as if sensing my presence, twists in his chair and spots me. He gets awkwardly to his feet and we stand and stare at each other for several long seconds.

Sue and Hugh just sit there, grinning at me like a couple of lemons. I still don't move.

'Don't forget these!' Sue's voice cuts into our little bubble.

Bay reaches over and takes something from her. 'I . . . I brought you something,' he says finally, walking towards me. In his arms he's holding a pair of bright yellow wellington boots, with an enormous bunch of flowers poking out of each one.

I take them and hug them to me with one arm.

'I read — I mean, I *heard* your letter,' I say.

'And?' he asks. He's smiling at me, but clearly nervous that this might turn out to be a public re-run of earlier.

'And, I'm sorry,' I say. 'I should have trusted you.'

'Well, I reckon I can let you off due to special circumstances,' he says, not taking his eyes off me.

I nod my thanks.

'But, did it . . . I don't know . . . did it help at all?' he asks.

I nod again. There's so much I want to say, but I feel like I'm going to have to choke the words out around a lump that has mysteriously appeared in my throat.

Bay seems to understand. He steps forward, closing the distance between us until we're almost touching.

'It was you,' I whisper. I can't tear my eyes off him. 'The letter. It was you. The you I know *and* this you.

It was the link I was missing.'

Bay reaches out, takes my free hand and laces his fingers through mine. I feel the hard calluses of his garden-rough hand and smile up at him.

'Then, we're okay?' The little quaver in his voice goes straight to my heart.

'More than,' I say. Reaching up, I kiss him gently, the wellies and flowers squashed between us.

39

The Beginning

> 'Every single second can be a new beginning. It's too easy to get caught up in the past and let your life slip by as you mourn the mistakes you've made, the decisions you regret or the paths you didn't take.
>
> 'Every single second can be a new beginning. But this time you're not a beginner . . . you start with a whole heap of experience and hope in your heart.'
>
> ©TheBeginnersGuideToLoneliness.com

As Bay swings Frank to a standstill at the top of the lane, I can't help but laugh. 'What? You don't want me to 'walk the track' again, do you? This isn't my first time, you know!'

Bay grins over at me. 'Just kidding!' he says, and we carry on, bouncing our way over the rough slates towards The Farm, where our friends are waiting for us.

Friends.

That word has more meaning to me now than it did just a few weeks ago. Doreen and Geoff. Moth, Messa and the others. Even Rowan. All friends. All on my side.

And then, of course, there's Bay. Over the past couple of days, there's barely been a moment's silence between us when we've been together. Hugh and Sue decided to head home the day after their epic sightseeing session, so while Bay's been at work, I've started pulling notes and ideas together for the book. In the evenings, though, we've spent every single second getting to know everything about each other. *Everything*.

I even told him about my mum. How it really was between us, and how it just got worse the more she drank. I told him about the relief I feel at no longer having to justify my life to her, no longer having to hear that I am her biggest disappointment. I told him about how guilty this all makes me feel.

I also told him that I should have been with her the night of the accident. If I hadn't ignored her call, I would have been driving, and maybe the accident wouldn't have happened at all. Or maybe I would have died too. There it is. There's the 'what if' that's at the heart of my phobia.

Of course, sharing hasn't miraculously made it all go away, but it feels like another step in taking back control of my life. Bay is definitely the best friend I could have ever hoped for. He's the best at a lot of other stuff too.

We've both been granted our wish to get back to The Farm before the course is over. Bay's colleague Greg has already been able to take back the reins of his project, though he'll be mostly directing his team from the comfort of his wheelchair.

* * *

As Frank bounces into the yard, my attention is brought firmly back into the present by Dennis barking in the seat between us.

'Oi, hound, what're you complaining about? We're

home!' I say, patting his head excitedly. He wags his tail, struggling against his seatbelt harness to stand up and peer properly through the windscreen. Then I see what he's barking at. Rowan is heading down the yard to meet us.

'Tori!' she squeals as I push the door open and struggle to hop down onto my stiff legs.

'Hey, Rowan!'

To my delight, she throws her arms around me and hugs me tight. I squeeze her back, but not for long as Dennis forces his way between us.

'Hello, idiot!' laughs Rowan, bending down to ruffle his fur. He promptly throws himself on his back, demanding a belly rub.

'I thought you were still grounded?' says Bay, throwing his arm around me.

Rowan looks up at us and grins. 'Nah, I made a deal with Dad,' she says, still tickling Dennis's stomach while he squirms, tongue lolling out of his mouth like a complete loon.

'Of course you did,' laughs Bay.

'Well, turns out that extra help around the house and with chores is more useful than keeping me off my phone, so . . . ' Straightening up, she takes her phone out of her jeans pocket and waves it at us.

'Shall we go find the others?' Bay asks me.

'Yay!' It's the only thing to say. I've missed them.

'No, wait . . . I've got to tell you something first!' says Rowan.

'Uh oh,' I say, coming to a halt. Rowan's smiling this time, but this feels a tad too familiar for my liking!

'Don't panic, it's something good. Guess what?'

'Rowan!' Ted's voice calls from the top of the yard. 'Stop hogging Tori and Bay! Your mum needs you.'

'But — ' she groans.

'Now.'

'Fine.' She slouches off up the path, Dennis following hot on her heels in pursuit of more belly rubs.

Ted reaches us and with a huge, tired grin, he flings his arms around Bay. 'So glad you could make it back!' he says.

'Me too,' says Bay.

'Tori!' Ted throws his arms around me too, and I squeeze him back, bobbly jumper and all.

'What was Rowan about to tell us?' I ask.

'Oh. Well, that's not for me to say. I think Lizzie wants to tell you.'

'But it's not bad news?' I check, worried that the chaos Nathan caused has had some kind of negative effect on The Farm.

Ted shakes his head. 'No bad news here.'

Bay takes my hand and we follow Ted towards the house. For a dizzying second I think he's about to lead us straight into the house itself, but instead he heads for the main fire pit, where everyone is hanging out around a lovely fire.

There's general pandemonium as they all rush over to us, and we find ourselves caught in the centre of a very happy, very huggy pile-up. It takes a good ten minutes before we're all perched back on the bales around the fire.

Doreen's right next to me, and one of my hands is in hers. My other hand is still in Bay's. The heat of their palms in mine heads straight up my arms, and my heart has never felt so warm. Maybe Doreen was right — perhaps they are turning me into a hippy.

'Go on then, Tori!' says Geoff, waving his cup of tea at me from across the fire. 'What's the big news you had to share with us?'

No, no, this isn't right. I'm the one meant to be finding out the news first!

'If I tell my news, will you tell me yours?' I ask Ted.

He looks at Lizzie, comfortably ensconced in a chair next to him, the little one nestled into her front.

'Deal,' says Lizzie. 'You first!'

'Okay. Well, the best thing ever happened when I was in London.'

'We can see that,' Doreen smiles at me, nodding at my hand clasped in Bay's.

I grin at her. 'Okay, you're right. The second best thing ever, then . . . '

Doreen chuckles, and Rowan nudges her from the other side. 'Shhh . . . or she'll never tell us!'

'Well, it's thanks to you really, Rowan. I met with a publisher when I was there. And they're interested in turning my blog into a book.'

A massive cheer goes up, and there are questions left and right and centre. I can't stop beaming as I say, 'Well, at least one good thing came from Nathan's article!'

'More than one good thing!' says Ted. 'Since you posted your response on your blog, our bookings have gone completely mad!'

'But . . . I haven't posted my review yet,' I say, perplexed. 'I wanted to finish the course first!'

'No, but you gave us a lovely mention in your post, and it's been incredible. So, thank you. Not just for that, but for everything,' he nods over at his baby daughter.

I shake my head, slightly embarrassed. I don't deserve this praise, this thanks.

'And that leads us to our next bit of news,' says

Lizzie, bouncing the baby on her lap.

I hold my breath.

'We've decided on a name for this little munchkin,' she says.

I let the breath out. Thank heavens, the spotlight is off me.

'We've decided to call her Victoria. After you.' Lizzie beams at me.

I don't know what to say, or where to look, so I turn to Rowan, who's grinning at me.

'She's going to be Vicca for short. Because you were amazing.'

That's it. They've finally broken me. I feel two huge tears break free and slide down my cheeks.

* * *

Moving back into the yurt with Bay and Dennis, even if it is only for a couple of nights, has to be one of the most joyous moments of my life so far. And given the amazing things that have happened to me over the past few days, that's saying something. This is the first place I've truly felt the sense of being at home, something I never felt for the house I grew up in, nor my London flat.

Speaking of the flat, that's something else I did while I was in London. I called my landlord. To be fair to the man, he was perfectly nice to me. I realized that I'd allowed my overactive imagination and anxiety-prone brain to turn him into the 'Big Baddy'. The poor guy was only doing what he had to do. I explained that I'd be able to pay him as soon as the advance for my book lands.

While we were on the phone, I also handed in my

notice on the flat. I'm not one hundred per cent sure what my next move is going to be, but with Bay in my life, I know it's going to be an exciting one.

* * *

I wake up to the sound of birds and the soft light of ridiculous o'clock creeping into the yurt. For a second, I just lie still and listen to the interweaving harmonies of the songbirds outside and the two sets of gentle snoring inside. I'm exactly where I want to be, snuggled up next to Bay with one of his arms wrapped around me. And Dennis is exactly where he wants to be, fast asleep on my bed over on the other side of the yurt.

I'm glad they're both asleep. I've got something I want to do, and the sounds of the early morning are beckoning. I'm ready.

I carefully slip out from under Bay's arm, pausing as he stirs in his sleep — and then I relax as he turns over and his breathing becomes deep and even once more.

I get dressed quickly and quietly and am just pulling my yellow wellies on by the door when a cold, wet nose and wagging tail demand my attention. Dennis is awake, and clearly quite keen to join me on my early morning mission. I ruffle his ears and briefly consider ordering him back to bed. But I change my mind and we set off together.

The morning is crisp and clear, and the fields teem with life. Last week's rain has made the greens even brighter and everything feels full of possibility, full of hope.

When I reach the top of the hill, I pause. I don't

want to turn back this time; I don't want to run away and hide. I've got one more thing to face while I'm here, and then I really will have done everything that this place has asked of me.

Coming back to The Farm in time to finish the retreat has meant a lot to me. I've been able to work with all the tutors some more, and I've had the chance to talk to both Ted and Lizzie about Mum's accident, our relationship and about my guilt and grief. I know I've still got a long way to go, but the steps I've already taken on the journey have shifted something deep inside of me.

I glance down at Dennis. He's sitting in the grass next to me, completely content to watch and wait for my next move. Question is, am I ready to make it?

'Ready,' I say quietly, and together we stride down the hill.

I duck under the trees at the bottom and pause again as the sound of the river reaches my ears. I take a deep breath in and let it out slowly. I can see running water. I can hear the pounding of the river. But it isn't taking me over.

Bending forward, I slip out of my wellingtons and peel off my socks. I roll up the legs of my trousers and straighten back up to stand, barefoot, on the shingle bank.

The sound of the river fills my ears. I take a step forward. Then another. I keep walking until my toes are right at the edge of the water. I pause.

I look behind me. Dennis is sitting by my boots, watching me, tail wagging and tongue lolling. I turn to face the river again. The sound of water is all around me. I take a deep breath in. For a brief second I see my mother's face, and then it's gone, replaced by the

water swirling in front of me. I breathe out.
I breathe in.
I'm ready.
I breathe out and step into the river.

Acknowledgements

My first thanks goes to my mum for all her gentle support, and to Pops for being the biggest champion of creativity I've ever met. I miss you both very much.

To my family — Dad and Jill, Rhian and Graham, Ross and Amberina, Sebby and Echo — thank you for all your love.

Huge thanks to the Books and the City team for scooping Tori out of the #OneDay submissions pile and wanting to read the rest of her story. A special shout-out to Bec Farrell and Sara-Jade Virtue for all your support and hard work — it has been amazing working with you.

A big cheer for all the authors and bloggers who have inspired me over the years, but special thanks to Heidi Swain, Darcie Boleyn, T. A. Williams, Kim Nash and Mary Lewis for being amazing friends and cheerleaders while I've been navigating the overwhelming waters of crafting a debut novel.

Special thanks to my Sapphire family for inspiring the Warriors. Thank heavens none of you are anything like Nat!

Greg Poulos, Leah Stevens and Sara Olsson — thank you for always being there, and for all your help. I look forward to the day we all finally get to hang out!

I undertook a lot of research while working on Tori's story and would like to give Mind.org.uk a shout-out for their wonderful online resources. I would also like to thank Suzanne Olenczyn for sharing her experiences with me. Any errors or inaccuracies are all on me.

To Mop — thank you for all the company and cuddles.

Jules, I've left you until last because I know you always skip to the end first — thank you for everything. I wouldn't have been able to do this if it weren't for you.

Other titles published by Ulverscroft:

TRAGEDY ON THE BRANCH LINE

Edward Marston

When Bernard Pomeroy, a young undergraduate at Corpus Christi College, finds a letter slipped under his door in the early hours of a rainy day, he flies into a panic. He hurries to the railway station. But he doesn't reach his destination alive. Inspector Colbeck and Sergeant Leeming are called upon to investigate this tragedy on the railway. It soon becomes apparent that Cambridge's hopes of success in the forthcoming Boat Race rested on Pomeroy's shoulders. With academic disputes, romantic interests and a sporting rivalry with Oxford in play, the Railway Detective will have his work cut out to disentangle the threads of Pomeroy's life in order to answer the truth of his death.

SPECIAL MESSAGE TO READERS

THE ULVERSCROFT FOUNDATION

( )

was es earch,
diagn les of
major lation

- T e
Hos
- T ıt
Orn
- F
trea
Opł
- T
Inst
- T
Oph
- T
Aust

You ɔn
by y
conti like
to h ıer

The Green, Bradgate Road, Anstey
Leicester LE7 7FU, England
Tel: (0116) 236 4325

website: .org.uk

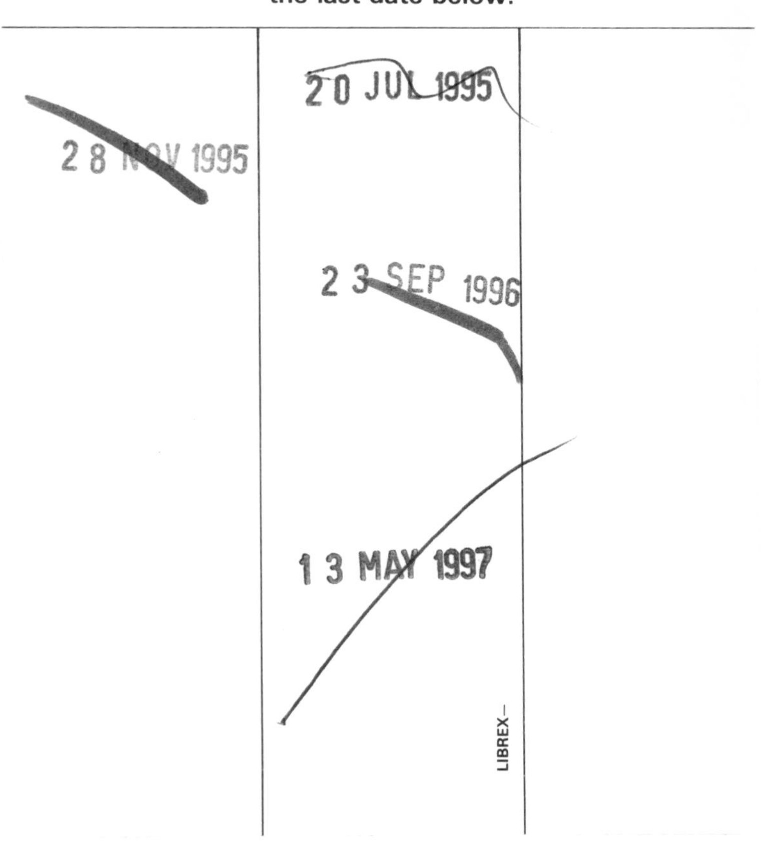
28 NOV 1995
20 JUL 1995
23 SEP 1996
13 MAY 1997
LIBREX

RISC Systems

C^3 INDUSTRIAL CONTROL, COMPUTERS AND COMMUNICATIONS SERIES

Series Editor: **Professor Derek R. Wilson**
Polytechnic of Central London, England

1. Reduced Instruction Set Computer—RISC—Architecture
   Daniel Tabak

2. Algorithms, Smart Chips and their Applications
   Ferenc Vajda

3. Dataflow Architecture for Machine Control
   Bogdan Lent

4. RISC Systems*
   Daniel Tabak

* *Cover artwork by Sylvia Watson, from a design by Yuval Roth-Tabak*

RISC Systems

Daniel Tabak

Professor of Electrical and Computer Engineering
George Mason University
Fairfax, Virginia 22030, USA

RESEARCH STUDIES PRESS LTD.
Taunton, Somerset, England

JOHN WILEY & SONS INC.
New York · Chichester · Toronto · Brisbane · Singapore

RESEARCH STUDIES PRESS LTD.
24 Belvedere Road, Taunton, Somerset, England TA1 1HD

Marketing and Distribution:

Australia and New Zealand:
Jacaranda-Wiley Ltd.
GPO Box 859, Brisbane, Queensland 4001, Australia

Canada:
JOHN WILEY & SONS CANADA LIMITED
22 Worcester Road, Rexdale, Ontario, Canada

Europe, Africa, Middle East and Japan:
JOHN WILEY & SONS LIMITED
Baffins Lane, Chichester, West Sussex, England

North and South America:
JOHN WILEY & SONS INC.
605 Third Avenue, New York, NY 10158, USA

South East Asia:
JOHN WILEY & SONS (SEA) PTE LTD.
37 Jalan Pemimpin 05-04
Block B Union Industrial Building, Singapore 2057

Library of Congress Cataloging-in-Publication Data

Tabak, Daniel, 1934–
RISC systems / Daniel Tabak.
p. cm.—(Industrial control, computers, and communications series; 4)
Includes bibliographical references.
ISBN 0-471-92694-9 (Wiley)
1. Reduced instruction set computers. 2. Computer architecture.
I. Title. II. Series.
QA76.9.A73T294 1990 90-30023
004.2′2—dc20 CIP

British Library Cataloguing in Publication Data

Tabak, Daniel, *1934–*
RISC systems.—(Industrial control, computers and communications series; 4).
1. Computer systems
I. Title. II. Series
004

ISBN 0 86380 100 5

ISBN 0 86380 100 5 (Research Studies Press Ltd.)
ISBN 0 471 92694 9 (John Wiley & Sons Inc.)

Typeset by MHL Typesetting Ltd., Coventry
Printed in Great Britain by Galliard (Printers) Ltd., Great Yarmouth

To my first grandson

Elior

Trademarks

UNIX is a registered trademark of AT&T.
Ethernet, Smalltalk 80 are registered trademarks of Xerox Corp.
Ada is a registered trademark of the US Government (AJPO).
CLIPPER and Intergraph are registered trademarks of Intergraph Corp.
MIPS, RISC/OS, UMIPS and RISCompiler are trademarks of MIPS Computer Systems, Inc.
NFS, SPARC, SunOS, Sun-4 are trademarks of Sun Microsystems, Inc.
VAX, VMS, Ultrix are trademarks of Digital Equipment Corp.
M88000, M68000, HYPERmodule are trademarks of Motorola, Inc.
PC/AT, ROMP, PC/RT, OS/2 are trademarks of IBM Corp.
VxWorks, VxADS are trademarks of Wind River Systems, Inc.
NuSuper, McCray is a trademark of YARC Systems Corp.
MACINTOSH, MULTIFINDER are trademarks of Apple Computer, Inc.
29K, Am29000 are trademarks of Advanced Micro Devices, Inc.
C EXECUTIVE is a registered trademark of JMI Software Consultants, Inc.
4.2 BSD, 4.3 BSD are trademarks of the Board of Regents of the University of California at Berkeley.
Dc18 is a trademark of Accel R8 Technology Corp.
80860, i860, 80960, 80386, 80486, Multibus II are trademarks of Intel Corp.
inmos, occam are trademarks of the INMOS Group of Companies.
Domain, Series 10000, Aegis are trademarks of Apollo Computer, Inc.
MS DOS is a trademark of Microsoft Corp.
Ridge 3200 is a trademark of Ridge Computers Co.
Pyramid, OSx are trademarks of Pyramid Technology Corp.
Butterfly, TC2000, GP1000, nX are trademarks of BBN, Inc.
pSOS+m is a trademark of Software Components Group, Inc.

Contents

Foreword

When Daniel Tabak wrote his first book on RISC architecture the technology was halfway between the development laboratory and the production environment. This second book coincides with the announcement that IBM is launching a RISC chip set styled 'America', with five instructions per cycle in an architecture using 184 instructions, and a 128-bit data bus from CPU to memory.

The fact that several manufacturers have already brought RISC chips to the market, e.g. Intel with the i860, Apollo's PRISM, Sun Microsystems with SPARC and, in Europe, the transputer from INMOS, does not diminish the importance of the turning point for RISC technology, namely IBM's endorsement of this important design approach, for high performance computer systems and workstations.

In my Editorial to Daniel Tabak's first book *RISC Architecture*, I wrote that 'the architecture of computer systems is one of the key elements in the future growth of silicon applications'. The growth in RISC technology has now reached the point where it represents a mature industry; and this emphasizes once more how the silicon industry rapidly absorbs new ideas and quickly turns those ideas into products.

Following closely on the heels of the technology of RISC processors is the technology of 'reconfiguration', as represented by Thorn's PARSYS machine in which RISC processors – in this case INMOS transputers – can be reconfigured so that many processors can be mapped onto the problem, rather than mapping the problem onto a single processor as in a traditional computer. However, this is still in the future for many users.

In this book, *RISC Systems*, Daniel Tabak has presented the 'state of the art' in RISC technology. This will be invaluable to engineers and students alike, because the remarkable growth of the silicon industry means that both students and engineers 'need to know' about the latest and most important design methodologies that RISC technology has made possible. This book is an important contribution to the subject and one which I know will be appreciated by its readers.

Derek Wilson
London 1990

Preface

Systems based on the Reduced Instruction Set Computer (RISC) concept have expanded tremendously since the appearance of *RISC Architecture* (D. Tabak, Research Studies Press Ltd, January 1987). There exist today about 10 systems which did not exist three years ago. RISC-type processors are used in numerous workstations, including 3D graphics, in high-performance computer boards, in multiprocessors, and in real-time systems. A definite need was felt for a concentrated documentation of recent powerful systems. Initially, a second edition of *RISC Architecture* was contemplated. Once the work started, it was realized that the material in the new edition would be more than twice the extent of that in the first. It was therefore decided that this should be a new book, called *RISC Systems*.

As its predecessor, the book is intended for advanced undergraduate and graduate students of electrical and computer engineering, computer science, and other fields having an interest in computing systems. It can also serve practising engineers and computer scientists. The text assumes a basic knowledge, by the reader, of computer organization and architecture (at the level of Hamacher or Hayes texts). The goal of the book is to present the basic principles of RISC along with the description of a number of leading commercial and experimental RISC systems. The above presentation is concluded with a comparative evaluation of RISC systems and a description of their applications.

The book is organized in 15 chapters, some of which are divided into sections and subsections. References are given at the end of each chapter. The references are denoted, in square brackets, by a double number, such as: 1.20, which means reference 20 of chapter 1.

The basic principles of RISC are concentrated in chapters 1 and 2. Chapter 1 introduces, in detail, the fundamental properties of RISC, after describing a number of CISC examples, as a contrast. Chapter 2 discusses the advantages of RISC from different points of view, along with its shortcomings.

Specific examples of RISC systems are covered in chapters 3 through 12. Chapter 3 describes the Berkeley RISC I and II – the first system identified by the name 'RISC'. The Microprocessor without Interlocked Pipeline Stages (MIPS) is presented in chapter 4. Initially, the original Stanford MIPS is covered, followed by the commercial one, created by the MIPS Computer Systems, Inc.

Chapter 5 is dedicated to a number of experimental systems. It starts with the IBM 801, which was chronologically the first RISC-type experimental system (although publicly announced after the Berkeley RISC). Subsequently, the Berkeley 'spin-offs' of RISC, the SOAR and the SPUR systems are described. The chapter continues with the presentation of the George Mason University (GMU) MIRIS and MULTRIS systems, the BGU single instruction computer and MODHEL systems, and GaAs-based systems.

Chapters 6 through 11 are dedicated to a specific manufacturer each. Chapter 6 covers the Motorola M88000 system; chapter 7, the Sun SPARC; chapter 8, the AMD 29000; chapter 9, the Intel 80960 and 80860; chapter 10, the Intergraph CLIPPER; and chapter 11, the Acorn and VLSI Technology system. Chapter 12 describes the Pyramid, Ridge, Apollo PRISM, INMOS TRANSPUTER, IBM ROMP, and the Hewlett Packard Precision Architecture.

The creators and manufacturers of various RISC systems have conducted numerous comparative experimental runs of standard benchmark problems. Selected results of these experiments, along with an evaluation discussion, are presented in chapter 13.

Chapter 14 is dedicated to the description of the numerous applications of RISC processors, including workstations, multiprocessors and real-time systems. Concluding comments are given in chapter 15.

A number of problems for students are offered at the end of the text. For the convenience of the reader, glossaries of abbreviations and basic definitions are also included at the back.

The author would like to express his appreciation to a number of colleagues and students for their valuable cooperation and comments. These include Dr Donna J. Quammen (GMU), the originating architect of MULTRIS, a former PhD advisee, Dr Helnye Azaria (GMU), the designer of the CMOVE and MODHEL systems, former and current students, contributors to the MULTRIS and MIRIS (at GMU), D. Richard Miller, David K. du Bose, Robert Senko, Gordon Leeuwrik, Dimitrios K. Fotakis, Jean M. Davila, Andrew Phillips, and Gary Bisaga. Particular thanks are due to Scott Goldstein, who also prepared some of the artwork in this text.

Valuable comments were obtained from representatives of some creators of RISC systems. Particularly helpful were Mr Dan Clarke (MIPS Computer Systems, Inc.), Professor John Hennessy (Stanford University), Mr Philip Brownfield (Motorola), Mr Max Baron (Sun Microsystems, Inc.), and Professor Veljko Milutinovic (Purdue University).

The author would also like to thank Professor Derek Wilson, the series editor and Mrs Veronica A. Wallace, Managing Director of Research Studies Press Ltd for valuable comments and continued support. The manuscript was processed by the GMU Word Processing Unit, under the direction of Ms Mary Blackwell. The promptness and excellence of the manuscript preparation are highly appreciated. Last but not least, the author would like to express his appreciation to his wife, Pnina, for her understanding and patience.

D.T.

1
The Concept of RISC

1.1 Introductory Comments

Within eight years since the term Reduced Instruction Set Computer (RISC) was first coined in 1980 [1.1], it underwent a rather remarkable development. There are about twenty industrial companies selling, manufacturing and developing RISC-type commercial products. Active research and development on various aspects of RISC is conducted in academia all over the world. Material on RISC, initially scattered in articles and reports, found its way into textbooks, monographs and chapters in books [1.2–1.7]. The RISC concept in digital computer design is a definite trend, practiced by many and to different extents.

The opposite and a rather established trend in computer design is the so-called Complex Instruction Set Computer – CISC. The CISC system is usually microprogrammed, endowed with a relatively large quantity of machine language instructions, addressing modes, instruction formats and a number of possible instruction lengths. Such a large 'menu' of possibilities of operation results in a highly complicated control unit in the Central Processing Unit (CPU) of the system. Before discussing, in detail, the concept of RISC, it would be beneficial to look at some examples of CISC-type systems. After doing that, the properties of RISC can be better appreciated. The CISC concept will therefore be exemplified next, followed by the definition of RISC in a subsequent section.

1.2 The Complex Instruction Set Computer – CISC

Some of the most prominent CISC examples would be the third generation (starting in the mid-sixties) mainframes, such as the IBM 360 and 370 families, followed by the 3080s and 3090s [1.8]. It would be erroneous to think that a CISC must necessarily be a large mainframe computer. In fact, a mini- or even a microcomputer can be designed to offer a large menu of instructions, addressing modes, instruction formats and sizes. To illustrate this point, the CISC systems selected as a detailed example are

(a) The Digital Equipment Corp. (DEC) VAX-11/780 [1.9–1.11], considered to be a superminicomputer, and

(b) The Motorola MC68020 Microprocessor [1.12–1.13].

EXAMPLE 1.2.1 *The VAX-11/780*
The VAX architecture features 304 instructions and 16 addressing modes. It is a 32-bit machine whose data and address paths are 32-bit wide. This means that its logical (virtual) address space is 2^{32} bytes or 4 Gigabytes. Its CPU has 16 32-bit registers R0, R1, . . . , R15. Register R15 serves a Program Counter (PC), and R14 as the Stack Pointer (SP).

The VAX supports a considerable number of different data types:

1. Integer
   (a) Byte 8 bits
   (b) Word 16 bits
   (c) Longword 32 bits
   (d) Quadword 64 bits
   (e) Octaword 128 bits
2. Floating Point
   (a) F form 32 bits, 8-bit exponent
   (b) D form 64 bits, 8-bit exponent
   (c) G form 64 bits, 11-bit exponent
   (d) H form 128 bits, 15-bit exponent
3. Packed decimal string, 0 to 16 bytes, 2 digits per byte.
4. Character string, 0 to 64K bytes, one character per byte.
5. Variable-length bit field, 0 to 32 bits.
6. Numeric string, 0 to 31 bytes.
7. Queue, greater than 2 longwords.

Among the VAX 16 Addressing Modes we have:

Immediate
Register
Register Deferred
Autodecrement
Autoincrement
Autoincrement Deferred
Absolute
Displacement
Displacement Deferred
Indexed

The VAX has an uncountable number of instruction formats. The general structure of the typical instruction is as follows:

Byte 1: Opcode
Byte 2: Operand Specifier 1
. . .
. . .
. . .

Operand Specifier 2

. . .

. . .

. . .

Operand Specifier k

. . .

. . .

. . .

$0 < k < 6$

An operand specifier may be as short as one byte and as long as 10 bytes. There may be 0, 1 and up to 6 operand specifiers. It is easy to see that VAX offers a great variety of instruction lengths and formats.

Some examples of VAX instructions:

ADDX3 – 3 operands ADD

The X can be either of the following:

B – B byte
W – Word
L – Longword
F – F Floating point
D – D Floating point
G – G Floating point
H – H Floating point

The same instruction can be operated with a variety of 7 types of operands, and there is also a two-operand ADDX2 instruction, with the same X options.

SUBP6 – Subtract Packed 6-Operand
MOVC5 – Move Character 5-Operand
CASEX – Case on X, which can be:
B – Byte
W – Word
L – Longword

And there are many other, similar instructions with numerous options.

As we can see from the above description the VAX architecture offers a very large menu of operation possibilities with an extensive list of instructions which can come in a variety of lengths and formats.

EXAMPLE 1.2.2 *The Motorola MC68020*

The Motorola 32-bit microprocessor MC68020 has 16 General Purpose CPU registers, 8 Data and 8 Address: D0, D1, . . . , D7 and A0, A1, . . . , A7. Only

A7 doubles as a User Stack Pointer (USP). Otherwise, the user is free to use these registers as he wishes in his program. The Program Counter (PC) is a separate register in the 68020.

The 68020 recognizes 7 data types:

1. Bits.
2. Bit Fields, 1 to 32 bits.
3. Binary Coded Decimal (BCD) Digits; Packed (2 digits/byte), Unpacked (1 digit/byte).
4. Byte Integers (8 bits).
5. Word Integers (16 bits).
6. Longword Integers (32 bits).
7. Quadword Integers (64 bits).

The 18 Addressing Modes of the 68020 are:

Register Direct.

1. Data Register Direct.
2. Address Register Direct.

Register Indirect.

3. Address Register Indirect.
4. Address Register Indirect with Postincrement.
5. Address Register Indirect with Predecrement.
6. Address Register Indirect with Displacement.

Register Indirect with Index.

7. Address Register Indirect with Index, 8-bit Displacement.
8. Address Register Indirect with Index, Base Displacement.

Memory Indirect.

9. Memory Indirect Post-Indexed.
10. Memory Indirect Pre-Indexed.
11. PC Indirect with Displacement.

PC Indirect with Index.

12. PC Indirect with Index, 8-bit Displacement.
13. PC Indirect with Index, Base Displacement.

PC Memory Indirect.

14. PC Memory Indirect Post-Indexed.
15. PC Memory Indirect Pre-Indexed.

Absolute.

16. Absolute Short.
17. Absolute Long.
18. Immediate.

The 68020 instructions can be of 1 Word (16 bits) and up to 11 Words in length. The general format is:

First Word	Operation Word (Opcode, Modes)
Second Word	Special Operand Specifiers (if any, 1 or 2 Words)
	Immediate Operand or Source Effective Address Extension (if any, 1 to 5 Words)
	Destination Effective Address Extension (if any, 1 to 5 Words)

Although the MC68020 has fewer instructions than the VAX, it offers quite an extensive menu with its 18 addressing modes and numerous instruction sizes.

All in all, the MC68020 as well as the VAX 11/780 (and many other CISC-type machines) have a great variety of data and instruction formats, addressing modes and instructions (such as the 304 VAX instructions). A direct consequence of this variety is a highly complicated control unit of the CPU, which is supposed to be able to differentiate between the numerous options and activate the appropriate control signals. For instance, even in the less sophisticated MC68000 the control unit takes up over 60% of the chip area. As will be seen later, it is less than 10% for the Berkeley RISC (see chapter 3).

A CISC system with a large menu of features implies a larger and more complicated decoding subsystem, preceding the complex control logic. Logic signals will usually have to propagate through a considerable amount of gates, increasing the duration of delays and slowing down the system. In a microprogrammed environment (and most CISCs are microprogrammed) increased complexity will directly result in longer microroutines and therefore their longer execution to produce all necessary microoperations and their control signals to execute an instruction.

One of the ways to increase the speed of execution on any computer is to implement pipelining [1.14]. For a pipeline with n stages, we can get the system to deal with n subsequent instructions simultaneously. Consider a simple two-stage instruction pipeline:

Stage one:	Fetch,	F
Stage two:	Execute,	E

Assume a simple model where each of the above stages takes just a single CPU cycle to complete. We get the following instruction-time (in CPU cycles) layout for three subsequent instructions:

	cycle:	1	2	3	4
instruction	i:	F	E		
	i+1:		F	E	
	i+2:			F	E

All three instructions are fully taken care of in four cycles. It should also be mentioned that instruction $i-1$ is executed during cycle 1, while instruction $i+3$ is fetched during cycle 4. At any cycle, two instructions are being worked on in this simple two-stage pipeline.

The above pipeline model does not occur in CISC systems. The instructions are of different length; while some can be fetched in a single cycle, others need more. Different instructions are executed in a different number of cycles. A more realistic example on a CISC can be the following:

	cycle:	1	2	3	4	5	6	7
instruction	i:	F	E	E	E			
	i+1:		F			E		
	i+2:			F	F		E	E

It takes now 7 cycles to execute 3 instructions (in the previous model it would take 6 cycles to handle all 3 instructions without a pipeline). Because of the disparity in instructions' lengths and execution times, some instructions have to be suspended and wait for a few cycles within the pipeline. Instruction i+3 can only be fetched starting with cycle 5 and its execution can commence no earlier than cycle 8.

The above example illustrates that there is a difficulty in implementing a pipeline efficiently in a CISC-type system. In actual systems instruction pipelines have more than 2 stages (usually 3 to 6). If there are considerable differences between lengths and execution cycles of different instructions, which can appear in the CPU in any order, the pipeline design and utilization will be much more complicated.

The complexity of a CISC system would imply a long design time with a significant probability of design errors. In a complex system the errors will take a long time to locate and correct. By the time a CISC system is designed, built and tested, it may become obsolete from the standpoint of the state of the art of the current computer technology, in which significant advances occur on a quarterly basis (sometimes even more frequently).

A large instruction set presents too large a choice for the compiler of any HLL (High Level Language). This in turn makes it more difficult to design the optimizing stage of a CISC compiler. This stage would have to be longer and more complicated in a CISC machine. Furthermore, the results of this 'optimization' may not always yield the most efficient and the fastest machine language code.

Some CISC instruction sets contain a number of instructions, particularly specialized to fit certain HLL instructions. However, a machine language instruction which fits one HLL, may not be suitable for another and this could constitute an excessive waste of effort for the designer. Such a machine language instruction would have a relatively low cost/benefit factor.

The above considerations have been on the minds of computer designers for many years. Eventually, a number of designers at different locations decided to deviate from the established CISC design patterns and to try a new, simplified system, with a much smaller menu of instructions, modes and formats. It is true that the very first computers of the first generation were simple enough. However, the existing technology at that time kept them at a low performance level. The upsurge of new LSI and VLSI technology paved the way for the emergence of new, relatively simple and yet high-performance computing systems. These systems became known as Reduced Instruction Set Computers (RISC), although it is not only the instruction set that got reduced in their design. There exists no formal definition of the RISC concept, universally acceptable. The next section formulates a definition of RISC, based on a significant set of existing systems of the above category and on some basic computer design considerations.

1.3 Definition of the Reduced Instruction Set Computer – RISC

Considering the pipeline operation example in section 1.2, one can see that an efficient system operation can be attained if all instructions take the same number of cycles for the fetch and execution stages. If the above take a single clock cycle, the operation will naturally be the speediest for a given technology. The designer should therefore strive to achieve a uniform series of single-cycle, fetch-and-execute operations for each instruction implemented on the computing system being developed.

A single-cycle fetch can be achieved by keeping all instructions at a standard size. The standard instruction size should be equal to the basic word length of the computing system, which is usually equal to the number of data lines in the system bus, connecting the memory (where the program is stored) to the CPU. At any fetch cycle, a complete single instruction will be transferred to the CPU. For instance, if the basic word size is 32 bits, and the data part of the system bus (the data bus) has 32 lines, the standard instruction length should be 32 bits.

Achieving uniform (same time) execution of all instructions is much more difficult than achieving a uniform fetch. Some instruction executions may involve simple logical operations on a CPU register (such as clearing the register) and can be executed in a single CPU clock cycle without any problem. Other instructions may involve memory access (load from or store to memory, fetch data) or multicycle operations (multiply, divide, floating point), and may be impossible to be executed in a single cycle. In order to achieve better performance the designer should strive to achieve a situation where most of the featured instructions are executable in a single cycle.

Ideally, we would like to see a *streamlined* and *uniform* handling of all instructions, where the fetch and the execute stages take up the same time for any instruction, desirably, a single cycle. This is basically one of the first and most important principles inherent in the RISC design approach. All instructions go from the memory to the CPU, where they get executed, in a constant stream. Each instruction is executed at the same pace and no instruction is made to wait. The CPU is kept busy all the time.

As argued earlier, some of the necessary conditions to achieve such a streamlined operation are:

(a) Standard, fixed size of the instruction, equal to the computer word length and to the width of the data bus.
(b) Standard execution time of all instructions, desirably within a single CPU cycle.

One might raise the following argument: why not pack two instructions into a single word, transferred into the CPU on the data bus? This would seem to enhance the speed. On the other hand, in most modern computers the standard word length is 32 bits. A 16-bit standard instruction would not be practical. Of course, a considerable number of simple single-operand instructions could be 16 bits. The trend in modern computer design is to have 3-operand instructions. This permits efficient encoding of operations with different source operands and a different destination in a single instruction (with a 2-operand format, two instructions would be required). A 32-bit format is needed for 3-operand instructions. This will also permit a larger range for immediate values and address displacements. Since it is impractical to have instructions of half-word (16 bits) length, they should all be a full word (32 bits) long. Having instructions of both 16- and 32-bits would be contrary to the principle of uniformity in size of all instructions, and would not permit a continuous streamlined handling at all times.

Having all of the instructions of the same length is not in itself sufficient to ensure streamlined handling for all cases. It is also essential to have relatively simple decoding and control subsystems. A complex control unit will introduce extra delays in producing control signals, which in turn will tend to interfere with the expected streamlining and uniform handling of all instructions. An obvious way of significantly reducing the complexity of the control unit is to provide a reduced number of choices (a reduced menu) of instructions, instructions and data formats and of addressing modes. A reduction in the number of operation possibilities will simplify the design and speed up the operation of the decoding subsystem, since it will have many less items to distinguish. Since there are fewer instructions and addressing modes, the control unit needs less logic circuitry to implement them. For a reduced menu, the control unit will be simpler and less costly to design, manufacture and test. The reduction of the operations menu was the primary point made by the original proposers of RISC [1.1].

How much is reduced? There is no definite answer to this question. One can only inspect the menu of the existing RISC-type systems, comparing them to the CISCs (such as the VAX with 304 instructions, 16 addressing modes and over 10 different instruction lengths). Based on a number of existing systems (discussed in chapters 3–12) one can tentatively adopt the following constraints for a RISC menu:

Number of instructions, less than or equal to 128,
Number of addressing modes, less than or equal to 4,
Number of instruction formats, less than or equal to 4.

Realizing that it might not be practical to hope that all instructions will execute in a single cycle, one can request that at least 75% should.

Which instructions should be selected to be on the reduced instruction list? The obvious answer is: the ones used most often. It has been established in a number of earlier studies [1.1–1.7, 1.15] that a relatively small percentage of instructions (10–20%) takes up about 80–90% of execution time in an extended selection of benchmark programs. Among the most often executed instructions were data moves, arithmetic and logical operations. Another criterion for selection would be the *general* support of High Level Languages (HLL). This is an important consideration, supporting the reduction of the *semantic gap* [1.16] between the basic machine design and the HLLs, particularly since over 90% of all programming is done in HLL. The term 'general' support is stressed, as opposed to the support of a particular HLL. In other words, one should strive to provide features which tend to support HLLs in general (such as support for procedure handling, parameter passing and process management), as opposed to a particular HLL (such as Pascal or FORTRAN). We shall return to discuss this important aspect in subsequent sections and chapters.

It was mentioned earlier in this section that one of the reasons preventing an instruction from being able to execute in a single cycle, is the possible need to access memory to fetch operands and/or store results. The conclusion is therefore obvious – we should minimize as much as possible the number of instructions that have to access memory during the execution stage. This consideration brought forward the following RISC principles, adopted on all of the existing systems of this category:

(a) Memory access, during the execution stage, is done by load/store instructions only.
(b) All operations, except load/store, are register-to-register, within the CPU.

Most of the CISC systems are microprogrammed, because of the flexibility that microprogramming [1.4] offers the designer. Different instructions usually have microroutines of different length. This means that each instruction will take a different number of cycles to execute. This contradicts the principle of a uniform, streamlined handling of all instructions. Such treatment can be achieved using hardwired control, which is also faster. Therefore, RISC-type systems should have *hardwired control*. An exception to this rule can be made when each instruction has a one-to-one correspondence with a single microinstruction. That is, each microroutine consists of a single control word. Such a design can be as fast and as efficient as one which uses hardwired control, and still let the designer benefit from the advantages of microprogramming. This approach has been adopted on the GMU MIRIS [1.3] (see section 5.3).

In order to facilitate the implementation of most instructions as register-to-register operations, a sufficient amount of CPU general purpose registers has to be provided. A sufficiently large register set will permit temporary storage of intermediate results, needed as operands in subsequent operations, in the CPU register file. This, in turn, will reduce the number of memory accesses by reducing the number of load/store operations in the program, speeding up its run time.

Table 1.1 RISC Definition

A RISC system satisfies the following properties:

(1) Single cycle execution of all (at least most, over 75%) instructions.

(2) Single-word standard length of all instructions, equal to the basic system word length and data bus width, permitting a uniform, streamlined treatment of all instructions.

(3) Small number of instructions, not to exceed 128.

(4) Small number of instruction formats, not to exceed 4.

(5) Small number of addressing modes, not to exceed 4.

(6) Memory access by load/store instructions only.

(7) All operations, except load/store, are register-to-register, within the CPU.

(8) Hardwired Control Unit.

(9) A relatively large (at least 32) general purpose CPU register file.

A minimal number of 32 general purpose CPU registers has been adopted, *de facto*, by most of the industrial RISC systems designers.

A summary of the basic points of RISC definition, discussed in this section, is given in Table 1.1. It is not a rigorous, acceptable by all, definition. In fact, some systems, advertised as RISC-type, violate some of the points in Table 1.1. The above points should be viewed as a guideline, explaining the nature of a RISC. Loosely speaking, a system satisfying the majority of these points, could be accepted as a RISC. Naturally, the more of these points are satisfied, the closer is the system to being a 'fully-fledged RISC'.

Why did the RISC approach in computer design capture a considerable part of industry within a relatively short time? What are its advantages and what are its shortcomings? These questions will be taken up in chapter 2. The remaining sections of this chapter will be dedicated to the discussion of some design practices adopted in many RISC systems, and to a historical survey of RISC development.

1.4 Practices of RISC Systems

In addition to the basic properties, forming the essence of RISC systems, described in section 1.3, there are a number of features practiced in many actual RISC systems. These features are not necessarily unique to RISC-type systems. In fact, they can well be adopted on any CISC. Some of them are indeed featured on a variety of CISC-type systems.

One of the most important practices in computer design, to be discussed here, is the machine support of High Level Languages (HLLs). Although most of the programming is done in HLLs, the basic computer design of earlier generations did not provide any hardware-based support to HLL features, such as array management, handling of procedure parameter passing, typing and classification of information, process and memory management. Usually, there existed a wide *semantic gap* between the HLL and the machine design [1.16]. In the early generations of computers this gap had to be narrowed and bridged by software. A wide semantic gap would in general cause more complicated and hence more costly and less reliable system software. Lately, many new systems (such as the VAX, for instance) started to incorporate features supporting HLLs in their basic design, thus narrowing the semantic gap.

The support of HLL features is mandatory in the design of any computing system, be it RISC or CISC. It is a rather complicated matter and has to be approached very carefully. Loading the design with a great number of HLL features and instructions (some of which may be used rather rarely), may result in a very complex and low-throughput system. A better approach is to investigate statistically the frequency of use of various HLL features, running a substantial number of benchmark programs, written in HLLs. Such experimental work has been performed by the Berkeley team during the design of their RISC I and RISC II [1.2, 1.17, 1.18]. This investigation suggested that the procedure call/return is the most time-consuming operation in typical HLL programs. The percentage of time spent on handling local variables and constants turned out to be the highest, compared to other variables. Based on that, the Berkeley team decided to support HLLs in their RISC design by supporting efficiently the handling of local variables, constants and procedure calls, while leaving less frequent HLL operations to instruction sequences or subroutines. In other words, the Berkeley team decided to support HLLs by enhancing the performance of the most time-consuming HLL features and operations. Many other subsequent RISC designs followed this policy, obtaining reasonable HLL support and narrowing the semantic gap, while maintaining the simplicity or 'low complexity' of the designed system.

One of the mechanisms supporting the handling of procedures and their parameter passing in particular, is the feature of the *register window*. It was adopted by the Berkeley RISC designers and later featured on the Pyramid (section 12.1) and on the Sun SPARC (chapter 7).

The register file is subdivided into groups of registers, called windows. A certain group of i registers, say r 0 to r(i – 1) are designated as *global registers*. The global registers are accessible to all procedures running on the system at all times. On the other hand, each procedure is assigned a separate window within the register file. The window base (first register within the window) is pointed to by a field called *Current Window Pointer* (CWP), usually located in the CPU's

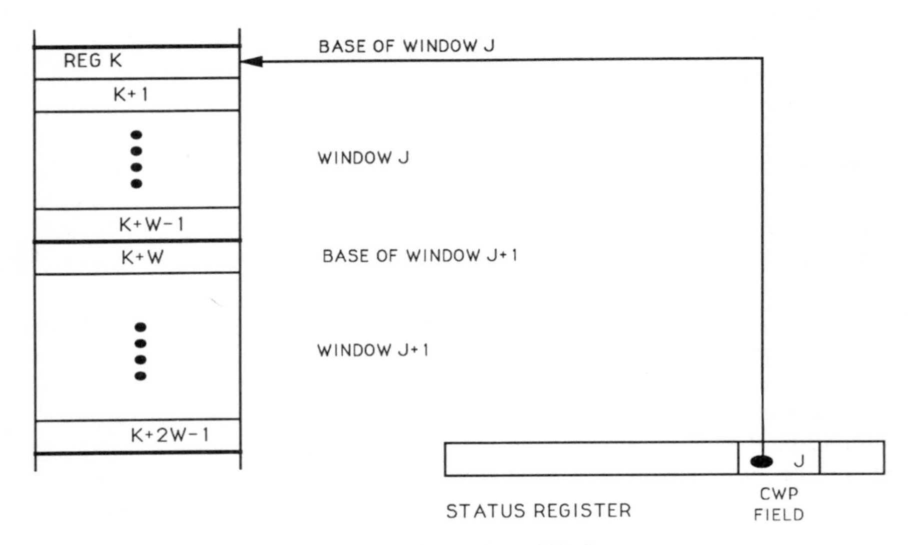

Figure 1.4.1 Register Windows

Status Register (SR), as illustrated in Figure 1.4.1. If the currently running procedure is assigned the register window j, taking up registers K, K+1, . . . , K+W−1 (where W is the number of registers per window), the CWP contains the value j, thereby pointing to the base of window j. If the next procedure to execute takes up window j+1, the value in the CWP field will be incremented accordingly to j+1.

Register windowing can be particularly adapted to efficient parameter passing between calling and called procedures by partial overlapping of the windows, as illustrated in Figure 1.4.2. The last N registers of window j are the first N registers of window j+1. If the procedure taking up window j calls a procedure, which in this design will necessarily be assigned the next window j+1, it can pass N parameters to the called procedure by placing their values into registers (K+W−N) to (K+W−1). The *same* registers will be automatically available to the called procedure without any further movement of data. Naturally, the procedure call will cause the CWP field to be incremented by one. In a computer with a small register file, parameters are passed by placing them on stack or any other data structure in memory. Extra traffic on the CPU to memory bus is necessarily involved, taking up additional time.

Although register windowing has been implemented primarily on RISC-type systems, the concept is not directly connected with RISC principles. Theoretically, register windowing could be implemented also on a CISC. However, an important point has to be noted. Modern implementations involve the use of VLSI chips. A CISC control unit takes up about 50% of the chip area, leaving very little space

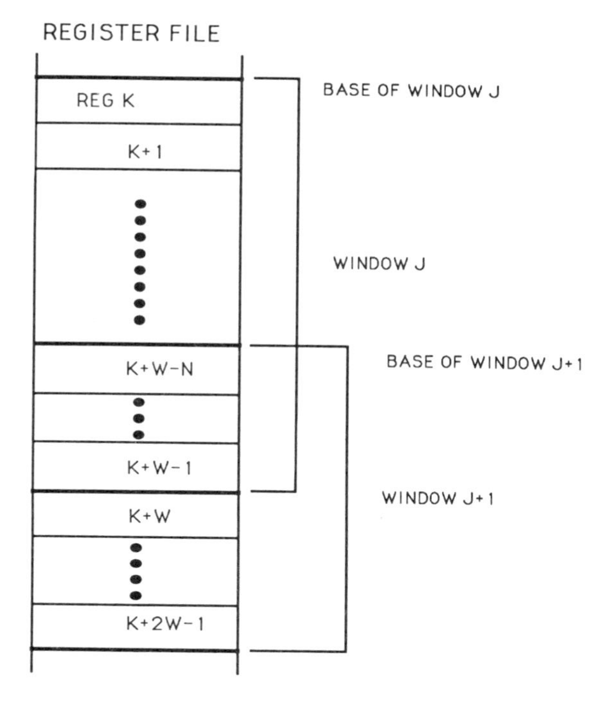

Figure 1.4.2 Partially Overlapping Windows

for other subsystems, and basically not permitting a large register file, needed for an efficient implementation of windowing. A RISC control unit takes up about 10% of the chip area, yielding the necessary space for a large register file.

Most modern computers use a number of parallel processing approaches to speed up operations. In particular the method of *pipelining* is widely used [1.14]. Pipelining was already featured in the third generation computers, such as the CDC 6600 and it became widely used later on (VAX 8600, MC68020 and many others). Pipelining was widely used on various CISC systems even before the RISC approach became popular and the concept is not directly connected with that of RISC. However, it was argued in section 1.2 that a streamlined RISC can handle pipelines more efficiently. Pipelining is indeed implemented in practically all modern high-performance RISC systems.

Another design feature, which became very popular on some RISC systems, is that of the *delayed branch*. The problem occurs in systems where instructions are prefetched (they always are in a system implementing an instruction pipeline), right after a conditional branch. If the branch condition is not satisfied (an unsuccessful branch), then the next instruction which was prefetched is executed, since no branch is to be performed, and no time is lost. If, on the other hand, the branch condition is satisfied (a successful branch), the next prefetched instruction is to be flushed and another instruction, pointed to by the branch address, is to be fetched in its place. The time dedicated to the prefetching of the flushed instruction is lost. Such loss of time can be remedied by using the delayed branch approach.

Consider the following example:

```
CLR     R2        ;  clear register R2
CMP     R1, 10    ;  check the difference (R1)-10
BZ      adr 1     ;  if (R1)-10=0 branch to adr 1
Next instruction  ;  otherwise execute next instruction.
```

(R1) is the contents of register R1. The nature of the 'Next instruction' is immaterial (can be any) and ';' represents the beginning of a comment. The next instruction was prefetched and will be flushed if (R1)=10. The first instruction can be placed between the branch and the next instruction, as follows:

```
CMP     R1, 10
BZ      adr 1
CLR     R2
Next instruction
```

The reshuffling of the instructions does not change the result. The instruction 'CLR R2' is now prefetched following the branch. Applying the *delayed branch* principle and assuming a successful branch, the execution of the branch (placing the value of the branch address 'adr 1' into the Program Counter) is delayed, until the following prefetched instruction 'CLR R2' is executed. No time is lost and there is no change in the intended program operation since R2 had to be cleared anyway before the branch and it did not influence the branch condition (check if another register, R1, contains the value 10).

The delayed branch technique can be implemented on any system, be it RISC or CISC. It so happens that it was actually implemented on some RISC systems.

There is another problem associated with the handling of instruction pipelines. Consider the following sequence of instructions:

```
load memr, r1    ;  load CPU register r1 from memory location memr
add r1, r2, r3   ;  (r1) + (r2) = r3
```

The r1, loaded from memory by the first instruction, is needed as an operand in the execution of the next instruction. It is important that the add instruction should use the new value in r1, attained after the completion of the load. Assuming both instructions can be fetched in a single fetch cycle (F), the load from memory would usually require an extra execute cycle (E). We have the following pipeline scheme:

load	F	E	E
add		F	E

The add is ready to execute before the new value in r1 is available. Unless appropriate steps are taken, the old value in r1 may be used, yielding an incorrect result.

A method, currently used to deal with such a case, is called *scoreboarding*. A special CPU control register, called the *scoreboard register*, is set aside for this purpose. Assume that there are 32 CPU registers. The scoreboard register would then be 32 bits long. Each of its bits represents one of the 32 CPU registers. For instance, bit 0 represents r 0, bit 1 represents r1 and so on. In general, if register ri is involved as a destination in the execution of any instruction, bit i in the scoreboard register will be set. As long as bit i is set, any subsequent instruction in the pipeline will be prevented from using ri in any way until bit i is cleared. This will happen as soon as the execution of the instruction, which caused bit i to be set, is completed.

In the previous example, bit 1 of the scoreboard register will be set until the load is complete. The execution of the add will be held (H cycle) until bit 1 is reset:

```
load    F  E  E
add        F  H  E
```

A cycle may be lost, but the final result is correct. Scoreboarding is used in the Motorola 88000 (chapter 6) and other systems.

In summary, some features implemented on RISC systems, but not necessarily directly connected with the RISC definition, are:

(a) HLL support
(b) Implementation of register windows
(c) Pipelining
(d) Delayed branch
(e) Scoreboarding

1.5 A Historical Survey of RISC

The term RISC was first coined by the University of California Berkeley group, directed by Patterson and Seguin [1.1–1.3, 1.17, 1.18]. The group produced the first experimental RISC-type CPUs on a single chip: RISC I and RISC II (chapter 3). Subsequently, the Berkeley group developed some special purpose RISC-type systems: the Smalltalk on a RISC, SOAR, and the Symbolic Processing Using RISCs, SPUR (section 5.2). Looking into the substance, rather than the name 'RISC', it turns out that the Berkeley group was not the first to adopt this concept.

Patterson [1.18] credits Seymour Cray (developer of the CDC 6600 family and founder of Cray Research, Inc.) with some basic design ideas of stressing CPU register-based operations; using memory access through LOAD/STORE instructions; and pipelined execution (features implemented in RISC). John Cocke of IBM is credited with the basic ideas leading to the development of the IBM 801 [1.18, 1.19], particularly expressed in pushing compiler technology with fast, simple instructions for text and integer applications. The IBM 801 project, initiated in 1975, but first officially publicized only in 1982 (the Berkeley RISC was announced in October 1980), was managed by G. Radin. According to a private communication by I. Barron, Managing Director of INMOS Ltd, UK, ideas for a RISC-type system have been under development by some INMOS personnel in parallel with IBM (without intercommunication between them), and which predated the work at Berkeley.

Shortly after the Berkeley RISC, another single-chip RISC-type processor, called MIPS (Microprocessor without Interlocked Pipeline Stages), was announced by a Stanford University team, directed by J.L. Hennessy [1.20]. The Stanford MIPS architecture was later ported into a commercial RISC-type processor, manufactured by MIPS Computers, Inc. (chapter 4).

Some authors see in the third generation CDC 6600 a model and a prototype of RISC [1.21]. The argument for this statement is that the CDC 6600 had hardwired control, a minimum number of instructions and memory access by load and store instructions only. It should be remembered on the other hand [1.22, chapter 43] that the CDC 6600 had two CPU instruction lengths of 15 and 30 bits, while its Peripheral Processing Units, PPUs, dealt with 12- and 24-bit instructions. The 24 CPU registers were subdivided into 3 types: 18-bit 8 Index, 8 Address Registers, and 8 60-bit floating point registers (the basic word length of the CDC 6600 was 60 bits). Although the CDC 6600 had some RISC properties, if the whole picture is considered, with its different options, the CDC 6600 can be viewed as a 'RISC prototype' only by a long stretch of the imagination.

A number of commercial products, marketed as RISC-type systems, was announced in the mid-eighties [1.3]. These include the Pyramid, Ridge, Inmos Transputer, IBM RT, Hewlett Packard, and others (chapter 12). Additional high-performance RISC-type products were announced in the second half of the eighties: MIPS R3000 (chapter 4), Motorola M88000 (chapter 6), Sun SPARC (chapter 7), AMD 29000 (chapter 8), Intel 80960 and 80860 (chapter 9). A number of DARPA-sponsored GaAs-based RISC-type systems, developed by a number of manufacturers, were announced [1.23]. Pioneering research in GaAs RISC systems was performed by Milutinovic [1.23].

A new Microcoded RISC (MIRIS) system was proposed and developed at the George Mason University [1.3]. Despite the fact that it is microcoded, it achieves a streamlined execution of all instructions by keeping a one-to-one correspondence between each machine language instruction and a single micro-instruction, and by avoiding the instruction decoding process (section 5.3). The MIRIS basic ideas were developed in an M.S. thesis by D. du Bose, advised by D. Tabak. A subsequent development of a Multitasking RISC [1.24] system, MULTRIS, conducted at GMU by D. Quammen, D.R. Miller, D. Tabak and a team of graduate students, is currently underway.

Some earlier RISC-related studies, conducted at the Ben Gurion University (BGU) of the Negev in Beer Sheva, Israel were part of a PhD thesis by Helnye Azaria, advised by Daniel Tabak [1.3]. Some of the work on the Single Instruction Computer has been inspired by earlier work of Lipovski and Tabak and Lipovski [1.3].

References

1.1 D.A. Patterson, D.R. Ditzel, 'The Case for the RISC', *Computer Architecture News*, **8**, No. 6, pp. 25–33, Oct. 15, 1980.
1.2 M.G.H. Katevenis, *Reduced Instruction Set Computer Architectures for VLSI*, MIT Press, Cambridge, MA, 1985.
1.3 D. Tabak, *RISC Architecture*, Research Studies Press, UK and Wiley, NY, 1987.
1.4 J.P. Hayes, *Computer Architecture and Organization, 2nd edn*, pp. 211–218, McGraw Hill, NY, 1988.
1.5 R.Y. Kain, *Computer Architecture, Vol. 1*, pp. 47–56, Prentice-Hall, Englewood Cliffs, NJ, 1989.
1.6 P. Chow, J. Hennessy, 'Reduced Instruction Set Computer Architectures', Ch. 2 in V.M. Milutinovic, ed., *Computer Architecture*, pp. 48–83, North-Holland, NY, 1988.
1.7 C.E. Gimarc, V.M. Milutinovic, 'RISC Principles, Architecture, and Design', Ch. 1 in V.M. Milutinovic, ed., *High-Level Language Computer Architecture*, pp. 1–64, Computer Science Press, NY, 1989.
1.8 D. Gifford, A. Spector, 'Case Study: IBM's System/360-370 Architecture', *Comm. ACM*, **30**, No. 4, pp. 292–307, April 1987.
1.9 T.E. Leonard, ed., *VAX Architecture Reference Manual*, Digital Press, Bedford, MA, 1987.
1.10 H.M. Levy, R.H. Eckhouse, Jr, *Computer Programming and Architecture: The VAX-11*, Digital Press, Bedford, MA, 1984.
1.11 G.M. Schneider, R. Davis, T. Mertz, *Computer Organization and Assembly Language Programming for the VAX*, Wiley, NY, 1987.
1.12 *MC68020 32-Bit Microprocessor User's Manual, 2nd edn*, Prentice-Hall, Englewood Cliffs, NJ, 1985.
1.13 J.F. Wakerly, *Microcomputer Architecture and Programming; The 68000 Family*, Wiley, NY, 1989.
1.14 K. Hwang, F.A. Briggs, *Computer Architecture and Parallel Processing*, McGraw Hill, NY, 1984.
1.15 D.A. Fairclough, 'A Unique Microprocessor Instruction Set', *IEEE MICRO*, **2**, No. 2, pp. 8–18, May 1982.
1.16 G.J. Myers, *Advances in Computer Architecture, 2nd edn*, Wiley, NY, 1982.
1.17 D.A. Patterson, C.H. Sequin, 'A VLSI RISC', *IEEE COMPUTER*, **15**, No. 9, pp. 8–21, Sept. 1982.
1.18 D.A. Patterson, 'Reduced Instruction Set Computers', *Comm. ACM*, **28**, No. 1, pp. 8–21, Jan. 1985.

1.19 G. Radin, 'The 801 Minicomputer', *IBM J. R&D*, **27**, No. 3, pp. 237–246, May 1983.

1.20 J.L. Hennessy, 'VLSI Processor Architecture', *IEEE Trans. on Computers*, **C-33**, No. 12, pp. 1221–1246, Dec. 1984.

1.21 C.G. Bell, 'RISC: Back to the Future?', *Datamation*, June 1, 1986, pp. 96–108.

1.22 D.P. Siewiorek, C.G. Bell, A. Newell, *Computer Structures: Principles and Examples*, McGraw Hill, NY, 1982.

1.23 V.M. Milutinovic, ed., *Special Issue of IEEE COMPUTER*, **19**, No. 10, Oct. 1986.

1.24 D.J. Quammen, D.R. Miller, D. Tabak, 'Register Window Management for a Real-Time Multitasking RISC', *Proc. 22nd Annual Hawaii Int. Conf. on System Sciences, HICSS-22*, **1**, pp. 135–142, Jan. 3–6, 1989.

2

RISC Advantages and Shortcomings

2.1 Introductory Comments

Computer designers may have different goals and criteria, but the following are universal for practically all systems:

(a) Maximize speed of operation or minimize execution time.
(b) Minimize cost; development cost and sale price.

The maximization of speed, or minimization of program execution time can be achieved in a number of ways. One way to speed up the system is by improving the technology of the components, achieving operation at higher frequencies. This means working with a *shorter clock cycle* T. Different instructions take a different *number of cycles* C to execute. Speed up can be achieved by a judicious architectural design, minimizing the average number of clock cycles per instruction. The overall time needed to run a given program, the *program time* PT, depends of course on the *number of instructions* (I) in it. We can write:

$$PT[\text{sec.}] = ICT\ [(\text{instr.})(\text{cycles/instr.})(\text{sec./cycle})] \qquad (2.1)$$

$$\text{instr.} = \text{instruction},\ \text{sec.} = \text{seconds}$$

Naturally, we would want to minimize PT. The shorter the PT, the higher is the *speed* S, which is proportional to the inverse of PT.

$$S = K/PT = K/(ICT)\ [\text{instr./sec.}] \qquad (2.2)$$

where K is a coefficient of proportionality with a dimensionality of [instr.].

In the subsequent discussion of RISC advantages, it will be argued that RISC systems are particularly adept for maximizing S while keeping the cost down, thus achieving important computer design goals.

The advantages of RISC will be discussed from a number of points of view:

VLSI realization,
Computing speed,
Design cost and reliability,
HLL support.

RISC shortcomings and criticism will be presented subsequently, followed by a summarizing discussion at the end of this chapter.

2.2 RISC and VLSI Realization

The VLSI viewpoint argumentation was one of the principal points presented by the original RISC proponents in 1980 [1.1]. As argued in chapter 1, a RISC has relatively few instructions, few addressing modes and few instruction formats. As a result, a relatively small and simple (compared to CISC) decode and execute hardware subsystem of the control unit is required. This yields the following results when we contemplate the realization of a computing system by VLSI chips:

(a) The chip area, dedicated to the realization of the control unit (the so-called *control area*) is considerably reduced. For example, the control area on RISC I constitutes 6% of the chip area [1.17]; on RISC II, 10%; and on the Motorola MC68020, 68%. In general, the control area for CISCs takes over 50% of the chip area [1.17]. Therefore, on a RISC VLSI chip, there is more area available for other features. There is a higher chance of fitting a whole CPU plus some additional commodities onto a chip (i.e. cache, floating point unit, part of the main memory, memory management unit, I/O ports).

(b) As a result of the considerable reduction of the control area, the RISC designer can fit a large number of CPU registers (138 in RISC II) on the chip. This in turn enhances the throughput and the HLL support, as will be argued in the following paragraphs.

(c) By reducing the control area on a VLSI chip, and filling the area by 138 identical registers, we actually increase the *regularization factor* of the chip. The regularization factor is defined [2.1] as the total number of devices on the chip, excluding ROMs, divided by the number of drawn devices (such as registers, ALUs, counters and other subsystems). It is the effective number of devices on the chip that we get for each device that we draw. Basically, the higher the regularization factor, the lower the VLSI design cost. While the regularization factor for MC68000 was 12, it was 25 for RISC I [2.2].

(d) The GaAs VLSI chip realization technology is currently limited by a relatively low density (about 30000 transistors/chip). Therefore, since a RISC reduces the control area, it represents an attractive approach for GaAs, single chip, CPU realization [1.23].

2.3 The Computing Speed Aspect

As explained in chapter 1, the essence of a RISC is its uniform, streamlined handling of all (at least most) of the instructions. The RISC design approach is particularly suitable for a more efficient handling of pipelines (compared to CISC). As a result of the uniformity of instruction size and duration of execution, wait or hold periods in the pipeline are reduced to a minimum. These factors contribute significantly to the increase in computing speed.

A simpler and a smaller control unit in a RISC has fewer gates. This results in shorter propagation paths (fewer gates to propagate through) for the control unit signals, yielding a faster operation.

A significantly reduced number of instructions, formats and modes, results in a simpler and smaller decoding system. As in the case of the simpler control unit, the decoding operation is faster on a RISC.

A hardwire-controlled system with a reduced control unit will in general be faster than a microprogram-controlled one. Particularly if the latter has instructions corresponding to microroutines of different lengths, some of which may be considerably long.

A relatively large (32 or more) CPU register file tends to reduce CPU-memory traffic to fetch and store data operands. Data items which are needed often can be kept in CPU registers. This tends to save computing time, particularly for programs handling large amounts of data.

A large register set can also be used to store parameters to be passed from a calling to a called procedure, to store the information of a process which was preempted by another, and to store the information of an interrupted program. Without an adequate CPU register file, all of the above information would have to be stored in memory. This would cause extra CPU-memory traffic for the storage and, later, for the eventual restoration of the above information. All in all, a considerable amount of computer time can be saved by a large register set in a number of different events.

The delayed branch technique (section 1.4) also contributes to the enhancement of speed by preventing the flushing (and thus a waste) of prefetched instructions in case of a successful branch.

From the quantitative point of view, we can say that the RISC design contributes to the reduction of the program run time, PT (eqn (2.1)), or to the increase of speed, S (eqn (2.2)), by reducing the number of clock cycles per instruction, C. This follows from the basic characterization of RISC, which minimizes the number of cycles (ideally, one) needed to execute each instruction (section 1.3).

2.4 Design Cost and Reliability Considerations

A relatively small and simple control unit in a CPU will usually yield the following design costs and design reliability benefits:

(a) It will take a shorter time to complete the design of a RISC control unit, thus contributing to the reduction in the overall design costs.

(b) A shorter design time would reduce the probability that the end product will be obsolete by the time the design is completed.

(c) A simpler and smaller control unit will have a reduced number of design errors and, therefore, a higher reliability. Moreover, it will be easier (than in a CISC) to locate and correct those errors.

(d) Because of the simplicity and low number of instruction formats (one or two) and the fact that all instructions have the same standard length, instructions will not cross word boundaries and an instruction cannot wind up on two separate pages in a Virtual Memory (VM). This eliminates a potential difficulty in the design of a virtual memory management subsystem. Some of the modern, commercial RISC-type products have very powerful memory management units, such as in the Motorola M88000 family (chapter 6).

2.5 High Level Language (HLL) Support

Several of the modern CISC systems, such as Digital VAX 11/780 or VAX-8600 [1.9], have many features in their machine design which support directly functions which are common in HLLs (procedure management, array operations, array index testing, information typing and protection, memory management and others). Several CISC systems have machine language instructions which are either identical or very similar to some HLL instructions. As it turns out, the RISC design also offers some features which directly support common HLL operations and simplify the design of certain HLL Compilers.

(a) Since the total number of instructions in a RISC system is small, a compiler (for any HLL), while attempting to realize a certain operation in machine language, will usually have only a single choice, as opposed to a possibility of several choices in a CISC. This will make that part of the compiler shorter and simpler in a RISC.

(b) The availability of a relatively large number of CPU registers in a RISC permits a more efficient code optimization stage in a compiler, by maximizing the number of faster register-to-register operations and minimizing the number of slower memory accesses.

(c) The 'register window' arrangement (see section 1.4) in a RISC CPU permits fast parameter passing between procedures and constitutes a direct support of HLL handling of subroutines and procedures.

(d) All in all a RISC instruction set presents a reduced burden on the compiler writer. This in turn would tend to reduce the time of preparation of RISC compilers and their costs [1.1, 1.17].

(e) A simplified instruction set in a RISC provides an opportunity to eliminate a level of translation at runtime, in favor of translating at compile time (since the RISC compiler is simpler).

2.6 RISC Shortcomings

RISC shortcomings are directly related to some of its points of advantage. The principal RISC disadvantage is its reduced number of instructions. Since a RISC has a small number of instructions, a number of functions, performed on CISCs by a single instruction, will need two, three or more instructions on a RISC. This in turn will cause the RISC code to be longer. More memory will have to be allocated for RISC programs and the instruction traffic between the memory and the CPU will be increased [2.3]. Recent studies have shown [1.17] that, on average, a RISC program will be about 30% longer than a CISC program, performing the same function. This is because only a minority of the instructions are used most of the time [1.15], and this minority is usually featured on RISC systems. This consideration has been taken seriously by most commercial RISC systems manufacturers. In fact, a number of commercial RISCs feature more than 100 instructions (chapters 6–12), compared to less than 40 on the Berkeley RISC and the Stanford MIPS (chapters 3, 4). Even the commercial MIPS, featured by MIPS Computer Systems, Inc., has more than 100 instructions (chapter 4).

A controversial feature of a number of RISC systems is the large (sometimes over 100 registers) CPU register file. Some of its potential advantages are quite obvious. By keeping data values, to be used as operands in the program, in the CPU register file, the overall data traffic between the memory and the CPU is reduced. If the register set is small, many intermediate results, even if needed later in the program, have to be stored in memory, only to be fetched again at a later time. With a large register set, intermediate results and any other data can be kept in CPU registers for as long as they are needed. A large register set also permits efficient parameter passing between procedures, as argued in section 1.4. With a small register set all of the parameters have to be stored in memory, and fetched from it whenever needed, increasing the CPU-memory data traffic.

In a multitasking environment, the processor is switched quite often between different tasks. Each task has a certain set of data associated with it, called the *task context*, or the *task state*. The context of the interrupted task has to be saved. It is usually saved in memory and later retrieved when the interrupted task is reinstated. If the CPU has a large register file and the task context is limited to a finite subset of the CPU registers, the context can be saved in *another subset* of the CPU register file, saving on CPU-memory traffic. The same can be said about saving the basic information of an interrupted program. A large enough CPU register file can be configured by the designer to serve, optionally, as a stack or a data queue if needed [1.24]. Without a large CPU register file, the above data structures have to be configured in the memory and any communication with them constitutes extra CPU-memory data traffic. Having a large number of identical registers on the CPU chip increases its regularization factor (section 2.2) and thus reduces the VLSI design and manufacturing cost.

On the other hand, having a large, on-chip, CPU register file is plagued with disadvantages. The register address decoding system will be more complicated for a larger register file, increasing the access time to any of its registers. The use of window pointers (section 1.4) in some systems also tends to increase the register address decode time. Elaborate window management policies may also complicate the CPU logic, raising the cost and slowing down the operation. A large register file takes up more space on a chip. Some designers, such as those of the Motorola 88000, decided that it was more important to place a Floating Point Unit (FPU) on the CPU chip, instead of having it on a separate coprocessor and have only a modest (32) CPU register file primarily managed by software (chapter 6). Having the FPU on chip certainly speeds up all floating point operations.

In all systems where all of the CPU registers are saved in memory during a context switch, a large register file will take more time to store and, later, to retrieve. In addition, some compiler techniques make more efficient use of relatively small register files (16 to 32 registers), such as on the MIPS (chapter 4). The advantages and disadvantages of a large (over 32) CPU register file, discussed above, are summarized in Table 2.6.1.

As can be seen, the question of the optimal size of the CPU register file is a controversial one, requiring additional research. Despite some obvious advantages, there are studies putting the benefit of a large register set in doubt [2.3, 2.4]. The simulation experiments in these studies were conducted with somewhat contrived rather than actual models of widely used computers. For this reason, the recommendations resulting from the above are indicative rather than conclusive. More extensive experimental results are needed.

The register file implementation on a number of actual RISC systems is summarized in Table 2.6.2. As can be seen from the table there is a wide spectrum of register file implementation in many experimental and commercial systems. Considerable experience, particularly with the commercial systems, is needed in order to arrive at some definite conclusions. In the meantime, the question of the size of the CPU register file will remain debatable.

An alternative to a large register file is the use of a cache memory [1.14, 1.22, 2.5]. The cache is now implemented in practically all modern computing systems. In order to compare the relative merits of a cache and a register file, let us list some of their properties:

	Cache	*CPU Register File*
1.	Addressed as locations in memory-long addresses.	Separate register addressing-short addresses.
2.	Has to be at least about 4 KBytes to be effective.	About 128 registers (512 bytes) will have significant effect on performance.
3.	Information loaded in units of blocks (lines).	Information can be loaded individually to each register.
4.	On the average, access slower compared to register file.	Faster access.

Table 2.6.1 Large CPU Register File

ADVANTAGES:

1. Speed up of operations by reducing CPU-memory traffic.
2. Procedure parameters passing support within the CPU.
3. Multitasking context switching and interrupt handling support within the CPU.
4. On-chip stack and/or queue of data.
5. Increase in the chip regularization factor.

DISADVANTAGES:

1. Longer access time.
2. If window pointers are used, longer to decode register address.
3. Register file takes up more chip space.
4. Elaborate window policies complicate CPU logic.
5. Advanced compiler technology makes efficient use of relatively small register files.
6. If all CPU registers are saved on a context switch, a large register file will take more time to store.

5. Information loaded based on prefetch and replacement policies.	Any information can be loaded at any time by the user.
6. Usually inaccessible by the user.	Usually fully accessible by the user.

Since cache addresses are actually memory addresses (usually 32 bits) they would take longer to decode than register file addresses (7 bits for 128 registers). Moreover, 3 direct register addresses can be easily packed into a 32-bit instruction format. With memory addressing, single word instruction length (32 bits), a three-operand addressing would necessarily be indirect. This would imply a longer access time compared to the direct mode. If the cache is on the same chip with the CPU, the access time will be comparable to that of a register file. However, how much cache can we put on a chip? The Motorola MC68030 has 512 bytes and the National Semiconductor NS32532 has 1536 bytes (of instruction and data total) on chip cache. Experience has shown that in order to attain a decent hit ratio (say above 0.85) the cache size should be at least 4 KBytes or even 8 KBytes [1.22]. Therefore, in order for the cache to be effective, most of it must be off

Table 2.6.2 Register File Implementation on RISC Systems

LARGER REGISTER FILE (over 32)	REGISTERS
WINDOW MANAGEMENT POLICY	
RISC II (Ch. 3)	138
MIRIS (Section 5.3)	2048
MULTRIS (Section 5.3)	1024
Pyramid (Section 12.1)	528
SPARC (Ch. 7)	128
NO WINDOWS	
Intel 80960 (Ch. 9)	84
AMD 29000 (Ch. 8)	192
MODERATE REGISTER FILE (32)	
IBM 801 (Section 5.1)	32
MIPS (Ch. 4)	32
Motorola 88000 (Ch. 6)	32
PRISM (Section 12.3)	32
HP Precision Architecture (Section 12.6)	32
SMALL REGISTER FILE (LESS THAN 32)	
Ridge (Section 12.2)	16
Acorn (Ch. 11)	16
Transputer (Section 12.4)	6
IBM ROMP (Section 12.5)	16
CLIPPER (Ch. 10)	24

the CPU chip. On the other hand, a 128-register CPU file can fit on chip, while providing considerable performance advantages [1.17, 1.18]. All in all, the CPU register file access is faster compared to that of the cache. This argument will be weakened in the future, with the appearance of larger caches on a CPU chip, such as the 4 KBytes instruction and 8 KBytes data caches on the Intel 80860 (chapter 9).

In many systems the user has no direct control over the manipulation of the cache. The cache is usually managed either by the hardware or by the Operating

System (OS) routines. On the other hand, the CPU register file is usually general purpose (or most of it) and fully accessible by the user.

Some other RISC shortcomings [2.6]:

(a) Hardwired control, implemented on most RISCs, is less flexible, more error prone, more difficult to find and correct errors [2.5], more difficult to handle complex instructions.

(b) Single word instructions make it impossible to use direct memory addressing for a full 32-bit address. For this reason, some manufacturers have allowed a small part of the instructions to have double-word length (Intel 80960, chapter 9). The use of such instructions is decided by the programmer; one can write complete programs with single-word instructions only.

2.7 Concluding Comments

As can be seen from the preceding sections in this chapter, the RISC concept has both advantages and shortcomings. It has encountered opposition right from its inception [2.7], and the controversy has continued over the years [2.8]. Notwithstanding the controversy, there are about 20 commercial computer products (15 described in the subsequent chapters of this text) announced as RISC-type by their manufacturers. To be sure, most of them do not adhere to all of the RISC properties, specified in chapter 1. Some are more 'RISCy' than others; however, all of them strive to achieve a uniform and streamlined handling of all (or at least most) of the instructions.

The applications of RISC processors are widening as time goes on (see chapter 14). Although most of the RISC applications, so far, were as processors in workstations, some computer systems developers plan to use RISC processors as individual CPUs in multiprocessors. For instance, the Motorola M88000 family (chapter 6) will be used in the new generation of the BBN Butterfly multiprocessor, and the AMD 29000 (chapter 8) will be used on the NYU Ultracomputer.

Recent market studies [2.9, 2.10] predict a spectacular growth of RISC products implementation. A study made by Information Network (San Francisco) predicts that total revenues for 32-bit RISC chips will grow from $17 million in 1987 to $505 million in 1992 [2.9]. RISC computer sales will grow from 7% of the total computer market (in 1987) to 44.5% in 1992. RISC-based workstations will grow from $300 million in 1987 to $2.89 billion in 1992. According to studies made at Askmar Partners (Menlo Park, CA), between 35,000 to 40,000 RISC units were shipped in 1988 and 118,000 are projected to be shipped in 1989. MIPS Computer Systems (chapter 4) led the market in 1988 with close to 20,000 units, while Intergraph's CLIPPER (chapter 10) and Sun's SPARC (chapter 7) shipped 11,000 and 9,000 respectively. It is projected that in 1989 and 1990

(260,000 units) MIPS' share will be well over 50% of the total RISC market. In 1990 Motorola RISC sales (M88000, chapter 6) are projected to exceed those of the CLIPPER and be about equal to those of the SPARC. The above statistics and projections indicate that despite some shortcomings, the RISC approach is here to stay. It has already attained a leading role in the computer technology, a role which it is predicted will grow.

References

2.1 W.W. Lattin *et al.*, 'A Methodology for VLSI Chip Design', *LAMBDA*, Second Quarter 1981, pp. 34–44.

2.2 D.A. Patterson, 'A RISCy Approach to Computer Design', *Proc. COMPCON 1982*, pp. 8–14, San Francisco, CA, 1982.

2.3 M.J. Flynn, C.L. Mitchell, J.M. Mulder, 'And Now a Case for More Complex Instruction Sets', *IEEE COMPUTER*, **20**, No. 9, pp. 71–83, Sept. 1987.

2.4 D.W. Wall, 'Register Windows vs. Register Allocation', *Proc. Conf. on Programming Language Design and Implementation (SIGPLAN '88)*, pp. 67–78, Atlanta, GA, June 22–24, 1988.

2.5 J.P. Hayes, *Computer Architecture and Organization, 2nd edn*, McGraw Hill, NY, 1988.

2.6 R. Weiss, 'RISC Processors: The New Wave in Computer Systems', *Computer Design*, May 15, 1987, pp. 53–73.

2.7 D.W. Clark, W.D. Strecker, 'Comments on "The Case for the RISC"', *Computer Architecture News*, **8**, No. 6, pp. 34–38, Oct. 15, 1980.

2.8 R.P. Colwell *et al.*, 'Computers, Complexity and Controversy', *IEEE COMPUTER*, **18**, No. 9, pp. 8–19, Sept. 1985.

2.9 M.C. Ballou, 'RISC Market to Boom Over Next Five Years, Study Finds', *Digital Review*, Aug. 15, 1988.

2.10 D. Gianatasio, 'RISC Will Dominate Market Within 5 Years, Report Says', *Digital Review*, Jan. 30, 1989, p. 62.

3

The Berkeley RISC

3.1 Introductory Comments

After discussing some general issues regarding RISC-type systems, the Berkeley RISC will be presented in this chapter. The Berkeley RISC I and RISC II are the first systems bearing this name and the first to be realized on a VLSI chip. In this chapter, unless stated otherwise, the term 'RISC' will imply the specific Berkeley RISC system (I or II, as specified).

The aspects of Architecture, Organization and Realization of RISC I and II will be described. By 'Architecture' we mean the image that the computing system presents to the machine language programmer and the compiler writer [1.16]. This usually includes the complete list of all CPU registers, flip-flops and other parts accessible to the user by any instruction, data and instruction formats, the complete instruction set and any other details that the programmer has a need to know.

By 'Organization' one should understand the complete details of the configuration, interconnections and other pertinent data of all the subsystems included in the computer, such as ALU, control subunits, I/O ports, buses, pins and others. By 'Realization' one should understand the details of the hardware structures and circuit components chosen to construct the system. Details about the VLSI technology, materials and other pertinent data are to be mentioned. Although all aspects will be presented, a particular stress will be given to the architectural properties of RISC.

3.2 RISC Architecture

3.2.1 General Description

The RISC is a 32-bit machine, with each byte in memory individually addressed. It recognizes the following integer, signed (2's complement) and unsigned data formats:

Word	32-bits
Half word	16-bits
Byte	8-bits

The RISC does not have a floating point facility. In a word or a half word, the least significant byte has the lowest address. All data items in memory are aligned in such a way that they do not cross word boundaries. If we start storing in the memory byte items, their addresses will be 0, 1, 2, 3, 4, 5 . . . and so on. For half-words we will have only even addresses 0, 2, 4, 6 . . . and for words: 0, 4, 8, 12 (addresses 0 and those divisible by 4). The data bus between the CPU and the memory is 32-bits wide and every memory-read operation fetches 4 bytes at a time into the CPU.

An example of a memory packing could be the following:

bits 31 — 24	23 — 16	15 — 8	7 — 0	*word*
byte 3	byte 2	byte 1	byte 0	0
half word 6		half word 4		4
half word 10		half word 8		8
half word 14		half word 12		12
word 16				16

The bits in a word are numbered so that bit 0 is the least significant, and bit 31 the most significant.

The CPU has a total of 138 32-bit working registers, R0, R1, . . ., R137 available to the user. However, each program or procedure, running on the RISC, 'sees' only 32 CPU registers. The multiple registers are used for parameter passing between calling and called procedures and for the storage of local variables by each procedure. This point will be elaborated in more detail later on. The first ten registers R0, R1, . . ., R9, called the *global registers*, are seen by all of the procedures running on the RISC and they contain the global variables of the program. Register R0 contains always zero (R0 = 0) and it is used to synthesize addressing modes and operations which are not directly available on the RISC. It can be written into but its contents will remain zero nevertheless.

When a signed 8- or 16-bit data value is stored in a 32-bit register it is automatically sign-extended, while being placed in the register's least significant part. The remaining, most significant part of the register is filled with the sign of the data value (1 for negative, 0 for positive). In the case of 8- or 16-bit unsigned data values, it works similarly; only the most significant part of the register is filled with zeros.

A whole word (32-bits) is used to specify addresses in RISC. Thus, the RISC logical address space is 2^{32} bytes or 4 Gbytes.

3.2.2 *The Instruction Formats*

The RISC is a 3-address (operand) machine with two sources and a destination specified in the instruction. There are also some two- and single-address (operand) instructions. The RISC architecture distinguishes two basic instruction formats:

(a) The Short-Immediate Format
This format is used for all register-to-register instructions and for register-indexed load, store and control-transfer instructions.

31 — 25	24	23 — Rd — 19	18 — Rs — 14	13	12 — S2 — 0
OPCODE	SCC	DEST	SOURCE 1	IM	SOURCE 2
7	1	5	5	1	13

The individual fields of the instruction format have the following interpretation:

OPCODE	7-bits, contains the operation code of the instruction. Although there is space for 128 opcodes, the RISC I has 31 and the RISC II only 39 instructions.
SCC	1-bit, when set this bit determines whether the condition codes (flags) of the CPU will be affected by the instruction.
DEST	5-bits, determines one out of 32 possible destination registers, Rd.
SOURCE 1	5-bits, one of the source registers, Rs (out of 32).
IM = 0	the low order 5 bits of the SOURCE 2 field (13-bits) specify the second source register; 8 bits of SOURCE 2 are unused.
IM = 1	SOURCE 2 is interpreted as a 13-bit, sign-extended constant.
SOURCE 2	13-bit, represents the second source operand S2, as explained above.

(b) The Long-Immediate Format

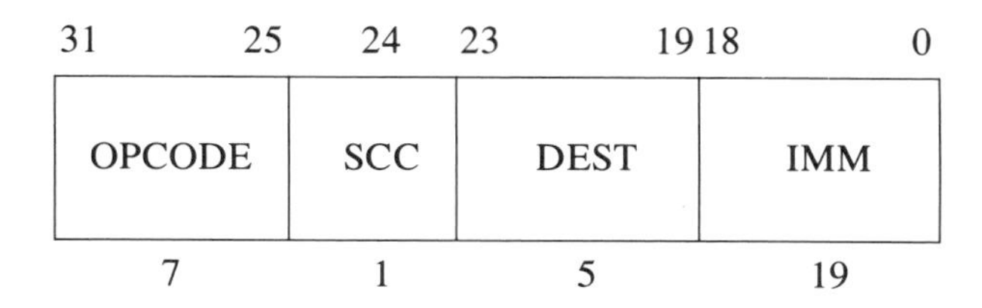

This format is used for all PC-relative instructions and for all branches. The OPCODE and the SCC field are interpreted as in the Short-Immediate Format.

DEST 5-bits, interpreted in two ways:
(a) As a 5-bit destination register, Rd,

(b) For branch instructions, its 4 least significant bits constitute the *condition code*, while the leftmost bit is unused.

IMM 19-bits, interpreted as a sign-extended constant.

3.2.3 The Addressing Modes

Formally, there are two basic addressing modes:

(1) Indexed mode, (Rx) S2
Effective Address = Rx + S2
(2) PC-Relative, Y
Effective Address (EA) = PC + Y

Mode (1) can be used to synthesize the following modes:

(a) Base-Absolute (Direct), Rx = Rb, S2 = imm
EA = Rb + imm
(b) Register Indirect, Rx = Rp, S2 = R0 = 0
EA = Rp
(c) Indexed for a linear byte array a[i], assuming Ra points to the base of a[.], Rx = Ri, S2 = Ra
EA = Ra + Ri

3.2.4 The Instruction Set

The RISC I has 31 instructions and the RISC II has 39. RISC II has all of the 31 RISC I instructions plus an extra 8 LOAD/STORE (5 LOAD, 3 STORE) instructions. All of the 8 extra RISC II instructions use the PC-Relative addressing mode, while the original LOAD/STORE instructions of RISC I (but also available on RISC II) use the Indexed mode.

The complete list of the RISC II 39 instructions is given in Table 3.1. The additional 8 instructions of RISC II are indicated. The RISC instructions are subdivided into 4 categories:

1. Arithmetic-Logic Instructions (12).
2. Memory Access: LOAD/STORE Instructions (16).
3. Branch and CALL Instructions (7).
4. Miscellaneous Instructions (4).

The instructions are listed in Table 3.1 in the above order.

In the Operation column of Table 3.1, when we write Rs + S2, we mean – the contents of Register Rs plus either the contents of the register, specified by S2 or the immediate constant, specified by S2. The above sum can serve as an effective address in memory, and the contents of the memory location, starting at that address, are denoted by M[Rs + S2]. Of course, different ['addends'] can be substituted in this expression:

M[Rx + S2]
M[PC + Y]

but the meaning remains the same.

The jump conditions, expressed by COND, are the following [1.2]

Hexadecimal Code	Assembly Notation	Name of Condition
0	—	Unconditional jump
1	GT	Greater Than
2	LE	Less or Equal
3	GE	Greater or Equal
4	LT	Less Than
5	HI	Higher Than
6	LOS	Lower or Same
7	LO or NC	Lower Than or No Carry
8	HIS or C	Higher or Same or Carry
9	PL	Plus
A	MI	Minus
B	NE	Not Equal
C	EQ	Equal
D	NV	No Overflow
E	V	Overflow
F	ALW	Always

Some of the instructions in RISC I have different mnemonics [1.17] than those in RISC II [1.2]:

RISC I	RISC II
SUBR	SUBI
SUBCR	SUBCI
LDL	LDXW
LDSU	LDXHU
LDSS	LDXHS
LDBU	LDXBU
LDBS	LDXBS
STL	STXW
STS	STXH
STB	STXB
JMP	JMPX
CALL	CALLX
CALLINT	CALLI
RETINT	RETI

Table 3.1 RISC II Instruction Set

	Instruction Name	Assembly Notation		Operation
	Arithmetic-Logic Instructions			
1.	Integer Add	ADD	Rs, S2, Rd	Rd <-- Rs + S2
2.	Add with Carry	ADDC	Rs, S2, Rd	Rd <-- Rs + S2 + C
3.	Integer Subtract	SUB	Rs, S2, Rd	Rd <-- Rs - S2
4.	Subtract with Carry	SUBC	Rs, S2, Rd	Rd <-- Rs - S2 - C
5.	Integer Subtract Reverse	SUBI	Rs, S2, Rd	Rd <-- S2 - Rs
6.	Subtract Reverse with Carry	SUBCI	Rs, S2, Rd	Rd <-- S2 - Rs - C
7.	Logical AND	AND	Rs, S2, Rd	Rd <-- Rs and S2
8.	Logical OR	OR	Rs, S2, Rd	Rd <-- Rs or S2
9.	Logical Exclusive OR	XOR	Rs, S2, Rd	Rd <-- Rs XOR S2
10.	Shift Left	SLL	Rs, S2, Rd	Rd <-- Rs shifted by S2
11.	Shift Right Logical	SRL	Rs, S2, Rd	Rd <-- Rs shifted by S2
12.	Shift Right Arithmetic	SRA	Rs, S2, Rd	Rd <-- Rs shifted by S2
	LOAD/STORE Instructions			
13.	Load Long	LDXW	(Rx) S2, Rd	Rd <-- M[Rx + S2]
14.	Load Short Unsigned	LDXHU	--- " ---	--- " ---
15.	Load Short Signed	LDXHS	--- " ---	--- " ---
16.	Load Byte Unsigned	LDXBU	--- " ---	--- " ---
17.	Load Byte Signed	LDXBS	--- " ---	--- " ---
18.	Load Relative Long II	LDRW	Y, Rd	Rd <-- M[PC + Y]
19.	Load Relative Short Unsigned II	LDRHU	--- " ---	--- " ---
20.	Load Relative Short Signed II	LDRHS	--- " ---	--- " ---
21.	Load Relative Byte Unsigned II	LDRBU	--- " ---	--- " ---
22.	Load Relative Byte Signed II	LDRBS	--- " ---	--- " ---
23.	Store Long	STXW	Rm, (Rx) S2	M[Rx + S2] <-- Rm
24.	Store Short	STXH	--- " ---	--- " ---
25.	Store Byte	STXB	--- " ---	--- " ---
26.	Store Relative Long II	STRW	Rm, Y	M[PC + Y] <-- Rm
27.	Store Relative Short II	STRH	--- " ---	--- " ---
28.	Store Relative Byte II	STRB	--- " ---	--- " ---

	Instruction	Assembly Notation		Operation
	Branch and CALL Instructions			
29.	Conditional Jump	JMPX	COND, (Rx) S2	PC <-- Rx + S2
30.	Conditional Relative Jump	JMPR	COND, Y	PC <-- PC + Y
31.	Call and Change Window	CALLX	Rd, (Rx) S2	Rd <-- PC, next PC <-- Rx + S2 CWP <-- CWP - 1
32.	Call Relative and Change Window	CALLR	Rd, Y	Rd <-- PC, next PC <-- PC + Y CWP <-- CWP + 1
33.	Return and Change Window	RET	COND, (Rx) S2	PC <-- Rx + S2 CWP <-- CWP + 1
34.	Call an Interrupt Pr	CALLI	Rd	Rd <-- last PC, next CWP <-- CWP - 1
35.	Return from Interrupt Pr	RETI	COND, (Rx) S2	NXTPC <-- Rx + S2, next CWP <-- CWP + 1
	Miscellaneous Instructions			
36.	Load Immediate High to Restart Delayed Jump	LDHI	Rd, Y	Rd <31:13> <-- Y, Rd <12:0> <-- 0
37.	Load Last PC (Save Value for Restarting Pipeline) Pr	GETLPC	Rd	Rd <-- last PC
38.	Load Status Word	GETPSW	Rd	Rd <-- PSW
39.	Set Status Word Pr	PUTPSW	Rm	PSW <-- Rm

Comments

II - Instruction available on RISC II only (not on RISC I).
Pr - Priviledged (System) Instructions.
S2 - Either a CPU register or a 13-bit immediate constant.
M[Rx + S2] - Memory location contents, whose effective address starts at Rx + S2.
Y - immediate 19-bit constant.
Rd, Rx, Rm - CPU registers. When in an equation - their contents.
Long - 32-bit word
Short - 16-bit word
COND - Branch condition (specified in the text). When COND=0, it represents an unconditional branch.
CWP - Current Window Pointer, points to the window of the currently active procedure.

However, their operation is essentially the same.

The opcodes of the RISC II instructions are the following [1.2]:

	000XXXX	001XXXX	010XXXX	011XXXX
XXX 0001	CALLI	SLL		
XXX 0010	GETPSW	SRA		
XXX 0011	GETLPC	SRL		
XXX 0100	PUTPSW	LDHI		
XXX 0101		AND		
XXX 0110		OR	LDXW	STXW
XXX 0111		XOR	LDRW	STRW
XXX 1000	CALLX	ADD	LDXHU	
XXX 1001	CALLR	ADDC	LDRHU	
XXX 1010			LDXHS	STXH
XXX 1011			LDRHS	STRH
XXX 1100	JMPX	SUB	LDXBU	
XXX 1101	JMPR	SUBC	LDRBU	
XXX 1110	RET	SUBI	LDXBS	STXB
XXX 1111	RETI	SUBCI	LDRBS	STRB

For instance, to obtain the opcode of AND, we take the 3 bits of the column with the 4 bits of the row to form: 001 0101.

3.2.5 The CPU Registers

As mentioned before, the RISC has 138 32-bit working registers R0, R1, . . . , R137, available to the user, 32 registers per program or procedure. The first 10 registers R0, R1, . . . , R9 are called the *global registers*. They are visible to *all procedures* running in the system. In addition, each procedure sees 22 *window registers*, R10 to R31 (see Figure 3.1), subdivided into three groups:

Name	Number of Registers	Registers
HIGH	6	R31 to R26
LOCAL	10	R25 to R16
LOW	6	R15 to R10

There can be a total of 8 windows. Each window is pointed to by a 3-bit field CWP (Current Window Pointer) of the Processor Status Word, PSW (bits 10–12). The PSW register (13 bits) is visible to the user and can be manipulated

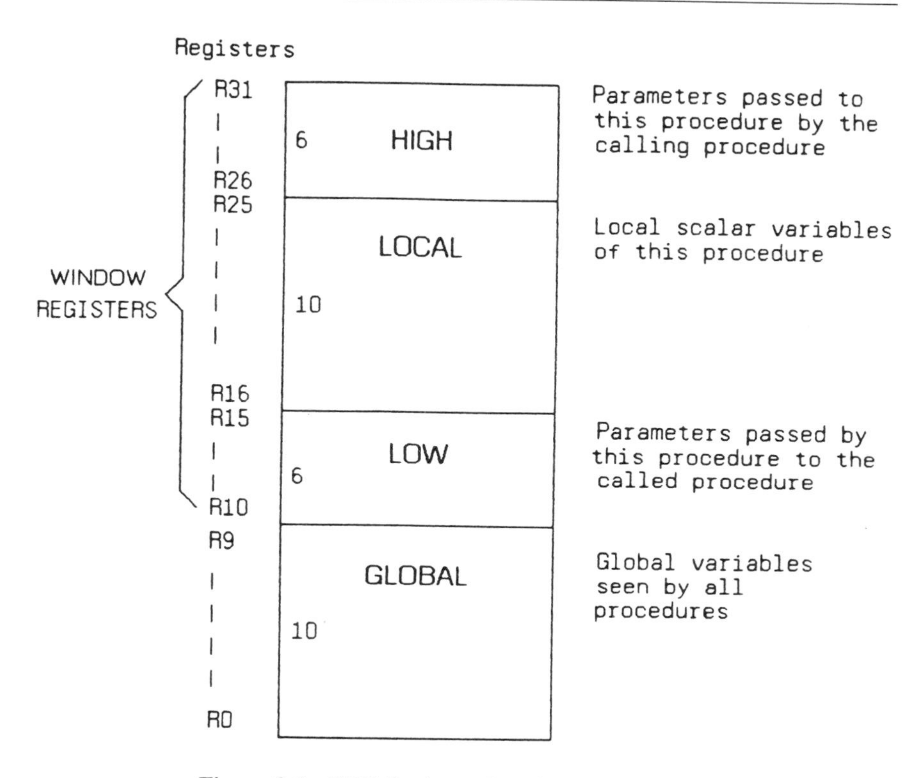

Figure 3.1 CPU Registers Seen by Each Procedure

by the GETPSW and PUTPSW (privileged) instructions. Each window is identified by a *window number*, ranging from 0 to 7.

Registers R16 to R25 (LOCAL) of each procedure contain the local scalar variables of that procedure. Registers R10 to R15 (LOW) of the procedure contain the parameters passed by this procedure to the procedure that it is calling. Registers R26 to R31 (HIGH) contain the parameters passed to this procedure by the procedure which called it (see Figure 3.2).

The Processor Status Word (PSW) is a 13-bit register, structured as follows:

12 10	9 7	6	5	4	3	2	1	0
CWP	SWP	I	S	P	Z	N	V	C

------- CC's --------

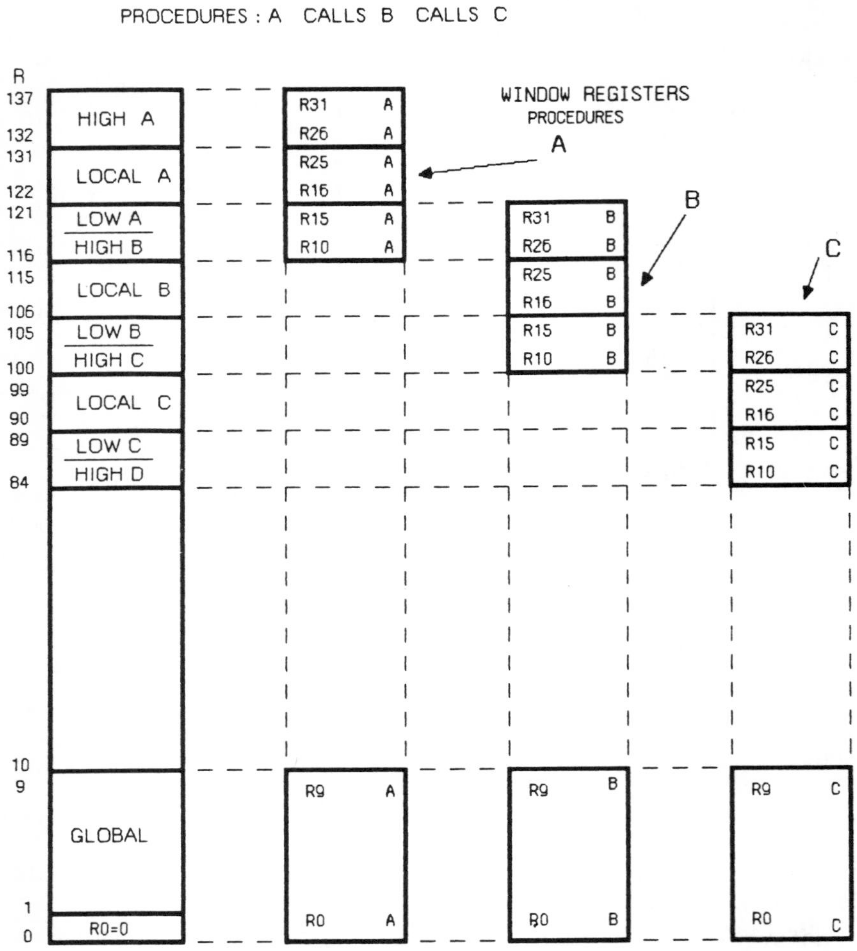

Figure 3.2 RISC Working Registers

where:

- CWP – Current Window Pointer, 0 to 7, specifies the window of the currently active procedure.
- SWP – Saved Window Pointer, identifies the youngest window that has been saved in memory. Not visible to the regular user.
- I – Interrupt enable bit
- S – System mode bit
- P – Previous system mode bit
- CC – Condition Codes (Flags):
  - Z – Zero

N – Negative
V – oVerflow
C – Carry

The CPU working registers can be identified by an addressing pair:

Window Number. Register Number

```
Register   Window Number.  Reg. assignment

  137                         7.25      Window 7 locals
  ---                         ---
  ---                         ---
  ---                         ---
  128                         7.16
- - - -              - - - - - - - - - - -
  127           6.31          7.15      Window 6 input arguments
  ---           ---           ---       Window 7 passed arguments
  ---           ---           ---
  ---           ---           ---
  122           6.26          7.10
- - - -              - - - - - - - - - - -
  121           6.25
  ---           ---
  ---           ---
  ---           ---

  112           6.16                    Window 6 locals
- - - -              - - - - - - - - - - -
  111           6.15          5.31      Window 6 passed arguments
  ---           ---           ---       Window 5 input arguments
  ---           ---           ---
  ---           ---           ---
  ---           ---           ---
  ---           ---           ---
  ---           ---           ---
  32            ---           1.16      Window 1 locals
- - - -              - - - - - - - - - - -
  31            0.31          1.15      Window 0 input arguments
  ---           ---           ---
  ---           ---           ---
  ---           ---           ---
  26            0.26          1.10      Window 1 passed arguments
- - - -              - - - - - - - - - - -
  25            0.25                    Window 0 locals
  ---           ---
  ---           ---
  ---           ---
  16            0.16
- - - -              - - - - - - - - - - -
  15            0.15          7.31      Window 0 passed arguments
  ---           ---           ---
  ---           ---           ---
  ---           ---           ---
  10            0.10          7.26      Window 7 input arguments
- - - -              - - - - - - - - - - -
  9                                     Global Registers
  ---
  ---
  ---
  0
```

The Window Number ranges from 0 to 7 and the current value is always stored in the CWP field of the PSW. The Register Number ranges from 10 to 31. Each procedure occupies a specific window and has a Window Number assigned to it. The window distribution in the register file has the form [1.2] shown on page 39.

As we can see, the registers dedicated to the windows (R10–R137) are arranged in a *circular organization*, with 8 windows (labeled 0 to 7) occupying the register file at any one time. In fact, there is a virtually unbounded capability of the absolute procedure nesting depth. Whenever there is a procedure call and there is no more space in the register file, a *register file overflow* (trap) occurs, and the parameters are pushed on stack (in the main memory). The SWP points to the youngest window that has been saved in memory. Mechanically, the criterion for a register file *overflow* is the event when a *call* instruction attempts to modify CWP so that it becomes equal to SWP. Symmetrically, there is also an *underflow trap* when a *return* instruction attempts to modify CWP so that it becomes equal to SWP. Tamir and Sequin [3.1] have investigated this aspect of RISC architecture and concluded that the best strategy, for most practical cases, is to save only one window per overflow trap. For 8 windows there can be actually 7 nested procedure activations.

Other CPU registers visible to the user (all 32-bits):

Instruction Register (IR) – contains the instruction to be executed next.

Program Counter (PC) – contains the address of the next-to-be-executed instruction (in IR). Used for PC-relative addressing mode.

Next PC (NXTPC) – contains the address of the instruction to be executed subsequently after the one contained in the IR.

Last PC (LSTPC) – contains the address of the instruction which just finished executing. Not visible to the regular user. Its purpose is to hold the value to the PC when an instruction is aborted due to an interrupt. The PC, in turn, holds the value of the NXTPC, while NXTPC is used for fetching the first instruction of the interrupt handler (interrupt service routine).

All three PCs always have a 0 least significant bit, since RISC instructions are always half-word aligned in the main memory. The three PCs are needed for the handling of delayed jumps and interrupts, to be discussed later in this chapter.

3.2.6 RISC Pipeline

Most of the RISC operational instructions are of the register-to-register type:

$$Rs1 \text{ op } Rs2 \rightarrow Rd$$

Here, the second source operand S2 is one of the CPU registers Rs2 (the alternative being a 13-bit immediate value). The above operation can be easily subdivided into three principal stages:

(1) Read Rs1 and Rs2 (or get PC or IMM).
(2) Perform the operation on Rs1 and Rs2.
(3) Write the result into the destination register Rd.

LOAD and STORE instructions, the only ones that access memory, require an additional cycle to complete their execution.

The RISC I has a basic two-stage pipeline. Each instruction cycle has the form:

	Instruction Execute		
Instruction Fetch	Read	Operate	Write

And a sequence of instructions I1, I2, I3 . . .:

Fetch I1	Execute I1		
	Fetch I2	Execute I2	
		Fetch I3	Execute I3 . . .

The RISC II separates the last stage of the execute subcycle, namely the writing into Rd, into another pipeline stage. Thus, the RISC II instruction pipeline has three stages:

Fetch I1	Compute I1	Write		
	Fetch I2	Compute I2	Write	
		Fetch I3	Compute I3	Write . . .

Usually, the pipelining issue belongs to the organization of the computing system, rather than to its architecture. It may be completely transparent to the user, who does not really have a need to know about it (such as with the VAX 8600 which is a pipelined machine with an architecture identical to the VAX 11/780). However, in RISC, due to the *delayed jump* facility (see section 1.4), at least the compiler writer has to be aware of the pipeline. Therefore, in RISC it is a part of the architecture. The burden of the delayed jump is taken up by the compiler writer. To facilitate the implementation of the delayed jump there are 3 PCs: NEXTPC, PC and LSTPC, as specified in the previous section.

Only one memory access at a time (fetch instruction, LOAD, STORE) is possible on the RISC. Therefore, during the execute stage of a LOAD or STORE instruction, there is no possibility of fetching the next instruction and the pipeline is *suspended* for a whole cycle.

3.2.7 *RISC CPU-Memory Data Interface*

The RISC architecture supports three basic data types:

Words	32-bits
Half-words	16-bits
Bytes	8-bits

The CPU memory data bus is 32-bits wide and 4 bytes are always transmitted along it. All instructions are 32-bits long and they are aligned along word boundaries (addresses divisible by 4 in the byte-addressable memory). Thus, there is no particular problem in the instruction-fetching operation.

In a memory-read (LOAD instruction) operation a whole word is always read into the CPU, even if the LOAD instruction involved only a byte or a half-word (16 bits). For instance, a word at address 20 is composed of 4 bytes at addresses 20, 21, 22, 23 (or 2 half-words at addresses 20 and 22). If we LOAD byte 21, say into register R5, the whole 32-bit word at address 20 will be read into the CPU. However, only byte 21 will be loaded into the least significant byte of R5. If the LOAD was signed (LDXBS or LDRBS), the byte in R5 will be sign extended. If it was unsigned (LDXBU or LDRBU), the three most significant bytes of R5 will be filled with zeros. The LOAD operation works similarly with half-words.

For memory-write (STORE instruction) operations the CPU always transmits a full 32-bit word, notwithstanding the exact data item specified by the instruction. If the STORE involves a byte or a half-word, only that part of a word in memory is to be overwritten. The two least significant bits of the 32-bit Effective Address (EA), supplied by the CPU, establish the byte within the word that is to be overwritten. In addition we use two special control outputs from the CPU:

WIDTH code W
WIDTH code H

The word overwriting rules are as follows:

				Word bits to be overwritten			
Instr.	WIDTH code W	WIDTH code H	EA 1:0	31:24	23:16	15:8	7:0
STW	ON	OFF	00	W	W	W	W
STH	OFF	ON	00			W	W
			10	W	W		
STB	OFF	OFF	00				W
			01			W	
			10		W		
			11	W			

EXAMPLE: Given EA = 00007A61 (hex)
WIDTH code W = WIDTH code H = 0

Obviously EA ⟨1:0⟩ = 01 and according to the above rules we overwrite bits ⟨15:8⟩ in the word at address 00007A60 (hex).

3.2.8 *Interrupt*

The exceptions of the RISC are subdivided into two categories:

Interrupts (external)
Traps (internal)

The main Interrupts and Traps and their corresponding Interrupt Vectors (addresses for the Interrupt Service Routine) are:

Interrupts	Vectors (hexadecimal)	
Reset pin pulsed high	8000	0000
Interrupt Request pin pulsed high	8000	0010
Traps		
Illegal opcode	8000	0000
Privileged opcode in user mode (while S=0)	8000	0000
Address misalignment	8000	0000
Register File Overflow	8000	0020
Register File Underflow	8000	0030

The priorities of the above are:
8000 0000 highest priority
8000 0030 medium priority (30,20 cannot occur simultaneously)
8000 0020
8000 0010 lowest priority

The Reset pin interrupt is non-maskable. All other interrupts can be disabled by setting bit I=0 in the PSW.

Suppose I=1 (interrupt enabled) and an interrupt request arrives in the middle of an instruction cycle of instruction i. The following, hardware-based, events will occur automatically:

(1) Instruction i is aborted; it will not complete its execution. A memory write (STORE) that may have started will be allowed to complete.
(2) Instruction i + 1 that may have been prefetched during cycle i is discarded. It is replaced by a hardwired instruction

CALLI R25 (with SCC=0)

which places the value in LSTPC into the register R25. The LSTPC contains at this point the value in PC, when the interrupt request arrived.

(3) The PSW is modified as follows:
 I=0 (disable interrupts)
 P=S (S bit saved into the P bit)
 S=1 (transfer into system mode)
(4) The Interrupt Vector value is loaded into NXTPC. This value constitutes the address of the next instruction to be fetched and executed by the CPU.

In addition, between points (2) and (4), the value in NXTPC must also be saved. We have:

NXTPC → PC → LSTPC

Subsequently the interrupt service routine (interrupt handler) must save the value in LSTPC by its first instruction, which is

```
GETLPC     R24 ;     R24 ← LSTPC
```

After the completion of the interrupt handling the PC values are to be restored by [1.2]:

```
JMPX    ALW, (R25) 0
RETI    ALW, (R24) 0
```

where ALW is the 'always' condition (see section 3.2.4).

3.3 RISC Organization

The organization of RISC I is sketched in Figure 3.3 and that of RISC II in Figure 3.4. Only a part of the RISC subsystems and their interconnections is shown in these figures. One of the main differences between the RISC I and II organizations is that RISC I has a 3-bus Register File Cell (buses A, B, C), while RISC II Register File Cell has only two buses (A and B). In addition, the RISC I register file has fewer (78) registers. The redesign of the Register File Cell in RISC II permitted the achievement of a more compact cell – about 2.5 times smaller than the 3-bus RISC I cell. The saving in the chip area gave the designers more flexibility in the allocation of the chip area to other on-chip resources. To make the 2-bus pipeline operation more effective and to avoid idle time in the utilization of the register file, a third stage has been introduced into the instruction pipeline (see section 3.2.6). The writing of the result of instruction i, into the register file, occurs while the ALU is executing instruction i + 1 and at the same time instruction i + 2 is being fetched.

The abbreviations used in Figures 3.3 and 3.4 are:

PSW	Processor Status Word register
IMM	Immediate latch
DIMM	Data In/Immediate latch
AI, BI	two input latches to the ALU

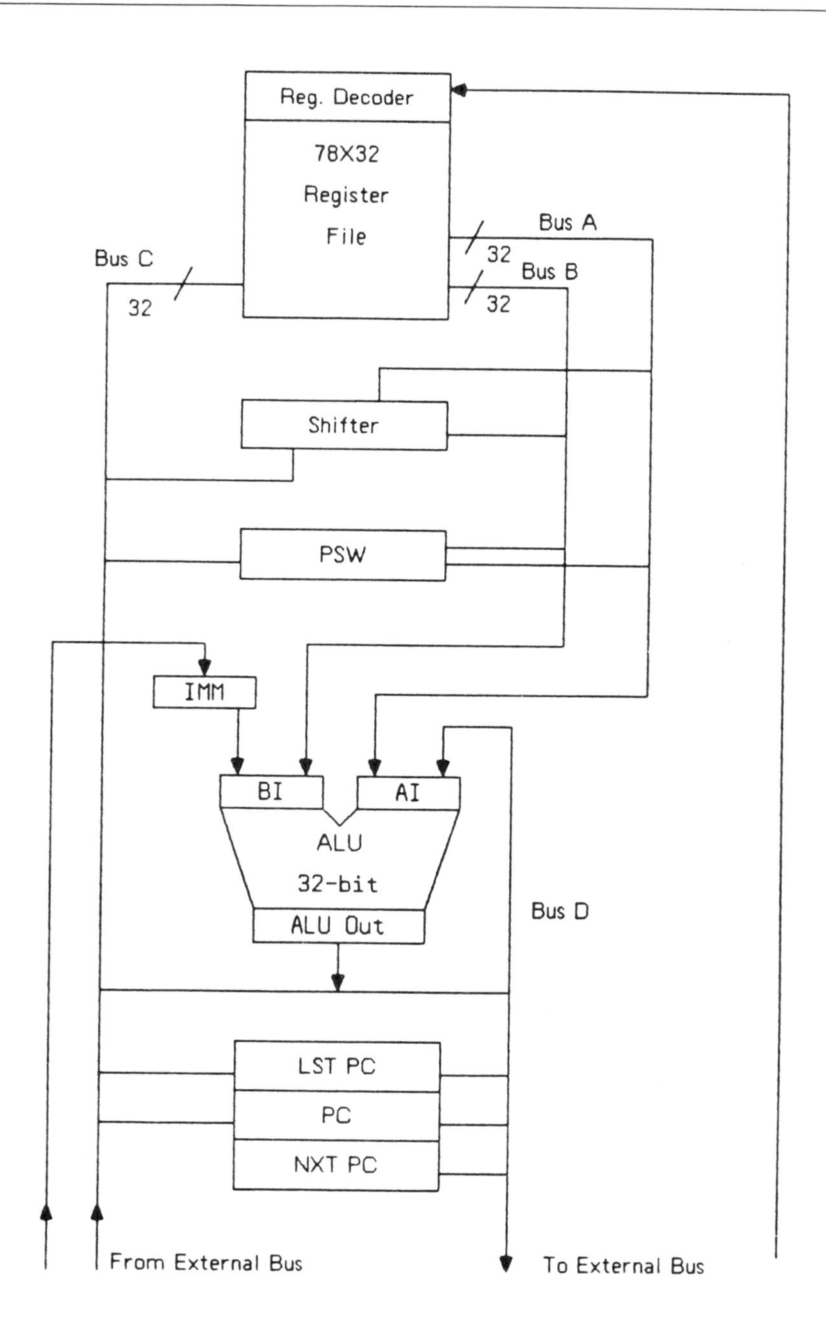

Figure 3.3 RISC I Organization

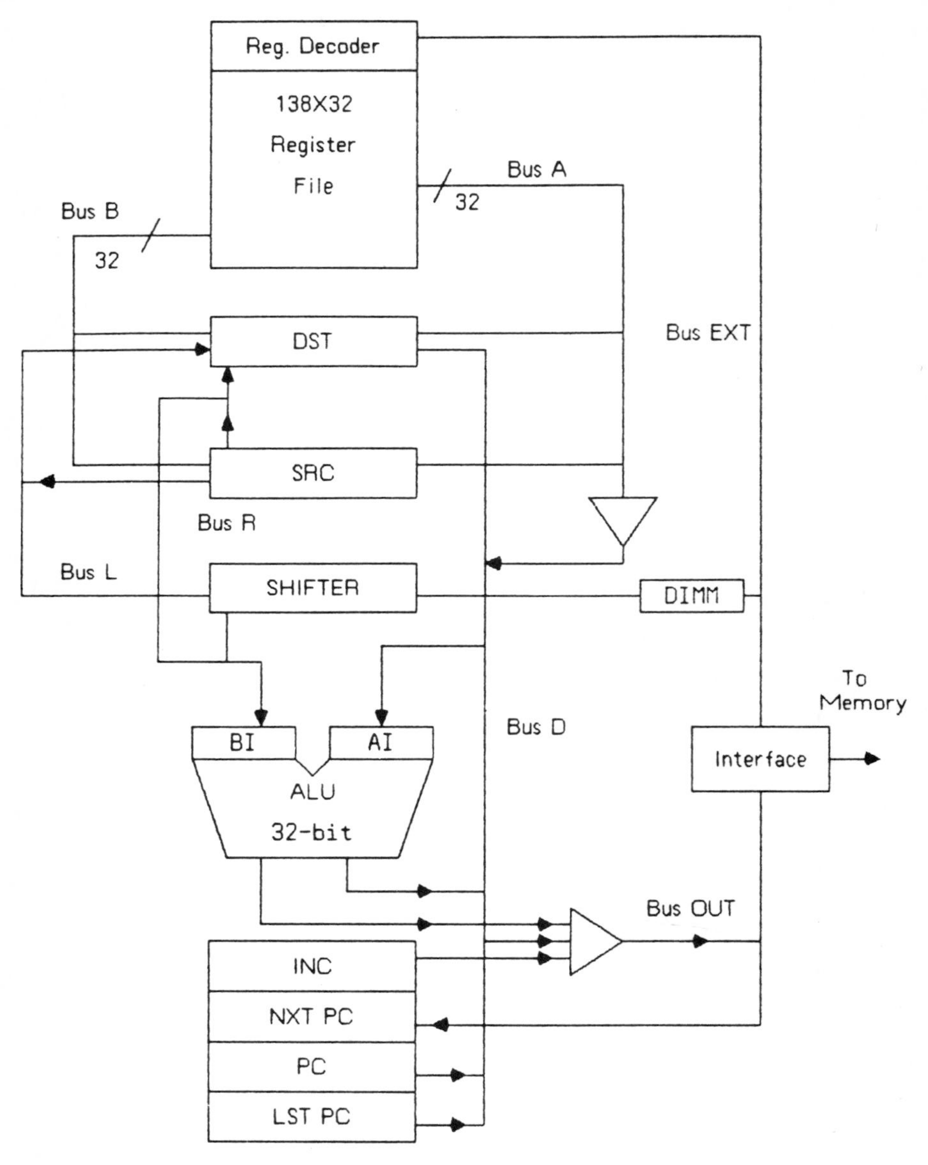

Figure 3.4 RISC II Organization

INC	Incrementer
DST	Destination latch, serving as a temporary pipeline latch
SRC	Source latch for the shifter

The communication between the RISC chip and the outside devices is established through a set of the following interconnection pins [1.2]:

name	bits
Address/Instruction/Data	32
Clock phases (in)	4
Reset (in)	1
Interrupt Request (in)	1
Interrupt Acknowledge (out)	1
WIDTH code W (out)	1
WIDTH code H (out)	1
Read/Write (out)	1
System Mode (out)	1
Instruction/Data (out)	1
Instruction Length (in)	1
Total	45

3.4 RISC Realization

The RISC I was realized on a single NMOS (lambda at 2 microns) chip in 1981 [1.17]. Some of its design metrics, compared to the Z8000 and MC68000 commercial microprocessors, were:

Metric	Z8000	MC68000	RISC I	RISC II
Total devices	17500	68000	44000	41000
Total minus ROM	17500	37000	44000	41000
Drawn devices	3500	3000	1800	
Regularization factor	5.0	12.1	25	20
Area, MIL^2	60000	69000	124000	
Size of Control, MIL^2	37000	35000	7000	
Percentage of control	53%	50%	6%	10%
Time to first silicon (months)	30	30	19	
Design effort (man * months)	60	100	15	18
Layout effort (man months)	70	70	12	12

From the above data we can see the considerably higher regularization factor, lower control area share, and lower design and layout effort of RISC, as argued in the discussion of the RISC advantages in chapter 2. It should also be noted that RISC is a 32-bit machine, while Z8000 and MC68000 are 16-bit machines (notwithstanding the 32-bit CPU registers of 68000).

The RISC II was realized in 1983, using the same NMOS technology as in the RISC I. It used smaller geometries, i.e., lambda = 1.5, was about half the size of RISC I and it runs with a 12 MHz clock (330 ns per instruction, compared to 500 ns, 8 MHz, of RISC I).

As the semiconductor technology becomes more advanced and more transistors can be incorporated on a chip, the next subsystem to be included on chip will be the instruction cache. This will be the key and primary ingredient that produces an improvement in the overall throughput. In the meantime, an extra instruction cache NMOS chip, which incorporates 44500 transistors for use in conjunction with RISC II, has been proposed [1.2, 3.2].

References

3.1 Y. Tamir, C.H. Sequin, 'Strategies for Managing the Register File in RISC', *IEEE Trans. on Computers*, **C-32**, No. 11, pp. 977–989, Nov. 1983.

3.2 D.A. Patterson, 'RISC Watch', *Computer Architecture News*, **12**, No. 1, pp. 11–19, March 1984.

4
The Stanford and Commercial MIPS

4.1 Introductory Comments

The Stanford MIPS [1.6, 1.7, 1.20, 4.1–4.5] was the second RISC processor, developed in academia, and following the Berkeley RISC very closely on the time scale. However, as will be seen from the subsequent description, it is considerably different from the Berkeley system. The basic differences, to be elaborated in the next section, are a relatively small CPU register set and more extensive reliance on software on the Stanford MIPS, compared to the Berkeley RISC.

A commercial RISC processor [4.6], based on a significantly extended Stanford MIPS, was brought to industry through MIPS Computer Systems, Inc. (Sunnyvale, CA), and currently (1989) features the R2000 and R3000 processors. The architecture of the commercial MIPS will be described in section 4.3. It should also be noted that the basic MIPS architecture was adopted by DARPA in its support for the development of new GaAs-based RISC systems.

4.2 The Stanford MIPS

The MIPS RISC-type machine was developed at the Stanford University between 1981–1983. The MIPS acronym stems from 'Microprocessor without Interlocked Pipeline Stages'. The exact meaning of this will be explained later in this section.

The MIPS is a 32-bit machine. Its standard Word is defined to be 32-bits long and it is *word addressable*. However, *byte addressing* in MIPS is supported using a set of instructions for manipulating *byte pointers*, which are single addresses, whose two low order bits are used to specify a byte within a word.

The MIPS Instruction Set is defined at two levels:

1. *User Level* – or *Assembly Language Instruction Set*, defines instructions that are *unpacked*, that is all have a standard length of 32 bits, and have no pipeline dependencies or branch delays.
2. *Machine Level* – low level, run by the processor. Generated only by a single program, the *Reorganizer*. The Reorganizer does all implementation-dependent optimization and isolates the user level instruction set from the implementation details.

Each macroinstruction is similar to a single microinstruction (the control is hardwired), requiring very simple and fast decoding. All instructions are executed within the same time interval, a *single data memory cycle*. The instructions have either two or three operands. There are four *addressing modes*:

1. Immediate;
2. Based with Offset;
3. Indexed;
4. Base Shifted.

The MIPS instructions are subdivided into four groups (types) of *instruction pieces*:

1. ALU;
2. Load/Store;
3. Control Flow;
4. Special Instructions.

Up to two simple (and possibly unrelated) instruction pieces are packed together, during *reorganization*, into an instruction word of 32 bits.

(1) *ALU pieces:* All register-to-register, two or three operand formats. Use less than a half of an instruction word.
(2) *Load/Store pieces:* Use 16 to 32 bits. When they are less than 32 bits, they are packaged with an ALU piece which is executed during the execution stage of the pipeline.
(3) *Control Flow pieces:* Include straight jumps, compare instructions and relative jumps. All branch instructions have a delay in their effect of one instruction; the next sequential instruction is always executed.
(4) *Special Instructions:* Support procedure and interrupt linkage.

There is no direct floating point operation support on MIPS; a coprocessor is needed for this type of operation. There is support for page faults, externally generated interrupts, and internally generated traps (arithmetic overflow and software generated exceptions). Support for an off-chip instruction cache implementation is provided.

Some examples of MIPS instruction pieces, classified by four groups, are provided as follows:

(1) *ALU*
Add src1,src2,dst; src2 + src1 → dst
Sub src1,src2,dst; src2 − src1 → dst (Subtract)
Total instructions in this group: 13

(2) *Load/Store*
Ld[src1 + src2],dst; M[src1 + src2] → dst (Load)
Mov src,dst ; src → dst (Move)
St src1,A[src] ; src1 → M[A + src] (Store)
Total: 10

(3) *Control Flow*
Bra dst ; PC+dst→PC (Branch)
Jmp dst; dst→PC (Jump)

Total: 6

(4) *Special*
SavePC A; PC→M[A]

Total: 2

Total MIPS Instructions: 31

There are no condition codes for conditional jumps. Instead, there are *compare and branch* operations.

There is a 16 32-bit CPU register file (32 registers on a more recent model MIPS-X), organized as a two-port structure. The large register file with the register window, as in the Berkeley RISC, has not been adopted in the Stanford MIPS system. On the other hand, in addition to the PC, there are 4 registers to hold the 4 previous PC values. They are needed to backtrack and restart instructions in case of a fault. In addition, there is a register to hold the *future* PC value, a feature which supports the branch instructions. The branch address for a conditional branch is calculated for a given instruction and stored in the future PC register. Only if the specified condition is satisfied, is the contents of future PC transferred into the regular PC. The above four registers are not architecturally visible.

Although the *virtual address* is 32 bits long, packaging constraints permitted only 24 address pins. Thus, the *physical address space* is 2^{24} = 16 MWords (32 bits each), equal to 64 Mbytes. The MIPS has separate Instruction and Data Memories, and their accesses are interleaved.

The MIPS supports a large, uniform addressing space for each process and fast context switching between processes. A process is defined as the smallest unit of programming activity which can be scheduled to run on a processor. Each process address (virtual address) space is 4 GWords = 2^{32} Words (1 Word = 32 bits). Each process has its own process identification number incorporated into the virtual memory address. Not all of the virtual to physical address translation could be included on the same chip. The hardware design supports the inclusion of an off-chip Translation Lookaside Buffer (TLB) for the address translation.

The general tendency in the MIPS design was to shift complexity from hardware to software. Its instruction set easily maps into a microinstruction set involving very simple decoding. The compiler, however, is required to be more sophisticated than the Berkeley RISC, because it performs a compact and time efficient mapping between higher-level instruction constructs and the simplified instruction set. The advantages of moving the complexity from hardware to software are:

(a) Complexity is paid for (in computing time) only once during compilation.
(b) Design effort is concentrated on the software, rather than on constructing

a complex hardware engine, which is hard to design, debug and efficiently utilize. VLSI environment makes hardware simplicity important.

There exist presently Pascal, FORTRAN and C compilers for the MIPS. A MIPS compiler incorporates two basic parts:

(1) *Code Generator* – produces a stream of simple operations, independent of all resource interaction, branch delays and instruction combinations.
(2) *Code Reorganizer* – performs the following operations on the *generated code*:
   (a) Assembles and packs one or two independent operations (instruction pieces) into each 32-bit instruction word.
   (b) Moves appropriate instructions into the words following each delayed branch.
   (c) Reorders instructions within each basic block to eliminate resource conflicts.

The above code reorganization saves, on the average, about 30% of execution time.

The MIPS has a 5-stage instruction pipeline, with three active instructions residing in the pipeline at any time. One instruction is initiated every two clock cycles. The stages of the pipeline and their individual tasks are as follows:

Stage Name	Task
1. IF – Instruction Fetch	Send PC value, fetch instruction, increment PC.
2. ID – Instruction Decode	Decode instruction.
3. OD – Operand Decode	Compute effective address of operand, fetch operand, use ALU.
4. OS/EX (SX) – Operand Store/ Execution	Send operand to memory if store, use ALU if execution.
5. OF – Operand Fetch	Receive operand if load.

Naturally, not all of the pipeline stages are needed for each instruction. The timing of the pipeline stages for a sequence of instructions looks as follows:

Instr.	Cycle:	1	2	3	4	5	6	7	8	9	10
i		IF	ID	OD	SX	OF					
i+1				IF	ID	OD	SX	OF			
i+2						IF	ID	OD	SX	OF	
									. . .	and so on	

Taking, for instance the sequence of CPU cycles 5 and 6, we see that during this two-cycle period the ALU is busy with stages OD and SX of instruction (i+1), the Instruction Memory is busy with stages IF and ID of instruction i+2, while the Data Memory is busy with stage OF of instruction i and stage SX of instruction (i+1). We can observe an efficient utilization of resources in this pipeline organization.

Considering the general operation and management of a pipeline, one can envisage an event when one component of an instruction in a pipeline may refer to a value that is computed in an earlier instruction. Because the earlier instruction may still be executing, the value may not be available, and a *pipeline timing hazard* is present. A hardware mechanism, called a *pipeline interlock*, prevents the latter instruction from continuing until the needed value is available. An interlock mechanism adds significantly to the hardware overhead. Its elimination from the hardware allows a simpler design. Interlocks can be eliminated by *reordering* the instructions and by inserting NOP operations, wherever necessary. In MIPS, the reordering to eliminate interlocks is done by the code *reorganizer* within the compiler. Since MIPS does not have hardware interlocks (the problem is handled by software), its name is *M*icroprocessor without *I*nterlocked *P*ipe *S*tages.

The *delayed branch* principle is also practiced in the MIPS design. Each branch instruction always executes one succeeding instruction. If the branch instruction references memory, as in an indirect jump, two succeeding instructions are fetched and executed. If an exception occurs during a branch, three consecutive PC values are saved in CPU registers, especially predesigned for this purpose.

The MIPS CPU organization is shown in Figure 4.1. It has a 32-bit full CLA (Carry Look Ahead) ALU. The total ALU delay is 80 ns. The CPU has two 32-bit bidirectional buses, sixteen 32-bit general purpose registers and two memory interfaces, one for data and one for instructions. The masking unit allows a machine address to be converted to a process virtual address. It also detects attempts to access illegal addresses and it raises an exception in such a case.

The MIPS was realized with NMOS, 2-micron technology. With a 4 MHz, 250 ns clock cycle, it achieves a performance of 2 VAX 780 MIPS (Millions Instructions Per Second). It has 84 pins, allocated as follows:

Address	24
Data	32
Status Out	8
Status In	7
Clock, Power	9
Control	4
Total	84

The chip contains an equivalent of over 24,000 transistors and its regularity factor is 12. Its area is relatively subdivided as follows:

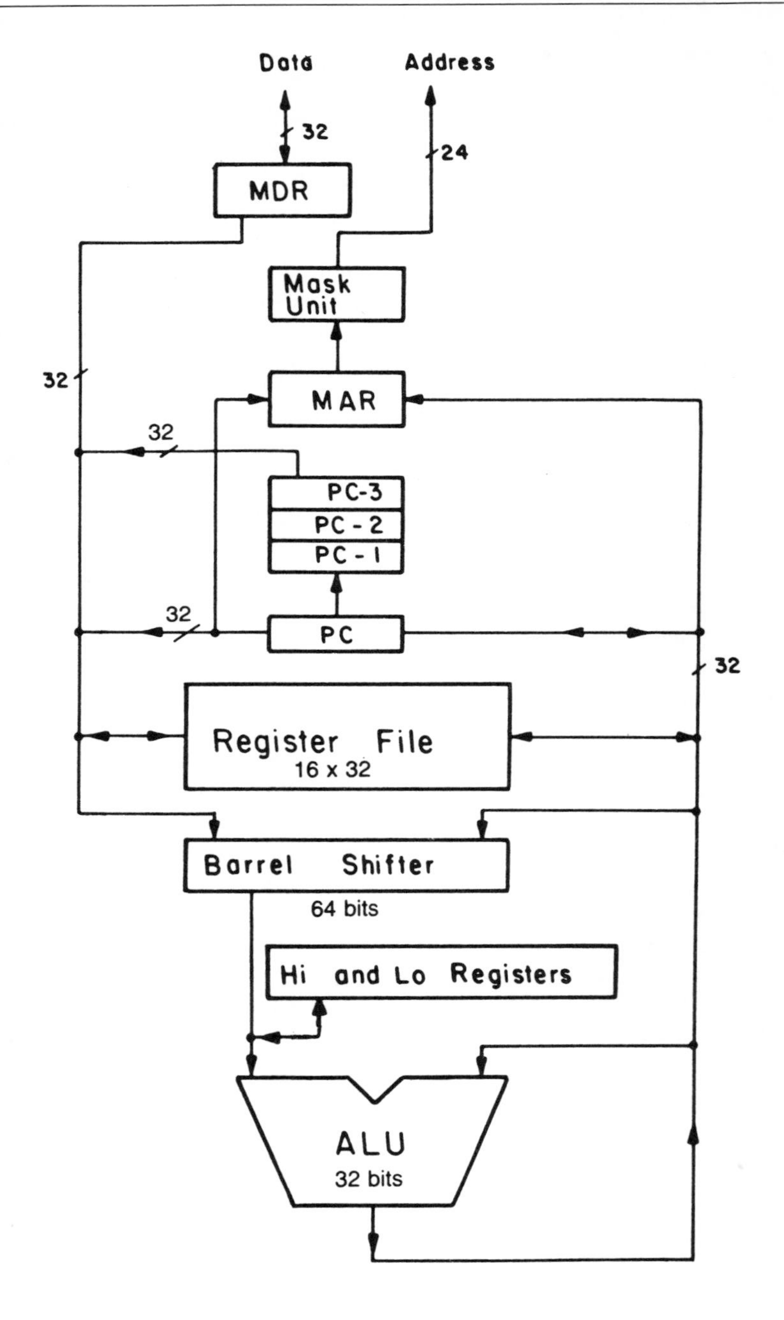

Figure 4.1 MIPS Organization

Datapath	39.2%
Control	18.2%
Periphery	42.6%
Total	100.0%

Compared to the Berkeley RISC, the MIPS control area is almost double; however, still considerably lower than the 50% of the CISCs. Another major difference is the regular CPU register file on MIPS; only 16 registers, compared to the 138 on RISC II. There are, however, 32 registers on the MIPS-X.

The MIPS-X is a 2-micron CMOS, 150,000 transistors chip. Its performance is about 20 Millions of Instructions Per Second (MIPS) at 20 MHz. It is much closer to the commercial R2000, described in the next section.

4.3 The Commercial MIPS

4.3.1 MIPS Architecture

The MIPS architecture [4.6–4.9], described in this section, is currently implemented on the R2000 and R3000 processor chips, which differ primarily in the technology of their realization. The differences between the two will be specified later in this section. For the sake of simplicity the R2000 notation will be used, with the understanding that the architecture of the R2000 and R3000 is the same.

A block diagram of the R2000 chip (and R3000) and its internal information flow paths is shown in Figure 4.2. The processor consists of two principal parts [4.6]:

(1) The CPU – a RISC-type, 32-bit processor.
(2) CPO – a System Control Coprocessor, containing the basic logic of a Memory Management Unit (MMU) and Cache Control.

The CPU includes a 32 × 32 general purpose register file, an ALU, a shifter, a Multiplier/Divider, an Address Adder, and a Program Counter (PC). The CPO Cache Control logic can handle separate, off-chip Instruction and Data Caches from 4 to 64 KBytes each for the R2000 and up to 256 KBytes for the R3000. The MMU includes a 64-entry, fully associative Translation Lookaside Buffer (TLB) for Virtual (Logical) to Physical (Real) memory address mapping of the 4 GByte virtual address space. The R2000 generates all addresses and handles memory interface control for up to three additional tightly-coupled external coprocessors.

The user-visible CPU registers are illustrated in Figure 4.3. The 32 general purpose registers r 0 to r31 can be used freely with the following two exceptions:

r 0 is permanently hardwired to a zero value, as in the Berkeley RISC (chapter 3),

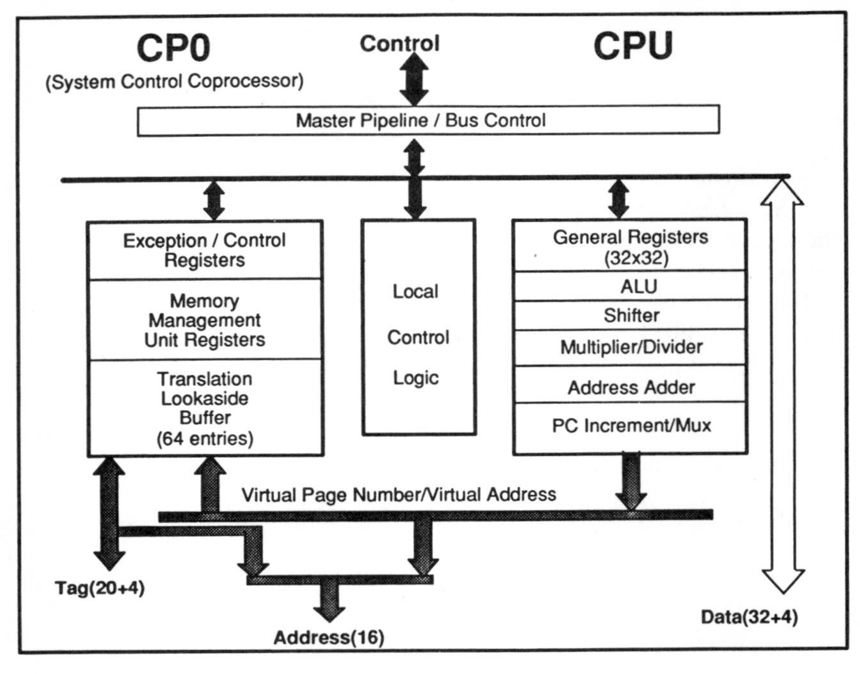

Figure 4.2 R2000 (R3000) Block Diagram
(*Courtesy of MIPS Computer Systems, Inc.*)

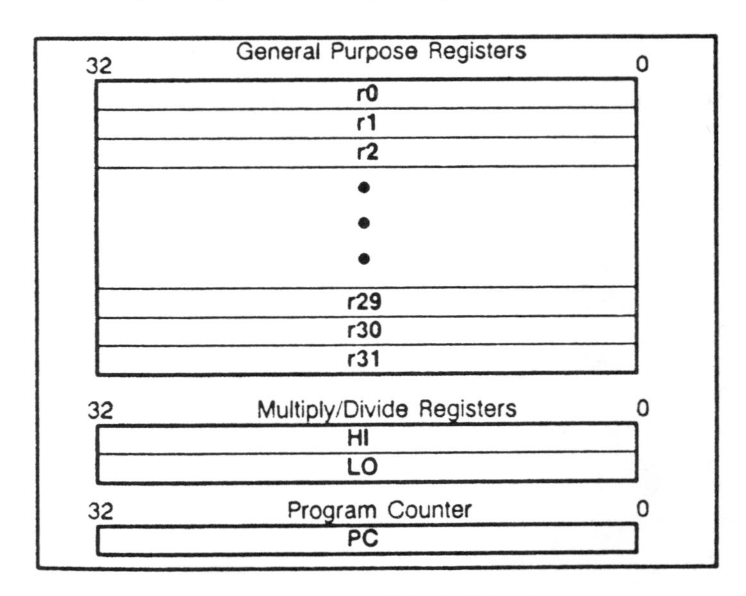

Figure 4.3 R2000 (R3000) CPU Registers
(*Courtesy of MIPS Computer Systems, Inc.*)

r31 serves as the Link Register for Jump And Link instructions (to be explained later).

The two Multiply/Divide Registers HI and LO store the double-word, 64-bit product of multiply operations and the quotient and remainder of divide operations.

The R2000 architecture defines the following basic data types:

Word	32 bits
Half Word	16 bits
Byte	8 bits

The memory is byte addressable. The byte ordering within a word stored in memory (4 bytes) can be configured (configuration occurs during hardware reset) in two ways:

(1) *Big-endian* (as in M68000 and IBM 370 families), where the most significant byte in a word is byte 0, and the least significant, byte 3;

byte 0, byte 1, byte 2, byte 3

(2) *Little-endian* (as in Intel 80 × 86, NS32000 and VAX families), where the most significant byte in a word is byte 3, and the least significant, byte 0;

byte 3, byte 2, byte, 1, byte 0

Half word accesses must be aligned on an even byte boundary, and word accesses on a byte boundary divisible by four.

The R2000 has three instruction formats, illustrated in Figure 4.4. The instructions must be aligned on word boundaries.

The Addressing Modes are:

1. Register
2. Immediate
3. PC Relative
4. Register Indirect (Base Register), with or without offset.

The instruction set of the R2000 is summarized in Table 4.1. The instructions are subdivided into the following groups:

(1) *Load/Store:* all I-type (Figure 4.4), the only ones to move data between memory and CPU registers. The only memory addressing mode supported in this group is base register plus 16-bit, signed immediate offset.
(2) *Computational:* R- or I-type (Figure 4.4), perform arithmetic, logical and shift operations (register-to-register only).
(3) *Jump and Branch:* change the control flow of a program. Jumps use the PC Relative addressing mode with the J-type (Figure 4.4) format (for subroutine calls) or the Register Indirect with the R-type format (for returns). Branches use PC Relative with 16-bit offset with the I-type format. Jump and Link instructions save a return address in r31.

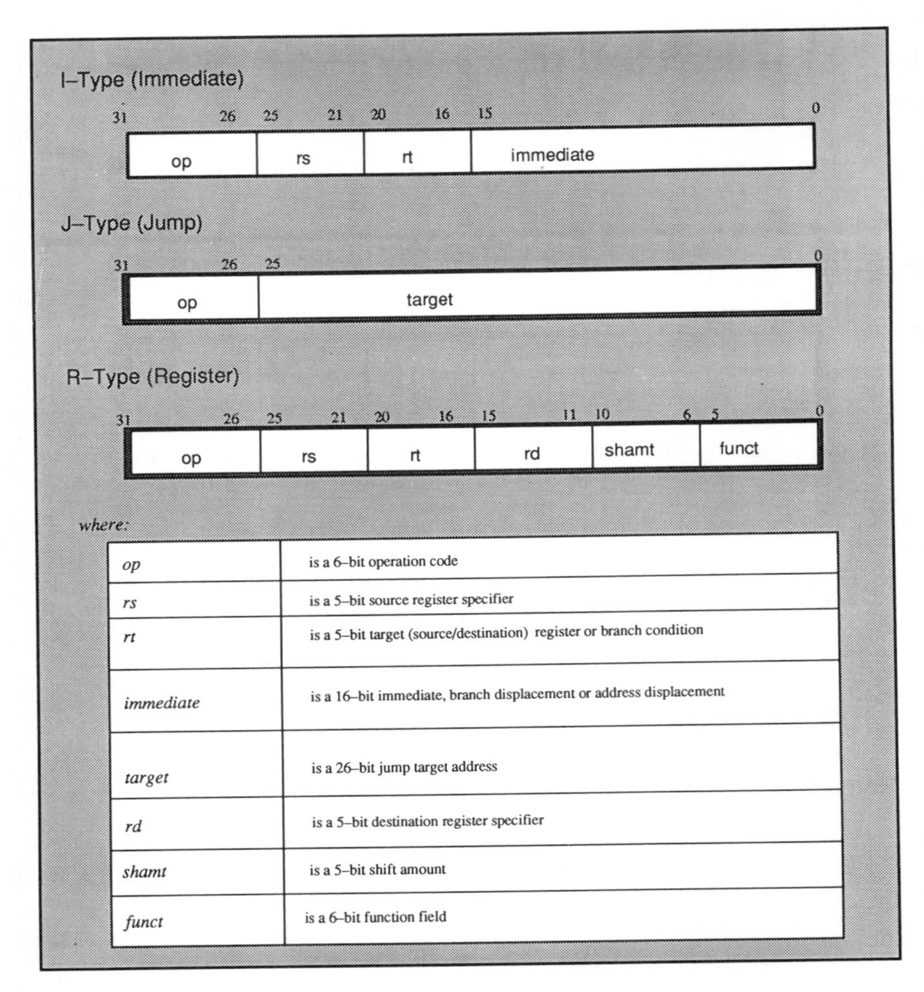

Figure 4.4 R2000 (R3000) Instruction Formats
(*Courtesy of MIPS Computer Systems, Inc.*)

(4) *Coprocessor:* perform operations in coprocessors. Coprocessor Loads and Stores are I-type.

(5) *Coprocessor O:* perform operations on the CPO registers to manipulate the MMU and exception handling facilities.

(6) *Special:* always R-type, perform various tasks, such as system calls and movement of data between special and general registers.

A number of examples of MIPS instructions are presented in the following paragraphs.

Table 4.1 R2000 Instruction Summary
(Courtesy of MIPS Computer Systems, Inc.)

OP	Description
	Load/Store Instructions
LB	Load Byte
LBU	Load Byte Unsigned
LH	Load Halfword
LHU	Load Halfword Unsigned
LW	Load Word
LWL	Load Word Left
LWR	Load Word Right
SB	Store Byte
SH	Store Halfword
SW	Store Word
SWL	Store Word Left
SWR	Store Word Right
	Arithmetic Instructions (ALU Immediate)
ADDI	Add Immediate
ADDIU	Add Immediate Unsigned
SLTI	Set on Less Than Immediate
SLTIU	Set on Less Than Immediate Unsigned
ANDI	AND Immediate
ORI	OR Immediate
XORI	Exclusive OR Immediate
LUI	Load Upper Immediate
	Arithmetic Instructions (3-operand, register-type)
ADD	Add
ADDU	Add Unsigned
SUB	Subtract
SUBU	Subtract Unsigned
SLT	Set on Less Than
SLTU	Set on Less Than Unsigned
AND	AND
OR	OR
XOR	Exclusive OR
NOR	NOR
	Shift Instructions
SLL	Shift Left Logical
SRL	Shift Right Logical
SRA	Shift Right Arithmetic
SLLV	Shift Left Logical Variable
SRLV	Shift Right Logical Variable
SRAV	Shift Right Arithmetic Variable
	Special Instructions
SYSCALL	System Call
BREAK	Break

OP	Description
	Multiply/Divide Instructions
MULT	Multiply
MULTU	Multiply Unsigned
DIV	Divide
DIVU	Divide Unsigned
MFHI	Move From HI
MTHI	Move To HI
MFLO	Move From LO
MTLO	Move To LO
	Jump and Branch Instructions
J	Jump
JAL	Jump And Link
JR	Jump to Register
JALR	Jump And Link Register
BEQ	Branch on Equal
BNE	Branch on Not Equal
BLEZ	Branch on Less than or Equal to Zero
BGTZ	Branch on Greater Than Zero
BLTZ	Branch on Less Than Zero
BGEZ	Branch on Greater than or Equal to Zero
BLTZAL	Branch on Less Than Zero And Link
BGEZAL	Branch on Greater than or Equal to Zero And Link
	Coprocessor Instructions
LWCz	Load Word from Coprocessor
SWCz	Store Word to Coprocessor
MTCz	Move To Coprocessor
MFCz	Move From Coprocessor
CTCz	Move Control to Coprocessor
CFCz	Move Control From Coprocessor
COPz	Coprocessor Operation
BCzT	Branch on Coprocessor z True
BCzF	Branch on Coprocessor z False
	System Control Coprocessor (CP0) Instructions
MTC0	Move To CP0
MFC0	Move From CP0
TLBR	Read indexed TLB entry
TLBWI	Write Indexed TLB entry
TLBWR	Write Random TLB entry
TLBP	Probe TLB for matching entry
RFE	Restore From Exception

1. Load Word: LW rt, offset (rs)
   The I-type format is used (Figure 4.4). The rt field represents the destination CPU register. The rs field points to the base register. The immediate field contains a 16-bit offset (sign extended to 32 bits), added to the contents of rs, to form the memory address, whose contents are loaded into rt.
2. Subtract: SUB rd, rs, rt; rd ← (rs) − (rt), R-type format
3. Multiply: MULT rs, rt

R-type format (rd field not used). The contents of the 32-bit registers rs and rt are multiplied. The 64-bit product is placed into two special registers, HI (most significant 32 bits) and LO (least significant 32 bits).

4. Divide: DIV rs, rt; (rs)/(rt)
   R-type format (rd field not used). The quotient is loaded into the LO register, and the remainder into HI.
5. Jump: J target; J-type format
   The 26-bit target field is shifted left two bits, combined (on the left) with the 4 most significant bits of the current PC value, to form the jump target address. The program unconditionally jumps to the calculated address, with a *delay* of one instruction. The *delayed branch* feature (see chapter 1) is implemented on the R2000.
6. Jump And Link: JAL target
   Used as a subroutine call. Works exactly the same way as the Jump, except that the address of the instruction after the delay slot, (PC) + 8, is placed in the *link register*, r31.
7. Branch on Equal: BEQ rs, rt, offset
   I-type format. The contents of registers rs and rt are compared. If equal, the program branches to a new target address, with a *delay* of one instruction. The new target address is computed from the sum of the address of the instruction in the delay slot (following BEQ) and the 16-bit offset, shifted left two bits and sign-extended to 32 bits.

All Load operations have a *latency of one instruction*. That is, the data being loaded from memory into a CPU register is not available to the instruction immediately following the Load, but to the next instruction (the second instruction after the Load).

The Load/Store opcode contains two bits, called *Access Type*, which indicate the size of the data item to be loaded or stored, as shown in Table 4.2. Regardless of access type or byte-numbering order (big or little endian), the address specifies the byte which has the *smallest byte address* of all the bytes in the addressed field. The bytes within the addressed word that are used can be determined directly from the access type and the two low-order bits of the address, as shown in Table 4.2. Only the combinations shown in this table are permissible.

4.3.2 MIPS Instruction Pipeline

The R2000 instruction pipeline consists of five stages, as shown in Figure 4.5:

(1) *IF – Instruction Fetch*
   Access the TLB and calculate the address required to read an instruction from the I (Instruction)-cache (off-chip). The instruction is not actually read into the CPU until the beginning of the next pipeline stage RD.
(2) *RD – Read*
   Complete instruction fetch. Read any required operands from CPU registers (RF = Register Fetch), while decoding the instruction.

Table 4.2 Byte Specifications for Load/Store
(*Courtesy of MIPS Computer Systems, Inc.*)

Access Type	Low-Order Address Bits	Bytes Accessed							
		Big-Endian				Little-Endian			
1 0	1 0	31			0	31			0
1 1 (word)	0 0	0	1	2	3	3	2	1	0
1 0 (triple-byte)	0 0	0	1	2			2	1	0
	0 1		1	2	3	3	2	1	
0 1 (halfword)	0 0	0	1					1	0
	1 0			2	3	3	2		
0 0 (byte)	0 0	0							0
	0 1		1					1	
	1 0			2			2		
	1 1				3	3			

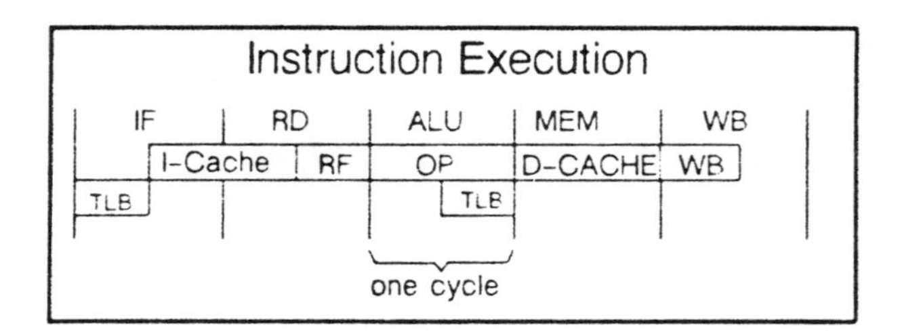

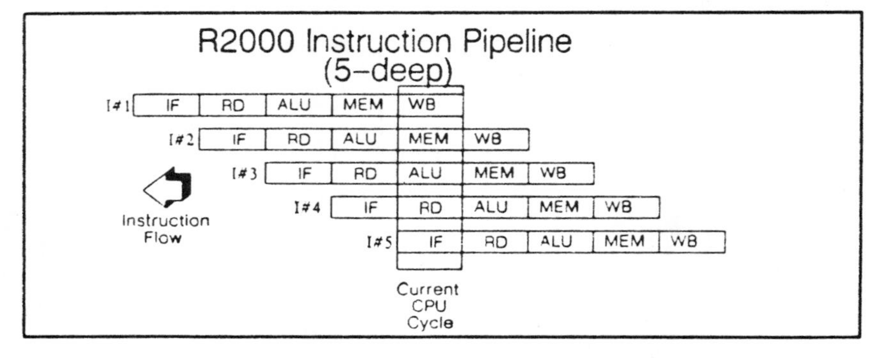

Figure 4.5 R2000 (R3000) Instruction Pipeline
(Courtesy of MIPS Computer Systems, Inc.)

(3) *ALU*
Perform the required operation on instruction operands.

(4) *MEM – Access Memory*
Access D (Data)-cache (off-chip) for Load or Store instructions.

(5) *WB – Write Back*
Store ALU results or value loaded from D-cache into the register file.

Each of the above steps requires approximately one CPU cycle. The R2000 uses the delayed instruction technique not only for jumps and branches but also for the Load instruction. This is illustrated by a sequence of 3 instructions in Figure 4.6. Instruction 1 (I#1) is a Load instruction. The data from the load is not available until the end of the I#1 MEM cycle – too late to be used by I#2 during its ALU cycle, but available to I#3 for its ALU cycle. Therefore, software must ensure that I#2 does not depend on data loaded by I#1. Usually, a compiler can reorganize instructions so that something useful is executed during the delay slot or, if no other instruction is available, can insert a NOP (no operation) instruction in the slot. MIPS Computer Systems statistics show that 70% of the Load delay slots are filled with useful instructions.

A similar example for a Branch case is shown in Figure 4.7. Instruction 1 (I#1) in this case is a Branch instruction. I#1 must calculate a branch target address, and that address is not available until the beginning of the ALU cycle of I#1 –

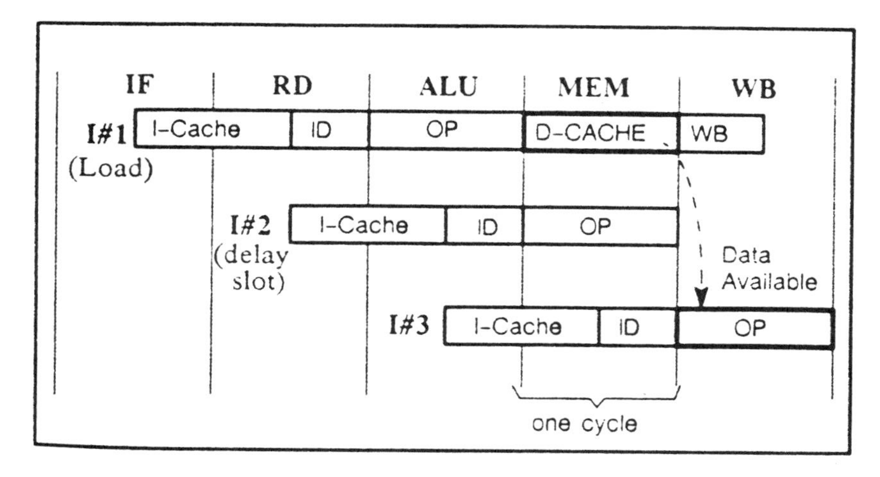

Figure 4.6 The Load Instruction Delay Slot
(*Courtesy of MIPS Computer Systems, Inc.*)

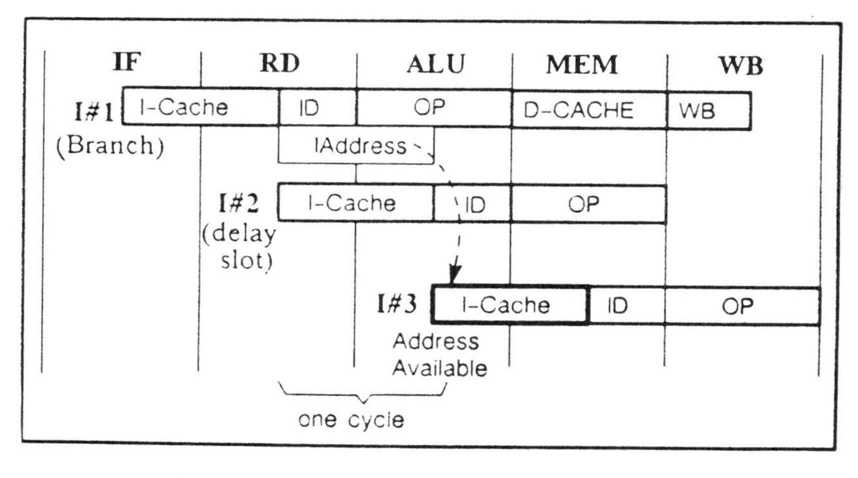

Figure 4.7 The Jump/Branch Instruction Delay Slot
(*Courtesy of MIPS Computer Systems, Inc.*)

too late for the I-Cache access of I#2 but available to I#3 for its I-Cache access. The instruction in the delay slot (I#2) will always be executed before the branch or jump actually occurs. This is precisely the case of the delayed branch, as described in chapter 1. Again, the reorganizer will move useful instructions into this branch delay slot and MIPS Computer Systems statistics show that this happens about 50% of times.

4.3.3 *The R2010 Floating Point Accelerator*

The R2010 Floating Point Accelerator (FPA) operates as a coprocessor for the R2000 Processor and extends the R2000's instruction set to perform arithmetic operations on values in floating-point representations. The R2010 FPA, with associated system software, fully conforms to the requirements of ANSI/IEEE Standard 754-1985, *IEEE Standard for Binary Floating-Point Arithmetic*. In addition, the MIPS architecture fully supports the Standard's recommendations. Figure 4.8 illustrates the functional organization of the FPA. The R3010 FPA is faster, but architecturally identical to the R2010. Both support the 32- and 64-bit IEEE Standard floating point formats.

The R2010 contains 32 32-bit Floating-point General-purpose registers FGR0, FGR1, . . ., FGR31. These registers can also be used as 16 64-bit Floating Point Registers FPR0, FPR2, . . ., FPR30. Register FPR0 is formed from FGR0 (least significant 32 bits) and FGR1 (most significant 32 bits). In general, FPRi (i even) is formed from FGRi (least) and FGRi+1 (most).

There are also two Floating-point Control Registers (FCR):

(1) Control/Status Register FCR31, used to control and monitor exceptions, hold result of compare operations, and establish rounding modes.
(2) Implementation/Revision Register, FCR0, holds revision information about the FPA.

MIPS coprocessors can have up to 32 FCRs, but only two are implemented on the R2010.

The R2010 features 17 instructions, subdivided into four groups:

(1) Load, Store, Move, transfer data between memory, the CPU and the FPA registers.
(2) Computational, perform single and double precision floating point Add, Subtract, Multiply, Divide, Absolute Value, Move and Negate.
(3) Conversion, from fixed-point to single or double floating point, or from floating- to fixed-point.
(4) Compare, between contents of registers, setting a condition bit in the Control/Status register based on the results.

The R2010 has a six-stage instruction pipeline, illustrated in Figure 4.9:

(1) IF – Instruction Fetch, the CPU calculates the address of the instruction to be fetched from the I-Cache.
(2) RD – Read, FPA decodes the instruction.
(3) ALU, FPA begins execution.
(4) MEM, if it is a Load or Store instruction, the FPA uses this stage to complete the D-Cache access.
(5) WB, used by the FPA solely to deal with exceptions.
(6) FWB, used by the FPA in the same manner at WB by the R2000 CPU (see subsection 4.3.2).

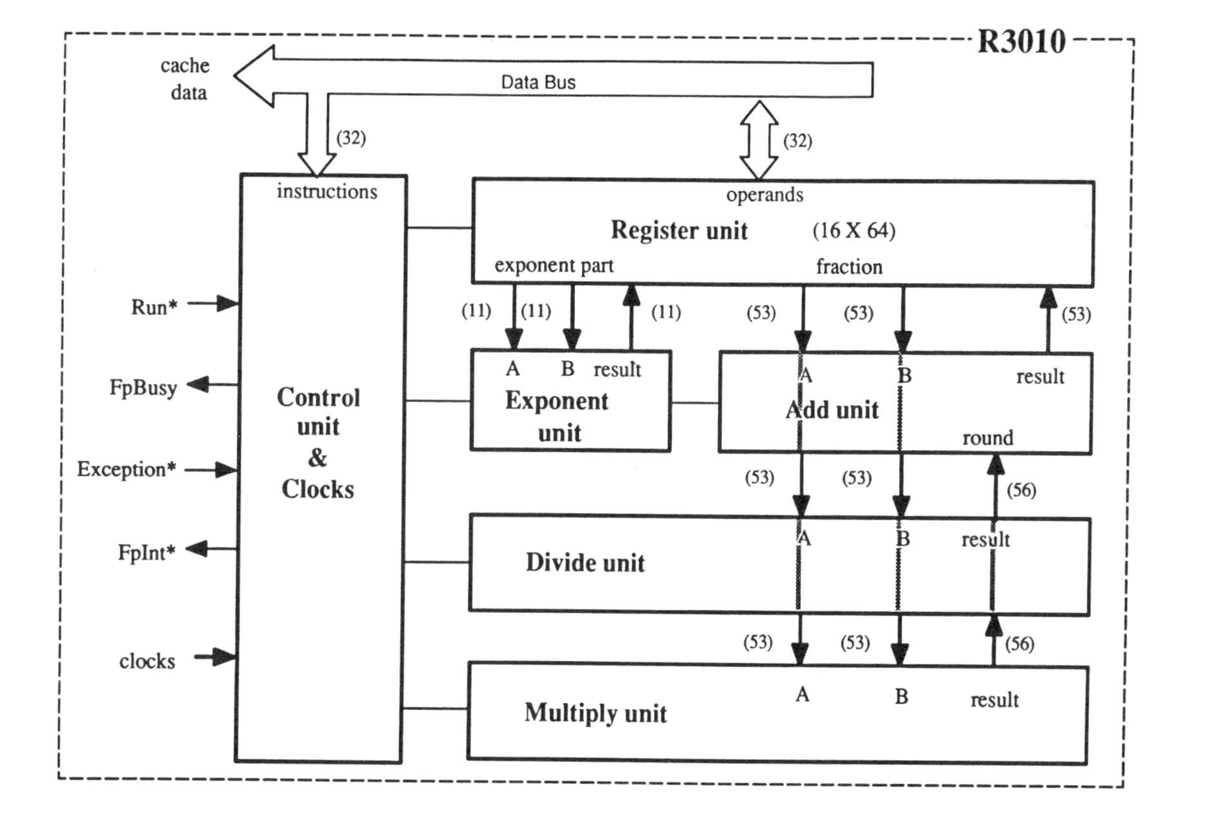

Figure 4.8 R3010 (R2010) Block Diagram
(*Courtesy of MIPS Computer Systems, Inc.*)

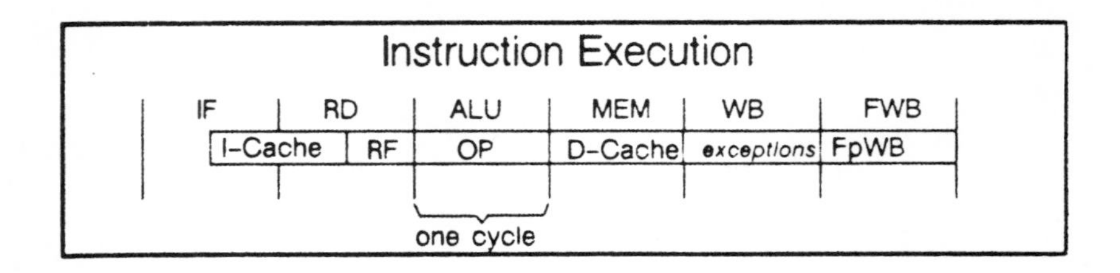

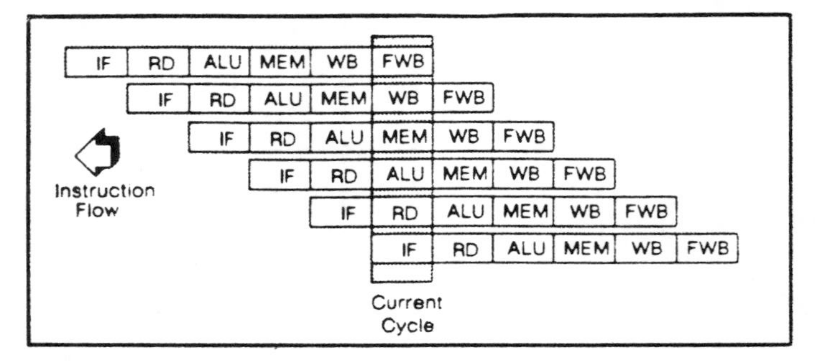

Figure 4.9 R2010 (R3010) Instruction Pipeline
(*Courtesy of MIPS Computer Systems, Inc.*)

4.3.4 MIPS Products

The R2000, R2010, R3000 and R3010 chips are available from Integrated Device Technology (IDT), Inc. (Santa Clara, CA), LSI Logic Corp. (Milpitas, CA), and Performance Semiconductor Corp. (Sunnyvale, CA). Early in 1989 an agreement was made between MIPS and NEC of Japan and Siemens of W. Germany to produce and market these components.

Both R2000 and R3000 contain all MMU and Cache Control circuitry within the chip. This includes a 64-entry TLB for fast virtual to physical address translation. The cache itself, separated into instruction (I-Cache) and data (D-Cache) caches, is implemented outside of the chip using SRAMs, as illustrated in Figure 4.10. The maximal size of either the I- or D-cache can be 64 KBytes with the R2000 aand 256 KBytes for the R3000, for a total cache size of 128 KBytes (R2000) and 512 KBytes (R3000).

Caches for either the R2000 or R3000 are direct-mapped. The standard line (block) size for the R2000 is 1 word (4 bytes). The line size for the R3000 can be set for 1, 4, 8, 16 or 32 words (4, 16, 32, 64 or 128 bytes). The R3000 also contains extra logic to support cache coherency for multiprocessor operation. The standard page size for virtual memory operation is 4 KBytes.

The address, transmitted from the CPU, is the physical address. Its lower 16 bits are transmitted on the ADRLO to the caches and to the memory interface (Figure 4.10). The upper bits of the address, plus 3 parity and one valid bits, are transmitted on the TAG bus to the same destinations. Instructions or operands

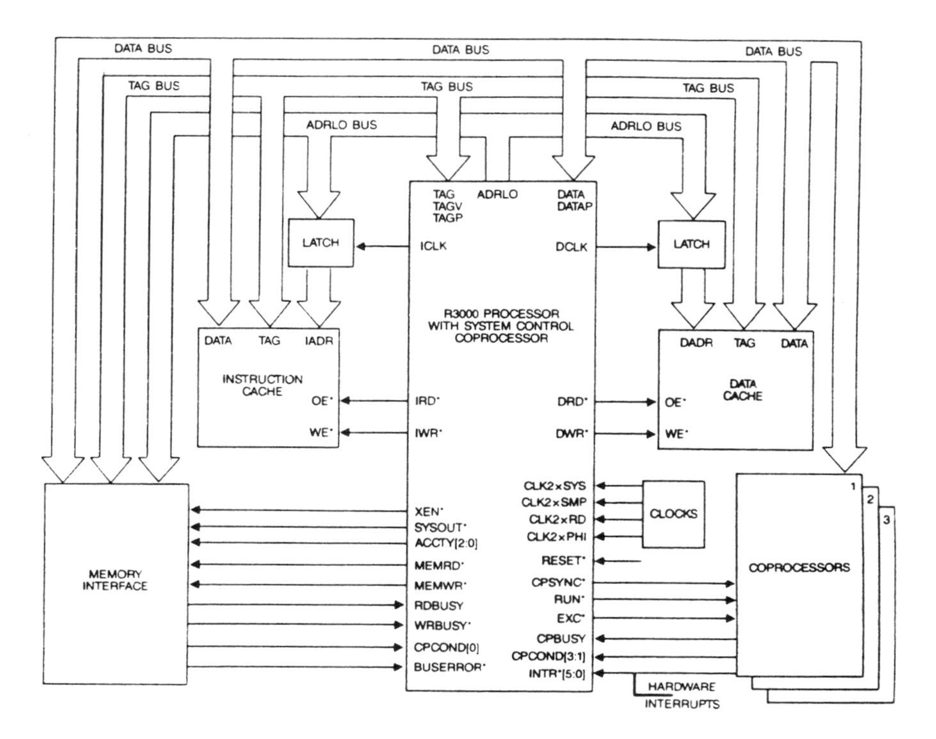

Figure 4.10 An R3000-Based System
(*Courtesy of MIPS Computer Systems, Inc.*)

are transmitted on the 32-bit (plus 4 parity bits) DATA bus, which is also connected to the coprocessors (such as the R3010) [4.7].

The essential properties of the multiple-sourced MIPS R2000 and R3000 chips are summarized in Table 4.3 [4.10]. MIPS R2000 and R3000 chips from NEC and Siemens are expected in 1989, as are 33 MHz versions of the R3000 chips from all the current semiconductor partners. In addition, NEC has announced its intention to produce an ECC version of the MIPS RISC architecture in 1990.

MIPS Computer Systems features a series of R2000- and R3000-based boards. They all feature a 4 GBytes Virtual (2 GBytes/Process) and 4 GBytes physical address spaces. All use the R2010 or R3010 FPA. All run under the Unix-based RISC/OS. Their different features are summarized in Table 4.4.

MIPS also features R2000-based microcomputers, such as RC2030, M/120 and M/1000. All use the R2010 FPA and run on the RISC/OS (also called UMIPS). Their properties are summarized in Table 4.5. The M/2000 system is R3000- and R3010-based. Its maximum clock frequency is 25 MHz (40 nsec cycle). It features 64 KBytes instruction and 64 KBytes data caches and up to 128 MBytes main memory. Its performance is 20 MIPS (sustained), 42000 Dhrystones/sec. and 14000 double precision KWhetstones/sec. It also runs on

Table 4.3 MIPS Sources

Manufacturer:	IDT		LSI Logic		Performance Semiconductor	
Feature						
Processor	79R2000	79R3000	LR2000	LR3000	R2000	R3000
Max. clock rate, MHz	16.7	25	16.7	25	20	25
Processor bus bandwidth, MB/sec.	133	200	133	200	160	200
VAX 780 MIPS	12	20	12	20	16	20
Technolgy, CMOS microns	0.8	0.8	1	1	0.8	0.8

the RISC/OS (see next subsection 4.3.5). A block diagram of the M/2000 system is shown in Figure 4.11.

4.3.5 MIPS Software

The MIPS features a Unix-based OS, called RISC/OS (also called UMIPS), capable of running both AT&T System V.3 and 4.3BSD applications. The system supports the RISCompiler subsystem for six programming languages [4.11]: C, FORTRAN 77, Pascal, Ada, COBOL and PL1. The compilation for all languages goes through the following stages:

(a) *HLL translation.*
(b) *Intercompilation unit*, translates the semantics of each language into an intermediate representation, called *U-Code*. The system provides the U-Code representation of a HLL with uniform compilation and optimization.
(c) *Optimization.*
(d) *Code Generation.*
(e) *Pipeline Scheduling.*

The above compiler system was tested on a benchmark program [4.11] that makes 10 million calls to a leaf procedure (a procedure that does not call any other procedure) with a loop – 100 calls each iteration. A MIPS M/120 system (see subsection 4.3.4) runs this program in 2.4 seconds. A VAX 11/780 runs this

Table 4.4 MIPS CPU Boards
(Courtesy of MIPS Computer Systems, Inc.)

RISCard CPUs	**R2412-3**	**R2412-5**	**R2600(2601)**	**R2800(2801)**	**R3200-8**	**R3200-6**
Processor	R2000	R2000	R2000	R2000	R3000	R3000
FPU (IEEE Std 754-1985)	R2010	R2010	none(R2010)	none(R2010)	R3010	R3010
Clock Frequency	12.5MHz	16MHz	12.5MHz	15MHz	20MHz	25MHz
Cycle Time	80nsec	62.5nsec	80nsec	66.7nsec	50nsec	40nsec
Mips Rating*	9mips	12mips	8mips	10mips	16mips	20mips
Instruction Cache	64KB	64KB	64KB	64KB	64KB	64KB
Data Cache	64KB	64KB	64KB	64KB	64KB	64KB
Cache Type	Write-thru	Write-thru	Write-thru	Write-thru	Write-thru	Write-thru
Write Buffers	32-bits, 4 stages	32-bits, 4 stages	32-bits, 4 stages	32-bits, 4 stages	32-bits, 4 stages	32-bits, 4 stages
CPU/Caches Bus BW	100MB/sec	128MB/sec	100MB/sec	120MB/sec	160MB/sec	200MB/sec
Memory Bus	Synchr.	Synchr.	Asynchr.	Asynchr.	Synchr.	Synchr.
Virtual Address Spare	4GB	4GB	4GB	4GB	4GB	4GB
Caches/Memory Bus BW	12MB/sec	16MB/sec	10MB/sec	10MB/sec	80MB/sec	100MB/sec
Interrupt Levels	6	6	6	6	6	6
Boot EPROM Size	on R2400	on R2400	256KB	256KB	256KB	256KB
RS-232C ports (full modem)	on R2400	on R2400	2 (1)	2 (1)	2 (1)	2 (1)
Time-of-Day Clock	on R2400	on R2400	yes	yes	yes	yes
Non-volatile RAM	on R2400	on R2400	yes	yes	yes	yes
Status LEDs	on R2400	on R2400	yes	yes	yes	yes
Power Dissipation	25W	25W	60W	60W	75W	75W
MTBF	40,000 hrs**	40,000 hrs**	25,000 hrs**	25,000 hrs**	40,000 hrs**	40,000 hrs**
Dimensions (mm)	140x396	140x396	367x280	367x280	367x400	367x400

Memory Modules	**R2450**	**R2850**	**R3250(R3251**
Size	8MB	16MB	32MB
DRAMs	1Mbit	1Mbit	1Mbit
Protection	Parity	ECC	ECC
VME Port	no	yes	yes
Block Mode DMA	n/a	no	yes
DMA Transfer Rate	see R2400	8MB/sec	20MB/sec
Power Dissipation	30W	45W	75W (55W)
MTBF	100,000 hrs**	45,000 hrs**	50,000 hrs**
Dimensions (mm)	140x320	367x280	367x400

System Motherboard	**R2400**
Boot PROM Size	64KB
RS-232C ports	4 (DB25S)
(full modem support)	(2)
Max Baud Rate	19.2K
Time-of-Day Clock	yes
Non-volatile RAM	yes
Status LEDs	yes
Memory Slots	6
DMA Transfer Rate	2.5MB/sec
AT-bus Slots	4
SCSI Controller	ANSI x3.131-1986
Max Transfer Rate	4.0MB/sec sync.
Ethernet Controller	IEEE 802.3
Data Rate	10Mbits/sec
Power Dissipation	80W
MTBF	45,000 hrs**
Dimensions (mm)	401x460

* Based on a suite of 12 benchmarks performed on a MIPS RISComputer System with the execution time set to a reference such that a VAX™ 11/780 running VMS software as released in 1987 is rated as 1.0 mips.

** Based on operation in the recommended operating temperature range of +10°C to +45°C.

Environmental	**All Cards**
Oper. Ambient Temp.	0°C to 55°C
Relative Humidity	20% to 85% non-condensing
Altitude	0 to 3,048m (10,000ft.)

Specifications are subject to change without notice.

program in 153 seconds (153/2.4 = 64). The M/120 is rated at 12 VAX 780 MIPS.

The RISCompiler C language product is fully compatible with the Kernighan and Ritchie specification [4.12]. ANSI extensions supported include Volatile Storage Class (required for OS global optimization when device drivers are included) and the prototype extension that is used for declaring function argument lists. The FORTRAN conforms to the ANSI X3.9-1978 specification for FORTRAN 77. It includes the features commonly found in Unix environments

Table 4.5 MIPS RISComputers
(*Courtesy of MIPS Computer Systems, Inc.*)

Unit	RC2030	M/120	M/1000	M/2000
Package Type	Desktop	Deskside	Pedestal	Rack Cabinet
Base System Price*	$17K to $20K	$30Kto $35K	$70K to $80K	$110K to $125K
Mips Rating**	12	13	10	20
Cost per mips***	$1400 to $1600	$2500 to $2900	$7000 to $8000	$5500 to $6500
Min./Max. Memory	8/16MB	8/48MB	16/80MB	32/128MB
Disk Type	3.5" SCSI	5.25" SCSI	8" SMD	8" SMD
Disk Capacity	3.65 GB	4.0 GB	2.0 GB	15.7 GB
Ethernet Ports	one	one	up to two	up to four
Peripherals in System Cabinet	172 MB disk, diskette	663/328MB disk, cart. tape, 4 AT slots	655MB disk, cart. tape, 6 VME slots	2.6GB disk, 1/2" mag tape, 13 VME slots
Other I/O Facilities	SCSI port, Exp. Cab. for disk drives	SCSI port, Exp. Cab. for disk drives	Expansion Cab. for disk drives and 1/2" tape	Expansion Cab. for disk, tape, & user devices
Software	Compatible across the product line.			
Benchmark Data:				
Dhrystones/sec.	31,000	31,000	23,700	47,400
KWhet/sec., DP	9,400	9,400	8,000	14,100
Linpack, DP FTN	1.8	2.1	1.5	3.9
First Customer Ship	Q2, 1989	Q2, 1988	Q3, 1987	Q3, 1988

* Base systems include RISC/os operating system software, minimum memory configuration, floating point unit, one disk drive and controller, a tape device, and an Ethernet controller. Other listed items are options. Prices are in U.S. dollars. Specifications and prices are subject to change without notice.

** Based on a suite of 12 benchmarks with the reference for execution time being a VAX 11/780 running VMS software as released in 1987 rated at 1.0 mips. The "MIPS Performance Brief" is available on request.

*** Other currently available multiuser and server systems typically cost $15,000 to $90,000 per mips, measured on a comparable basis. Specific data should be obtained directly from each of the other suppliers.

such as support for Unix system calls, preprocessors, byte data type, multiple-include facilities, short integers, and binary/octal/hex constants. A full compatibility with VMS FORTRAN is provided. The Pascal compiler conforms to the ANSI/IEEE 770-X3.99-1983 level 0 specification, and is consistent with common practice in the Unix/C programming environment. It has include-file processing and a compile-time macro facility. Extensions supported are separate compilation, constant expressions, otherwise clauses in case statements, interface to Unix calls and routines, bit operations, and lazy I/O for interactive input. The Ada compiler is validated at version 1.9 ACVC. The front-end and Ada tools are derived from Verdix's VADS Ada under license. MIPS provides as an option a real-time Ada operating environment suitable for embedded systems.

The AccelR8 Technology Corp. (Denver, CO) has recently announced a new software product *Dcl 8*, a DCL shell for the RISC/OS [4.13]. The Dcl 8 provides an interface for users more familiar with DEC's Command Language DCL, used on DEC's VMS OS. The Dcl 8 makes the operation with RISC/OS on a MIPS computer transparent to the user and very similar to that of a VMS-based system.

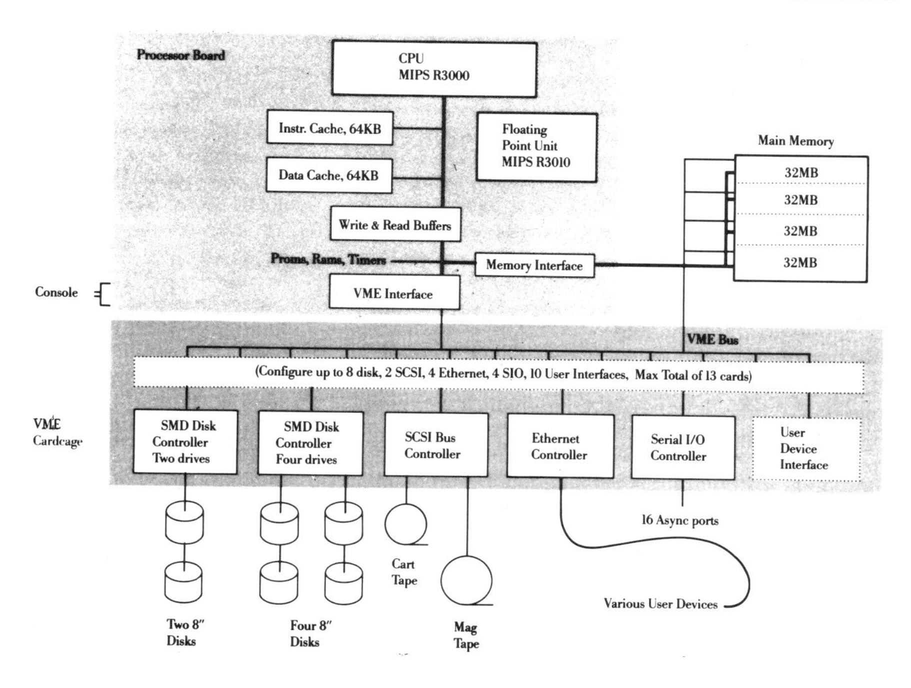

Figure 4.11 Functional Block Diagram of the M/2000 System (*Courtesy of MIPS Computer Systems, Inc.*)

References

4.1 J.L. Hennessy, T. Gross, 'Postpass Code Optimization of Pipeline Constraints', *ACM Trans. on Programming Languages and Systems*, **5**, No. 3, pp. 422–448, July 1983.

4.2 J.L. Hennessy *et al.*, 'MIPS: A VLSI Processor Architecture', *Proc. CMU Conf. VLSI Systems and Computations*, pp. 337–346, Computer Science Press, Rockville, MD, Oct. 1981.

4.3 J.L. Hennessy *et al.*, 'The MIPS Machine', *Proc. COMPCON 1982*, pp. 2–7, San Francisco, CA, 1982.

4.4 J.L. Hennessy *et al.*, 'Design of a High Performance VLSI Processor', *Proc. 3rd Caltech Conf. VLSI*, pp. 33–54, Pasadena, CA, March 1983.

4.5 S.A. Przybylski *et al.*, 'Organization and VLSI Implementation of MIPS', *J. of VLSI and Computer Systems*, **1**, No. 2, pp. 170–208, Spring 1984.

4.6 G. Kane, *MIPS R2000 RISC Architecture*, Prentice-Hall, Englewood Cliffs, NJ, 1987.

4.7 C. Hansen *et al.*, 'A RISC Microprocessor with Integral MMU and Cache Interface', *Proc. 1986 ICCD*, pp. 145–148, New York, Oct. 1986.

4.8 S. Stritter *et al.*, 'Engineering a RISC Hardware Environment', *Proc. 1986 ICCD*, pp. 138–141, New York, Oct. 1986.
4.9 J. Moussouris *et al.*, 'A CMOS RISC Processor with Integrated System Functions', *Proc. 1986 COMPCON*, pp. 126–131, San Francisco, March 1986.
4.10 B. Furlow, 'RISC – The Sound and the Fury', *ESD*, March 1989, pp. 49–57.
4.11 F. Chow, L. Weber, 'Optimizing the RISC Odds', *ESD*, Sept. 1988, pp. 73–76.
4.12 B.W. Kernighan, D.M. Ritchie, *The C Programming Language*, Prentice-Hall, Englewood Cliffs, NJ, 1978.
4.13 D.W. Haskin, 'Less RISCy Business', *Digital Review*, Nov. 7, 1988, pp. 55–64.

5
Experimental Systems

5.1 The IBM 801

As mentioned in section 1.5, the IBM 801 system was the first RISC-type system to be developed as an experimental computer. As attested by the system developers [1.19, 5.1], the following principles were examined during the design:

(1) System orientation towards the *pervasive use of HLL programming* and a sophisticated compiler.
(2) A *primitive instruction set* which can be *completely hardwired.*
(3) Storage hierarchy and I/O organization to enable the CPU to *execute an instruction* at almost *every cycle.*

Referring back to section 1.3 we can see that the above principles fit quite well to the points of definition of a RISC-type system. Since the development of the IBM 801 started in 1975, it can definitely be regarded as the first RISC-type machine, although it has never been called by that name.

The IBM 801 is a 32-bit machine. Both its addresses as well as arithmetic data are 32-bits long. Two's complement arithmetic is being used. Instructions are also fullword (32-bit) long, aligned on fullword boundaries in memory. In fact, all operands are aligned in memory on boundaries, consistent with their size. The instructions are executed in a single cycle of 66 ns, achieving an overall speed of 10 MIPS. There is a total of 120 machine language instructions. However, this instruction set is intended for the compiler writer only. The regular user is supposed to program in HLL only. A PL.8 (subset of PL/1) compiler has been developed along with the 801 system. The compiler also accepts Pascal programs, producing compatible object code so that PL.8 and Pascal procedures can call one another.

Memory is accessed by Load/Store instructions only. Only two addressing modes are used for memory access:

Base + Index
Base + Displacement

For Branch target specifications, the following three addressing modes can be used:

Absolute 26-bit address
Instruction Address Register (IAR) + Displacement
(signed 16- or 26-bit)

Register + Register

The last two addressing modes are not conceptually different from the two memory reference addressing modes. Thus, we really have only three different addressing modes on the 801. In general, instructions may have three register operands.

Multiplication is supported by the MULTIPLY STEP instruction. A 32×32-bit, 64-bit product, multiplication is accomplished in 16 cycles. Similarly, division is supported by the DIVIDE STEP instruction. A 64/32-bit, 32-bit quotient, 32-bit remainder division is accomplished in 32 cycles.

The 801 architecture supports a *Branch with Execute* feature. When the branch target is fetched, the CPU executes the instruction following the branch. This is practically the same as the delayed branch (section 1.4).

EXAMPLE The code sequence

```
LOAD R1,A
BNZ L       ; Branch on Non Zero
```

is converted by the compiler into a Branch with Execute sequence:

```
BNZX L      ; Branch on Non Zero and Execute
LOAD R1,A;  executed while the instruction
            ; at address L is being fetched.
```

There is a total of 32 CPU registers. That was a considerably large number for a system of 801's size in 1975, although it is substantially lower than the 138 of RISC II, completed in 1982. Of all the experimental RISC prototypes, the register window idea has been implemented on the Berkeley RISC and GMU MIRIS and MULTRIS only (in a way different from the Berkeley RISC though, as described in section 5.3).

The system's Cache memory is split into a

(1) Data Cache
(2) Instruction Cache

with asynchronous fetching of instructions and data from memory. A block diagram is shown in Figure 5.1. The Block (Line) size for either cache is 32 bytes. The basic store unit is 4 bytes = 32 bits. Explicit instructions for cache management have been defined. Thus, in the 801 system, the cache is a part of the architecture, visible to the programmer (at least to the compiler writer).

The hardware prototype of the IBM 801 has been realized with Motorola ECL (Emitter Current Logic) 10K DIP (Dual Inline Packages) MSI chips. It was completed in 1980.

5.2 The Berkeley SOAR and SPUR

After having completed the development of the RISC II in 1981, the Berkeley team continued with the design of two new, special purpose, RISC-type systems:

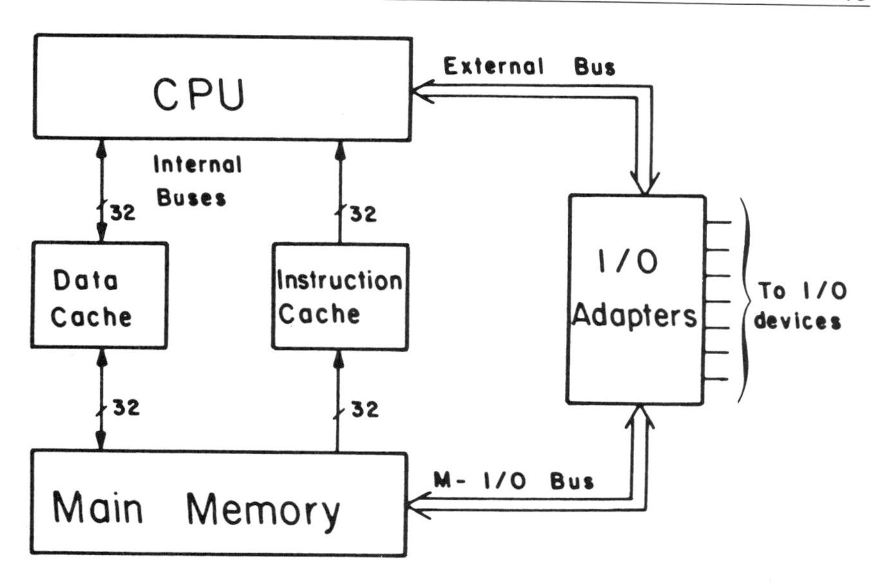

Figure 5.1 IBM 801 Interconnections

the Smalltalk On A RISC (SOAR) [5.2, 5.3] and the Symbolic Processing Using RISC (SPUR) [5.4, 5.5].

Smalltalk-80 is an object-oriented programming environment, developed by Xerox Corp. in Palo-Alto, CA, and implemented on their Dorado computing system [5.6, 5.7]. Before the creation of SOAR, Smalltalk-80 had to be run on relatively expensive computing systems. One of the main motivations of SOAR designers was to create a simple and inexpensive system, capable of running Smalltalk-80 in an efficient, high-performance manner. A number of architectural innovations were built into the SOAR to speed up Smalltalk-80 operations [5.2, 5.3].

Smalltalk-80 does not have type of operands declarations. This causes a significant overhead since a type check has to be performed before the execution of an operation. SOAR designers improved the Smalltalk-80 performance by introducing hardware supported *data tagging*. There are two types of tagged data: integers and pointers (as required by the Smalltalk-80 environment), denoted by the most significant bit in a 32-bit SOAR word (bit 31), as illustrated in Figure 5.2. For integers, bit 31=0, and for pointers, bit 31=1. Bits 28–30 are used as a *tag* field for pointers. The tag is actually used as a *generation tag*, associated with the object pointed to by the pointer. It is particularly used during store operations while reclaiming storage space. The SOAR reclaim policy requires that a list be updated whenever a pointer to a new object is stored in an old object. While computing the memory address, the store instruction compares the generation tag of the data being stored with the generation tag of the memory

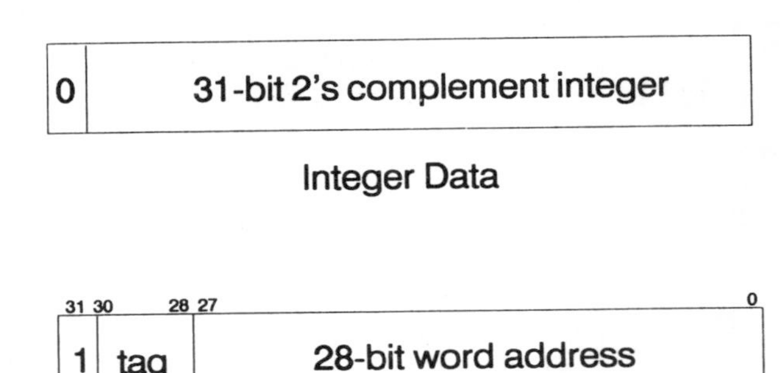

Figure 5.2 SOAR Tagged Data Formats

address. If the latter is smaller, the store is completed; otherwise, a list update exception is generated.

For arithmetic and comparison operations, SOAR assumes that the operands are integers and begins the execution of the operation immediately, simultaneously checking the tags. Most often (in over 92% of all cases) both operands are integers and the correct result is available after one cycle. If not (the operands are pointers), SOAR aborts the operation and traps to routines that carry out the appropriate computation for the data types.

SOAR architecture uses *compare-and-skip* instructions for integer comparisons. It does not have conventional condition codes. Conditional jumps are implemented by a sequence of a conditional skip and an unconditional jump. SOAR jump instructions contain the absolute address of the target instruction. Because no address computation is required, SOAR eliminates the instruction prefetch penalty for jumps. If the condition in the conditional skip is met the program skips the jump. Otherwise, the prefetched jump is executed.

SOAR has a standard 32-bit word instruction length. Most instructions take one cycle to execute. Loads, stores and returns are executed in two cycles. There are three basic instruction formats:

(1) Calls and jumps, with a 28-bit word address of target.
(2) Three-operand, with a 6-bit opcode and 5-bit fields of source 1, source 2 and destination registers. Source 2 can alternately serve as a 12-bit immediate constant.
(3) Store, with a 6-bit opcode and two source fields.

Memory is word addressed. Separate instructions insert or extract bytes from words. There are 21 instruction types including arithmetic (add, sub), logical (and, or, xor), shift (sll, srl, sra), byte manipulation (insert, extract), load/store (including load/store multiple, loadm, storem), skip, trap, nop and program control (call, jump, ret).

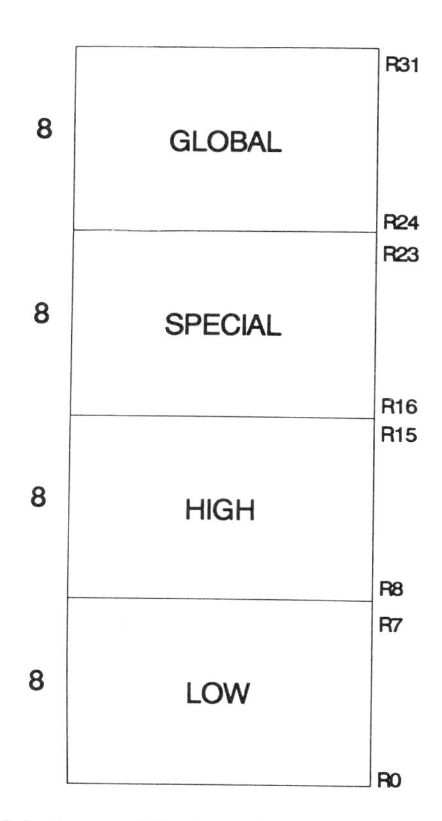

Figure 5.3 Register File for each Subroutine on the SOAR

SOAR, like RISC I and II, efficiently supports subroutine calls and returns by using the overlapping register window approach (chapter 3). Each subroutine running on the SOAR sees 3-bit CPU registers, as illustrated in Figure 5.3. The above 32 registers are subdivided into 4 groups of 8 registers:

(1) LOW, R0–R7, contain parameters passed to the called subroutine.
(2) HIGH, R8–R15, contain parameters received from the calling subroutine.
(3) SPECIAL, R16–R23, include:
  R16, rzero, always zero (as R0 on RISC I or II).
  R17, Program Counter, PC.
  R18, shb, Shadow B, input to ALU.
  R19, sha, Shadow A, input to ALU.
  R20, Saved Window Pointer, SWP (memory address of object leader of the most recently saved register window).
  R21, tb, Trap Base, base address of the interrupt and trap vector area.
  R22, Current Window Pointer, CWP (index of on-chip register set serving as a HIGH-window).

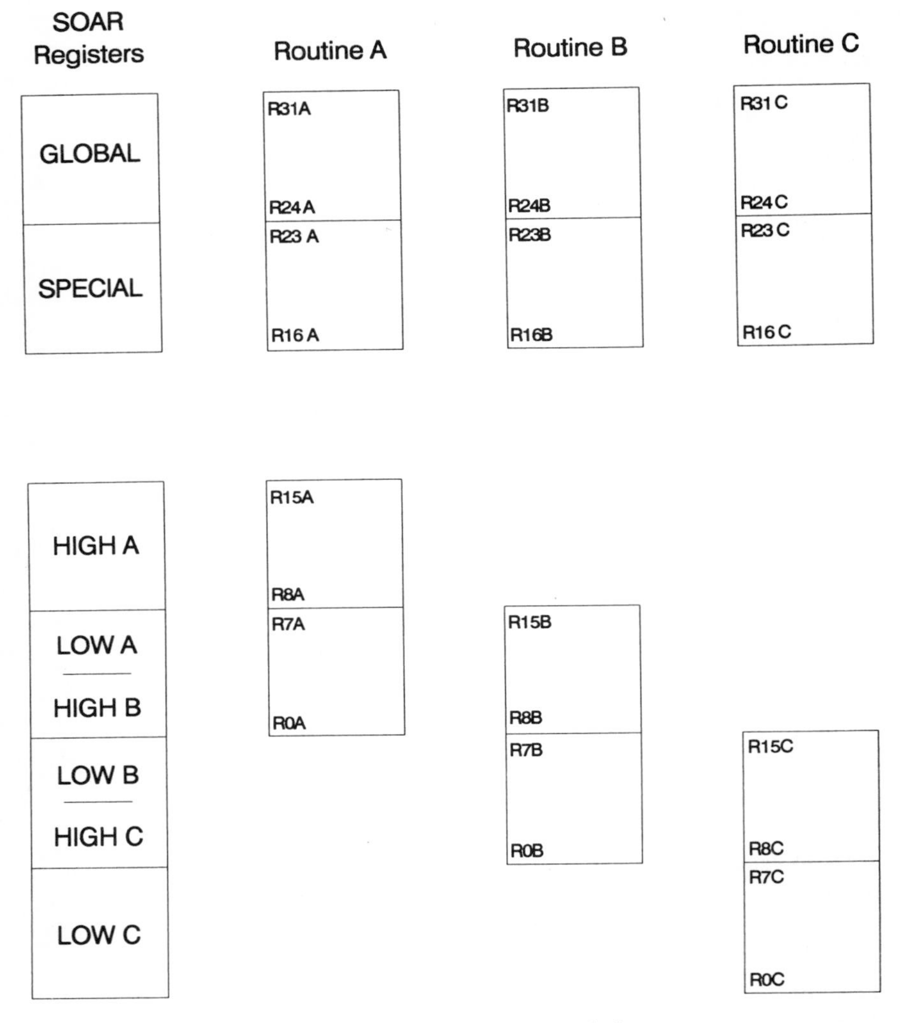

Figure 5.4 SOAR Register Windows

R23, Processor Status Word, PSW.

(4) GLOBAL, R24–R31, for system software such as trap handlers.

The register window arrangement for three consecutive nested routines A, B and C, is illustrated in Figure 5.4. It is understandably similar to that of the Berkeley RISC (chapter 3), although somewhat different. In addition to the 16 global and special registers, there are 64 window registers, permitting a 7-deep routine nesting on chip. The total number of CPU registers is 80. When the number of routine activations exceeds the on-chip register capacity, SOAR traps to a software routine that saves the contents of a set of registers in memory. Load- and store-multiple instructions, to speed register saving and restoring, are available. These instructions can transfer 8 registers in 9 cycles (1 instruction fetch and 8 data accesses). These instructions have the ability to operate on non-contiguous data; the increment between memory references is given by the source 2 field.

Another way SOAR supports subroutine handling and reduces overhead is by decreasing the time taken to find the target of a call. Once computed, the target's address is cached in the instruction stream for subsequent use [5.2]. This feature is called *in-line caching*. Subsequently, the SOAR call instruction contains the absolute address of its destination. A call or jump can be recognized by examining only one bit. This makes it possible to detect these instructions in time to send the incoming data back to the memory as an address. Thus, a call or jump executes in one cycle. The above call or jump handling mechanism is called the *fast shuffle*.

The SOAR return instruction performs one compulsory and three optional functions [5.2], specified by the low-order three opcode bits. The compulsory function is a transfer of control to the calling (or interrupted) routine. The optional functions are:

(1) Enable interrupts, yielding a return from interrupt instruction.
(2) Increment the CWP for returning from a normal call.
(3) Initialize local registers to zero, according to the Smalltalk-80 requirements.

Each call in Smalltalk-80 needs a new *activation record*, containing local variables and other data of the new object. SOAR caches activation records in the on-chip register file, achieving higher speed. If the number of activations exceeds the number of on-chip register windows, an overflow occurs. It is backed by an overflow stack in memory. Pointers to activation records are rare, so SOAR's hardware merely detects these and causes a trap at the appropriate time [5.2]. The first trap occurs when a reference to an activation record is created. Pointers to activation records have all the tag bits (Figure 5.2) set. When such a word is stored into memory, the tag check causes a trap. At the time of the trap, the high order bit of the activation record's return address is set. Setting this bit indicates that the activation record may outlive its parent. Since these records are normally allocated and freed Last-In-First-Out (LIFO), we label such anomalously long-lived activation records as non-LIFO. The return instruction then traps if the return address has the high order bit set – this lets software save this activation record [5.2].

To reduce the cost of trapping, SOAR implements *Shadow Registers* that catch the operands of the trapping instructions. A similar feature is implemented in the commercial Motorola M88000 system (chapter 6). SOAR does not support nested interrupts or traps in order to reduce complexity. There is an Interrupt Enable bit (bit 6) in the Program Status Word (PSW); it is reset upon an interrupt or trap. When an interrupt or trap occurs, the instruction that is executing is aborted before it can change any values in registers. The address of the aborted instruction is saved in R7. I/O interrupts are disabled by clearing the interrupt enable bit in the PSW. This freezes the Shadow Registers, which normally track the ALU inputs. A vector is constructed from the trap base register, the opcode of the aborted instruction, and the trap source. Finally, the control is transferred to the vectored location [5.2].

The SOAR datapath is illustrated in Figure 5.5. It contains a dual-port register file, ALU, PC, Memory Address Latch and a Destination Latch. The three-stage SOAR pipeline is illustrated in Figure 5.6. Because of the *fast shuffle* feature, described above, jumps and calls execute in a single cycle and cause no delay in the pipeline. Conditional branches are synthesized with a skip and an unconditional jump. This takes two cycles. The datapath allows two simultaneous reads or one write to the register file. Each execute cycle is divided into 3 nonoverlapping phases (Figure 5.6):

(1) Decode the instruction and precharge the bus.
(2) Read source registers onto the buses.
(3) Compute results in the ALU and, simultaneously, store back the result from the previous instruction into its destination register.

The result of instruction i is not actually stored into its destination register until the end of instruction i+1. Forwarding logic hides this delay; if instruction i+1 attempts to read the destination register of instruction i, the desired value is forwarded from the destination latch at the output of the ALU.

The SOAR is a 4-micron NMOS, 35700 transistors, 3 W power dissipation chip. Its performance is 400 nsec/instruction, or 2.5 MIPS. Its primary disadvantage is that it needs an extra 700 KBytes of memory to run Smalltalk-80, compared to the Dorado, which needs just one MBytes. This is a common RISC-type system disadvantage (section 2.6). A SOAR-based board, that operates with a Sun workstation, was constructed at Berkeley.

Another Berkeley RISC-spinoff system is the Symbolic Processing Using RISC (SPUR) workstation [5.4]. It was aimed at applying RISC concepts to the support of LISP programming environments [5.8]. The SPUR incorporates custom-designed processor nodes and off-the-shelf memory and I/O boards. SPUR may include up to 12 processor nodes, interconnected by the SPUR bus into a multiprocessor system. The T1 NuBus was chosen as the system bus.

The processor node board is composed of the following major parts:

(1) Custom designed VLSI, 32-bit, RISC-type CPU. It features 40-bit tagged (32-bits data, 8-bits tag) architecture and a load-store/register-register instruction set.
(2) A VLSI, custom designed, memory/cache management chip, implementing a cache coherency protocol and virtual memory management.
(3) A custom-designed floating point coprocessor [5.5], implementing the IEEE standard.
(4) A 128 KByte cache.

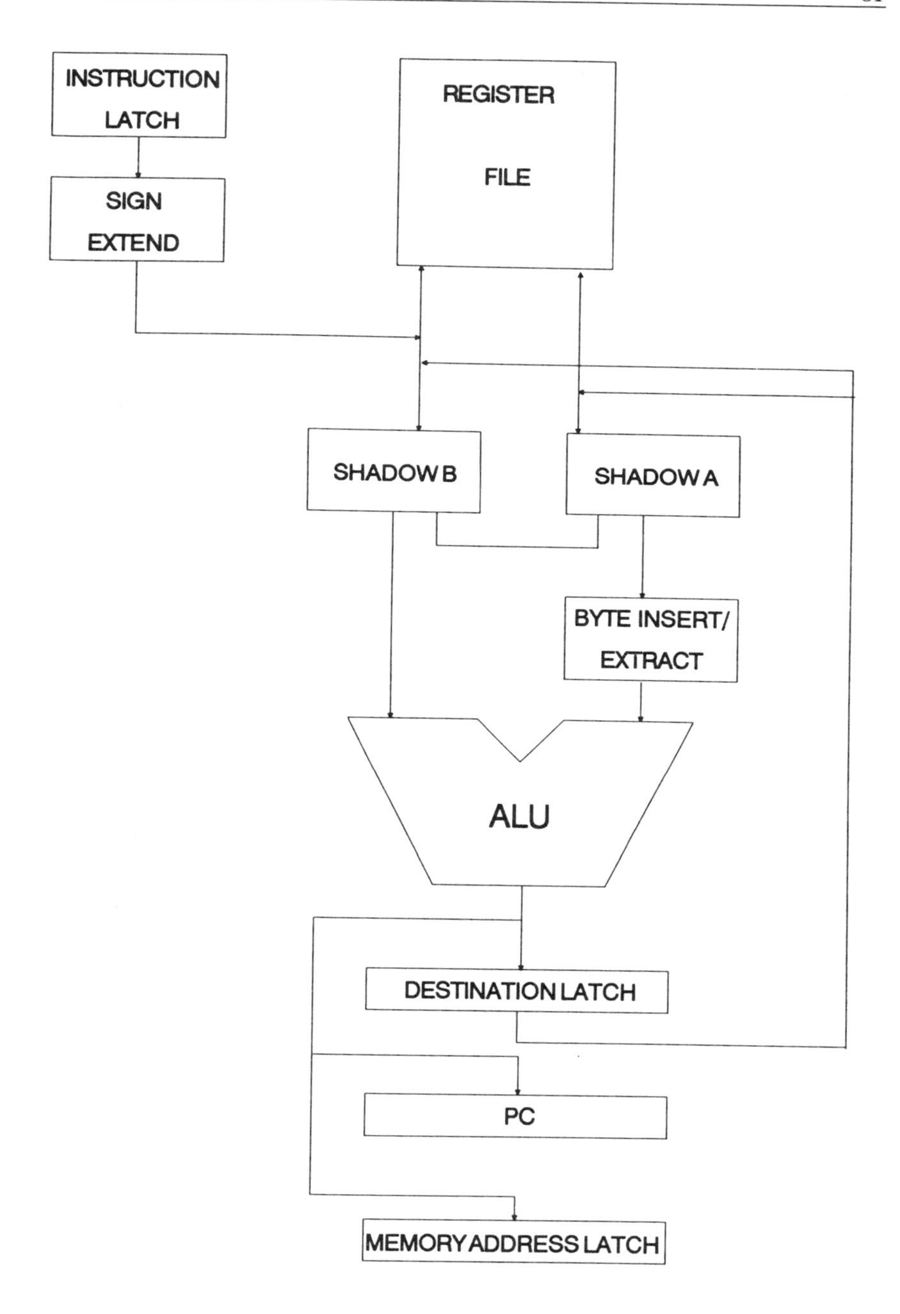

Figure 5.5 The SOAR Datapath

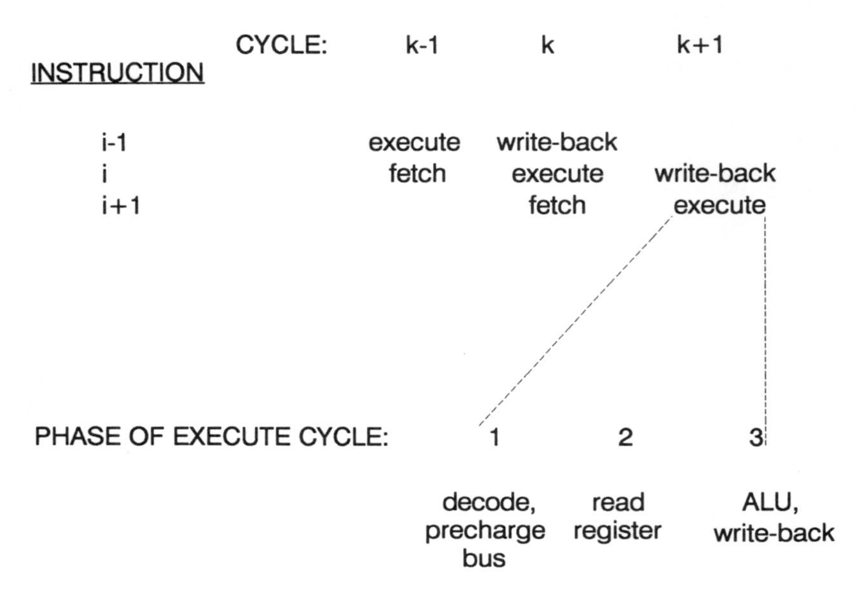

Figure 5.6 The SOAR Pipeline

The board features a 64-bit data bus to accommodate double-precision floating point values.

5.3 The GMU MIRIS and MULTRIS

A Microcoded RISC-type processor, MIRIS, was developed at the George Mason University (GMU) in Fairfax, Virginia [1.3, 5.9, 5.10]. A bit-sliced (AMD 2900) prototype was constructed.

As most other RISC systems, it is a 32-bit processor with 32-bit data paths. All instructions are 32-bit long and each instruction is primitive enough to execute in a single cycle. The current, bipolar technology, used for the prototype, permits work at 10 MHz, attaining a performance of 10 Millions of Instructions Per Second (MIPS).

The MIRIS is subdivided into two main parts (Figure 5.7):

(1) The Program Control Section (PCS), along with the Program Memory (PM). Its functions are:
  (a) Compute the address of the next instruction to be executed.
  (b) Fetch the instruction from PM into the Instruction Register (IR).
  (c) Decode the instruction, providing all of the necessary control signals on the control lines.
  (d) Provide the appropriate hardware logic to recognize and handle interrupts.

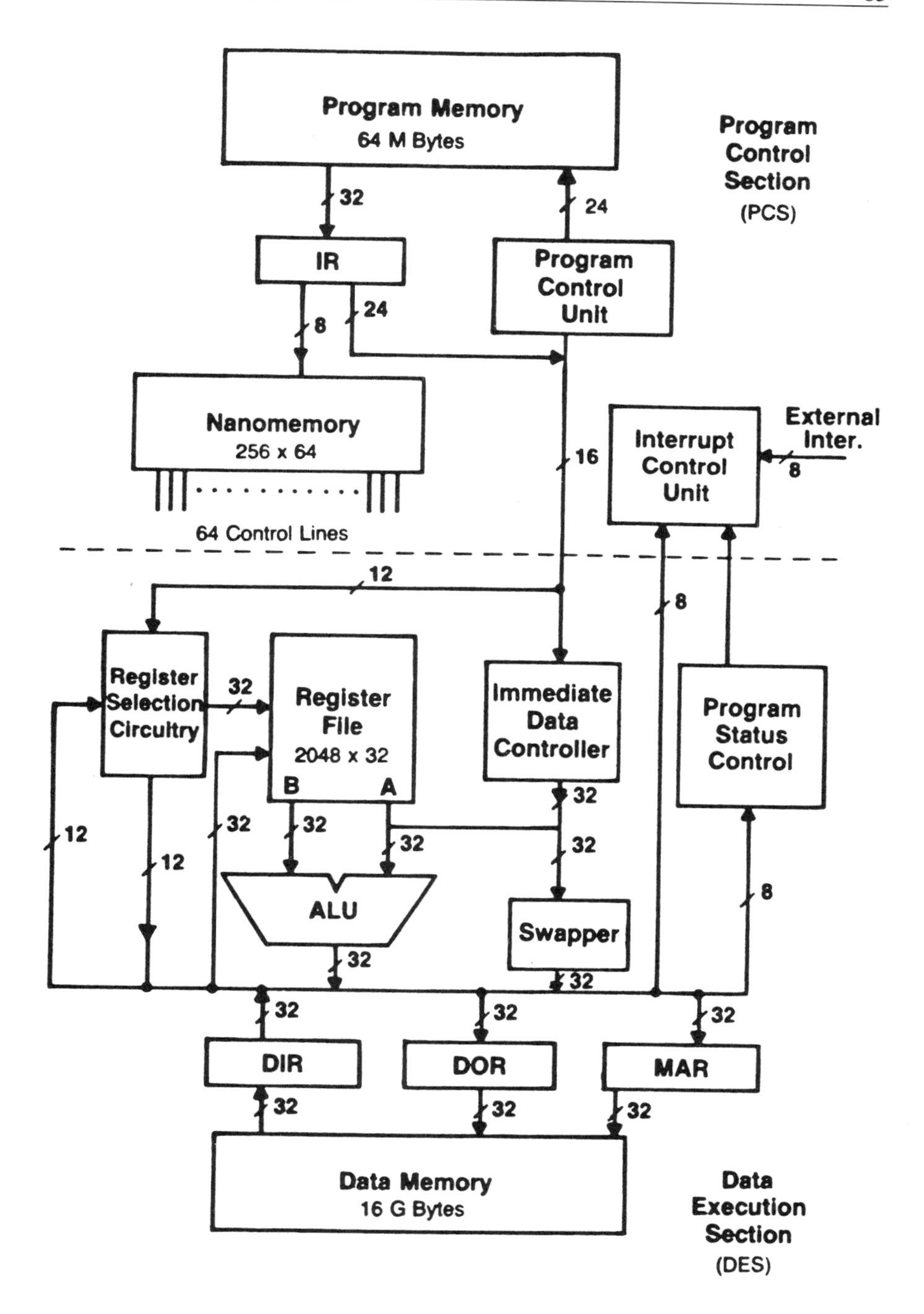

Figure 5.7 Microcoded RISC (MIRIS)

(2) The Data Execution Section (DES), along with the Data Memory (DM), are physically separate from the PM. Its functions are:
   (a) Execute all data processing tasks with the Arithmetic Logic Unit (ALU).
   (b) Store current operands and results in the Register File (RF).
   (c) Provide information about the status of the processor through an appropriate field of the Logical Status Word (LSW), allocated within the Program Status Control Unit (PSCU).
   (d) Interface with the Data Memory (DM) to Load/Store operands.

The basic difference between the MIRIS and the other research prototypes of RISC (Berkeley and Stanford machines, IBM 801) is that the control of MIRIS is microcoded, while that of the others is hardwired. However, the MIRIS microcode does not have the standard structure with numerous microsubroutines, as in other microcoded machines [1.22]. In MIRIS, each machine instruction always corresponds to just one 64-bit control word. All control words are stored in a maximum 256 × 64 Control Store PROM. Since, at the moment, there are only 64 instructions (no more than about 75 are expected at the end of the development), the Control Store is underutilized in the prototype. The most significant byte of each machine instruction is the opcode and at the same time – a direct address to the 256 × 64 ($256 = 2^8$) Control Store. No decoding is needed. The short access Control Store produces practically immediately (within 30 ns with the current realization) a 64-bit, horizontal Control Word (or Micro-instruction), capable of activating up to 64 control lines simultaneously. Thus, a *streamlined*, microcode-based, instruction execution is achieved. At the same time, the design benefits from the usual microcode advantages of greater flexibility for modifications and error recovery, while maintaining a high speed of instruction handling (no decoding, control lines activated within 30 ns).

The Control Store of MIRIS is very similar to the Nanomemory in the MC68000, and for this reason it has been so labelled. Of course, there is a big difference in the fact that MIRIS does not have the extra Micromemory level available in the MC68000 [2.5, p. 361]. This is illustrated in Figure 5.8.

The Program and Data Memories can be accessed simultaneously. In fact, while the result of instruction (i – 2) is being stored in DM, instruction (i – 1) may be executed by the ALU, while instruction i is being fetched and decoded (a practically immediate operation), thus forming a three-stage instruction pipeline.

The only data formats recognized by MIRIS architecture are:

8-bit Byte
16-bit Halfword
32-bit Word

Two's complement arithmetic is implemented.

The MIRIS has a set of 64 primitive instructions. Each instruction is executable within a single machine cycle and has a standard length of 32 bits. All instructions are subdivided into two major fields:

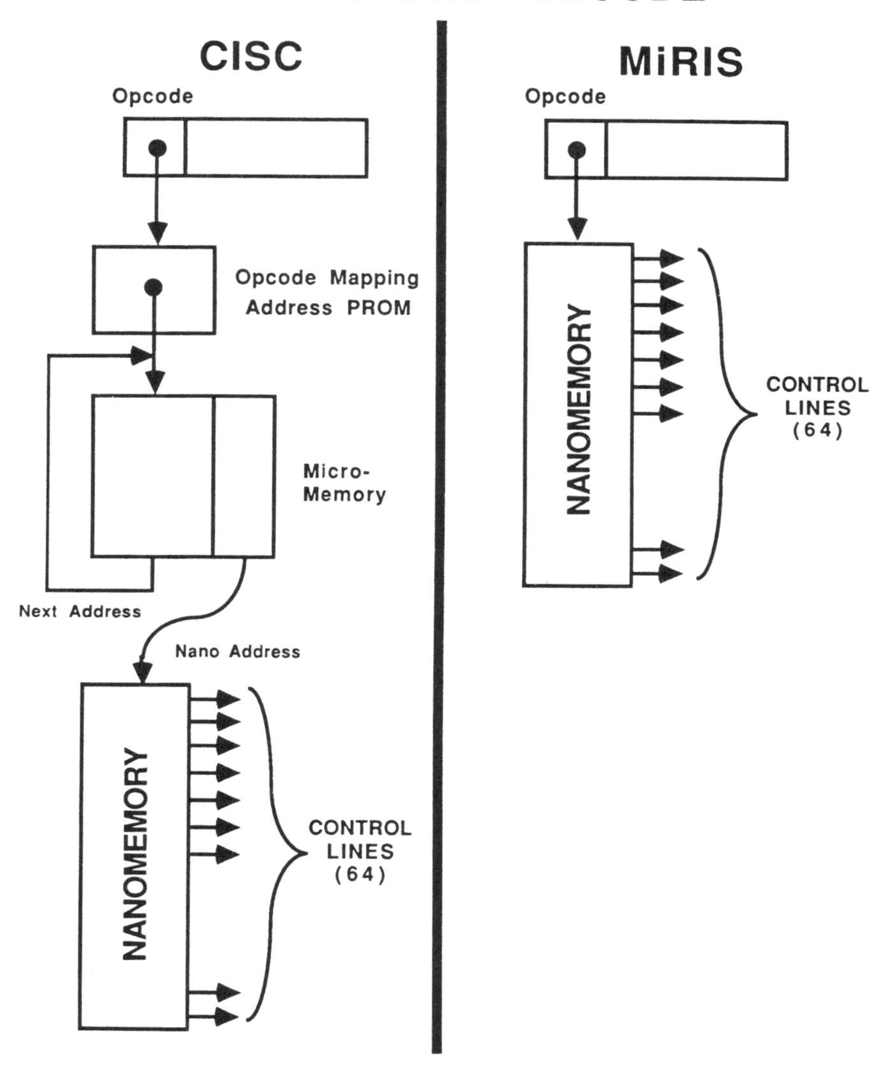

Figure 5.8 A CISC and MIRIS Microcode Hierarchy

bits 31–24: opcode
bits 23–0 : operand address.

There is a one-to-one correspondence between each type of machine instruction, fetched from PM, and a single control word (nanoword, nanoinstruction) in the 256 × 64 Nanomemory. The 8-bit opcode is just a direct address into the

Nanomemory (256 = 2^8) and no decoding is necessary. The machine has a capability of handling up to 256 primitive instructions. The design can be relatively easily expanded by adding new instructions if necessary, sometimes just by adding information to the Nanomemory PROM, while judiciously using the existing control lines interconnections.

The Program Memory (PM) is addressed only by a single 24-bit Direct Addressing Mode. It is Word (32-bit)-addressable. Thus, its size is 16 MWords or 64 MBytes. All in all, the MIRIS architecture recognizes four formats for the Operand Address field, as illustrated in Figure 5.9.

The value of the immediate operand is 16 bits wide within the address field. When transferred into a 32-bit register it can be placed in its high 31:16 or low 15:0 half word and either 0 or 1 extended, according to the IS encoding:

IS	Placement	Extension bit
00	low	0
01	high	0
10	low	1
11	high	1

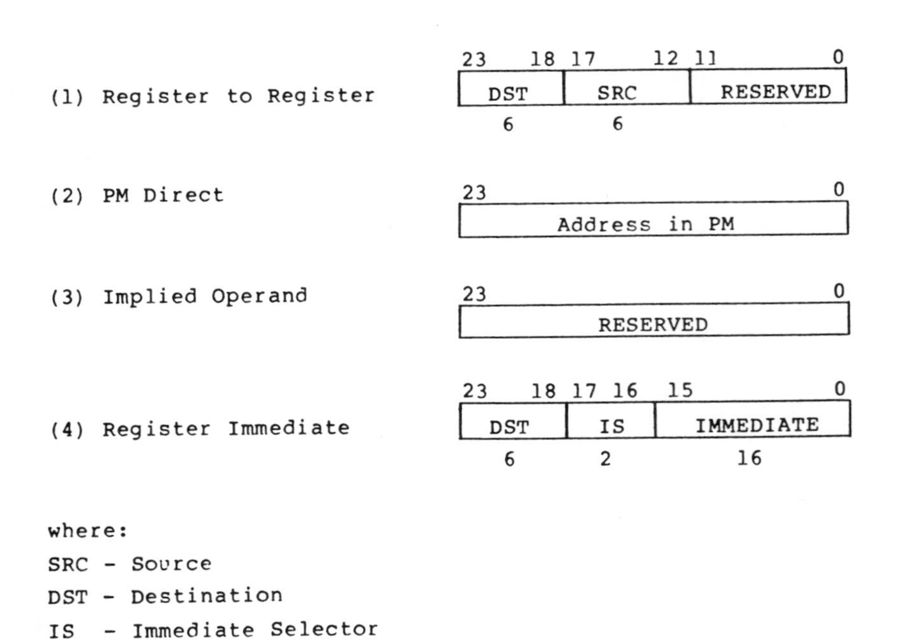

Figure 5.9 MIRIS Operand Addressing Formats

The SRC and DST fields are each 6 bits wide. If the MSB of either is not set (0), then the lower 5 bits are used to address only the 32 global registers R0–R31. Otherwise, the lower 5 bits are combined with the 6 bits of either Port A and Port B fields in the LSW to form the 11-bit address of one of the 2048 CPU registers.

Each process in the MIRIS can 'see' a maximum of 96 registers out of the whole Register File (RF). The RF is implemented as a dual port memory in which the SRC and the DST registers can be accessed simultaneously and the result can be stored back into the DST register – all within one CPU cycle (100 ns). This is one of the reasons for the expected high throughput of MIRIS.

The Logical Status Word (LSW) format is illustrated in Figure 5.10. It should be stressed that the LSW is not implemented in hardware as a single register. Its fields are realized in the Program Status Control Unit in different components. However, the contents of LSW in its entirety can be moved into any register using the available instruction:

SAVLSW DST ; DST ← (LSW)

The LSW can also be restored using:

RESLSW SRC ; LSW ← (SRC)

Generally, the saving of any information during a procedure call or an interrupt is done in the CPU register file instead of the Data Memory, thereby speeding up the operation.

As stated in the beginning of this section, the MIRIS system is organized as two basic parts (Figure 5.7):

(1) The Program Control Section (PCS)
(2) The Data Execution Section (DES)

31 24	23	22 16	15 12	11 6	5 0
MASK	I	RESERVED	C O N Z	PORT B	PORT A

where:

MASK	- 8-bit interrupt mask field
I	- Interrrupt Enable (I=1 : Enabled).
C	- Carry Flag
O	- Overflow Flag
N	- Negative Flag
Z	- Zero Flag
PORT B	- upper six bit register file address, port B
PORT A	- upper six bit register file address, port A

Figure 5.10 The MIRIS Logical Status Word (LSW)

The PCS is composed of the following main units.

(a) *Program Control Unit* (PCU)
Provides the address of the next instruction to be executed. It contains a 24-bit Program Counter (PC) register. The address is provided in a 24-bit direct format. The PCU is realized using 6 AMD2930 Program Control Unit chips. The chip contains a 17-register stack for nested subroutine return addresses.

(b) *Instruction Register* (IR)
Stores the whole instruction (32-bits), fetched from the Program Memory (PM). It is loaded with a new instruction every clock cycle (100 ns). The IR is realized by 4 TTL 74S374 chips.

(c) *Nanomemory*
A 256 × 64 PROM Control Store. Each 64-bit Control Word constitutes a horizontal microcode entry, equivalent to a specific MIRIS instruction. The 8-bit opcode, stored in the 8 most significant bits of IR, constitutes a direct address into the nanomemory. The nanomemory is realized by 16 AM27S21A (256 × 4 each) PROM chips, with an access time of 30 ns.

(d) *Interrupt Control Unit* (ICU)
Recognizes interrupts and passes control to interrupt service routines. Realized by an AMD2914 chip to handle 8 interrupt sources.

(e) *Program Memory* (PM)
Organized as a 16 MWord (64 MBytes) memory. Accessed by the PCU. Access time: 100 ns.

The DES includes the following:

(a) *32-bit Arithmetic Logic Unit* (ALU)
Performs all of the data processing operations. Realized by 8 AMD2903 chips along with AMD2902 chips for the Carry Look Ahead (CLA) logic circuitry.

(b) *Register File* (RF)
The maximal configuration contains 2048 32-bit registers, realized by AMD29705 chips. The current, reduced prototype contains only 128 registers. It is easily expandable to its full size.

(c) *Data Memory* (DM)
Technologically, approximately the same as the PM. Presently, it is of the same size, 64 MBytes. It can be extended to 2^{32} = 4 GBytes.

(d) *DM Interface Registers*
MAR – Memory Address Register
DOR – Data Output Register
DIR – Data Input Register
All three are 32-bit wide, realized by TTL 74S374 chips. The MAR contains

the address of the DM location accessed. The DOR serves as a buffer for data to be stored in DM, while DIR is a buffer for data fetched from DM.

(e) *Program Status Control Unit* (PSCU)
An auxiliary logic unit, used to store the status information of the processor. Includes the LSW register data. Realized by an AMD2904 chip.

(f) *Immediate Data Controller*
Supplies immediately data values to the ALU. Realized by 16 74LS253 chips.

(g) *Swapper*
Swaps half words and bytes within 32-bit words. In addition it can perform a 4-bit rotate left.

A Motorola 68000-based system serves as a front-end auxiliary coprocessor to handle the OS, I/O operations and diagnostics. The system memories are dual-port organized to permit simultaneous access by the service processor and by the MIRIS CPU. The overall MIRIS structure is shown in Figure 5.11. An example of an activation of an instruction is shown in Figure 5.12.

To summarize, the expected high throughput of MIRIS is due to the following factors:

(1) Streamlined handling of simple, primitive instructions.
(2) Avoidance of instruction decoding.
(3) Fast, horizontally microcoded Nanomemory.
(4) Large CPU dual-port register file (2048 × 32), which allows accessing two registers and store a result – all in one cycle of 100 ns. We have also an overall minimization of memory accesses.
(5) Register window (96 registers) mechanism for passing parameters. Only 48 registers are implemented in the prototype.
(6) Storage of data, due to an interrupt, in the register file, instead of in the main memory.
(7) Fast memory access; access time = 100 ns.
(8) All instructions executed in a single cycle of 100 ns.

The above was achieved (1987) in a bit-sliced AMD2900 (10 MHz) prototype. It stands to reason that an eventual, single-chip (excluding PM and DM) VLSI realization, may yield even better results.

The MIRIS project was extended for multitasking operation, exemplified by an intermediate model called Parallel RISC (PARIS) [5.10, 5.11]. The current generation multitasking system is called MULTRIS (MULTitasking RISC) [1.24]. The MIRIS does not feature floating point operations. A set of high-speed software floating point procedures was developed for the MIRIS. Their performance was found to be competitive with that of other systems such as IBM 370/148, NS32081 (10 MHz), MC68881 (8 MHz), Intel 8087 (8 MHz), VAX 11/750 and RISC II (12 MHz) with a Weitek coprocessor. For double-precision Whetstone it exceeded

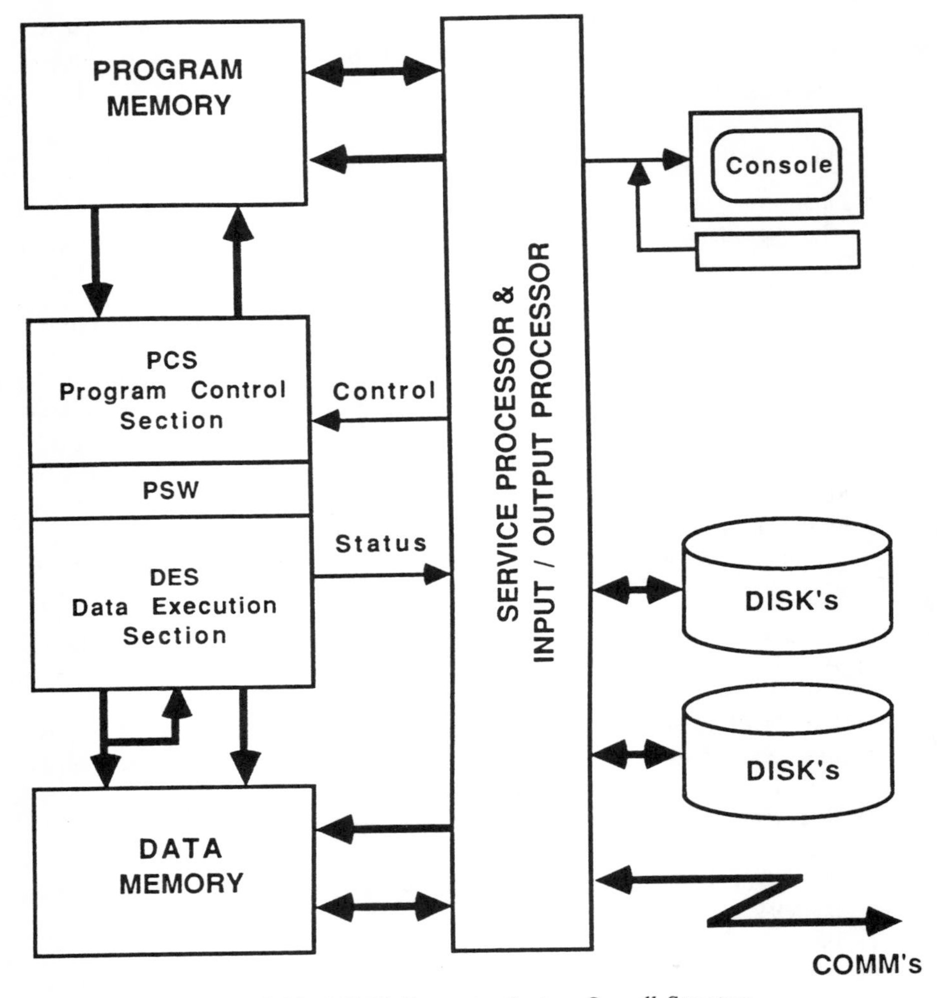

Figure 5.11 MIRIS Computer System Overall Structure

the Berkeley RISC II software performance (without a coprocessor) by an order of magnitude [5.12].

The goal in the MULTRIS development was to design a system which offers the advantages of general registers, register stacks, and cache, but which minimizes some of the problems associated with them [1.24], discussed in chapter 1. The concept is called 'Threaded Register Windows'. Currently the basic unit of the thread is a register window, each of which contains 16 32-bit registers. The size of this window is experimental, and may be changed later. These windows do not overlap as do those of the Berkeley RISC II (chapter 3), but dual pointers supported by the architecture allow access to both a *calling* procedure's activation

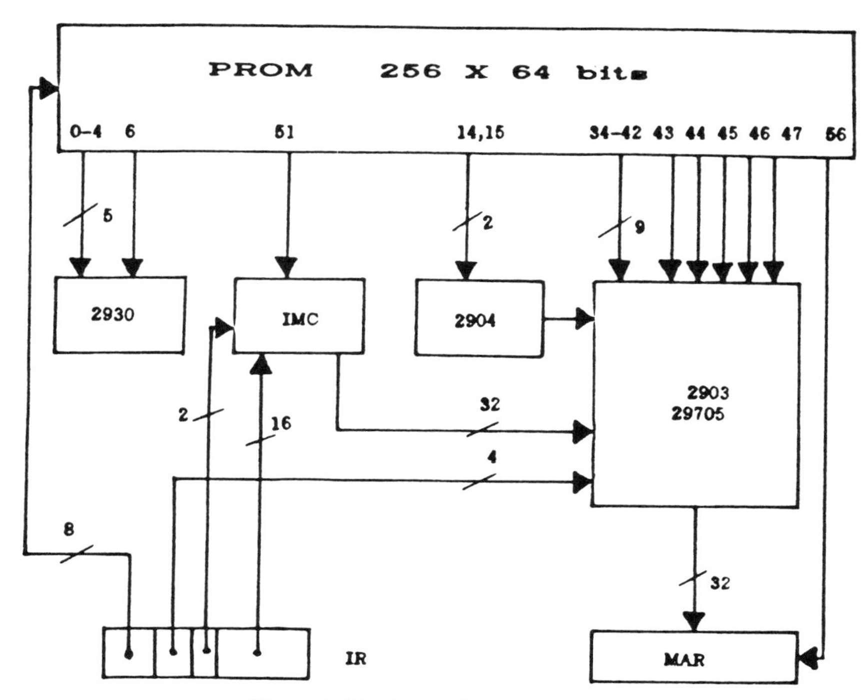

Figure 5.12 Instruction Interpretation
CAMAR SRC, IMM   MAR ← SRC + IMM

window and the *called* activation window – therefore any passed parameters need not be copies. The windows can be flexibly and dynamically configured to serve as:

(1) Activation Record Stacks: several windows may be dynamically linked together to form a stack to hold procedural activation records. Because no window overlap is required, the windows forming the stack need not be contiguous.
(2) General Purpose Traditional Data Stacks: the same linking approach can be used to form a traditional push/pop data stack. Implicit access to this stack is supported by the architecture.
(3) General Purpose Queues: the architecture also supports implicit access to queues made up of linked register windows.
(4) Statically allocated windows to hold vital information for an interrupt handler or the operating system.
(5) Isolated packets of frequently used global or object oriented data.

The overhead involved in forming the links is low, and the architecture supports constructs which make it transparent to application programs.

There are many advantages to these structures. The activation record stack allows the run time system to have multiple stacks (or at least the tops of them) resident on-chip at one time. This allows tasks to save their most recently used and needed data in the fastest storage available, and not copy it at the time of a context switch. The result of this will be to make the performance gains achieved by other RISC machines available to multitasking systems.

The queue structure will allow task communications to occur within the domains of the fast on-chip storage, and will also facilitate scheduling. The additional availability of traditional stacks is advantageous since this structure is sharable by all procedures. That is, it is not tied directly to the procedure control structures. This structure would be useful to a compiler; to hold data from large procedural activation records (those which require more than 16 words); or to support recursive algorithms, such as those used to handle trees and graphs [5.13].

The interior of the windows is accessed using a block relative address (register number). Therefore, the operand address is short, allowing for three operand instructions, and the compiler can assume that a dedicated set (one window) of registers is available for local and parameter storage. Dynamically allocated storage is initially allocated only in the windows. This is done by taking a 'free window' from a hardware supported (chip-resident) free-windows stack. Off-chip memory is allocated only if an overflow occurs. Which windows to overflow, or to underflow, can be computed in the background using information available from the operating system and guidance from the compiler. The additional processing time needed to choose which window to overflow can be regained by avoiding 'misses' and unnecessary memory allocations.

In the register window thread organization register access is implicit through window pointers contained in the processor state. The processor state, saved in two process status words (PSW1 and PSW2), includes references to six windows at any one time. Additionally, there is always an implicit reference to the global window, giving an access to a total of 7×16 registers. Access is restricted to only these windows. This allows the scope of a procedure to be inherently protected. Because of the limited address field, it is impossible to accidentally access data outside the windows which have been allocated to a process.

Figure 5.13 shows the organization of the processor state registers. Of the six windows, five are used to access user data. One, the 'Map Window' (MW in PSW1) is used to manage activation record stacks. The five data window references are:

(1) The Current Window (accessible through CUR in PSW2) – containing the activation record of the currently active procedure.
(2) The Old Window (accessible through OLD in PSW2) – containing the activation record of the current procedure's dynamic parent. Any parameters which are passed are accessed directly using this pointer.
(3) Stack/Queue Window 1 (accessible through SQW1 in PSW2) – this window may be treated as a data stack, the head or tail of a queue, or a general data window.
(4) Stack/Queue Window 2 (accessible through SQW2 in PSW2) – this window

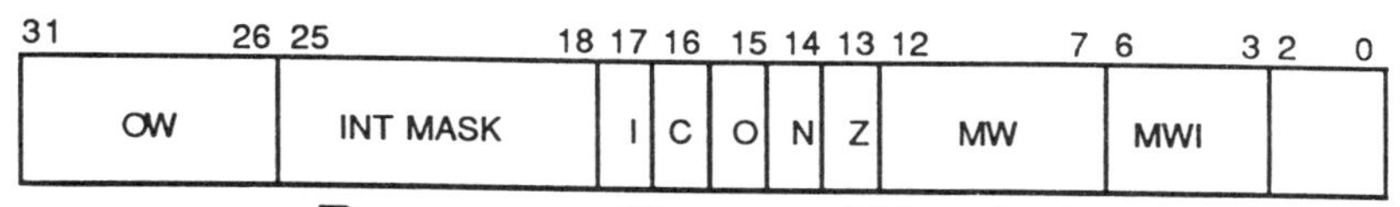

Program Status Word 1

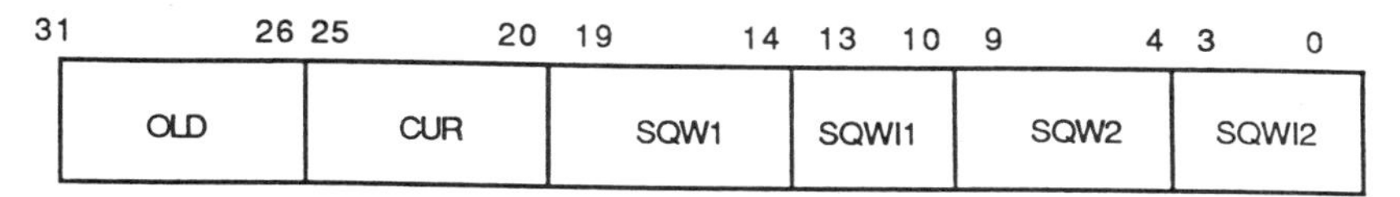

Program Status Word 2

CUR	Current activation record window pointer
OLD	Previous (caller's) activation record window pointer
SQW1	Stack/Queue Window 1 pointer
SQWI1	Stack/Queue Window 1 index
SQW2	Stack/Queue Window 2 pointer
SQWI2	Stack/Queue Window 2 index
OW	'Object' Window pointer
MW	Map Window pointer
MWI	Map Window index
ICONZ	Interrupt enable, carry, overflow, negative, and zero flags

Figure 5.13 Processor State Registers

may be treated as a data stack, the head or tail of a queue, or a general data window.

(5) An Object Window (accessible through OW in PSW1) – this window can be used to hold any additional program-controlled data pointer which, for example, can be used to access an object or frequently referred to globals.

The SQW pointers also have an intra-register displacement associated with them. A register address is expressed in the instruction using two fields. The first is a three-bit field indicating one of the windows; the second a four-bit field indicating one of the sixteen registers in that window.

Register windows which are resident in the processor can be referenced by a six-bit window pointer (this provides for up to 64 windows). When a window is spilled to memory, it is still necessary to maintain a reference to the data it contains. In this architecture, windows are most easily spilled to specific locations in memory called 'window frames'. These frames are located in a specific region of data memory. The approach permits windows, whether spilled or not, to be referenced via a 16-bit pointer. If the upper 10 bits of the pointer are all zero, then the window is resident in the register bank in the window specified by the lower 6 bits. Otherwise, the full 16-bit value is used to form a memory (byte) address by shifting it left 6 bits. This indicates that window frames can only occur on 64 byte boundaries in memory.

The activation record stacks are represented by a list of windows, as shown in Figure 5.14. Access to the top two windows is possible using the OLD and CUR pointers as described in the preceding section. To keep track of the 'thread' of windows allocated to the activation record stack, an additional window, the map window (MW) is needed. This serves as a map, or directory, of the stack. This map, which can be housed in any register window, contains a sequential list of six-bit window pointers identifying the register windows in the stack and defining their order. The return address value for each nested procedure call is stored here as well. There is also a flag field which indicates that the window has overflowed into memory. The MWI (Map Window Index) is used to index this window. If a procedure call depth greater than 15 exists in one task, the hardware will trap and create a link for an additional map window. One register (the link) is reserved to accommodate the doubly-linked list (two 16-bit pointers to either memory resident window frames, or to another register window).

If it becomes necessary to overflow a window from a particular activation stack into memory, the MW plays an integral role. To start an overflow, a memory resident window image, a 'window frame', is allocated and a pointer to it is saved in the 'downward' link of R0 in the MW. The previous contents of this link is copied to the 'downward' link in the first location of the allocated window frame (referred to as the 'MW image'). Next, the activation record window to be spilled is copied into a second memory window frame. The 16-bit pointer to this window frame is now saved in the MW image. When all 15 windows of this MW have been overflowed the MW itself can be spilled. Since each MW contains a pair of 16-bit pointers (in R0), the MW linkage can be maintained whether or not the MWs are in memory or registers. When this procedure chain is reactivated, the windows must be copied back to register windows before control is transferred to them. Only those procedures that are about to be reactivated need be copied back.

If access is required to a variable down the procedure chain, this map (whether resident in memory or in register windows) can be used to traverse the chain.

To facilitate communication in multitasking systems, the threaded register

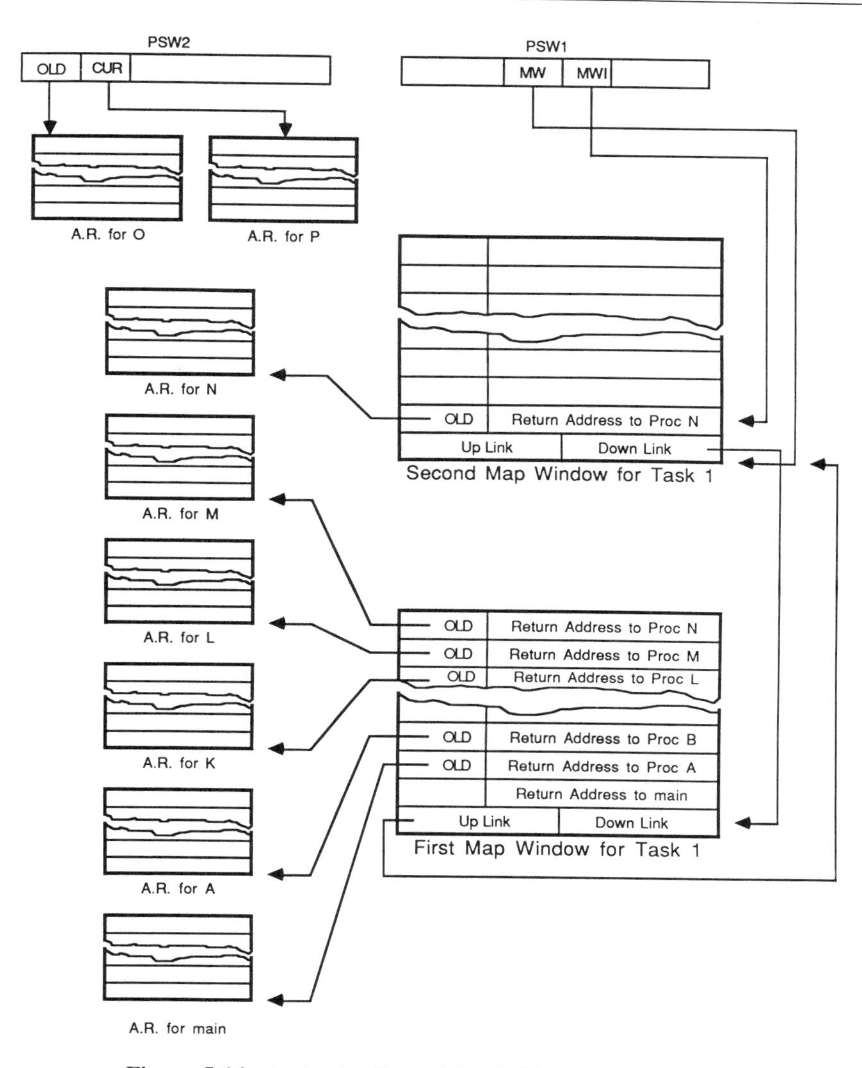

Figure 5.14 Activation Record Stack Thread Maintenance

windows can be reconfigured as queues or traditional push/pop stacks. The two SQW and SQWI fields are used to support these structures. Four special instructions alter these pointers; POP, PUSH, ENQUEUE and DEQUEUE. All four instructions add or remove the single word elements from the stack/queue which is pointed to by the SQW plus SQWI. After each instruction the SQWI is adjusted accordingly. When 15 elements have been pushed or queued, a software trap will link another window to the stack/queue.

The expandability of these structures, as illustrated in Figure 5.15, is especially

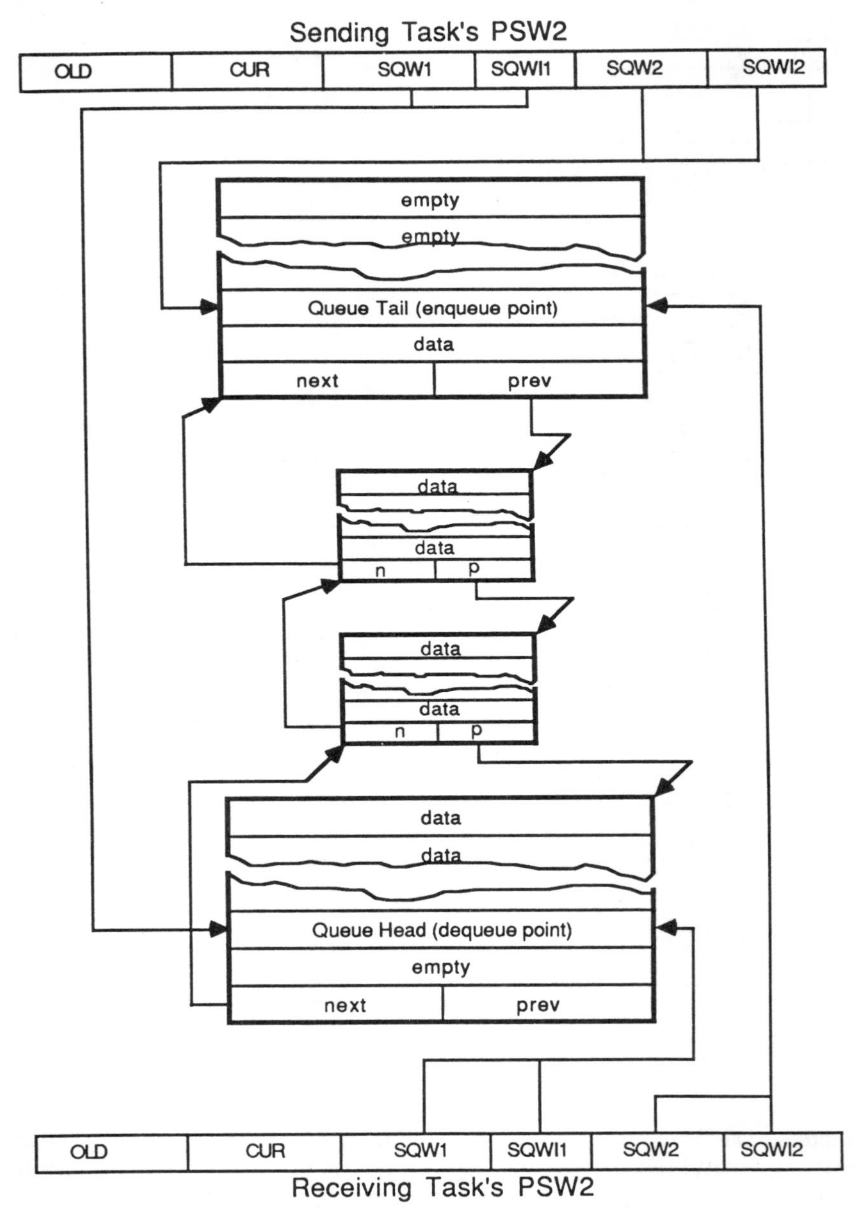

Figure 5.15 Queue Window Management

beneficial to queue management. In most conventional systems, queues are implemented in statically allocated storage and have a circular behavior. This requires that the memory allocated be sufficiently large to accommodate the entire queue, and that base and bound checks be done. Using the threaded register window concept the queue is register resident and occupies only the minimum number of windows needed to hold the current queue contents. As the queue grows and shrinks, register windows are automatically allocated and de-allocated. No checks for base/bounds need be performed.

The two SQWs allow access to both the head and the tail of a queue. However, frequently the entity which queues and the entity which dequeues are separate tasks. In Figure 5.15 two tasks are accessing the same queue. The source task uses SQW2 to reference the queue's tail. The receiving task uses SQW1 to reference the queue's head. The choice of using SQW1 or SQW2 is arbitrary and can be left to programming convention.

The queue empty condition or stack empty condition is not automatically determined by the hardware but requires software support. However, there is a hardware aid provided. If during the execution of one of the four instructions SQW1 = SQW2 and SQWI1 = SQWI2 condition codes will be set.

Parts of the stack/queue can be overflowed to the memory window frames. In this case the links of its neighbor windows are changed to point to the memory frame address. Two such window frame pointers are accommodated in register 0 of each window.

As with other operations presented here, this set of queue/stack operations is designed to hide as much of the register window granularity from the applications programs as possible, without paying a large performance penalty.

Since the total task state is provided in the two PSWs, task context switches can be accomplished by simply saving two words. This saves the configuration of the activation stack and all other window-based data structures. If these two words were saved in registers, saving the current state would require two register-to-register moves, plus any additional logic needed to determine the storage location. In order to optimize a task context switch, any saved scheduler data, such as the location of task control blocks, scheduling queues, etc. should be made available as soon as the scheduler is passed control.

To facilitate this, the architecture allows for a window to be pre-allocated for the scheduler's 'CUR' window. This window may be selected at system start-up, and a pointer to it saved in a special register called the Interrupt Control Register (ICR). There are 16 of these special registers, eight of which are reserved for hardware interrupt vectors. The other eight may be used for software traps. The ICR structure is shown in Figure 5.16. The window pointer field permits the static allocation of a window for use by each interrupt handler. This window remains allocated even after the handler returns. There are many advantages to this static allocation. First, it reduces the chances of a window underflow exception occurring at the time of an interrupt. Second, the static nature of the window makes it nicely suited to serving as a buffer for interrupts involving data transfer.

The 'CALLI' instruction is used for software traps. This instruction is similar to the CALL instruction except it need not select a window from the free list to be used as the new CUR window. Instead it checks the ICR window field. If it is non-zero, then the pre-allocated window is moved to CUR. This same process is used to service interrupts. It is not necessary to have a pre-allocated

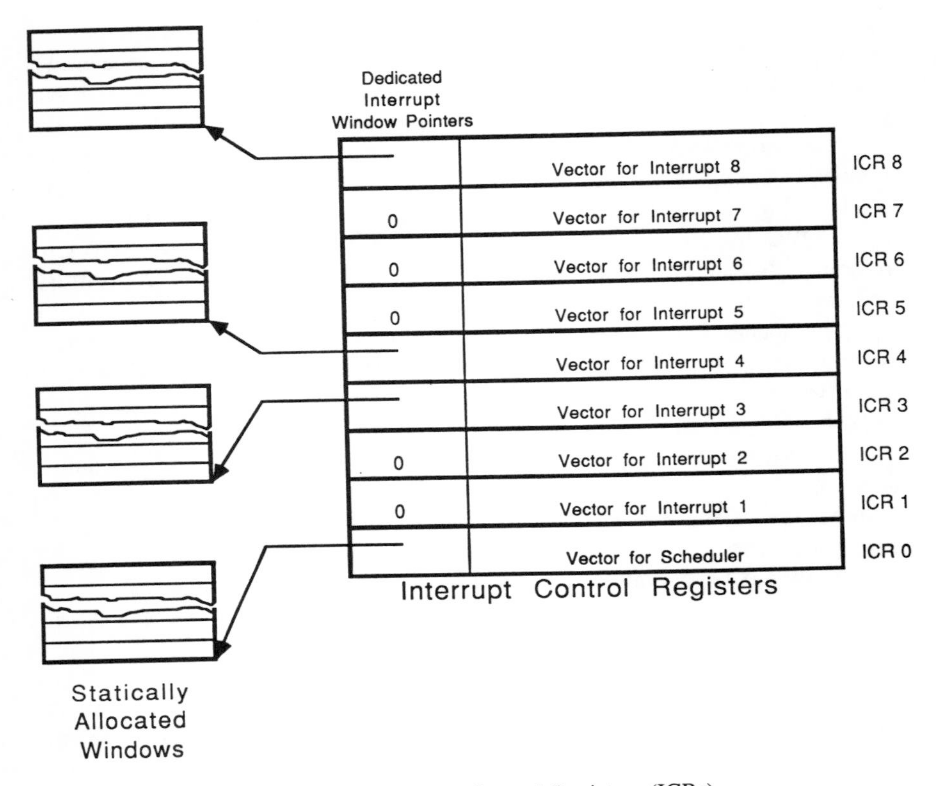

Figure 5.16 Interrupt Control Registers (ICRs)

window – a value of zero in this field causes the interrupt to be allocated a new window, just as in a procedure call.

By using an instruction similar to a procedure call to transfer control to the scheduler the PC and 'OLD' field of the currently active task is saved in that task's MW. Because of the symmetry of CALLI and CALL, once the selected task's PSWs have been loaded, the scheduler need only execute a return instruction (RET). The RETI instruction is provided for this. It is identical to RET except it does not return the window pointed to by CUR to the free list, unless the CUR entry in the interrupt's ICR is zero.*

A block diagram of MULTRIS is shown in Figure 5.17. It is to some extent similar to that of the MIRIS (Figure 5.7). The handling of the instructions, fetched from the Program Memory, is basically the same. There is a dual bus system for simultaneous transfer of even- and odd-numbered word data. All buses are 32-bits wide. The burst mode control is used for fast transfer of 16-register

* The paragraphs dealing with the Threaded Register Windows concept were written by Donna J. Quammen and D. Richard Miller.

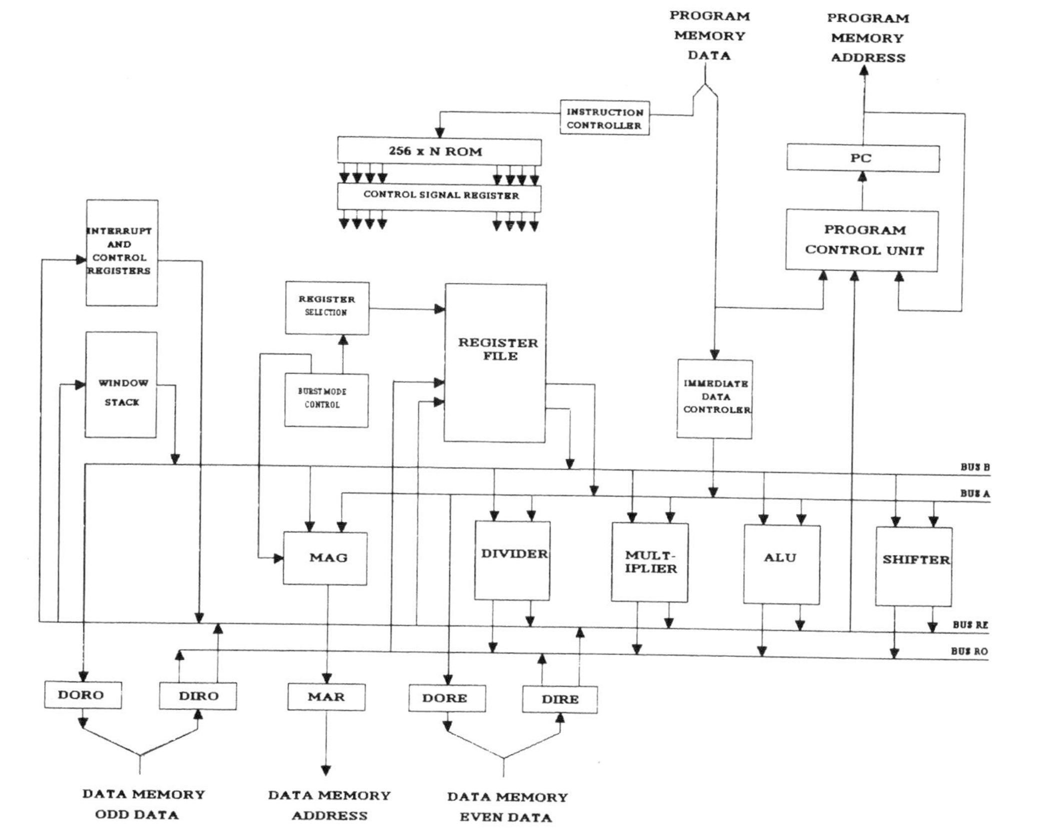

Figure 5.17 MULTRIS Block Diagram

windows to or from window frame locations in the Data Memory (dual-ported). MULTRIS contains a number of hardware units, in addition to the ALU, to speed up operations (multiplier, divider, shifter).

Notation used in Figure 5.17:

DIRE – Data Input Register Even
DIRO – Data Input Register Odd
DORE – Data Output Register Even
DORO – Data Output Register Odd
MAG – Memory (Data) Address Generator
MAR – Memory Address Register
PC – Program Counter
RE – Result Even
RO – Result Odd

A map of the Program Memory (PM) is shown in Figure 5.18. Since all instructions are of single-word length (32 bits), it is word-addressable. The byte-addressable Data Memory (DM) is illustrated in Figure 5.19. A map of the CPU registers file, consisting of 64 register windows (16 registers), along with the corresponding window frames in the DM, is shown in Figure 5.20. A list of free window frames, implemented as a stack in DM, is maintained. It is shown in Figure 5.21.

In addition to the PSW1 and PSW2 registers, shown in Figure 5.13, there are three control registers:

SSW – System Status Word,
OPR – Overflow Pointer Register,
RB – Implied Base Register,

and 16 Interrupt Control Registers (ICRs, also shown in Figure 5.16), illustrated in Figure 5.22.

MULTRIS architecture features 4 instruction formats, shown in Figure 5.23. There are three basic groups of instructions:

1. Data Movement (Tables 5.1 and 5.2),
2. Arithmetic-Logic (Table 5.3),
3. Program Control (Table 5.4).

The development of the MULTRIS is still underway. Performance simulation studies and VLSI implementation are planned in the future.

5.4 The BGU Single Instruction Computer

One of the principal characteristics of a RISC-type system (section 1.3) is a reduced number of machine language instructions. By continuing to reduce the number

MULTRIS ARCHITECTURE

PROGRAM MEMORY
(PM)

word (32-bit) addressed
since all instructions are
32-bits long

16 MWords
(64 MBytes)
$2^{24} \times 32$

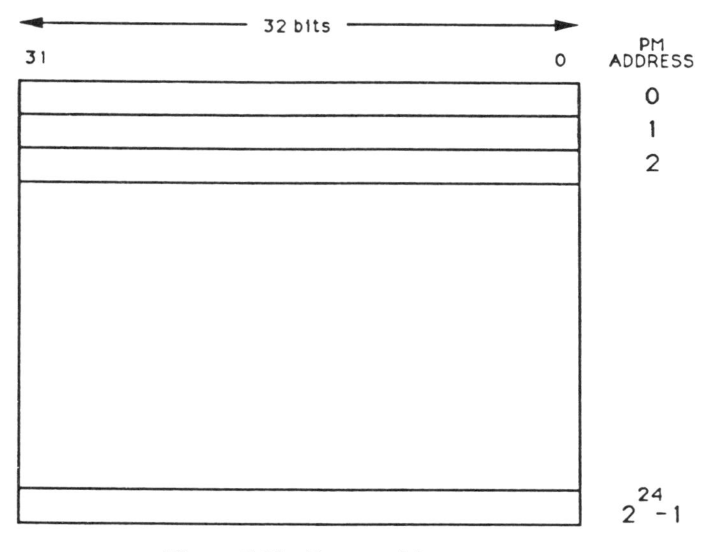

Figure 5.18 Program Memory

of instructions, eventually the limiting case of a Single Instruction Computer (SIC) will be achieved. Such a case has indeed been considered in the past by several researchers [5.14–5.18]. The idea of constructing and utilizing a SIC was originally proposed by Lipovski [5.14]. Since the single instruction, implemented in the above system, was MOVE, the whole idea was designated as the 'MOVE Architecture'. Subsequently, a Conditional MOVE option was added to the system

MULTRIS ARCHITECTURE

DATA MEMORY
(DM)

BYTE ADDRESSABLE AT ANY ADDRESS

HALFWORD ADDRESSABLE AT ANY EVEN ADDRESS

WORD ADDRESSABLE AT ANY ADDRESS DIVISIBLE BY 4

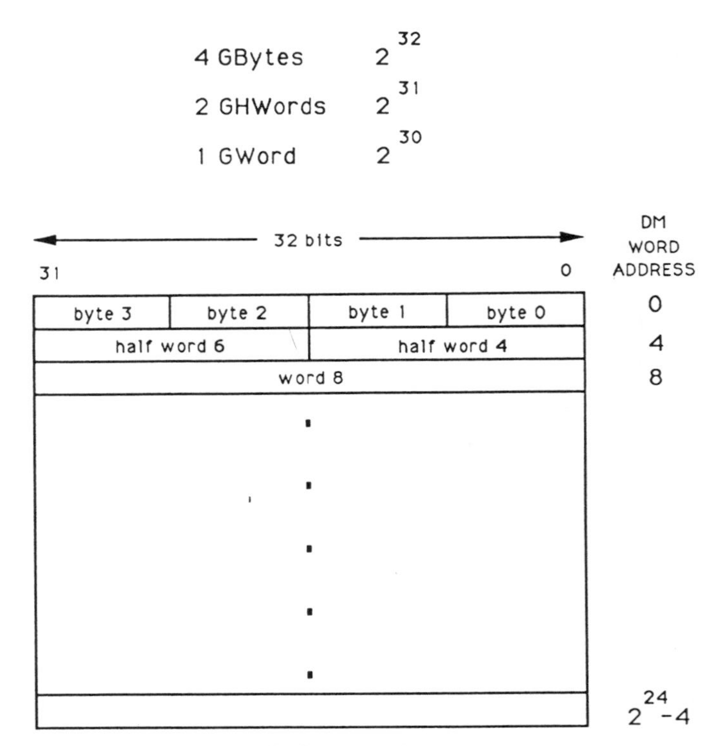

Figure 5.19 Data Memory

[5.15] and it has been renamed as 'CMOVE Architecture'. The choice of MOVE as the single instruction has not been random. It is usually the most often used instruction in many programs. Indeed, a recent study [1.15] reports that data movement instructions are used with a frequency of 45% on the average. This is the highest frequency; the second most frequent instructions are the program modification instructions at 29%. Theoretically, one could build a SIC with a different instruction; however, based on practical considerations of frequency of usage, the MOVE implementation is fully justified.

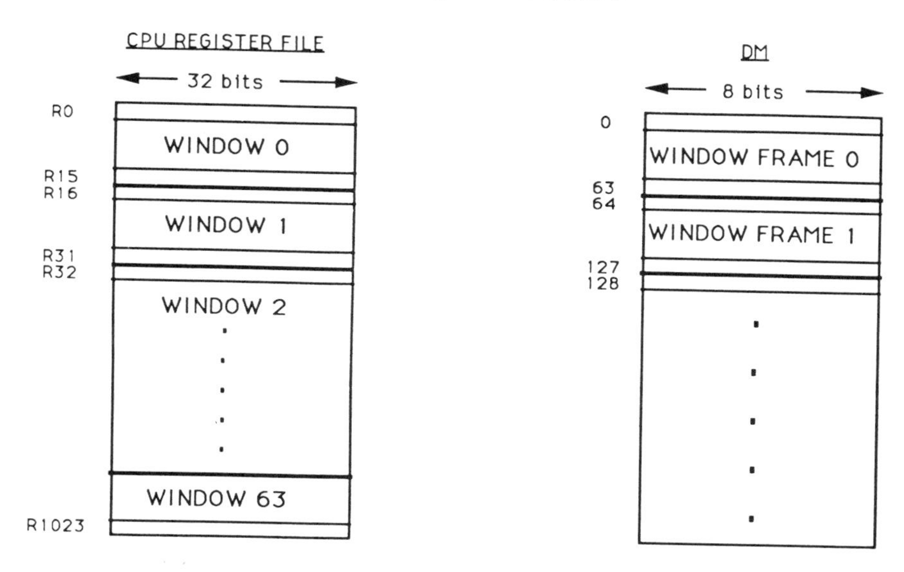

Figure 5.20 CPU Register File and DM Window Frames

A prototype of SIC (CMOVE Architecture) system of 8-bits was constructed, for the first time, in the Digital Laboratory of the Department of Electrical and Computer Engineering at the Ben Gurion University (BGU) of the Negev in Beer Sheva, Israel [5.18] in 1982.

The principal basic properties of a CMOVE architecture system can be summarized as follows:

(a) The system has a single instruction (no opcode, no opcode decoding) with the following general structure:

MULTRIS ARCHITECTURE

LIST OF FREE WINDOW FRAMES IN DM

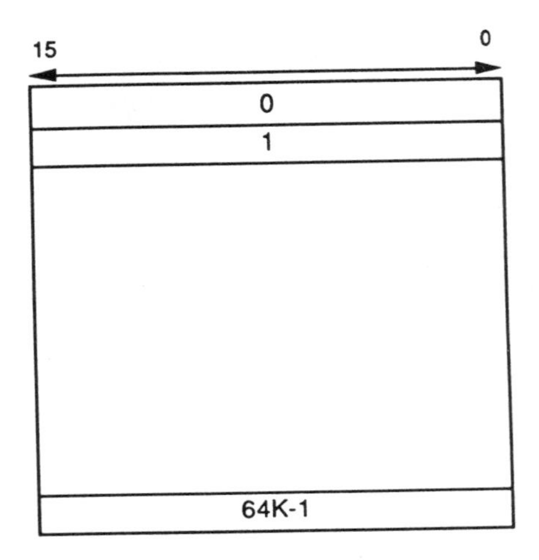

Implemented as a stack in DM., with the top of the stack in one of the CPU windows.

Figure 5.21 Free Windows Stack in DM

MOVE FROM SOURCE, TO DESTINATION

SOURCE represents the address of the source location in memory, while DESTINATION represents the address of the destination location in memory.

(b) The instruction is executed in two machine cycles, FROM and TO.

(c) There are four addressing modes for each of the two timing cycles:

FROM cycle	TO cycle	Code
Direct	Direct	00
Immediate	Conditional	01
Indexed X	Indexed X	10
Indexed S	Indexed S	11
X and S are index registers		

(d) There are two memories:
A Program Memory (PM) to store instructions
A Main Memory (MM) to store data
(alternatively identified as a data memory).

System Status Word, (SSW):

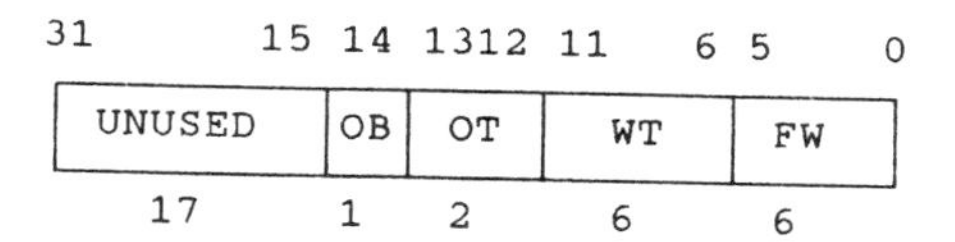

FW : FREE WINDOWS, number of free windows left on the window stack

WT : WINDOWS TRANSFERRED, number of windows transferred to memory

OT : OVERFLOW TYPE, 00 Regular Task Activation
01 LIFO Stack

OB : OVERFLOW BIT, set on window overflow

Overflow Pointer Register, (OPR):

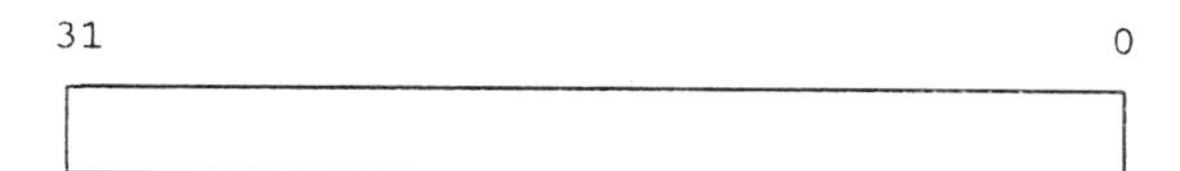

This register holds a data value that points to the beginning address in data memory where the first overflowed window is stored.

Implied Base Register, (RB):

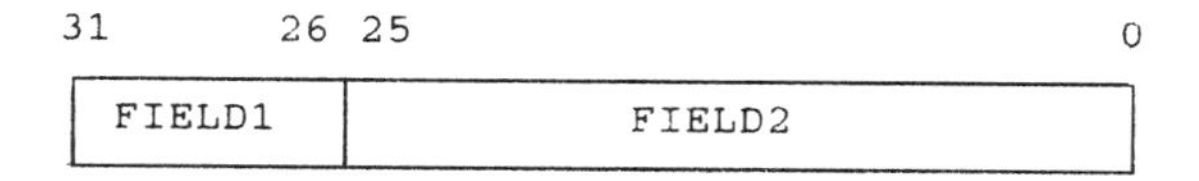

This register is used in any instruction that makes reference to RB.

Interrupt Control Registers, (ICRs):

31 26 25 0

FIELD1	FIELD2

FIELD1 : Dedicated Interrupt Window Pointer or 0

FIELD 2 : Interrupt Vector

Note: There are sixteen of the above Interrupt Control Registers.

Figure 5.22 Control Registers

MULTRIS ARCHITECTURE

INSTRUCTION FORMATS

R TYPE (REGISTER) FT=00

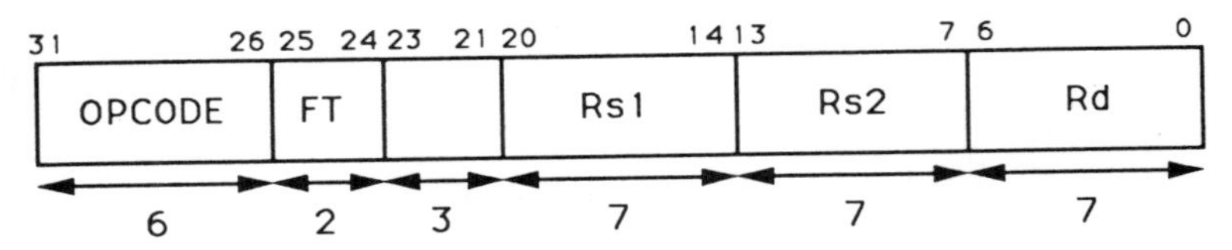

D TYPE (DISPLACEMENT) FT=10

J TYPE (JUMP) FT=11

I TYPE (IMMEDIATE, 2'S COMPLEMENT) FT=01

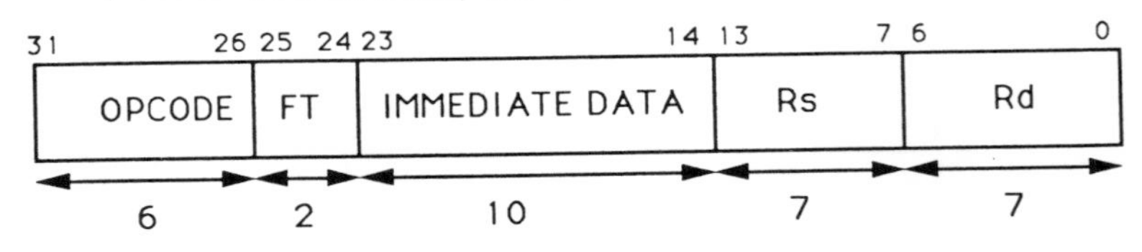

RS1 source register 1
Rs2 source register 2
Rd destination register
FT format

Figure 5.23 Instruction Formats

Table 5.1 MULTRIS Archiecture; Data Movement Instructions

LOAD INSTRUCTIONS		FORMAT
LDx (Rb,Ri),Rd	indirect based-indexed	
	DM address ((Rb)+(Ri)) ⟶ Rd	R
LDx disp(Rb),Rd	indirect base + displacement (10 bits)	
	DM address (disp + (Rb)) ⟶ Rd	I
LDx disp,Rd	indirect implied base + displacement (17 bits)	
	DM address (disp + (RB)) ⟶ Rd	D
LDC Imm,Rs,RC	load control register	
	Imm + (Rs) ⟶ RC RC = PSW1, PSW2, RB, SSW, OPR	I
STORE INSTRUCTIONS		
STx Rs,(Rb,Ri)		R
STx Rs,disp(Rb)		I
STx Rs,disp		D
STC Imm,Rc,Rd	store control register	
	Imm + (RC) ⟶ Rd	I

where x is H for half word, B for byte, or blank for word (default)

PUSH	Imm,Rs,SWP		I
	SWP -- stack window pointer = MW, SQW1, SQW2		
POP	0,SWP,Rd		I
ENQ	Imm,Rs,SWP	Enqueue	I
DEQ	0,SWP,Rd	Dequeue	I

(e) The CPU consists mainly of a Central Controller and auxiliary logic circuitry. It includes 8 registers, allocated in the first 8 addresses of MM: 0 to 7. The registers are:

Address	Register	Comment
0	PC	Program Counter
1	JSR	Subroutine Register
2	X	Index Register
3	X − 1	Contains always (X) − 1
4	S	Index Register
5	S − 1	Contains always (S) − 1
6	C	Counter Register
7	C − 1	Contains always (C) − 1

Table 5.2 MULTRIS Architecture; Window Load/Store Instructions

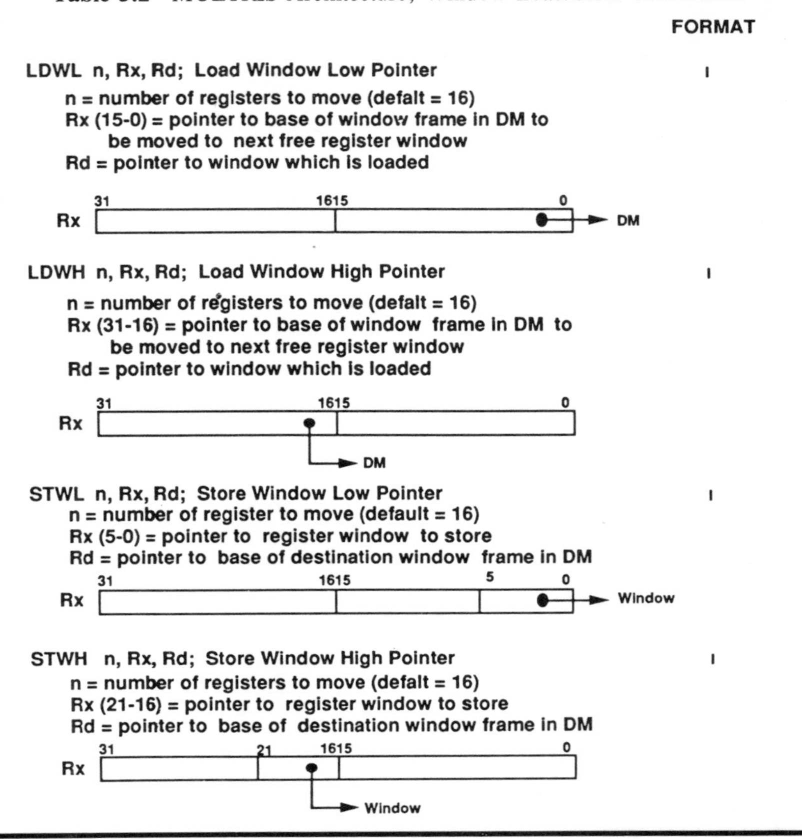

FORMAT

LDWL n, Rx, Rd; Load Window Low Pointer — I

n = number of registers to move (defalt = 16)
Rx (15-0) = pointer to base of window frame in DM to
be moved to next free register window
Rd = pointer to window which is loaded

LDWH n, Rx, Rd; Load Window High Pointer — I

n = number of registers to move (defalt = 16)
Rx (31-16) = pointer to base of window frame in DM to
be moved to next free register window
Rd = pointer to window which is loaded

STWL n, Rx, Rd; Store Window Low Pointer — I

n = number of register to move (default = 16)
Rx (5-0) = pointer to register window to store
Rd = pointer to base of destination window frame in DM

STWH n, Rx, Rd; Store Window High Pointer — I

n = number of registers to move (defalt = 16)
Rx (21-16) = pointer to register window to store
Rd = pointer to base of destination window frame in DM

(f) The CPU contains no ALU. Arithmetic and/or Logic operations are performed within I/O processors, denoted in this system as: Arithmetic Move Units (AMUs).

(g) For an m-bit word machine the single instruction format for each of the two cycles (FROM, TO) consists of m+4 bits, which is the word size of the Program Memory. It follows that:

m bits are used for the direct address either in MM or for the AMUs and the 4 control bits are defined:
2 bits for 4 addressing modes, listed in (c)
1 bit indicating MM or AMU space
1 bit for an interrupt flag.

The instruction format of a CMOVE is shown in Figure 5.24.

The conditional mode of the TO cycle is implemented using an extra N flip flop (flag), which is loaded, automatically, with the sign bit of the word moved

Table 5.3 MULTRIS Architecture; Arithmetic-Logic Instructions

		FORMAT
ADD Rs1,Rs2,Rd	(Rs1) + (Rs2) → Rd	R
ADD Imm,Rs,Rd	(Rs) + Imm → Rd	I
ADD Imm,Rd	(Rd) + Imm → Rd	D
SUB Rs1,Rs2,Rd	(Rs2) - (Rs1) → Rd	R
SUB Imm,Rs,Rd	(Rs) - Imm → Rd	I
SUB Imm,Rd	(Rd) - Imm → Rd	D
OR Rs1,Rs2,Rd	(Rs1) OR (Rs2) → Rd	R
OR Imm,Rs,Rd	(Rs) OR Imm → Rd	I
OR Imm,Rd	(Rd) OR Imm → Rd	D
AND Rs1,Rs2,Rd	(Rs1) AND (Rs2) → Rd	R
AND Imm,Rs,Rd	(Rs) AND Imm → Rd	I
AND Imm,Rd	(Rd) AND Imm → Rd	D
COM Rs,Rd	Complement Rs → Rd (Imm=0 implied)	I
SLL Imm,Rs,Rd	Shift Logical Left Rs by Imm → Rd	I
SLR Imm,Rs,Rd	Shift Logical Right Rs by Imm → Rd	I
SAL Imm,Rs,Rd	Shift Arithmetic Left Rs by Imm → Rd	I
SAR Imm,Rs,Rd	Shift Arithmetic Right Rs by Imm → Rd	I
MUL Rs1,Rs2,Rd	Signed (Rs1)*(Rs2) → Rd, Rd+1 Rd=most sig., Rd+1=least sig.	R
DIV Rs1,Rs2,Rd	Signed (Rs1)/(Rs2) → Rd (Quotient)	R
MOD Rs1,Rs2,Rd	Remainder (Rs1)/(Rs2) → Rd	R

last. If N = 1, the condition is considered to be satisifed and the conditioned move is performed. If N = 0, no move takes place and N is not affected.

Programming is done by the following symbolic notation:

$$A \leftarrow B$$

where B is the source and A, the destination symbolic address. If the move is conditional, we write

$$A\not{c} \leftarrow B.$$

Table 5.4 Program Control Instructions

Instruction	Action	Format
JMP adr.pm	adr.pm -> PC	J
JMP disp,(Rb,Ri)	disp(Rb)(Ri)->PC	I
JCC adr.pm (see CC table)	If CC=TRUE then adr.pm -> PC	J
JCC disp,(Rb,Ri) (see CC table)	If CC=TRUE then disp(Rb)(Ri)->PC	I
CALL adr.pm	adr.pm -> PC	J
CALL disp,(Rb,Ri)	disp(Rb)(Ri)->PC	I
CALLI adr.pm	adr.pm -> PC	J
CALLI disp,(Rb,Ri)	disp(Rb)(Ri)->PC	I
RET	N/A	N/A
RETI	N/A	N/A

Condition Code Table:

Code (CC)	Indication	State
Z	zero result	Z set
NZ	non-zero	Z reset
N	negative	N set
P	pos. or zero	N reset
O	overflow	O set
NO	no overflow	O reset
C	carry	C set
NC	no carry	C reset

	4	m
FROM	Control	Source Address
TO	Control	Destination Address

Figure 5.24 CMOVE Instruction Format

To move immediate numbers we use the symbol #,

$$A \leftarrow 20\#$$

number 20 (decimal) is moved into location A. All address references refer to MM or AMU (depending on the space allocated). Only the Program Counter (PC, at MM location 0) refers to the Program Memory (PM). The PC is normally incremented in each memory cycle (by one for FROM and by one for TO). A branch operation is performed as follows:

$$0 \leftarrow \text{ADDR}$$

or

$$\text{JMP} \leftarrow \text{ADDR}$$

where ADDR is a symbolic branch address. Naturally, an immediate branch address can also be specified:

$$\text{JMP} \leftarrow 100\#.$$

It should be noted that addresses refer to the MM, while in the case of JMP or PC, the addresses refer to the PM.

The instruction: call a subroutine, say SUB1, is written:

$$1 \leftarrow \text{SUB1}$$

or

$$\text{JSR} \leftarrow \text{SUB1}.$$

The PC content, which is the address of the following instruction, is stored automatically in a special RTS register and restored to the PC after a return from the subroutine. The instruction: return from a subroutine, is written:

$$\text{JMP} \leftarrow \text{JSR}.$$

Each of the registers X, S and C has a companion register $X-1$, $S-1$ and $C-1$, respectively which contains, automatically, its decremented value. Thus,

$$X \leftarrow X-1$$

decrements X, while

$$X-1 \leftarrow X$$

increments X.

In order to perform any arithmetic or logic operation one has to use a special AMU, wired for the specific operation. For instance, in an AMU wired for addition, there would be an interconnection shown in Figure 5.25. Moving the addends into registers A and B will automatically yield their sum in C.

The SIC was intended from its inception to serve as a *special purpose*

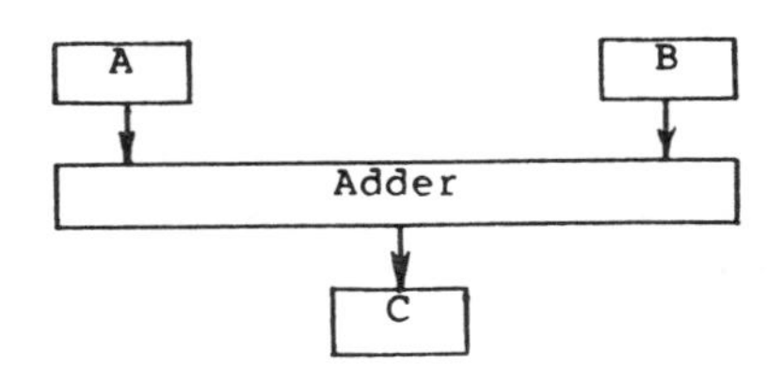

Figure 5.25 AMU Adder Configuration

controller only. For this reason it has not been mentioned in the previous chapters along with other RISC-type systems. Any comparison between the SIC and the other systems with respect, for instance, to the ability to handle complicated software, such as OS or HLL Compilers, would not be useful because the SIC has not been designed for such an implementation.

The implementation for which the SIC has been intended is for cases requiring very simple controllers with relatively brief and simple software. Particularly in large scale systems, where a large number (hundreds, possibly thousands) of such controllers may be required, it may be more economical to use a very simple controller, instead of a full scale off-the-shelf microprocessor CISC, with numerous but unnecessary instructions. An example of a potential use of a SIC-type controller could be the control of a signalized traffic intersection.

A complete design of a SIC prototype, using AMD2900 bit-sliced equipment has been performed [5.17, 5.18]. Although only an 8-bit prototype has been constructed, the design can be readily implemented for any m-bit system. Since the realization equipment is known, precise performance evaluation can be made for any generated software. For a preliminary comparison with existing 16-bit microprocessors, a 16 × 16 multiplication subroutine was generated for a 16-bit CMOVE system operating at 8 MHz. The CMOVE multiplication subroutine consists of a series of shifts and adds (performed by moves from one register to another), executed within an AMU (Arithmetic MOVE Unit). It was compared with the following microprocessors, which have a multiplication instruction in their assembly language:

Intel 8086 at 8 MHz
Motorola 68000 at 8 MHz
Zilog 8000 at 4 MHz

The 16 × 16 multiplication in microseconds:

CMOVE	3.500
8086	18.125
68000	9.250
8000	17.500

Even if the CMOVE is run at 4 MHz, it would perform the 16 × 16 multiplication in 7 microseconds. The regular 2900 operating frequency is actually 10 MHz and the CMOVE can perform the above operation in 2.8 microseconds [5.17].

It should be pointed out that the above comparison studies were actually performed in 1981, taking into account the equipment available at that time. A distributed multiprocessing system, composed of hundreds of CMOVE processors, has also been designed [5.19].

5.5 The BGU MODHEL System for RISCS Investigation

The objective of this section is to describe a special purpose computing system MODHEL, which has been developed to serve as a tool to investigate the properties of various RISC-type models.

There are quite a few models of RISC-type systems, each with a different combination of instructions in its instruction set. The question arises: which combination of instructions is a better choice? How do you choose an instruction set? Once an instruction set has been chosen, what will be the properties of the system? In order to attempt to answer the above questions, a special research tool, the MODHEL System [5.20–5.22], has been proposed. It is a RISC-type system, which can be optionally activated as a different system with a different combination of instructions. The MODHEL is an experimental research system which is not intended to perform as a universal computer. The primary designation of MODHEL is to serve as an investigation tool in the study of the computing systems within the RISC Space (RISCS). Some results of studies of this type will be presented later in this section.

The particular and unique property of the MODHEL is that it consists of Modules of Instruction Subsets. Each module contains a group of two to six different instructions and each module can be activated or deactivated during any specific operation of the system. In this way, a variety of RISC-type systems can be created and tested out on the same physical installation.

The current design contains eight instruction modules with the following instruction allocation:

Module	Notation	Instructions
0	M_0	Data Movement Instructions; MOVE, CMOVE
1	M_1	Program Control Instructions; JMP, JMPR, CALL, CALLR, RET
2	M_2	Arithmetic Instructions I; ADD, ADDC, SUB, SUBC
3	M_3	Shift and Rotate Instructions; SHIFT, ROTATE (Left, Right)
4	M_4	Logic Instructions; OR, AND, NOT, XOR
5	M_5	Arithmetic Instructions II; MULT, DIV
6	M_6	I/O Instructions; IN, OUT
7	M_7	Reserved; Option for Multiprocessing Support

Activating module M_0 only makes the MODHEL almost identical to the SIC or the CMOVE system, described in the previous section. Activating all of the 8 modules makes MODHEL very close to the RISC I with its 31 instructions. As will be seen in the following description, the architectures of MODHEL and RISC I (or II) are very close (see also chapter 3). Activation of any other combination of modules will yield a different RISC-type system within the RISC computing space (RISCS). The following notation will be adopted: activation of module 0 only yields a system denoted by M_0,

activation of modules 0, 1: M_{01}
activation of modules 0, 1, 2: M_{012}
activation of modules 0, 2, 3: M_{023},

and so on.

No matter which combination of modules has been selected, the MODHEL has the following architectural properties.

(a) Word length: 32 bits.
(b) The MODHEL has a stack oriented architecture.
(c) There are two separate memories:

31 29	28	27	26	25	24	23 19	18	17 13	12 5	4 0
MOD	MR	TF	CU	DI	R	SRC/DST	IJ	SRC1	ADDR	SRC2
3						5		5	8	5

where:

MOD	Module identifier (000 to 111).
MR	Access Memory or Register.
TF	TO MM cycle or FROM MM cycle.
CU	Conditional or Unconditional Move.
DI	Direct or Indirect Addressing Mode.
R	Relative address, when R=0, 18 least significant bits of the instruction form an address.
SRC/DST	Source or Destination Register.
IJ	Indirect Jump. Used by a Slave processor in a multiprocessing configuration to bring an address from the shared MM to its own PC.
SRC1	Source Register.
ADDR	8-bit address component.
SRC2	Index Register (when DI=1).

Figure 5.26 MODHEL Instruction Format

Program Memory (PM) to store programs;
Main Memory (MM) to store data.
All instructions, data items and addresses are each 32-bits long.

(d) MM is accessed by MOVE TO/FROM MM only (equivalent to STORE/LOAD of RISC). Data is processed when it is in one of the CPU registers only.

(e) There is a single 32-bit Instruction Format, shown in Figure 5.26.

(f) There are four Addressing Modes:

1. *Direct* to MM, 18 bits: SRC1, ADDR, SRC2.
2. *Indexed* to MM: SRC1, ADDR + (SRC2).
3. *Register Indirect* to MM: (SRC2).

$$SRC1 = ADDR = 0$$

4. *Immediate* in fields SRC1, ADDR, SRC2: 18 bits.

(g) There is a total of 138 CPU registers, with 32 (10 global, 22 window) seen by each procedure, as in RISC II (chapter 3).

The primary function of MODHEL is to serve as a research tool for RISCS investigations and it has been indeed used in such capacity [5.21].

In order to be able to make a comparison with previous studies, the same benchmark programs as in [1.17] have been used (described in section 13.2):

Puzzle A
Puzzle B
Ppuzzle
Qsort.

The following modules of the MODHEL have been used:

Module	Number of instructions
0	6
1	5
2	4
3	4

A total of MODHEL configurations have been tested:

MODHEL configuration	Total number of instructions
M_0	6
M_{01}	11
M_{02}	10
M_{012}	15
M_{0123}	19

For each benchmark program, the dynamic count (for a program run) of the occurrence of the instructions was taken. This was done for all MODHEL configurations, one after the other, listed above. The M_0 module, which has only MOVE-type instructions, is equivalent to the CMOVE system, described in section 5.4. The arithmetic operations are performed in the AMU in such a system. The dynamic count was then compared with the results of [1.17] for the Berkeley RISC I and for the VAX 11/780. The results, specified in millions of occurrences of instructions, are as follows:

System:	VAX	RISC I					
Program			M_0	M_{01}	M_{02}	M_{012}	M_{0123}
Puzzle A	10.01	10.11	20.55	20.55	15.05	15.05	10.11
Puzzle B	8.23	10.11	20.38	20.38	15.05	15.05	10.11
Ppuzzle	5.33	7.10	12.59	12.59	7.86	7.86	7.10
Qsort	1.05	1.63	2.26	2.08	1.70	1.70	1.70

The four benchmark programs activated from 17%–36% of data movement instructions, 43%–65% of arithmetic instructions and from 17%–25% of program control instructions, including subroutine calls and returns. This is a reasonable mix for a test and it fits, in a general way, the results in [1.15]. The above results indicate that even if we use the 15-instruction configuration M_{012} and compare it to RISC I, we use 50% more instructions for Puzzle A and B, 10% more for Ppuzzle and only 4% more for Qsort. For the M_{0123} configuration the number of instructions, used dynamically, becomes practically identical to that of RISC I for all benchmarks. The M_{0123} contains 19 instructions, about 61% of RISC I. The above results are only indicative and, as yet, inconclusive. More experimentation work in RISCS is needed in order to be able to draw definite conclusions, which could provide an answer to the questions posed at the beginning of this section. The results obtained so far can only serve as an indication (but not as a proof) that RISC-type systems, with a very small number of instructions (even less than the 31 instructions of the Berkeley RISC I), can run the same benchmarks as the RISC I or the VAX 11/780 at a comparable speed. The MODHEL system can be used in a variety of experiments with a great number of benchmark programs in studies aimed to provide some answers to the above questions.

5.6 GaAs RISC Systems

Since 1984 the US Defense Advanced Research Project Agency (DARPA) has been supporting the development of RISC-type, GaAs-based processors [5.23–5.28]. The primary developers of these processors are Control Data Corp. (CDC) jointly with TI, McDonnell-Douglas (McD), and Radio Corp. of America (RCA). All of the above processors are based on the Stanford MIPS architecture (chapter 4).

The primary advantage of GaAs is that it can be operated with a clock frequency that is about five times faster than CMOS for the same power consumption. Its main disadvantage is the low realizable density, permitting no more than about 30,000 transistors/chip. Therefore, the low-resources and options RISC-architecture becomes an excellent and, at the moment, only candidate for GaAs realization.

The high switching speed, or very low gate delay of a GaAs, while being of great advantage, causes additional design problems. The problem is the ratio between off-chip and on-chip memory access times, illustrated in the following example showing some typical values:

	GaAs	CMOS
On-chip access, An (nsec)	1	10
Off-chip access, Af (nsec)	10	30
r = Af/An	10	3

For silicon CMOS the above ratio r may range from 2 to 4 and the problem posed to the designer is moderate. On the other hand, in GaAs the r ratio changes from 5 to 20 (depending on the physical placement and capacity of the memory). That is, the off-chip access time is by one or two orders of magnitude longer than that of the on-chip. This extreme disparity between on- and off-chip access times has some very serious design consequences. Consider the execution of a load instruction. The processor sends the address of the data item, to be loaded into one of its registers, to the off-chip memory, while holding on to the destination register (Rd) address. During the time that it takes for the memory address to reach the memory module and for the fetched value to arrive back to the processor, the CPU could complete about 10 internal cycles. However, since the load instruction is not yet completed, the CPU may be prevented from implementing its full speed. This is because some of its resources are busy keeping the destination register address for the load instruction. The Rd may also be required as an operand of a subsequent instruction and only an updated value of Rd will yield correct results.

It follows from the above discussion that unless the designer takes some very particular steps it may not be possible to utilize the high speed of GaAs to its full extent. One possible way to alleviate the problem of the load instruction is to send out the Rd address along with the memory address and receive it back with the fetched data. This would release the appropriate CPU resources for other activities during the off-chip memory access delay [5.27]. This alone would not solve, however, the problem of a possible immediate need for an updated value of Rd by some subsequent instructions. The problem may be at least partially alleviated by introducing *memory access pipelining* (similarly to what is done in M88000, section 6.3, but with more pipeline stages) in addition to that of the processor. An additional approach would be to use an optimizing compiler that would change the order of instructions, if possible, to separate dependencies which are too close to each other in the program. The importance of an optimizing compiler is more critical in GaAs than in Silicon. In GaAs design the compiler becomes an integral part of the architecture [5.27]. Since the component count on the GaAs chip is severely limited, many traditional hardware functions must be transferred into the compiler. A great part of the actual design of GaAs systems, surveyed in the following, reflects the discussion above.

The CDC system features a CPU, a Floating Point Coprocessor (FCOP) and two Memory Management Units (MMU), one for each cache. All of the above chips have less than 10,000 gates, share a common instruction bus, and are pipelined. The processor operates with a 5 ns clock cycle (200 MHz) and has demonstrated a 91 MIPS rate in simulations. The CPU has 39, the FCOP 31, and the MMU 6 instructions. The operands used are 8, 16, and 32 bits. The IEEE 754-1985 Floating Point Standard is implemented.

The CPU contains a 24 32-bit general purpose registers. It has a six-stage pipeline:

1. Instruction Fetch — I1
2. Instruction Fetch Receive — I2
3. Execute — EX
4. Memory Access 1 — M1
5. Memory Access 2 — M2
6. Write Register — WR

Hardware pipeline interlocks are provided. A two-cycle branch delay is filled (in most cases) by the optimizing compiler.

The FCOP is also pipelined and contains four 64-bit registers, a status register, and a 64-bit barrel shifter. All FCOP instructions, executed in parallel with those of the CPU, require more than one cycle to execute.

One of the MMUs contains the instruction and the other the data cache. Each cache has 1024 32-bit words. The block size is 8 words. Cache access time is 1.0 to 1.5 ns. The page size for Virtual Memory operation is 2 KBytes.

Optimizing compilers for Ada and Pascal are an integral part of the architecture. The compilers are responsible for maintaining parallelism among the different coprocessor units.

The McD system consists of a CPU, two Floating Point Units (FPU), a system controller, and external memory.

The CPU (less than 10,000 gates) has a four-stage pipeline:

1. Instruction Fetch — IF
2. ALU Operation — ALU

3. Operand Fetch OF
4. Write Back WB

Only a single branch delay slot is to be filled by the compiler. No hardware pipeline interlocks are present. The pipeline is fully restartable after faults or interrupts. The CPU register file of 32 32-bit registers includes:

16 General Purpose registers
8 Optional General Purpose registers
8 Control registers.

The system controller performs functions that could not be placed on the CPU and FPU chips, such as interrupt handling, clock control, and I/O interface. The FPU (6000 gates) implements the IEEE 754-1985 Standard. The compiler is an integral part of the architecture. It performs global code optimization, global registers allocation, and scheduling for pipeline optimization.

The RCA [5.27] system consists of a CPU, FPU and a memory controller. The CPU has a 16 32-bit register file and a nine-stage pipeline. It uses a carry-select adder and a full barrel shifter. The register file has one read and one write port, however, two reads or writes per clock cycle are allowed. The system is targeted to operate at 200 MHz.

All of the above systems are under current experimental development.

References

5.1 M.E. Hopkins, 'A Perspective on the 801/RISC', *IBM Systems Journal*, **26**, No. 1, pp. 107–121, 1987.

5.2 D.M. Ungar, *The Design and Evaluation of a High Performance Smalltalk System*, MIT Press, Cambridge, MA, 1987.

5.3 D.M. Ungar, D.A. Patterson, 'What Price Smalltalk?', *IEEE Computer*, **20**, No. 1, pp. 67–74, Jan. 1987.

5.4 R.H. Katz, D.A. Patterson, 'A VLSI RISC Multiprocessor Workstation', *Proc. ICCD 86*, pp. 94–96, New York, Oct. 1986.

5.5 G.D. Adams, 'Functional Specification and Simulation of a Floating Point Coprocessor for SPUR', *Report No. UCB/CSD 87/311*, Computer Science Div., Univ. of California, Berkeley, CA, Aug. 1986.

5.6 L.P. Deutsch, *The Dorado Smalltalk-80 Implementation: Hardware Architecture's Impact on Software Architecture*, Addison-Wesley, Reading, MA, 1983.

5.7 A.J. Goldberg, D. Robson, *Smalltalk-80: The Language and its Implementation*, Addison-Wesley, Reading, MA, 1983.

5.8 R.P. Gabriel, *Performance and Evaluation of LISP Systems*, MIT Press, Cambridge, MA, 1985.

5.9 D.K. duBose, D.K. Fotakis, D. Tabak, 'A Microcoded RISC', *Computer Architecture News*, **14**, No. 3, pp. 5–16, June 1986 (also presented at the 19th Microprogramming Workshop, New York, Oct. 1986).

5.10 D.K. duBose, 'Extended RISC', M.S. thesis, George Mason University, 1988.

5.11 D.J. Quammen, D.K. duBose, D. Tabak, 'A RISC Architecture for Multitasking', *Proc. 21st Hawaii Int. Conf. on System Science, HICSS-21*, **1**, pp. 230–237, Jan. 1988.

5.12 J.M. Davila, A.J. Philips, D. Tabak, 'Floating Point Arithmetic on a RISC', *Microprocessing and Microprogramming*, **23**, No. 1-5, pp. 179–184, 1988.

5.13 A.V. Aho, J. Hopcroft, J. Ullman, *The Design and Analysis of Computer Algorithms*, Addison-Wesley, Reading, MA, 1975.

5.14 G.J. Lipovski, 'The Architecture of a Simple, Effective, Control Processor', in M. Sami, J. Wilmink and R. Zaks (eds.), *Microprocessing and Microprogramming, EUROMICRO 76*, North-Holland, Amsterdam, pp. 7–18, 1976.

5.15 G.J. Lipovski, 'On Conditional Moves in Control Processors', *Proc. 2nd Rocky Mountain Symp. on Micro Computers*, pp. 63–94, Pingree Park, CO, 1978.

5.16 D. Tabak, G.J. Lipovski, 'MOVE Architecture in Digital Controllers', *IEEE Trans. on Computers*, **C-29**, No. 2, pp. 180–190, Feb. 1980.

5.17 H. Azaria, D. Tabak, 'Bit-Sliced Realization of a CMOVE Architecture Microcomputer', *EUROMICRO Journal*, **6**, No. 6, pp. 373–380, Nov. 1980.

5.18 H. Azaria, D. Tabak, 'Design Considerations of a Single-Instruction Microcomputer – A Case Study', *Microprocessing and Microprogramming*, **11**, No. 3, 4, pp. 187–194, March/April 1983.

5.19 H. Azaria, D. Tabak, 'A CMOVE Distributed Processing System', in L. Richter, P. Le Beaux, G. Chroust (eds.), *Implementing Functions: Microprocessors and Firmware*, North-Holland, Amsterdam, 1981.

5.20 H. Azaria, D. Tabak, 'The MODHEL Microcomputer for RISCS Study', *Microprocessing and Microprogramming*, **12**, No. 3, 4, pp. 199–206, Oct./Nov. 1983.

5.21 H. Azaria, 'Preliminary Analysis of RISC Architectures Performance', *Microprocessing and Microprogramming*, **14**, No. 3, 4, pp. 133–137, Oct./Nov. 1984.

5.22 I. Shallom, H. Azaria, 'Architectural Concepts of an Optimal Instruction Set Selection Procedure Machine', *Microprocessing and Microprogramming*, **16**, No. 2, 3, pp. 113–119, Sept./Oct. 1985.

5.23 C.E. Gimarc, V.M. Milutinovic, 'RISC Principles, Architecture, and Design', in V.M. Milutinovic (ed.), *HLL Computer Architecture*, Ch. 1, pp. 1–64, Computer Science Press, NY, 1989.

5.24 H. Vlahos, V.M. Milutinovic, 'GaAs Microprocessors and Digital Systems', *IEEE MICRO*, **8**, No. 1, pp. 28–56, Feb. 1988.

5.25 W.A. Helbig, V.M. Milutinovic, 'Architecture and Design of a 32-Bit GaAs Microprocessor', in V.M. Milutinovic (ed.), *HLL Computer Architecture*, Ch. 2, pp. 65–106, Computer Science Press, NY, 1989.

5.26 B. Furrow, 'RISC – The Sound and the Fury', *ESD Magazine*, March 1989, pp. 49–57.

5.27 W.A. Helbig, V.M. Milutinovic, 'A DCFL E/D-MESFET GaAs Experimental RISC Machine', *IEEE Trans. on Computers*, **38**, No. 2, pp. 263–274, Feb. 1989.

5.28 V.M. Milutinovic (ed.), 'Special issue on GaAs Microprocessor Technology', *IEEE Computer*, **19**, No. 10, Oct. 1986.

6
The Motorola M88000 System

6.1 General Description

Among the recently announced commercial RISC-type forerunners is the Motorola M88000 microprocessor family. It is a new system without any compatibility connections to the Motorola M68000 CISC family. Two initial chips were announced: the MC88100 and MC88200.

The M88000 family RISC processor MC88100 is a 1.5 micron (a 1.2 micron version is to appear) HCMOS, 180-pins chip [6.1–6.7]. It can achieve a peak performance of 17 MIPS or 6 MFLOPS at 20 MHz. It has an on-chip Floating Point (single and double precision IEEE P754 standard) capability. The M88000 architecture features 51 instructions, 7 data types (5 integer, 2 floating point), 3 data addressing modes, 4 instruction addressing modes and 3 instruction formats. All instructions are single word (4 bytes) long. As in any typical RISC (chapter 1), all operations are register-to-register and memory is accessed by load/store instructions only.

The second chip of the M88000 family is the MC88200 Cache Memory Management Unit (CMMU). Its technology and pin count is the same as that of the MC88100. It contains 16 KBytes of instruction or data cache, the memory management logic and address translation caches. An MC88100 CPU is usually configured with 2 CMMU chips, one for the instruction and the other for the data cache. The maximal configuration in the current packaging technology is for 8 CMMU chips, 4-instruction (total 64 KBytes) and 4-data cache (64 KBytes), a total of 128 KByte cache storage. A diagram showing an M88000 system configuration is illustrated in Figure 6.1.

The 88100 CPU is connected to the CMMUs through a Processor Bus (PBUS). It has separate instruction and data PBUSes. The PBUS is a synchronous bus with separate (non-multiplexed) 32 data lines and 30 address lines. The basic word of the 88000 has 32 bits or 4 bytes and it is aligned on addresses (it is byte-addressable) divisible by 4 (two least significant bits are zero). For this reason, 30 address bits are sufficient. The overall virtual address space is 4 GBytes for the user and 4 GBytes for the Supervisor (OS) address spaces, separately for instructions and data, for a total of 16 GBytes. The main memory physical address space is limited to 4 GBytes. Separate 4 GBytes of physical memory for instructions and data are possible, but may require separate instruction and data disk drives, and two Memory Buses (MBUSes).

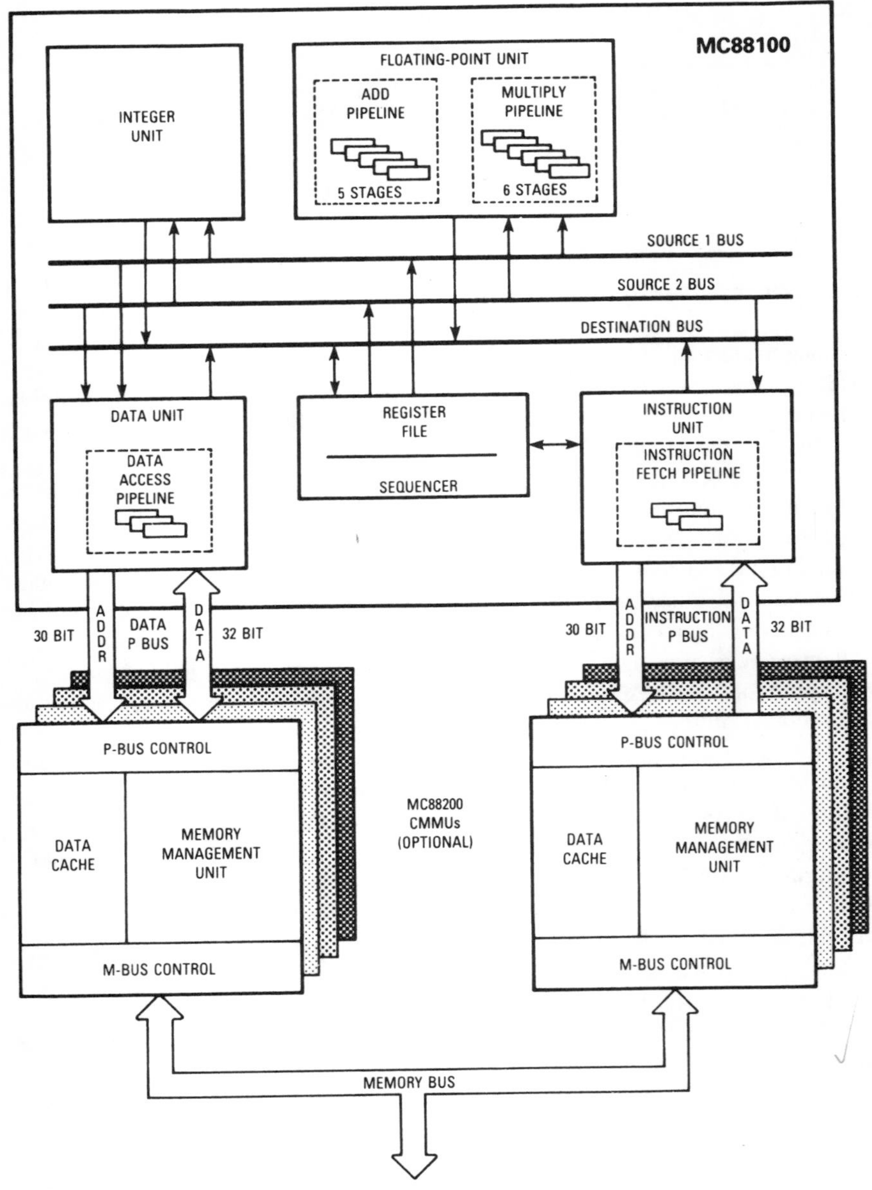

Figure 6.1 MC88100/MC88200 Block Diagram
(Reprinted with permission, courtesy of Motorola, Inc.)

Each CMMU is connected to the Memory Bus (MBUS), interconnected to the main memory and I/O interfaces. The MBUS is synchronous with 32 multiplexed data/address lines. Since the minimal cache configuration is 32 KBytes (16 KBytes code, 16 KBytes data), a high hit ratio can be assumed. Thus, most of the CPU-to-memory traffic will occur on the PBUS and only a small percentage on the MBUS. Therefore, the multiplexing of the MBUS will have an insignificant effect on the CPU-to-memory speed of operation.

The 88100 CPU has an on-chip Floating Point Unit (FPU), implementing single (32-bits) and double precision (64-bits) IEEE 754-1985 Standard. The FPU has a five-stage add and a six-stage multiply pipeline. The FPU is a particular case of a Special Function Unit (SFU) that can be placed on the MC88100. A total of up to 7 SFUs can be configured on future versions of the 88100.

6.2 System Architecture

The 88100 features 32 general purpose registers, 64 Integer Unit (IU) general control registers and 64 FPU control registers. Only 21 of the general and 11 of the FPU control registers are actually implemented. The actually implemented registers are illustrated in Figure 6.2. Of the 32 general purpose registers r0 to r31, only two are predefined by hardware design:

r0 – always contains zero (as in the Berkeley RISC, chapter 3);
r1 – contains the subroutine return pointer.

All other registers (as indicated in Figure 6.2) can be assigned by software. Observing the shown register assignment convention maintains compatibility with future processors of the M88000 family and Motorola-authorized software.

Among the CPU registers the Scoreboard Register is of particular interest. Its 32 bits are associated with each of the 32 general purpose registers. It is used for hardware synchronization of operations involving the general purpose registers. When an instruction is executed or dispatched, the *scoreboard* bit of the destination register is set, reserving that register for that instruction. Other instructions are executed or dispatched as long as their source and destination operands have clear scoreboard bits (i.e., as long as the registers are not in use). When an instruction completes execution, it clears the scoreboard bit of the destination register, freeing that register for use by other instructions.

The M88000 51 instructions, summarized in Table 6.1, are subdivided into the following groups:

Integer Arithmetic	8
Floating Point Arithmetic	12
Logical	4
Bit-field	8
Load/Store/Exchange	7
Flow Control	12
	Total 51

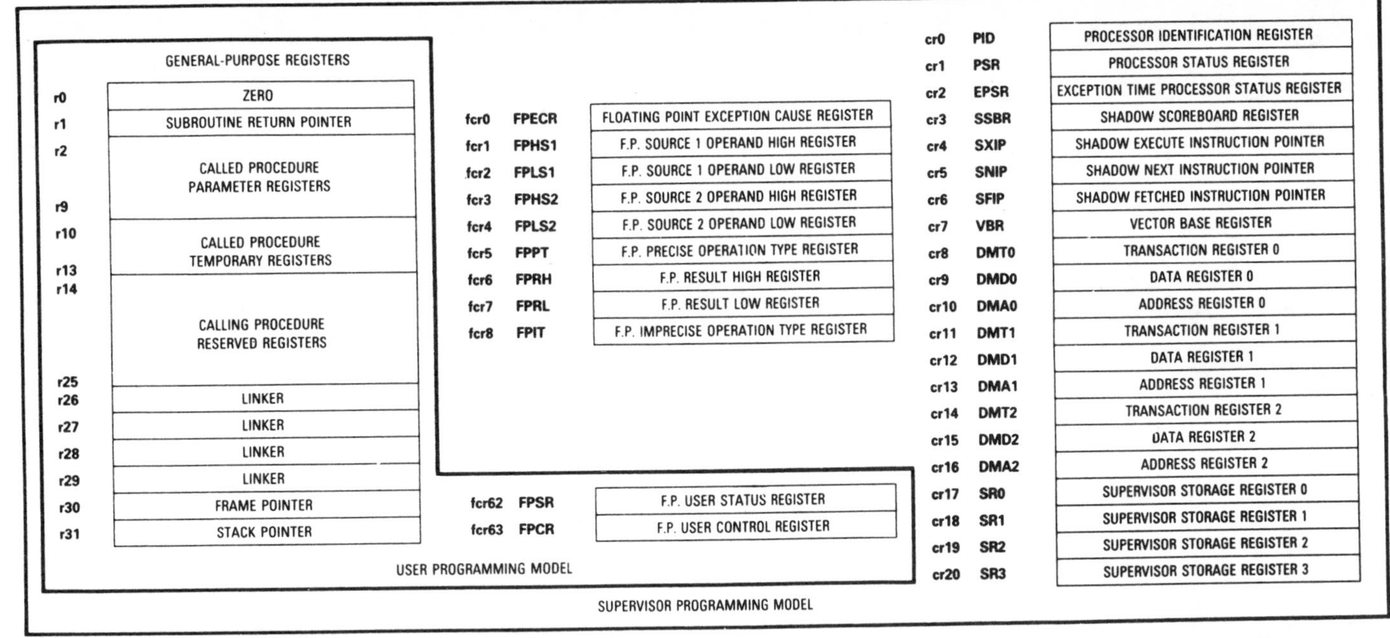

Figure 6.2 Programming Model
(Reprinted with permission, courtesy of Motorola, Inc.)

Table 6.1 Instruction Summary
(Reprinted with permission, courtesy of Motorola, Inc.)

Integer Arithmetic Instructions

Mnemonic	Description
add	Add
addu	Add Unsigned
cmp	Compare
div	Divide
divu	Divide Unsigned
mul	Multiply
sub	Subtract
subu	Subtract Unsigned

Floating-Point Arithmetic Instructions

Mnemonic	Description
fadd	Floating-Point Add
fcmp	Floating-Point Compare
fdiv	Floating-Point Divide
fldcr	Load from Floating-Point Control Register
flt	Convert Integer to Floating Point
fmul	Floating-Point Multiply
fstcr	Store to Floating-Point Control Register
fsub	Floating-Point Subtract
fxcr	Exchange Floating-Point Control Register
int	Round Floating-Point to Integer
nint	Round Floating-Point to Nearest Integer
trnc	Truncate Floating-Point to Integer

Logical Instructions

Mnemonic	Description
and	AND
mask	Logical Mask Immediate
or	OR
xor	Exclusive OR

Load/Store/Exchange Instructions

Mnemonic	Description
ld	Load Register from Memory
lda	Load Address
ldcr	Load from Control Register
st	Store Register to Memory
stcr	Store to Control Register
xcr	Exchange Control Register
xmem	Exchange Register with Memory

Flow-Control Instructions

Mnemonic	Description
bb0	Branch on Bit Clear
bb1	Branch on Bit Set
bcnd	Conditional Branch
br	Unconditional Branch
bsr	Branch to Subroutine
jmp	Unconditional Jump
jsr	Jump to Subroutine
rte	Return from Exception
tb0	Trap on Bit Clear
tb1	Trap on Bit Set
tbnd	Trap on Bounds Check
tcnd	Conditional Trap

Bit-Field Instructions

Mnemonic	Description
clr	Clear Bit Field
ext	Extract Signed Bit Field
extu	Extract Unsigned Bit Field
ff0	Find First Bit Clear
ff1	Find First Bit Set
mak	Make Bit Field
rot	Rotate Register
set	Set Bit Field

The M88000 is, for the moment, unique in offering the user an *optional delayed branch* capability, attained by placing '.n' after the instruction mnemonic, such as in jmp.n (just writing 'jmp' would be a regular, undelayed jump).

Only load/store and the exchange register with memory (xmem – an indivisible instruction for semaphore handling) instructions can access memory. All other operations are executed within the CPU.

The 88000 architecture recognizes seven data types:

1. Bit fields, 1 to 32 bits, signed and unsigned
2. Byte, 8 bits, signed and unsigned
3. Half-word, 16 bits, signed and unsigned
4. Word, 32 bits, signed and unsigned
5. Double-word, 64 bits, signed and unsigned
6. Single Precision Floating Point, 32 bits (IEEE)
7. Double Precision Floating Point, 64 bits (IEEE).

Types (2), (3) and (5) are used only on load and store instructions.

There are three data Addressing Modes:

Register Indirect with Unsigned Immediate,
Register Indirect with Index,
Register Indirect with Scaled Index,

and four instruction Addressing Modes:

Register with 9-bit Vector Number
Register with 16-bit Signed Displacement
Instruction Pointer Relative (26-Bit Signed Displacement)
Register Direct.

The MC88100 basic instruction formats are illustrated in Figure 6.3. For some addressing modes the subopcode and the S2 fields are used to store immediate values.

The M88000 instructions are 3-operand ones. For instance:

add r5, r4, r1; $r5 \leftarrow (r4) + (r1)$

or

div r11, r1, r2; $r11 \leftarrow (r1)/(r2)$

Floating point operations permit the mixing of single and double precision operands.

EXAMPLE: fmul.dss r1, r4, r8; $r1, r2 \leftarrow (r4) \times (r8)$
s = single precision
d = double precision

The double precision product of the contents of r4 and r8 (single precision each) will be placed in registers r1, r2 (most significant part in r1).

The MC88100 Processor Status Register (PSR), also denoted as cr1 (Figure 6.2), is illustrated in Figure 6.4. It contains information about the current operations of the processor. The processor can run either in the user or supervisor (OS) mode. This is established by bit 31 of the PSR (MODE). As in the commercial MIPS (chapter 4), big-endian or little-endian byte ordering in memory can be established, using bit 30(BO). The 88000 byte order can be changed dynamically, while the MIPS byte order is fixed at reset. The MC88100 CPU was designed for concurrent operation of its subunits. This will happen if bit 29(SER) of the PSR is reset. For diagnostic purposes or during debugging, serial operation may be selected by setting bit 29. Similarly, the floating point unit (FPU or SFU1) can be disabled by setting bit 3(SFD1). Bits 4–9 are reserved for similar purposes for future implementations of additional on-chip SFUs. The MC88100 implements the concept of Shadow Registers (similarly to the SOAR, chapter 5), which can be disabled by setting bit 0(SFRZ) of the PSR. These registers will be discussed later in this chapter.

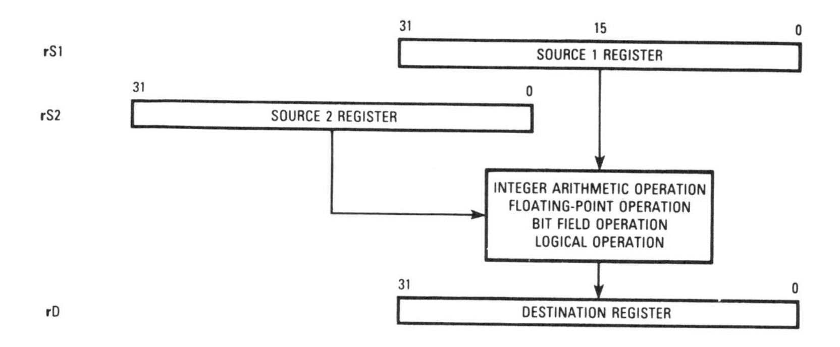

Instruction Format (Floating-Point)

31–26	25–21	20–16	15–5	4–0
1 0 0 0 0 1	D	S1	SUBOPCODE	S2

D The D field specifies the destination register which receives the result of the operation.

S1 The S1 field specifies the source 1 operand register. For the **int**, **nint**, **flt**, and **trnc** instructions, S1 must be zero.

SUBOPCODE This field identifies the floating-point instruction (**fadd**, **fcmp**, **fdiv**, **fmul**, **fsub**, **int**, **nint**, **flt**, and **trnc**).

S2 The S2 field specifies the source 2 operand register.

Instruction Format (Non-Floating-Point)

31–26	25–21	20–16	15–5	4–0
1 1 1 1 0 1	D	S1	SUBOPCODE	S2

D The D field specifies the destination register which receives the result of the operation. This field is ignored for instructions that do not generate results.

S1 The S1 field specifies the source 1 operand register. For bit scan and the **rte** instructions, this field is ignored.

SUBOPCODE This field identifies the non-floating-point instruction (**add**, **addu**, **and**, **cmp**, **div**, **divu**, **ext**, **extu**, **ff0**, **ff1**, **mak**, **mul**, **or**, **rot**, **rte**, **set**, **sub**, **subu**, **trnc**, and **xor**).

S2 The S2 field specifies the source 2 operand register. For the **rte** instruction this field is ignored.

Figure 6.3 Instruction Formats of the MC88100
(Reprinted with permission, courtesy of Motorola, Inc.)

cr1

31	30	29	28	27 … 10	9 … 4	3	2	1	0
MODE	BO	SER	C	0 0 0 0 0 0 0 0 0 0 0 0 0 0 0 0 0 0	1 1 1 1 1 1	SFD1	MXM	IND	SFRZ

```
MODE  =  0   Processor is in user mode
      =  1   Processor is in supervisor mode
  BO  =  0   Big Endian byte order in memory
      =  1   Little Endian byte order in memory
 SER  =  0   Concurrent instruction execution
      =  1   Serial instruction execution
   C  =  0   No carry/borrow generated
      =  1   Carry/borrow generated
SFD1  =  0   SFU1(FPU)enabled
      =  1   SFU1(FPU)disabled
 MXM  =  0   Misaligned memory accesses generate exceptions
      =  1   Misaligned memory accesses truncate
 IND  =  0   Interrupt enabled
      =  1   Interrupt disabled
SFRZ  =  0   Shadow registers enabled
      =  1   Shadow registers disabled
```

Figure 6.4 Processor Status Register – PSR (crl)
(*Reprinted with permission, courtesy of Motorola, Inc.*)

6.3 MC88100 Bus Interconnections and Pipelining

As illustrated in Figure 6.1, the MC88100 has two sets of Processor Buses, called PBUS; one for data and one for instructions. The functional diagram of the MC88100 is shown in Figure 6.5. The Data and the Instruction PBUS are connected to separate CMMUs.

The signals related to the Data PBUS start with a 'D', and those for the Instruction PBUS with a 'C' (for Code). Each side has separate, non-multiplexed 32-bit data and 30-bit address lines. The code is aligned on word address boundaries. Therefore, only the upper 30 address lines (CA31–CA2) are needed. On the Data PBUS there are additional 4 DBE3–DBE0 lines which can identify any byte in a word. The DS/U* and the CS/U* control lines differentiate between the Supervisor and the User modes of operation. The MC88100 receives reply signals on both sides: DR1, DR0 and CR1, CR0. Their encoding is:

(D)CR1	(D)CR0	
0	0	Reserved
1	0	Successful Memory Transaction
0	1	Memory Wait
1	1	Transaction Fault

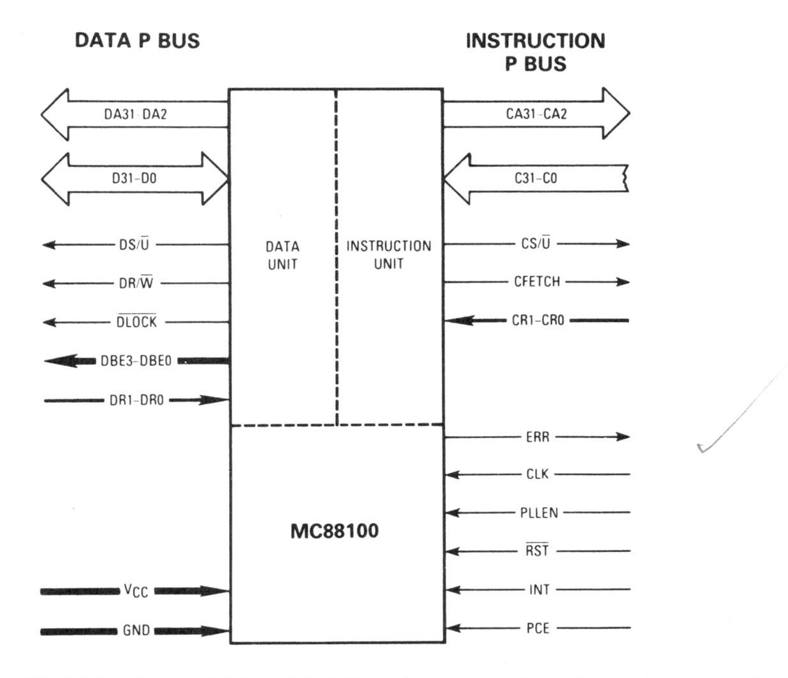

Function	Mnemonic	Type	Active	Count	Reset
Data Address	DA31–DA2	Output	—	30	High Impedance*
Data	D31–D0	I/O	—	32	High Impedance*
Data Supervisor/User Select	DS/$\overline{U}$	Output	—	1	High Impedance*
Data Read/Write	DR/$\overline{W}$	Output	—	1	High Impedance*
Data Bus Lock	$\overline{DLOCK}$	Output	Low	1	High Impedance*
Data Byte Enable	DBE3–DBE0	Output	High	4	High Impedance*
Data Reply	DR1–DR0	Input	—	2	Input
Code Address	CA31–CA2	Output	—	30	High Impedance*
Code	C31–C0	Input	—	32	High Impedance*
Code Supervisor/User Select	CS/$\overline{U}$	Output	—	1	Input
Code Fetch	CFETCH	Output	High	1	High Impedance*
Code Reply	CR1–CR0	Input	—	2	Input
Error	ERR	Output	High	1	Low
Reset	$\overline{RST}$	Input	Low	1	Input
Interrupt	INT	Input	High	1	Input
P Bus Checker Enable	PCE	Input	High	1	Input
Clock	CLK	Input	High	1	Input
Phase Lock Enable	PLLEN	Input	High	1	Input
Power	V_{CC}	—	—	18	—
Ground	GND	—	—	18	—

*These signals remain in the high-impedance state for one clock cycle after the $\overline{RST}$ signal is recognized as negated (high).

Figure 6.5 Functional Diagram of MC88100 Signals
(*Reprinted with permission, courtesy of Motorola, Inc.*)

The DLOCK* (* means a low asserted signal, denoted by a bar over the letter in the figure) signal is a memory lock signal used by the atomic xmem instruction. When DLOCK* is asserted, the CMMU does not allow the system memory to be accessed by any other bus master between the two xmem accesses.

The Phase Lock Enable (PLLEN) signal controls the internal phase lock circuit that synchronizes the internal clocks to the external clock (CLK) signal. Using phase lock circuitry assures better frequency precision. The Reset (RST*) signal is used to perform an orderly restart of the processor, bringing it to a known state and beginning program execution at address 0. The Error (ERR) signal is asserted when a bus comparator error occurs. It is used in the Checker Mode, to be described later in the chapter. The PBUS Checker Enable (PCE) signal differentiates at reset between a master (negated) and a checker (asserted) chip in the checker mode.

The MC88100 features an Instruction PBUS pipeline in the sense that the address of an access coincides with the reply phase of the previous instruction access. Figure 6.6 shows an example timing diagram for a read cycle with one wait cycle followed by a read access with no wait cycles. Since the reply (via CR1, CR0) for address phase 1 was 'wait', the address phase for the second access is repeated by the MC88100 until a successful transaction response to the first access is obtained. A similar pipeline is also implemented on the Data PBUS.

The FPU has two arithmetic pipelines, shown in Figure 6.1, a five-stage add and a six-stage multiply.

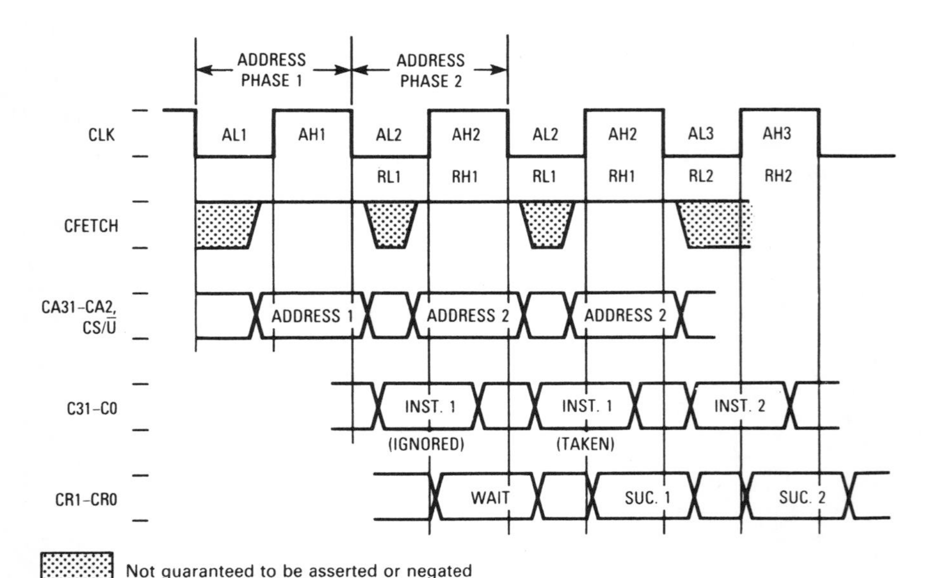

Figure 6.6 Instruction Prefetch with Wait Cycle
(*Reprinted with permission, courtesy of Motorola, Inc.*)

The MC88100 Instruction Unit which prefetches instructions from memory, performs the first steps of decoding, and provides the appropriate control signals, is organized as a three-stage pipeline, shown in Figure 6.7. Each stage contains its own Instruction Pointer (IP):

(a) *Execute Stage*
Executive Instruction Pointer, XIP, points to the instruction currently executing.

(b) *Next Stage*
Next Instruction Pointer, NIP, points to the following instruction being accessed and decoded.

(c) *Fetch Stage*
Fetch Instruction Pointer, FIP, points to the memory location of the next instruction to be accessed.

All of the above registers have their Shadow Registers SXIP, SNIP, SFIP, containing the same information as XIP, NIP and FIP, respectively, during a regular run. The information in the shadow registers is frozen when an exception occurs. This information is available upon a return from the exception, restoring the interrupted run.

The MC88100 Data Unit also features a three-stage pipeline – Stages 2, 1, 0, with the following tasks:

Stage 2 receives information from the register file and computes data access addresses. It contains a dedicated ALU for address calculations.

Stage 1 drives the external data address bus (DA31–DA2). If it is a store

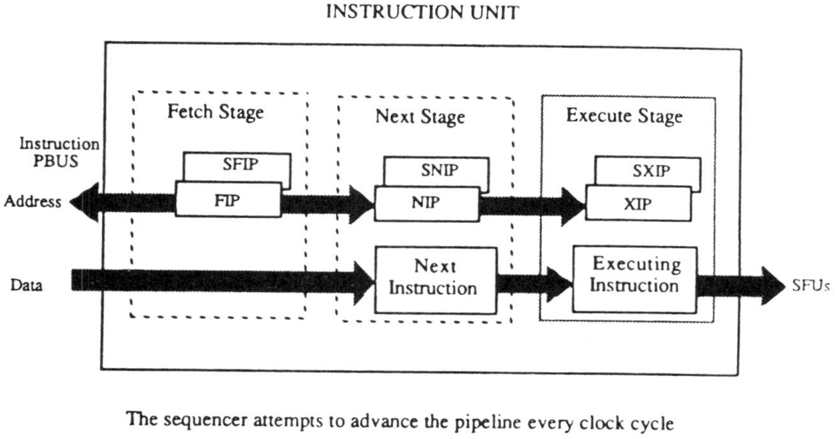

INSTRUCTION UNIT

Instruction PBUS
Address
Data
Fetch Stage
SFIP
FIP
Next Stage
SNIP
NIP
Next Instruction
Execute Stage
SXIP
XIP
Executing Instruction
SFUs

The sequencer attempts to advance the pipeline every clock cycle

Figure 6.7 Instruction Unit Pipeline
(Reprinted with permission, courtesy of Motorola, Inc.)

operation, it fetches data from the source register and drives the data bus (D31–D0).

Stage 0 monitors the reply from the memory (usually the DATA CMMU through DR1, DR0). If it is a load operation, it reads the data bus and writes to the destination register.

Each of the above stages has three registers:

DMTi
DMDi
DMAi, i = 0, 1, 2,

listed in Table 6.2 (they are also called cr8 to cr16). Their tasks:

DMTi – Data Memory Transaction registers, contain encoded information about the memory access, such as byte ordering, data access space (user/supervisor), double word access indicator, bus lock identifier, destination register encoding, data zero or sign extension indicator, byte enable bits, and read/write, valid/invalid indicators.

DMDi – Data Memory Data registers, contain the data value involved in the current access, of stage i.

DMAi – Data Memory Address registers, contain the address of the current data memory access, for each stage i.

Table 6.2 Data Unit Control Registers
(Reprinted with permission, courtesy of Motorola, Inc.)

Register Number	Acronym	Name
cr8	DMT0	Transaction Register #0
cr9	DMD0	Data Register #0
cr10	DMA0	Address Register #0
cr11	DMT1	Transaction Register #1
cr12	DMD1	Data Register #1
cr13	DMA1	Address Register #1
cr14	DMT2	Transaction Register #2
cr15	DMD2	Data Register #2
cr16	DMA2	Address Register #2

6.4 Processor Exceptions

The MC88100 recognizes the following types of exceptions:

(a) External interrupts, signaled via the Interrupt (INT) pin (Figure 6.5).
(b) Externally signaled errors, such as memory access fault (CR1, CR0 or DR1, DR0 pins, Figure 6.5).

(c) Internally recognized errors, such as divide by zero.
(d) Trap instructions.

There are two categories of exceptions:

(1) *Precise* – the exact processor context when the exception occurred is available, and the exact cause of the exception is known.

(2) *Imprecise* – the exact processor context is not known when the exception is processed, because concurrent operations have affected the information that comprises the context. EXAMPLE: with a floating point overflow, the FPU does not save the source operands internally, so it does not have a local copy of those operands when the exception is processed.

Exception processing begins at the next instruction boundary after an exception is recognized. The processor proceeds with the following steps:

(a) Freezes the execution context in *Shadow* and *Exception-Time Registers* (which also precludes other exceptions from occurring).
(b) Explicitly disables interrupts.
(c) Enters the Supervisor Mode of execution.
(d) Disables and freezes the FPU.
(e) Allows the Data Unit to complete pending accesses.
(f) Transfers instruction execution to the appropriate *exception handler routine*, pointed to by the *exception vector* associated with the particular exception.

During an exception, copies of some of the CPU registers are kept in *Shadow Registers*. During normal operation the shadow registers are updated on every clock cycle when shadowing is enabled (bit 0 of PSR, SFRZ = 0, Figure 6.4). The SFRZ is set by hardware when an exception is processed, disabling shadowing in order to preserve the processor context. It is reset by software by writing into PSR or by the rte (return from exception) instruction, enabling shadowing for the resumption of normal operation. The states of the appropriate control registers, after an exception occurs, are summarized in Table 6.3. The exception vectors of the MC88100 are listed in Table 6.4. Each exception vector is 8 bytes long, consisting of 2 instructions (2 words):

(1) Delayed branch into the exception handler routine.
(2) First instruction of the exception handler routine, always executed before branching.

The exception vectors are stored in the *Vector Table*, pointed to by the *Vector Base Register*, VBR (cr7). The VBR and the exception vector address formation are illustrated in Figure 6.8.

The exception priorities (top priority first) are:

1. Reset.
2. Instruction Access fault.

Table 6.3 General Control Register States after an Exception
(Reprinted with permission, courtesy of Motorola, Inc.)

Register	State
Processor Status Register (PSR)	Bits 31, 3, 1, and 0 set (supervisor mode, FPU and interrupts disabled, shadow registers frozen); all other bits unchanged.
Exception-Time Processor Status Register (EPSR)	Contains the value in the PSR before the exception occurred and after all data unit operations have completed or faulted.
Scoreboard (SB)	Cleared
Shadow Scoreboard (SSBR)	Contains the value in the scoreboard before the exception occurred.
Instruction Pointers (XIP, NIP, FIP)	FIP = exception vector address, V bits in NIP and XIP are cleared
Shadow Instruction Pointers (SXIP, SNIP, SFIP)	Contains XIP, NIP, and FIP values before the exception occurred. Instructions pointed to by the SNIP and SFIP have not been executed. The instruction pointed to by the SXIP may have been aborted or completed, depending on the exection type.
Vector Base Register (VBR)	Unchanged
Data Memory Transaction Registers (DMT0, DMT1, DMT2)	For a data access exception, DMT2, DMT1, DMT0 contain information on the memory transaction in progress. Valid bits are clear if no memory access exception has occurred.
Data Memory Address Registers (DMA0, DMA1, DMA2)	For a data access exception, DMA2, DMA1, DMA0 contain information on the memory transaction in progress. Undefined for all other exceptions.
Data Memory Data Registers (DMD0, DMD1, DMD2)	For a data access exception, DMD2, DMD1, DMD0 contain information on the memory transaction in progress. Undefined for all other exceptions.
General-Purpose Registers (**r31–r0**)	Unchanged
Floating-Point Control Registers	FPECR contains information on floating-point exceptions, floating-point precise registers contain information on procese exception, and floating-point imprecise registers contain information on imprecise exceptions; otherwise these are undefined. FPCR and FPSR are unchanged by exception recognition.

31 – 12	11 – 0
VECTOR TABLE BASE ADDRESS	0 0 0 0 0 0 0 0 0 0 0 0

VBR **cr7**

Bits 31–12 — Vector Table Base Address

Bits 11–0 — Reserved
Always contain zero. Not guaranteed to be zeros in future implementations.

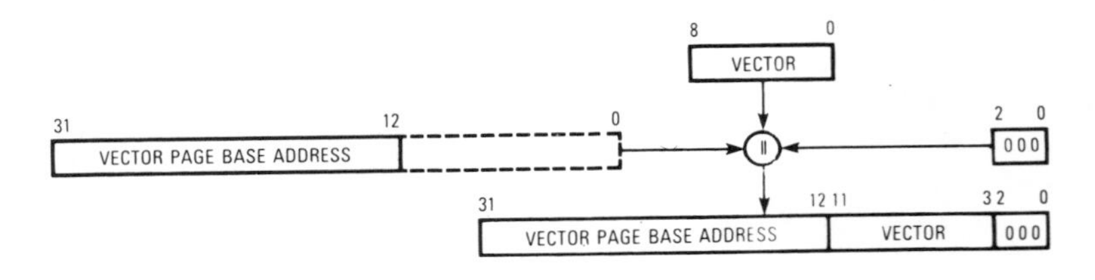

Figure 6.8 Exception Vector Address Formation
(Reprinted with permission, courtesy of Motorola, Inc.)

Table 6.4 Exception Vectors
(Reprinted with permission, courtesy of Motorola, Inc.)

Exception Number	Address	Definition
0	0	Reset (the VBR is Cleared Before Vectoring) Exception
1	VBR + $8	Interrupt Exception
2	VBR + $10	Instruction Access Exception
3	VBR + $18	Data Access Exception
4	VBR + $20	Misaligned Access Exception
5	VBR + $28	Unimplemented Opcode Exception
6	VBR + $30	Privilege Violation Exception
7	VBR + $38	Bounds Check Violation Exception
8	VBR + $40	Illegal Integer Divide Exception
9	VBR + $48	Integer Overflow Exception
10	VBR + $50	Error Exception
11–113		Reserved for Supervisor and Future Hardware Use Only
114	VBR + $390	SFU 1 Precise — Floating-Point Precise Exception
115	VBR + $398	SFU 1 Imprecise — Floating-Point Imprecise Exception
116	VBR + $3A0	SFU 2 Precise (see Note) Exception
117	VBR + $3A8	Reserved
118	VBR + $3B0	SFU 3 Precise (see Note) Exception
119	VBR + $3B8	Reserved
120	VBR + $3C0	SFU 4 Precise (see Note) Exception
121	VBR + $3C8	Reserved
122	VBR + $3D0	SFU 5 Precise (see Note) Exception
123	VBR + $3D8	Reserved
124	VBR + $3E0	SFU 6 Precise (see Note) Exception
125	VBR + $3E8	Reserved
126	VBR + $3F0	SFU 7 Precise (see Note) Exception
127	VBR + $3F8	Reserved
128–511		Supervisor Call Exceptions — Reserved for User Definition (Trap Vectors)

NOTE: SFU2 through SFU7 are not implemented. Executing an instruction that is coded for these SFUs causes a precise exception for that SFU.

3. Unimplemented opcode.
4. Privilege Violation.
5. Misaligned Access, Integer Overflow, Illegal Integer Divide, Trap Instructions, Bounds Check, SFU Precise.
6. Interrupt.
7. SFU Imprecise.
8. Data Access.

The principal exception processing phases are:

(a) *Exception recognition* – the processor saves the execution context in shadow registers and changes program flow to the exception handling routine. The saving of the context in memory is done by software in the exception handler.

(b) *Exception handling* – software (exception handler routine) corrects exception condition or performs the function initiated by a trap instruction.

(c) *Return from exception* – execution context restored, execution resumes at the program location where the exception occurred. The registers restored by the return from exception, rte, instruction are:

PSR from EPSR (cr2),
SBR from SSBR (Shadow Scoreboard Register, cr3),
FIP from SFIP (cr6),
NIP from SNIP (cr5).

The rte instruction fetches the instruction pointed to by SNIP and then the one by SFIP. The SXIP points to the instruction that caused the exception for a precise exception, and to the last instruction issued for an imprecise exception or interrupt. The hardware does not use SXIP on return from exception.

The following exceptions are *maskable*:

External Interrupts,
Misaligned Access,
Floating Point Imprecise.

6.5 The MC88200 CMMU

A block diagram of the MC88200 Cache Memory Management Unit, CMMU, briefly described in section 6.1, is shown in Figure 6.9. The MC88200 receives logical addresses from the MC88100 on the PBUS, translates them into physical addresses, while asserting the validity of the address mapping, and then drives the physical address on the MBUS (Figure 6.1), if necessary. The MC88200 contains a 16 KBytes on-chip cache with a high hit ratio.

The M88000 main memory can be subdivided in two ways:

(1) *Blocks*, 512 KBytes, used primarily for system software.
(2) *Segments*, 4 MBytes, subdivided into 1024 *Pages*, 4 KBytes each.

The MC88200 has two fully-associative *Address Translation Caches* (ATCs):

(a) *Block ATC* (BATC), 10 entries, pointing to 10 blocks in memory. Two of the above are hardwired to point to two fixed blocks, dedicated to memory-mapped peripheral devices. These two blocks are called 'control memory'.
(b) *Page ATC* (PATC), 56 entries, pointing to 56 page frames in memory.

When the MC88200 receives a logical address, its MMU logic performs the following four functions concurrently:

1. Identity translation (in case of physical address = logical address) if the

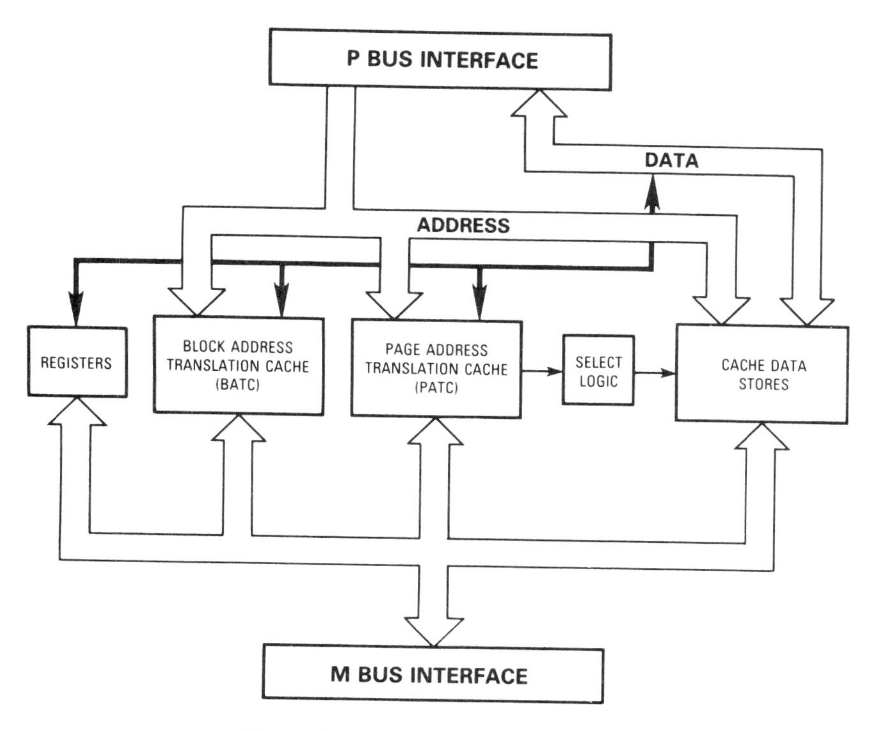

Figure 6.9 MC88200 Block Diagram
(Reprinted with permission, courtesy of Motorola, Inc.)

Translation Enable bit is clear in either the:
(a) Supervisor Area Pointer Register (SAPR), or
(b) User Area Pointer Register (UAPR).

2. Compare bits 31-19 of the logical address and the supervisor/user bit to each Logical Block Address (LBA) entry in the BATC. If there is a hit, then create a physical address by concatenating logical address bits 18-2 to the Physical Block Address (PBA) from the BATC entry.

3. Compare bits 31-12 of the logical address and the supervisor/unit bit to each Logical Page Address (LPA) in the PATC. If there is a hit, create a physical address by concatenating logical address bits 11-2 to the Page Frame Address (PFA) from the PATC entry. If there is a BATC and a PATC hit, then the BATC entry is used for address translation.

4. Data cache set selection is performed using bits 11-4 of the logical address. The cache line is selected at the end of address translation if there is a hit in the data cache.

If the logical address misses both ATCs, then the MMU creates a new PATC entry by performing a translation table search on the MBUS, which involves traversing a two-level table of descriptors in memory to find a new PFA, as illustrated in Figure 6.10. The newly acquired PFA is placed in the PATC along with its corresponding LPA and control bits. If the PATC is full, an entry is replaced using a First-In, First-Out (FIFO) scheme.

The 16 KByte on-chip data cache is 4-way set-associative (4 lines/set), consisting of 256 sets. Each line contains 4 words or 16 bytes. Each set has

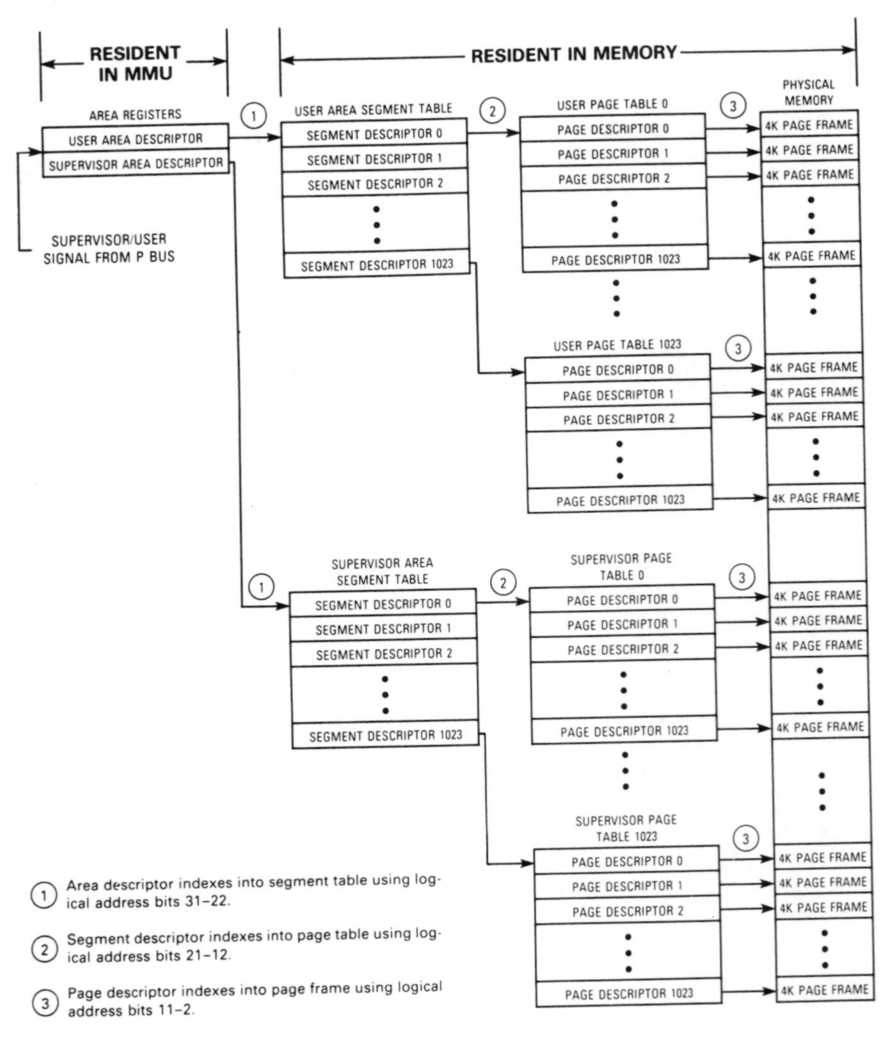

Figure 6.10 Translation Table Structure
(Reprinted with permission, courtesy of Motorola, Inc.)

associated LRU (Least Recently Used) information for line replacement [2.5]. A cache line contains 4 contiguous words from memory, loaded from quad-word aligned address (A3, A2, A1, A0 = 0). Each line has an associated address tag in the cache. The tag contains a 20-bit physical address that corresponds to the base address of a 4 KByte page in physical memory. There are also the following control bits associated with each line in the cache:

D, Disable Bit =	0	Line may be used
=	1	Line may not be used
VV, Valid Bits =	11	Invalid State
	10	Shared Unmodified State
	01	Exclusive Unmodified State
	00	Exclusive Modified State

The VV bits are particularly useful in implementing a cache coherency bus watching protocol in a multiprocessing configuration, and to support copy-back (see section 6.6).

The MC88200 bus signals are shown in Figure 6.11. The PBUS signals were discussed in section 6.3. The MBUS 32-bit data and address parts are multiplexed, forming the AD31-AD0 lines. There are 4 additional parity check lines ADP3-ADP0, each associated with a byte of the AD; ADP0 with AD7-AD0, and so on. There is also a Control Parity (CP) signal, which indicates the even parity of the MBUS control lines C6-C0. The Local Status signals ST3-ST0 indicate the MBUS status as follows (x means don't care):

Status	ST3	ST2	ST1	ST0
Error	1	x	x	x
Retry	0	1	x	x
Wait	0	0	1	x
End of Data	0	0	0	1
Phase completed successfully	0	0	0	0

The System Status signals SS3*-SS0* (* means low asserted) are generated by MBUS slaves in response to the MC88200 request and data phases. Their encoding is as follows:

Status	SS3*	SS2*	SS1*	SS0*
Error	0	x	x	x
Retry	1	0	x	x
Wait	1	1	0	x
End of Data	1	1	1	0
Phase completed successfully	1	1	1	1

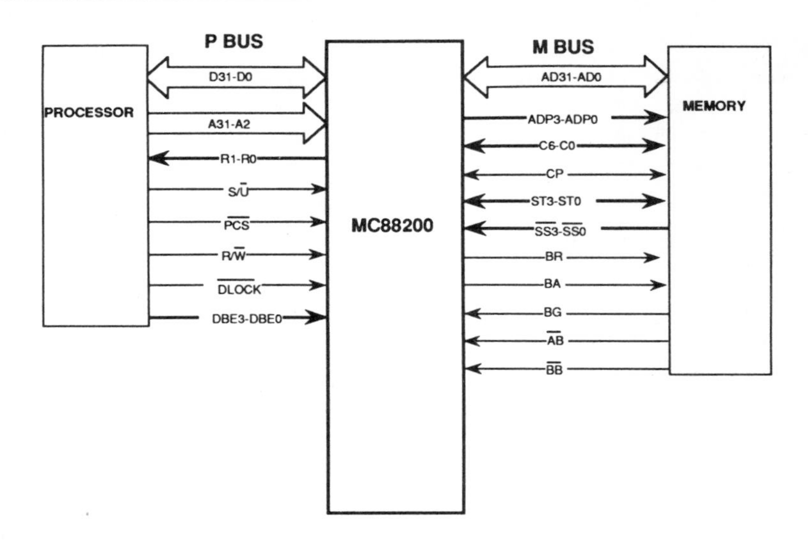

Function	Mnemonic	Type	Active	Count	Reset State
P BUS					
Address	A31–A2	Input	High	30	Ignored
Supervisor User	S $\overline{U}$	Input	High	1	Ignored
Chip Select	$\overline{PCS}$	Input	Low	1	Ignored
Data Byte Enable	DBE3–DBE0	Input	High	4	Ignored
Data	D31–D0	I O	High	32	High Imped
Read Write	R $\overline{W}$	Input	High	1	Ignored
Lock	$\overline{DLOCK}$	Input	Low	1	Ignored
Reply	R1–R0	Output	High	2	High Imped
00 — Reserved					
10 — Successful Transaction					
01 — Memory Wait					
11 — Transaction Fault					
M Bus					
Bus Request	BR	Output	High	1	Negated
Bus Grant	BG	Input	High	1	Ignored
Bus Acknowledge	BA	Output	High	1	Negated
Arbitration Busy	$\overline{AB}$	Input	Low	1	Ignored
Bus Busy	$\overline{BB}$	Input	Low	1	Ignored
Address Data	AD31–AD0	I O	High	32	High Imped
Address Data Parity	ADP3–ADP0	I O	High	4	High Imped
Control	C6–C0	I O	High	7	High Imped
Control Parity	CP	I O	High	1	High Imped
Local Status	ST3–ST0	I O	High	4	Active Input
System Status	$\overline{SS3}$–$\overline{SS0}$	I O	Low	4	Ignored

Figure 6.11 MC88200 Bus Signals
(Reprinted with permission, courtesy of Motorola, Inc.)

There are 5 bus arbitration signals:

BR Bus Request, asserted by the MC88200 to request bus ownership,

BA Bus Acknowledge, asserted by the MC88200 when it has been granted the bus in response to a bus request,

BG Bus Grant, generated by external arbitration logic, granting bus ownership to the MC88200,

AB* Arbitration Busy, indicates that one or more MBUS devices are performing a bus request. May prevent the MC88200 from issuing a BR.

BB* Bus Busy, indicates that some MBUS device is currently the bus master.

6.6 Diagnostic and Multiprocessing Configurations

The M88000 system can be configured in an automatic Fault-Detection MBUS Shadowing configuration, using an extra set of checker components, as shown

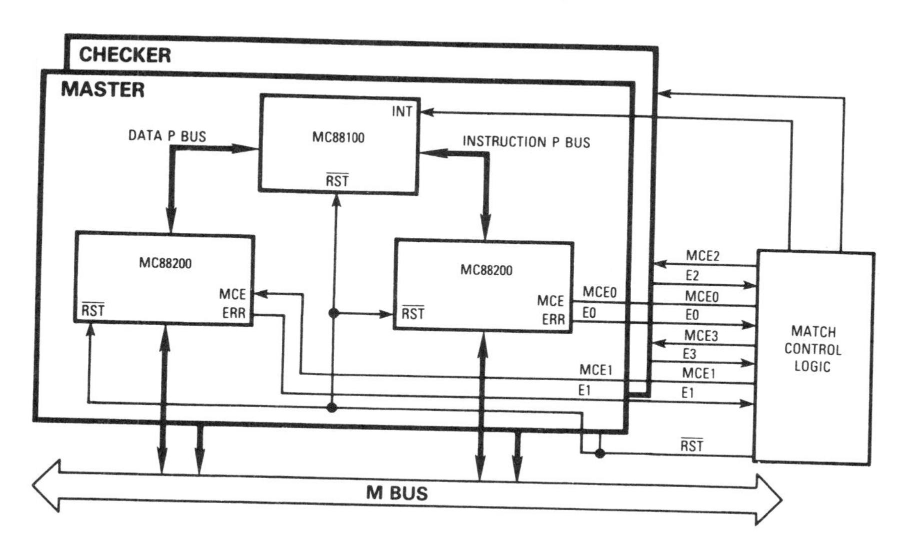

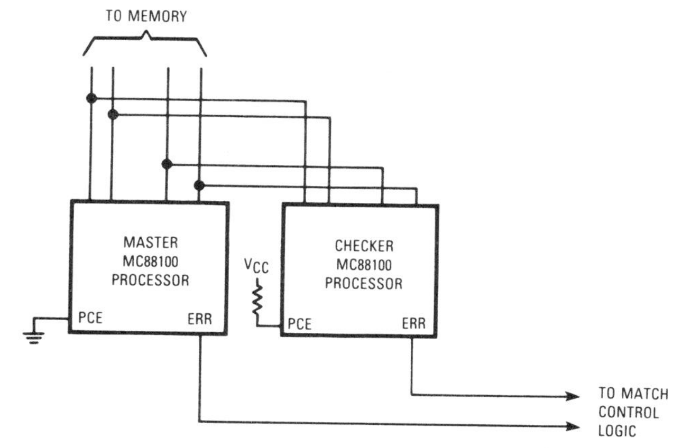

Figure 6.12 Basic Master/Checker Configuration
(Reprinted with permission, courtesy of Motorola, Inc.)

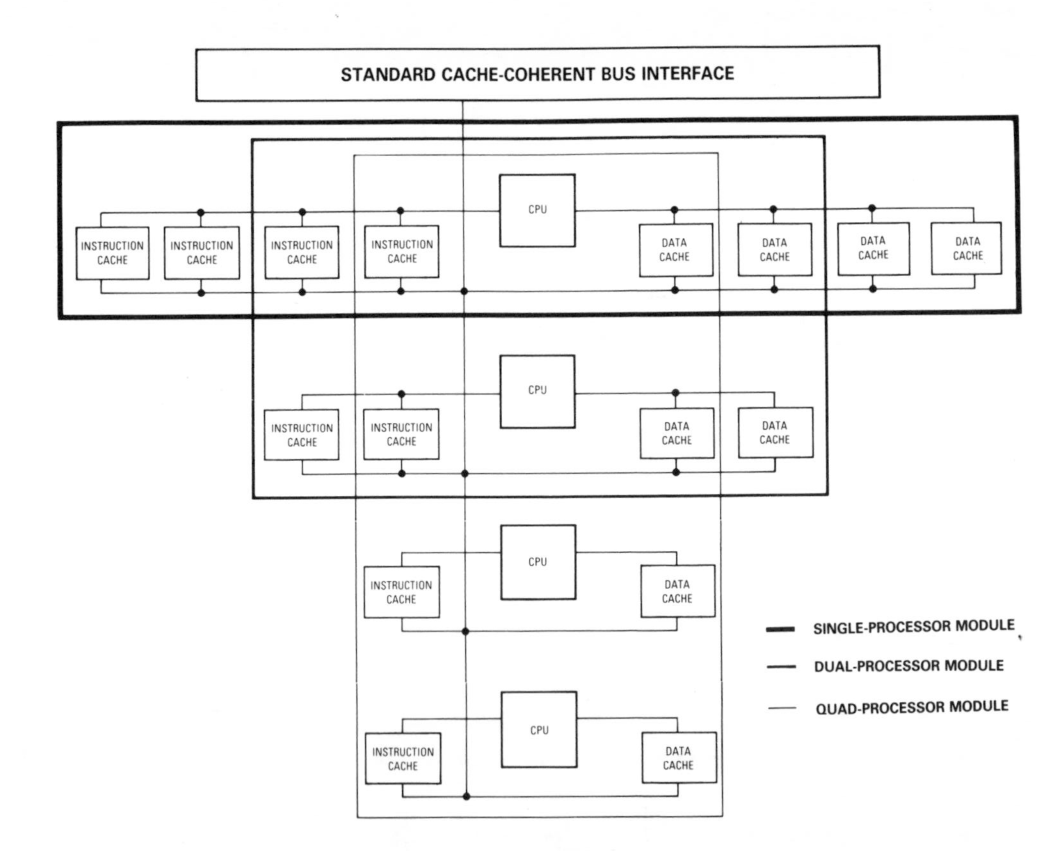

Figure 6.13 The HYPERmodule
(Reprinted with permission, courtesy of Motorola, Inc.)

in Figure 6.12. Every output signal on the MC88100 and the MC88200 has a comparator circuit to check that the signal on the output pin is the same as the input signal to the driver. An ERR (error detect) signal is asserted when any of the circuits finds a mismatch. ERR is valid one half clock after the mismatch occurs. Each bus on the MC88200 has a checker mode input that disables the device from driving output signals. The above properties allow the configuration shown in Figure 6.12 in which the active (master) component is coupled to one or more checker components (within the broken line limits). The checker components have access to the input code and data stream, and execute concurrently in lock step to compare output results. Checker components check every output signal but do not drive the signals. If the checker component detects a difference between the master component's results and its own results, it asserts the ERR signal to indicate that an error has been detected.

There is a multiprocessor, consisting of up to 4 MC88100 CPUs and up to 8 MC88200 CMMUs, called HYPERmodule. Its block diagram is shown in Figure 6.13. Its expected performance at 20 MHz is up to 50 MIPS, 20 MFLOPS or 100,000 Dhrystones. The MC88200 provides the capability to monitor the MBUS cache coherency in a multiprocessing environment. When the MC88200 is not the bus master, it monitors all global transactions of other bus masters to ensure that cached data remains consistent with main memory. When a device, connected to the MBUS, accesses information that is resident in the MC88200 cache, the MC88200 preempts the access and updates its cache and main memory as appropriate to ensure data consistency.

References

6.1 C. Melear, 'The Design of the 88000 RISC Family', *IEEE MICRO*, **9**, No. 2, pp. 26–38, April 1989.
6.2 MC88100 RISC Microprocessor User's Manual, MC88100UM/AD Motorola, Inc., 1988.
6.3 MC88200 Cache/Memory Management Unit (CMMU) User's Manual, MC88200UM/AD, Motorola, Inc., 1988.
6.4 J.H. Wharton, 'Architecture vs. Implementation in RISC Wars', *Microprocessor Report*, pp. 14–15, 1988.
6.5 G. Grey, 'The 88000 Faces of Multibus II', *ESD*, Sept. 1988, pp. 45–50.
6.6 R. Wilson, 'Motorola Unveils New RISC Microprocessor Flagship', *Computer Design*, May 1, 1988, pp. 21–24.
6.7 H. Falk, '88000 Designed for Use with Optimizing Compilers', *Computer Design*, May 1, 1988, pp. 30–32.

7

The Sun SPARC

7.1 General Description

The architecture of the Sun SPARC is not connected to any specific hardware realization. As a matter of fact, there are at least five chip manufacturers, producing different products, which implement the SPARC architecture. The SPARC stands for Scalable Processor Architecture [7.1–7.6]. The concept of 'scalability', as seen by the SPARC creators, is the wide spectrum of its possible price/performance implementations, ranging from microcomputers to supercomputers [7.1]. The scalability of the SPARC can also be interpreted in the amount of CPU registers that can be used in various versions of products, implementing the SPARC architecture. This is different from the M88000 (chapter 6) where the scalability could be viewed in adding Special Function Units (SFUs) on different future versions of the M88000 processor.

The Sun SPARC follows the Berkeley RISC design philosophy by its stressing the importance of the CPU register file and by implementing similar register window features.

The SPARC processor is subdivided into two basic units:

1. *Integer Unit* (IU), which performs the basic processing and integer arithmetic.
2. *Floating Point Unit* (FPU), which performs floating point calculations concurrently with the IU.

A block diagram of the IU is shown in Figure 7.1. There are two separate internal 32-bit buses: Address and Instruction/Data.

The IU Control/Status registers are:

(1) Program Counter, PC, contains the address of the instruction currently executed by the IU.
(2) Next PC, nPC, contains the address of the next instruction to be executed by the IU (assuming no trap).
(3) Processor State Register, PSR, contains the encoding of the processor status, including the condition code flags and the five-bit Current Window Pointer (CWP).
(4) Window Invalid Mask. WIM, composed of 32 bits wi(i=0, 1, . . . , 31), corresponding to a window. If wi=1, window i is considered to be invalid, and a trap condition exists.

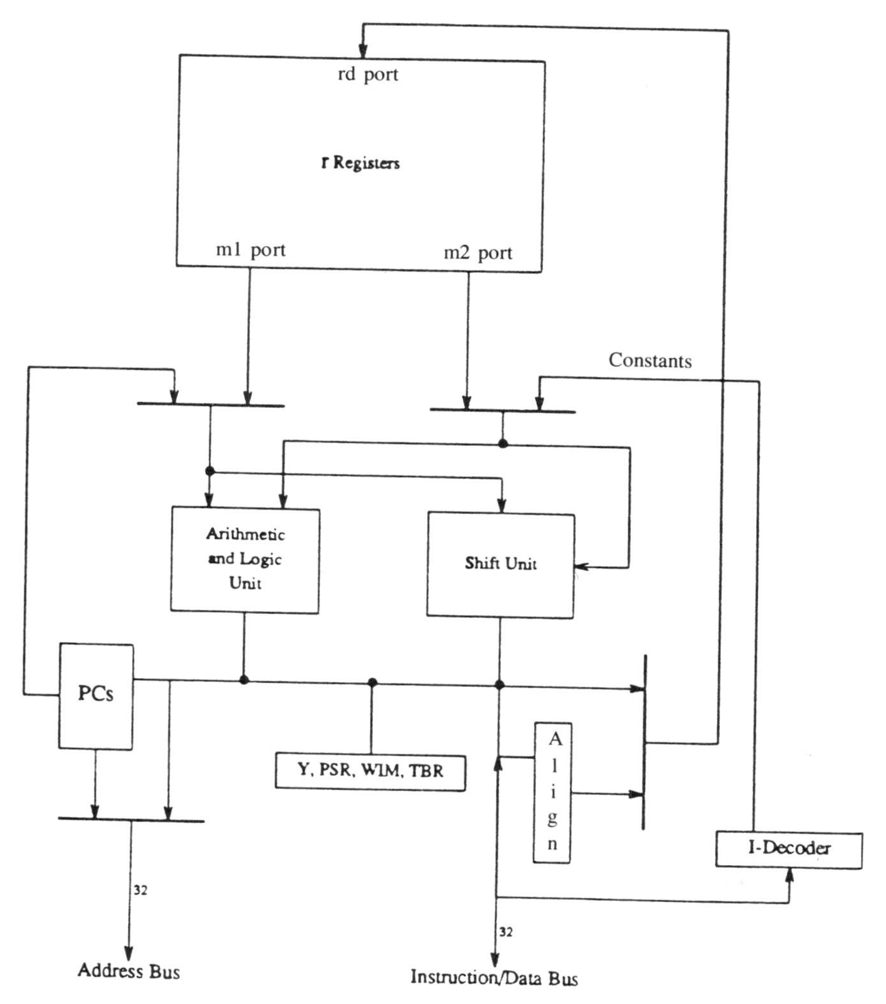

Figure 7.1 Integer Unit Block Diagram
(*© Copyright Sun Microsystems, Inc. 1987*)

(5) Trap Base Register, TBR, serves as a pointer to a trap handler. Includes the trap type encoding.
(6) Y Register, used to create 64-bit products in multiply step instructions.

7.2 SPARC Architecture

Each procedure, running on the SPARC, can use a total of 32 32-bit IU registers, r0–r31,

8 Global Registers
24 Window Registers

subdivided as follows (Figure 7.2):

r24–r31	ins
r16–r23	locals
r8–r15	outs
r0–r7	globals

As in the Berkeley RISC (chapter 3) the calling procedure passes parameters to the called procedure through its outs (r8–r15) registers, which are the ins registers of the called procedure. The window of the currently running procedure, called the Active Window, is pointed to by the CWP field in the PSR.

The number of windows (NWINDOWS) implementable on different versions of the SPARC, ranges from 2 to 32, for a total number of general purpose IU

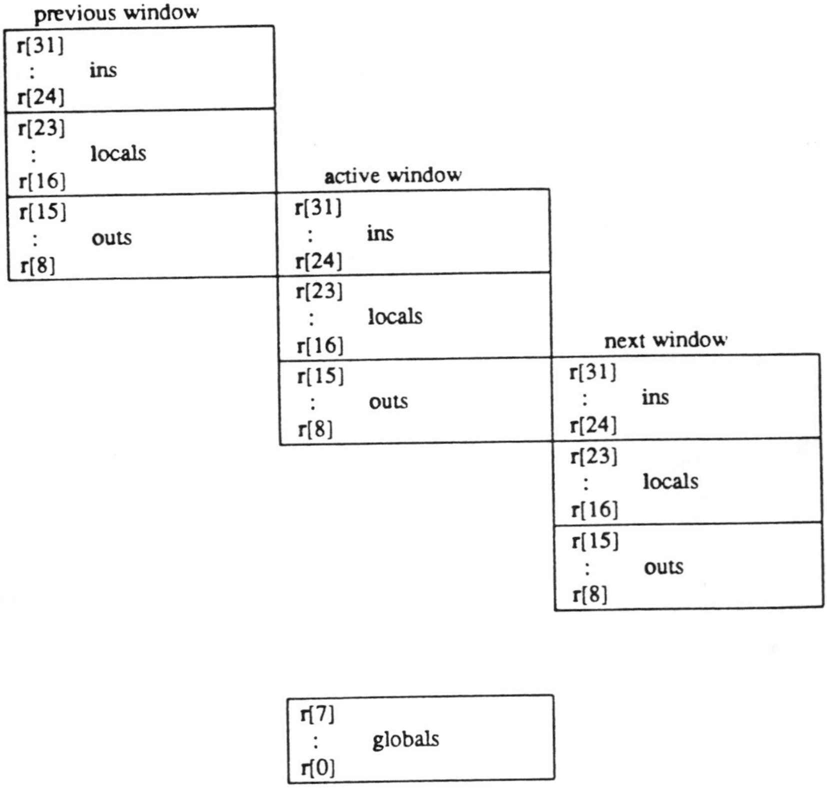

previous window
r[31] : r[24] ins
r[23] : r[16] locals
r[15] : r[8] outs

active window
r[31] : r[24] ins
r[23] : r[16] locals
r[15] : r[8] outs

next window
r[31] : r[24] ins
r[23] : r[16] locals
r[15] : r[8] outs

r[7] : r[0] globals

Figure 7.2 Three Overlapping Windows and Globals
(*© Copyright Sun Microsystems, Inc. 1987*)

registers (including globals) ranging from 48 to 548, respectively. Implemented windows are contiguously numbered 0 to NWINDOWS-1. An example of an 8-window implementation, where the windows are circularly interconnected, is shown in Figure 7.3.

Some of the SPARC IU registers have specially designated tasks. The r0 is hardwired to zero, as in the Berkeley RISC and the Motorola M88000. A CALL instruction writes its own address into the out register r15. The CWP is decremented with a SAVE instruction on a procedure call, and incremented by a RESTORE instruction on a procedure return. Procedures can also be called without changing the window.

Suppose that in the case of NWINDOWS=8 (Figure 7.3), window 0 is the currently running Active Window. In this case CWP=0. Since window 0 is the

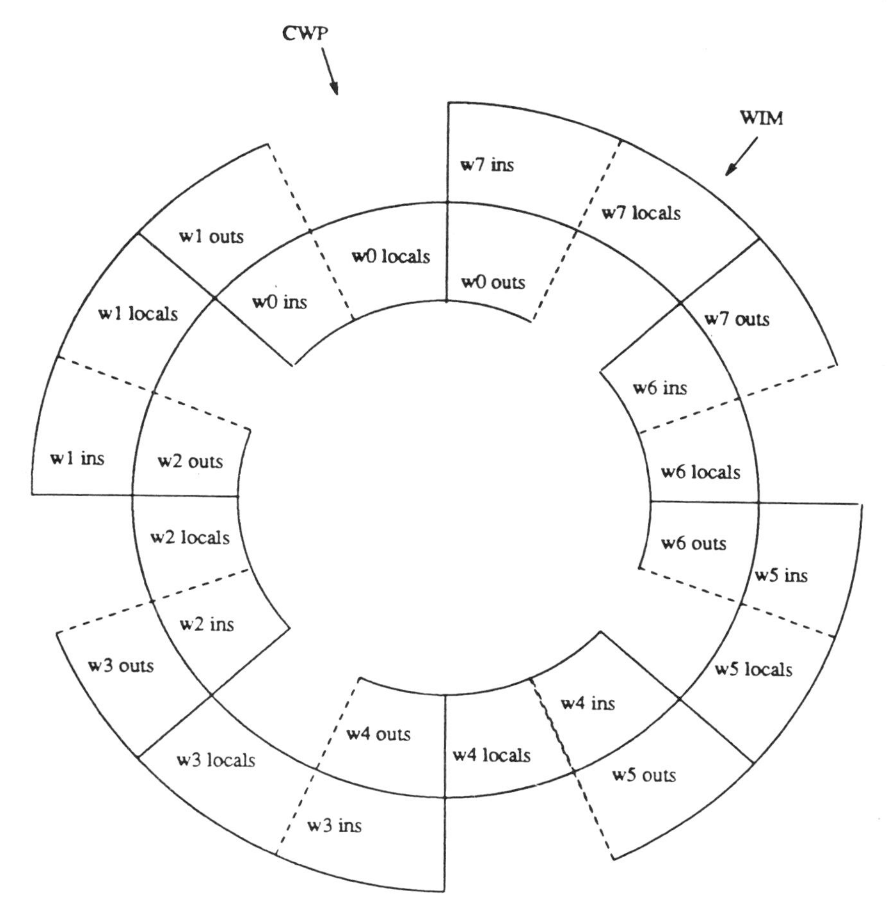

Figure 7.3 Circular Stack of Window Registers
(© *Copyright Sun Microsystems, Inc. 1987*)

last free window when the procedure, using window 0, calls another procedure, a window *overflow* occurs. A new register window wraps around to overwrite the previously used window 7, whose contents must be saved in the memory by software. After a return, and when the register file is out of windows, we have a window *underflow*. Software must restore previously used register windows in this case. A window overflow trap is caused by the overflow. The overflow trap handler uses the locals of window 7 for pointers into the memory where the overflowed window is stored. Window 7 is invalidated during the trap handling by setting bit 7 of the WIM register.

The SPARC FPU architecture features 32 32-bit Floating Point registers f0 to f31. They can contain 32 single precision or 16 double precision or 8 extended quad-precision floating point operands. Double precision operands are stored so that the most significant exponent (Figure 7.4) is in an even-numbered f register, followed by the f-part (mantissa) in the next odd-numbered register. There is a 32-bit Floating-point Status Register, FSR, containing FPU mode and status information. There is also a Floating-point Queue, FQ, consisting of one or more (scalable) 64-bit instruction/address pairs. It keeps track of floating point operations that are pending completion. If an implementation provides n entries in the FQ, at most n floating point operations can execute simultaneously in the FPU. For example, if the FPU has one adder and one multipler that can operate independently, then the FQ has no fewer than n=2 entries.

The SPARC architecture has a total of 69 basic instructions, 14 of which are for floating point operations. The instruction categories are:

1. Load/Store.
2. Arithmetic/Logical/Shift.
3. Control Transfer.
4. Read/Write Control Registers.
5. Floating Point Operate.
6. Coprocessor Operate.

The SPARC instructions are summarized in Table 7.1.

The SPARC architecture recognizes the following data types, shown in Figure 7.4:

Integer –		
Signed, unsigned byte	8 bits	
Signed, unsigned half-word	16 bits	
Signed, unsigned word	32 bits	
Doubleword	64 bits	
Floating Point – IEEE Standard		
Single precision	32 bits	
Double precision	64 bits	
Extended precision (nonIEEE)	exponent	15 bits
	mantissa	63 bits

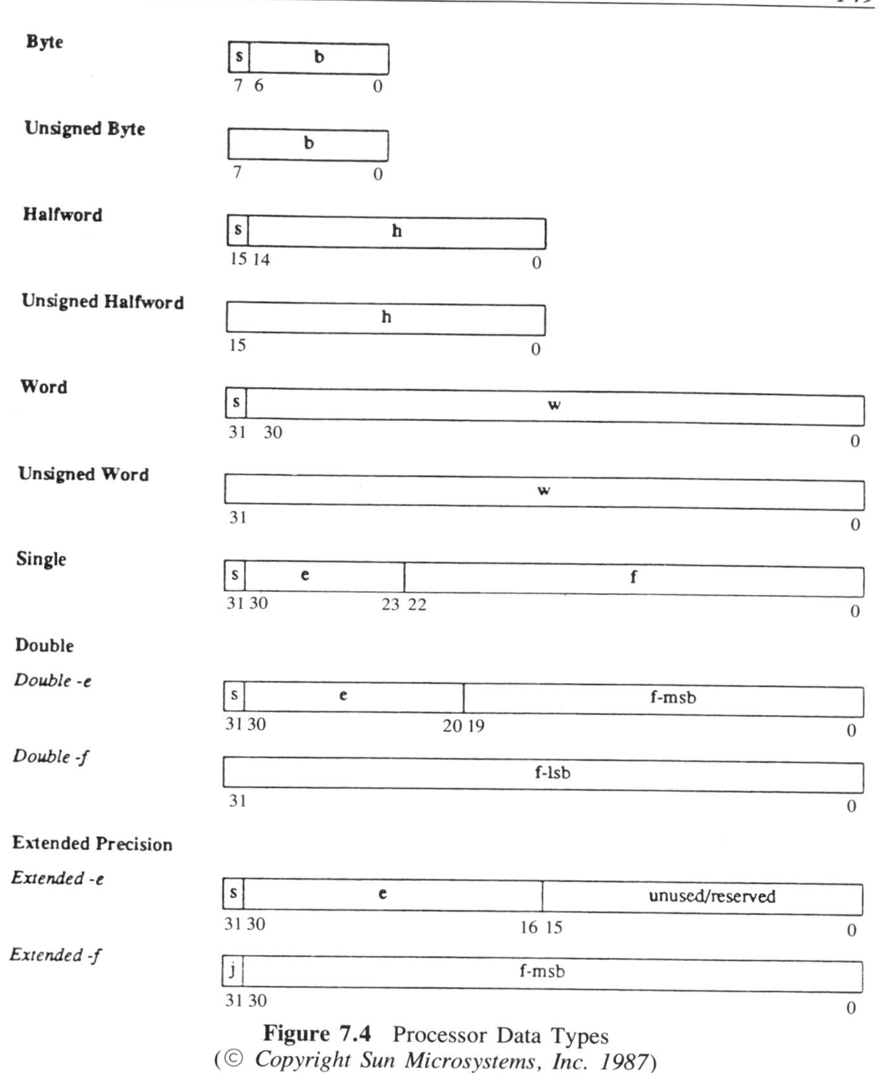

Figure 7.4 Processor Data Types
(© *Copyright Sun Microsystems, Inc. 1987*)

The half-words are aligned on 2 Byte address boundaries, words on 4 Byte boundaries, and doublewords on 8 Byte boundaries (Figure 7.5).

The SPARC architecture recognizes three basic instruction formats, shown in Figure 7.6. As one can see, it implements three-operand addressing, and all formats are of a single word length (32 bits).

The fields in the instructions have the following meaning:

op (bits 31, 30) – Format Field. There are three major formats:

Table 7.1 SPARC Instruction Set
(*© Copyright Sun Microsystems, Inc. 1987*)

Opcode	*Name*
LDSB (LDSBA†)	Load Signed Byte (from Alternate space)
LDSH (LDSHA†)	Load Signed Halfword (from Alternate space)
LDUB (LDUBA†)	Load Unsigned Byte (from Alternate space)
LDUH (LDUHA†)	Load Unsigned Halfword (from Alternate space)
LD (LDA†)	Load Word (from Alternate space)
LDD (LDDA)†	Load Doubleword (from Alternate space)
LDF	Load Floating-point
LDDF	Load Double Floating-point
LDFSR	Load Floating-point State Register
LDC	Load Coprocessor
LDDC	Load Double Coprocessor
LDCSR	Load Coprocessor State Register
STB (STBA†)	Store Byte (into Alternate space)
STH (STHA†)	Store Halfword (into Alternate space)
ST (STA†)	Store Word (into Alternate space)
STD (STDA†)	Store Doubleword (into Alternate space)
STF	Store Floating-point
STDF	Store Double Floating-point
STFSR	Store Floating-point State Register
STDFQ†	Store Double Floating-point Queue
STC	Store Coprocessor
STDC	Store Double Coprocessor
STCSR	Store Coprocessor State Register
STDCQ†	Store Double Coprocessor Queue
LDSTUB (LDSTUBA†)	Atomic Load-Store Unsigned Byte (in Alternate space)
SWAP (SWAPA†)	Swap r Register with Memory (in Alternate space)
ADD (ADDcc)	Add (and modify icc)
ADDX (ADDXcc)	Add with Carry (and modify icc)
TADDcc (TADDccTV)	Tagged Add and modify icc (and Trap on overflow)
SUB (SUBcc)	Subtract (and modify icc)
SUBX (SUBXcc)	Subtract with Carry (and modify icc)
TSUBcc (TSUBccTV)	Tagged Subtract and modify icc (and Trap on overflow)
MULScc	Multiply Step and modify icc
AND (ANDcc)	And (and modify icc)
ANDN (ANDNcc)	And Not (and modify icc)
OR (ORcc)	Inclusive-Or (and modify icc)
ORN (ORNcc)	Inclusive-Or Not (and modify icc)
XOR (XORcc)	Exclusive-Or (and modify icc)
XNOR (XNORcc)	Exclusive-Nor (and modify icc)
SLL	Shift Left Logical
SRL	Shift Right Logical
SRA	Shift Right Arithmetic
SETHI	Set High 22 bits of *r register*
SAVE	Save caller's window
RESTORE	Restore caller's window
Bicc	Branch on integer condition codes
FBfcc	Branch on floating-point condition codes
CBccc	Branch on coprocessor condition codes
CALL	Call
JMPL	Jump and Link
RETT†	Return from Trap
Ticc	Trap on integer condition codes

Table 7.1 *(cont'd)*

Opcode	*Name*
RDY	Read Y register
RDPSR†	Read Processor State Register
RDWIM†	Read Window Invalid Mask register
RDTBR†	Read Trap Base Register
WRY	Write Y register
WRPSR†	Write Processor State Register
WRWIM†	Write Window Invalid Mask register
WRTBR†	Write Trap Base Register
UNIMP	Unimplemented instruction
IFLUSH	Instruction cache Flush
FPop	Floating-point Operate: FiTO(s,d,x), F(s,d,x)TOi FsTOd, FsTOx, FdTOs, FdTOx, FxTOs, FxTOd, FMOVs, FNEGs, FABSs, FSQRT(s,d,x), FADD(s,d,x), FSUB(s,d,x), FMUL(s,d,x), FDIV(s,d,x), FCMP(s,d,x), FCMPE(s,d,x)
CPop	Coprocessor operate

† privileged instruction

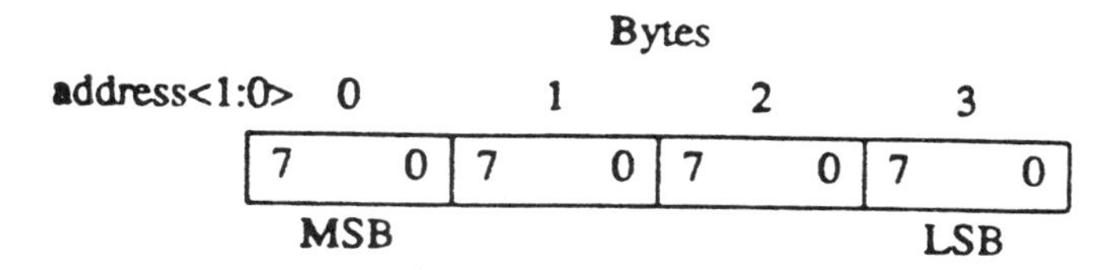

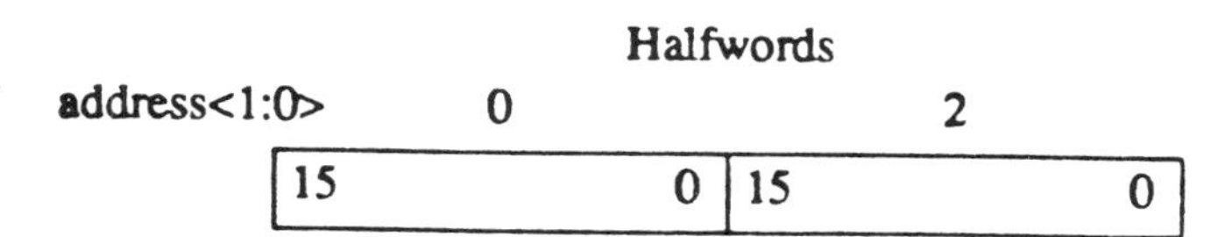

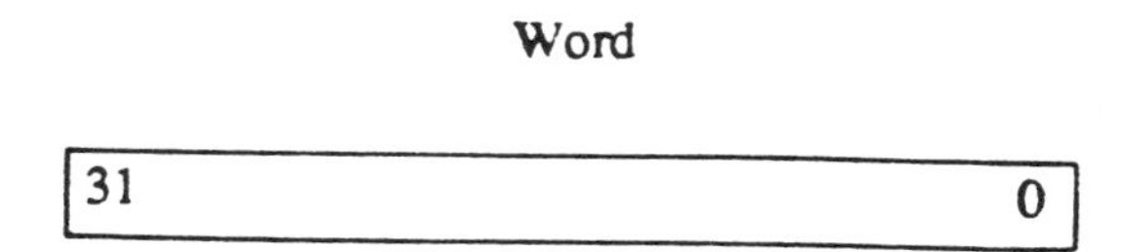

Doubleword

address<2>

0	63	32
1	31	0

Figure 7.5 Address Conventions
(© *Copyright Sun Microsystems, Inc. 1987*)

Format 1: CALL

op	disp30
31	29 … 0

Format 2: SETHI and Branches (Bicc, FBfcc, CBcc)

op	rd		op2	imm22
op	a	cond	op2	disp22
31	29	28	24	21 … 0

Format 3: Remaining instructions

op	rd	op3	rs1	i	asi	rs2
op	rd	op3	rs1	i	simm13	
op	rd	op3	rs1	opf		rs2
31	29	24	18	13	12	4 … 0

Figure 7.6 SPARC Instruction Formats
(*© Copyright Sun Microsystems, Inc. 1987*)

	op	Instruction
(1)	01	Call
(2)	00	Bicc, FBfcc, CBccc, SETHI
(3)	10 or 11	all other instructions

op2 (bits 24-22, Format 2) – selects the instruction as follows:

op2	Instruction
000	UNIMP
010	Bicc
100	SETHI
110	Fbfcc
111	CBccc

rd (bits 29-25) – selects the source register for store instructions and the destination register for all other instructions.

a (bit 29) – annul bit. Changes the behavior of the instruction encountered immediately after a control transfer.

cond (bits 28-25) – selects the condition code for format 2 instructions.

imm22 (bits 21-0) – a 22-bit constant value used by the SETHI instruction.

disp22 (bits 21-0) – a 22-bit sign-extended word displacement for branch instructions.

disp30 (bits 29-0) – a 30-bit sign-extended word displacement for PC-relative call instructions.

op3 (bits 24-19) – selects one of the format 3 opcodes.

i (bit 13) – selects the type of the second ALU operand for non-floating-point operation instructions.

i=0: the second operand is in a register, rs2,

i=1: the second operand is sign-extended simm13.

asi (bits 12-5) – 8-bit address space identifier generated by load/store alternate instructions.

rs1 (bits 18-14) – selects the first source operand from either the r or the f registers.

rs2 (bits 4-0) – selects the second source operand from either the r or the f registers.

simm13 (bits 12-0) – a sign-extended 13-bit immediate value used as the second ALU operand when i=1.

opf (bits 13-5) – identifies a floating-point operate (FPop) or a coprocessor operate (CPop) instruction.

The load and store instructions (the only ones to access memory) generate a 32-bit byte address. In addition to the address, the processor always generates an address space identifier (9-bit asi), interpreted as follows:

asi (decimal)	assignment
0–7	Implementation-definable
8	User instruction space
9	Supervisor instruction space
10	User data space
11	Supervisor data space
12–255	Implementation-definable

EXAMPLES:

LDSB addr, rd; load signed byte from memory at address addr into register rd.
LD addr, rd; load word into rd.

There are 2 Load/Store memory Addressing Modes:

1. register 1 + register 2
2. register + signed 13-bit constant

Most of the arithmetic-logical instructions have dual versions (such as ADD and ADDcc) which modify the integer condition codes (icc) as a side effect.

EXAMPLES:

ADD rs1, rs2, rd; (rs1) + (rs2) → rd, no icc modification.
ADDcc rs1, rs2, rd; (rs1) + (rs2) → rd, icc modified.

The SETHI (set high 22 bits of rd) instruction writes a 22-bit constant from the instruction into the high-order bits of the destination register rd. It clears the low-order 10 bits, and does not change the condition codes. It can be used to construct a 32-bit constant using two instructions. It is used in the following form (format 2):

SETHI const22, rd

There are five types of control transfer instructions:

(1) Conditional branch (Bicc, FBfcc, CBccc)
(2) Jump and Link (JMPL)
(3) Call (CALL)
(4) Trap (Ticc)
(5) Return from trap (RETT)

Each of the above can be further categorized according to whether it is:

(a) PC-relative or register-indirect,
(b) delayed or non-delayed.

A *PC-relative* control transfer computes its target address by adding the (shifted) sign-extended immediate displacement to the program counter (PC). A register indirect instruction computes the target address according to one of the memory addressing modes listed earlier.

A control transfer instruction is *delayed* if it transfers control to the target address after a one-instruction delay. This is basically the delayed branch feature described in chapter 1.

The a (annul) bit changes the behavior of the delay instruction. This bit is only available on conditional branch instructions (Bicc, FBfcc and CBccc). If a=1 on a conditional branch (except BA, FBA and CBA) and the branch is not taken, the delay instruction is annulled (not executed). If the branch is taken, the a bit is ignored and the delay instruction is executed. BA, FBA and CBA instructions are a special case; if a=1 in these instructions the delay instruction is not executed if the branch is taken, but it is executed if the branch is not taken.

The effect of the a bit can be summarized as follows:

a	type of branch	delay instruction executed?
1	Unconditional	No
	Conditional, taken	Yes
	Conditional, not taken	No
0	Unconditional	Yes
	Conditional, taken	Yes
	Conditional, not taken	Yes

A procedure that requires a register window is invoked by executing both a CALL (or JMPL) and a SAVE instruction. A procedure that does not need a register window, a so-called *leaf routine*, is invoked by executing only a CALL (or a JMPL). Leaf routines can use only the *out* registers.

The CALL instruction stores PC, which points to the CALL itself, into register r15 (an *out* register). JMPL (Jump and Link) stores PC, which points to the JMPL instruction into the specified r register (EXAMPLE: JMPL addr, rd).

The SAVE instruction is similar to an ADD instruction, except that it also decrements the CWP by one, causing the active window to become the previous window, thereby saving the caller's window.

EXAMPLE: SAVE rs1, rs2, rd;
The operands rs1 and rs2 are from the previous (old) window and the destination rd is in the new window, addressed by the new CWP.

A procedure that uses a register window returns by executing both a RESTORE and a JMPL instruction. A leaf procedure returns by executing a JMPL only. The RESTORE instruction (also similar to an ADD) increments the CWP by one, causing the previous window to become the active window, thereby restoring the caller's window. Also, the source registers for the addition are from the current window while the result is written into the previous window. Both SAVE and RESTORE compare the new CWP against the WIM to check for window overflow or underflow.

The SPARC architecture features the following multiprocessor operation support instructions:

swap – exchanges the contents of an IU register with a word from memory, while preventing other memory accesses from intervening.
ldstub – (atomic load and store unsigned byte) reads a byte from memory into an IU register and then rewrites the same byte in memory to all 1's, while precluding intervening accesses. Can be used to construct *semaphores*.

7.3 SPARC Realization

At the moment there are five major SPARC licensed manufacturers that, according to Sun Microsystems, Inc., are either producing SPARC compatible chips or will produce chips in the near future [7.7]. A non-profit organization, called SPARC International, was formed by Sun Microsystems, Inc. in 1988. It includes Sun Microsystems and other companies interested in the development and applications of the SPARC. One of its main goals is to control the direction of evolution of the SPARC. The main SPARC manufacturers are:

1. Fujitsu Microelectronics, Inc., MB86900, 1.5 micron CMOS, 20,000 gate logic-array technology, 10 MIPS integer processor, 1.1 MFLOP DP LINPACK FPU. MB86901, 1.2 micron CMOS, 15 MIPS integer, 2.7 MFLOP DP LINPACK FPU.
2. Cypress Semiconductor, CY7C601, 0.8 micron full custom CMOS IV, 24 MIPS integer processor, 4.5 MFLOP DP LINPACK FPU.
3. Bipolar Integrated Technology, Inc. (BIT), VLSI-density ECL Technology, 50 MIPS integer processor, 15 MFLOP DP LINPACK FPU.
4. LSI Logic Corp., 1.0 micron semicustom CMOS, 20 MIPS integer processor, 3 MFLOP DP LINPACK FPU.

5. TI, 0.8 micron full custom CMOS, 24 MIPS IU, 4.2 MFLOPS DP LINPACK FPU.

The performance of the above, compared to the VAX 11/780, in units of MIPS, is summarized in Table 7.2. All of the above implement the floating point unit on a separate coprocessor chip or chips. The Fujitsu and the BIT implement 7 windows, and Cypress, 8 windows in the IU.

The Fujitsu MB86900 is a 16.67 MHz Integer Unit (IU) chip interconnecting to a companion chip MB86910 Floating Point Controller (FPC). The FPC provides a tightly coupled interface to the Weitek W1164 multiplier and W1165 ALU for a peak performance of 2.6 MFLOPS for single, and 1.5 MFLOPS for double precision arithmetic, on Linpack benchmarks. Floating point operations can occur concurrently with instructions executed on the MB86900 IU. Sun software tools (licensed to Fujitsu) included Optimizing C, Pascal and FORTRAN compilers, software simulator and assembler, running on Sun workstations under Unix.

A recently announced top Fujitsu SPARC Architecture product is the S-25 or MB86901 IU, CMOS, 179 pin, 25 MHz chip. The MB86901 can interconnect directly with the following auxiliary new chips:

MB86911 Floating Point Controller (FPC), 25 MHz, interfacing directly to the Texas Instruments (TI) Floating Point Processor (FPP) SN74ACT 8847, operating at 3.3 MFLOPS, single precision, and 2.7 MFLOPS, double precision.

MB86920 Memory Management Unit (MMU), 25 MHz. Supports three-level page tables management for 4 KBytes pages. Includes a fully associative 64-entry page descriptor cache and LRU (Least Recently Used) logic for replacement management of an external cache memory.

Fujitsu offers an MB86901-based EBO1 evaluation VME 25 MHz board set. It includes the MB86920 MMU and may optionally include the MB86911 FPC with the TI8847 FPP. It also includes a 128 KByte direct-mapped cache (32 byte line size), 4K × 20 bit Tag RAM, up to 256 KByte EPROM and 2 KByte EEPROM.

The BIT IU features a five-stage pipeline and a 72-line Data In bus, in addition to the separate 32-bit Address and Data Out buses. Additional BIT products include:

Table 7.2 Performance Comparison of SPARC Chips Expressed in VAX 11/780 MIPS

Chip	Technology	CPU Frequency, MHz	Speed, MIPS
Fujitsu, MB86900	CMOS (1.5m)	16.67	10
Fujitsu, MB86901	CMOS (1.2m)	25	15
Cypress	CMOS (0.8m)	33	24
LSI Logic	HCMOS (1.0m)	33	20
BIT	ECL	80	50
TI	CMOS (0.8m)	33	24

B3120/B2120 Floating Point ALU
B3110/B2110 Floating Point Multiplier/Divider/Square Root; providing non-pipelined peak throughput of 60 MFLOPS for the chip set
64 × 18 five port register file
16 × 16 multiplier
16 × 16 multiplier-accumulator.

The BIT IU interconnects to a 128 KByte Direct-Mapped Virtual Address Cache, which supplies information to the IU through the 72-line Data In bus. Operating System (OS) support is provided with SunOS [7.2] with compilers supported by Sun.

Cypress Semiconductors produces a set of SPARC family chips through its Ross Technology, Inc. subsidiary. The following chips are featured [7.8, 7.9]:

CY7C601	SPARC Architecture CPU
CY7C602	Floating Point Unit (FPU)
CY7C604	Cache Controller and Memory Management Unit (MMU)
CY7C605	Multiprocessor Cache Controller and MMU
CY7C608	Floating Point Controller (FPC)
CY7C609	Floating Point Processor (FPP)
CY7C157	16K × 16 Static Cache RAM (CRAM), 20 ns access

The 601 is a 0.8 micron CMOS, 207 pin grid array package, 33 MHz chip. Its pinout and internal data flow block diagram are shown in Figure 7.7. The 601 features a 4-stage instruction pipeline. Its performance is 24 VAX MIPS with a 150 ns interrupt response. It has 136 general purpose 32-bit CPU registers. Its peak power consumption is 3.3 Watts.

The 602 (equivalent to the TI 8848 FPU) combines the functions of the 608 FPC and the 609 FPP (equivalent to TI 8847 FPU), that is, it contains a floating point processing unit and a floating point unit controller on the same chip. A pinout and a block diagram of the 602 are shown in Figure 7.8. The 602 FPU can be interconnected directly to the 601 CPU without any 'glue logic' (external directly connected logic). The 602 has a three-deep floating point queue which stores both instructions and addresses. The 602 meets the IEEE 754-1985 Standard for single and double precision formats. The 602 has a 32 × 32 floating point register file. Its performance is 4.2 double precision LINPACK MFLOPS. The chip is a 144 pin grid array package.

The 604, 0.8 micron CMOS chip comprises a Cache Tag and an MMU. It can be combined with two CY7C157 16K × 16 CRAMs to form a complete 64 KBytes direct-mapped cache, and like the 602, the 604 and 157 interface directly to the 601 without any glue logic. Cache size can be scaled up by using additional 604 and 157 chips. The cache line size is 32 bytes. Write through and copy back policies can be implemented. There are 2048 direct-mapped cache tag entries. The MMU part of the chip supports 4096 contexts. The virtual memory page size is 4 KBytes. There is an on-chip, 64-entry fully associative Translation

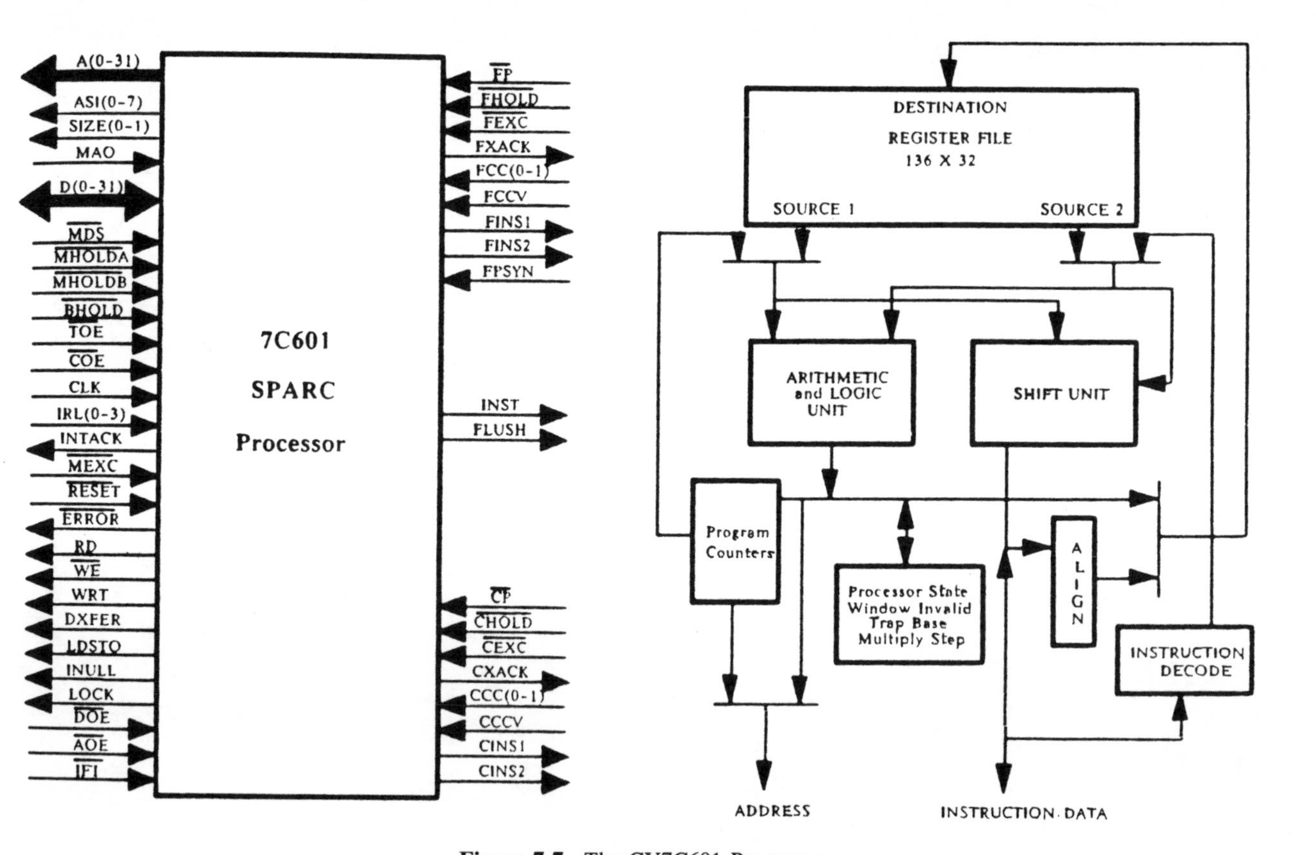

Figure 7.7 The CY7C601 Processor
(*Courtesy of Ross Technology, Inc.*)

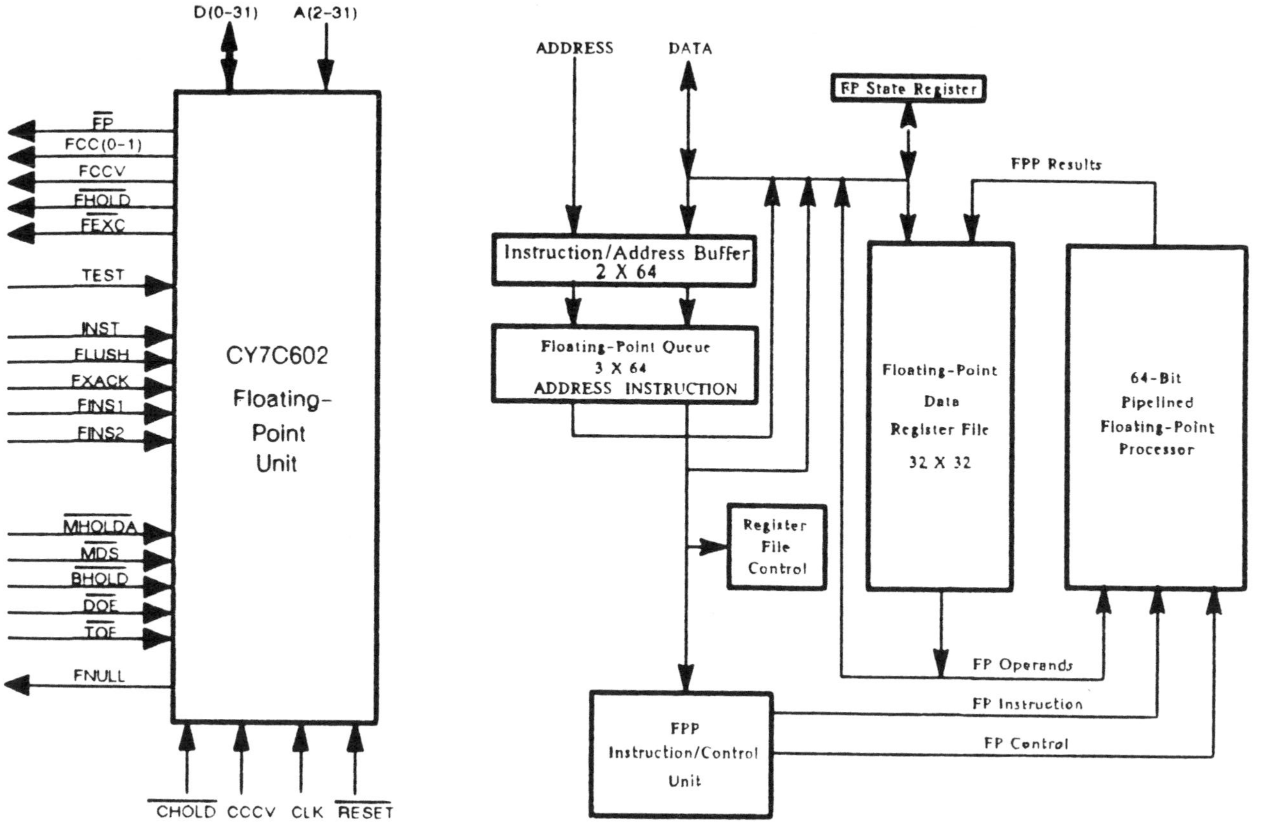

Figure 7.8 The CY7C602 Floating Point Unit
(*Courtesy of Ross Technology, Inc.*)

Lookaside Buffer (TLB) for fast virtual to physical address translation. The 604 chip can be in either a 243 pin grid array package or 207 quad flatback.

The 605 Multiprocessor Cache Controller and MMU is a superset of the 604 (same technology, pins and basic parameters). It includes, in addition to the 604 features, multiprocessor support and a dual cache tag set: 2048 virtual tags and 2048 physical tags. The 605 implements a special cache coherency protocol which uses the dual set of tags for bus snooping.

Both the 604 and the 605 offer cache entry and TLB entry locking. This capability is required in real-time applications where predictable response time is needed.

LSI Logic features the L64811 SPARC architecture CPU. The top product is a 1 micron, HCMOS, 33 MHz, 20 MIPS, 179 pin chip. Its integer performance is 38000 Dhrystones/sec. There is also a 25 MHz, 15 MIPS, L64801 CPU. The L64811 has 136 CPU registers and a 4-stage instruction pipeline. Designed by LSI Logic, this part is pin compatible with the CY7C601. There is also a Floating Point Unit (FPU) L64814 planned. At the moment there is a Floating Point Controller (FPC) L64812 which operates with the TI 8847 FPU. An MMU/Cache Controller L64815 will also be available.

Future SPARC implementations will include a 100 MIPS ECL version from Metaflow and a 250 MIPS GaAs version from Prisma [7.10]. Metaflow and Prisma are architecture licensees of the SPARC.

New 40 MHz floating-point coprocessors, designed to work with the SPARC IV, were recently announced by Weitek. They are the Abacus 3170, designed to work with the Fujitsu chips, and the Abacus 3171, designed to work with the Cypress family. Both chips integrate a floating-point data path and a floating point controller onto a CMOS, 143 pin chip. The data path contains a 64-bit multiplier, a 64-bit ALU, a 64-bit divide/square root unit and a 16 × 64-bit register file. The chips implement the IEEE 754-1985 Standard.

References

7.1 R.B. Garner, 'SPARC – Scalable RISC Architecture', *Sun Technology*, **1**, No. 3, pp. 42–55, Summer 1988.

7.2 S.R. Kleinman, D. Williams, 'Sun OS on SPARC', *Sun Technology*, **1**, No. 3, pp. 56–63, Summer 1988.

7.3 S.S. Munchnick, 'Optimizing Compilers for SPARC', *Sun Technology*, **1**, No. 3, pp. 64–77, Summer 1988.

7.4 The SPARC Architecture Manual, Version 7, Sun Microsystems, Inc., Part no. 800-1399-08, Rev. 8, Oct. 22, 1987.

7.5 J.A. Steinberg, 'RISCy Business', *Digital Review*, June 20, 1988, pp. 43–45.

7.6 D. Weaver, K. Ingram, M. Baron, 'A Software Bid for SPARC', *ESD*, Sept. 1988, pp. 109–112.

7.7 M. Namjoo, 'SPARC Implementations: ASIC vs. Custom Design', *Proc. 22nd Annual Hawaii Conf. on System Science, HICSS-22*, **1**, pp. 19–22, Jan. 1989.

7.8 *Cypress RISC Seminar Notebook*, Cypress Semiconductor, San Jose, CA.

7.9 M. Slater, 'SPARC Chip Looks for Fresh Cache', *ESD*, March 1989, p. 20.

7.10 R. Wilson, 'SPARC Wars Ignite in Rush to Sun's Architecture', *Computer Design*, Nov. 15, 1988, pp. 21–23.

8

The AMD 29000

The AMD 29000 (or Am29000) 32-Bit RISC Processor is a 1.2 micron CMOS, 169 pins chip [8.1–8.6]. It can achieve a sustained performance of 17 MIPS at 20 MHz and 20 MIPS at 30 MHz. The processor is organized as a 4-stage pipeline: Fetch, Decode, Execute, Write-Back. Pipeline interlocks are implemented by hardware. The chip has three non-multiplexed, 32-bit buses interconnecting to it, as illustrated in Figure 8.1:

1. Data, bidirectional to and from Data Memory and interfaces.
2. Address, going out to all memories and interfaces.
3. Instruction, coming in from Instruction Memory.

The overall bus bandwidth is 240 MBytes/sec. As one can see, the Am29000 implements the Harvard Architecture, using separate Instruction and Data Memories (not just separate caches). However, a data and an instruction cache can be placed within the blocks in Figure 8.1. The Am29000 does not implement floating point; it is implemented on a separate Am29027 Arithmetic Accelerator chip. In the future Am29090 product floating point will be implemented on-chip.

The Am29000 is subdivided into the following subunits, shown in Figure 8.2:

1. *Instruction Fetch Unit*. Consists of:
   (a) Instruction Prefetch Buffer. 4 words (4×32).
   (b) Branch Target Cache. $2 \times 64 \times 32 = 512$ Bytes = 128 instructions. Two-way set-associative, containing the first four target instructions of a number of recently taken branches (up to 32). Its average hit rate is 60%.
   (c) PC Unit.
2. *Execution Unit*. Consists of:
   (a) Register File, each register 32 bits,
   192 General Purpose Registers.
   23 Special Purpose (Status and Control) Registers.
   (b) Address Unit, evaluates addresses and assembles immediate data.
   (c) ALU, includes multiplication/division steps.
   (d) Field Shift Unit, includes n-bit shift, byte or half-word extract or insert, word from doubleword.
3. *Memory Management Unit* (MMU)
   Includes a *Translation Lookaside Buffer* (TLB), composed of two sets of 32

64-bit address translation entries, 2 × 32 × 64. Accessed by Supervisor data move operations only. Entries are replaced by the Least Recently Used (LRU) policy.

The general purpose registers, numbered 0 to 255, are assigned as follows:

Register number	Assignment
0	Indirect Pointer Access
1	Stack Pointer, SP
2–63	Not implemented
64	Global Register 64
65	Global Register 65
.	.
.	.
.	.
127	Global Register 127
128	Local Register 125
129	Local Register 126
130	Local Register 127
131	Local Register 0
132	Local Register 1
.	.
.	.
.	.
254	Local Register 123
255	Local Register 124

It is assumed in the above that register 1(SP) contains the number 131, thus establishing that register 131 will be Local Register 0.

The general purpose registers are specified by an 8-bit field; if its MSB=1, it refers to a local register, if its MSB=0, it refers to a global register. Global register 0 specifies that an indirect pointer is to be used as the source of the register number; there is an indirect pointer for each of the instruction operand/result registers. Global register 1 contains the Stack Pointer (SP) to address local registers. A shadow copy of gloal register 1 is maintained by CPU hardware for local register addressing. It is set only with results of arithmetic and logic instructions. Specification of global register 0 as a source or destination operand causes an indirect access to general purpose registers. The absolute register number is provided by an indirect pointer contained in a special purpose register. Indirect pointers are set by a move to special register, floating point, multiply, divide, setip and emulate instructions.

The local register file implements a simple SP and offset addressing mode

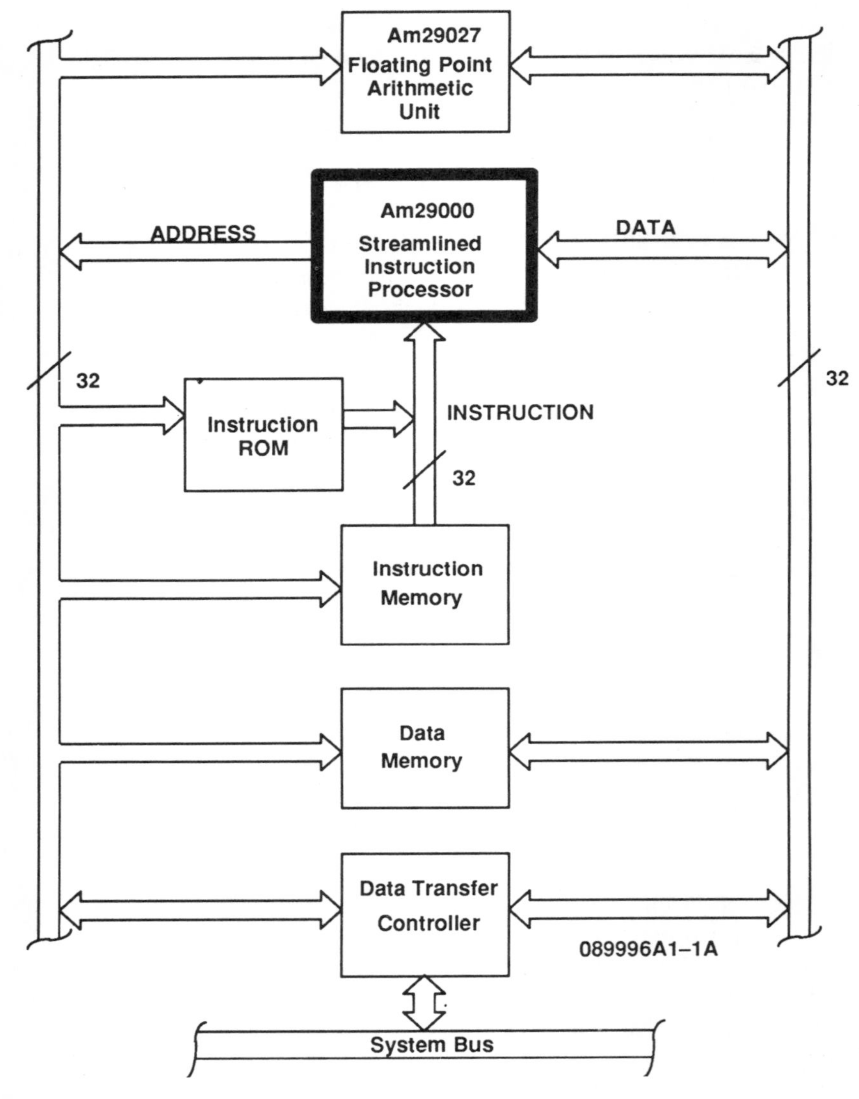

Figure 8.1 Simplified System Diagram

(the SP is the global register 1, as explained above). The offset is the register number taken from the instruction itself. Using this mechanism, a compiler can allocate procedure activation records (that is, stack frames) in registers as well as on the run-time stack in main memory. Most or all of the activation record can be allocated in CPU registers, saving on CPU-memory traffic. The number

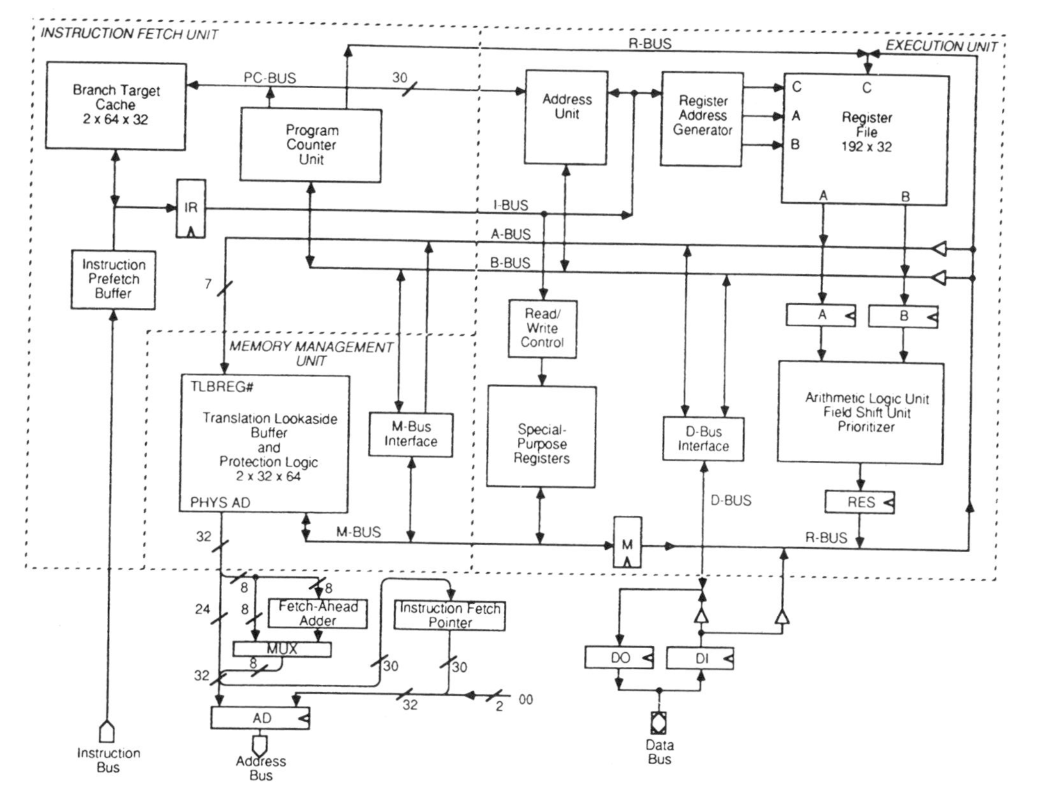

Figure 8.2 Am29000 Data Flow

of registers allocated in the Am29000 register file can be programmed to match exactly the size of the activation record. This feature is somewhat similar to that of the MULTRIS (section 5.3). However, the MULTRIS management of the CPU register file is much more versatile. Both the Am29000 and the MULTRIS are inherently suited for multitasking operations, such as those encountered in real-time applications.

The Am29000 architecture features 112 instructions of the following types:

Integer Arithmetic	29
Compare	21
Logical	7
Shift	4
Data Movement	17
Constant	3
Floating Point	15
Branch	9
Miscellaneous	7
	Total 112

In addition, there is a set of 21 reserved opcodes for instruction emulation and future expansion. The Am29000 instruction set is listed in Table 8.1. Instructions are 32-bit long, aligned on word-address boundaries.

The Am29000 features a 3-address, 4-field (8-bits/field) instruction format. The most significant field is for the opcode. The instruction format is shown in Figure 8.3.

EXAMPLE: ADD rc, ra, rb; rc ← (ra) + (rb)

The data types recognized by the Am29000 architecture are

Byte	8 bits
Half Word	16 bits
Word	32 bits
Double Word	64 bits

Bytes and Half Words in a Word can be numbered either by starting from the most (little-endian) or the least (big-endian) significant, as shown in Figure 8.4. The ordering can be established by setting a Byte Order bit in the Configuration Register (one of the special purpose registers), similarly to the M88000 (chapter 6). The Special Purpose Registers are shown in Figure 8.5.

The *Vector Area Base Address* register (Special Purpose Register 0, SPR0) specifies the beginning address of the interrupt/trap vector area. This address is constrained to begin on a 64 KByte address boundary in the memory. Thus, bits 15-0 of this register are zero. The *Old Processor Status* register (SPR1) and

Table 8.1 Am29000 Instruction Set
(*© Copyright AMD, Inc. 1988*)

Mnemonic	Instruction Name
ADD	Add
ADDC	Add with Carry
ADDCS	Add with Carry, Signed
ADDCU	Add with Carry, Unsigned
ADDS	Add, Signed
ADDU	Add, Unsigned
AND	AND Logical
ANDN	AND-NOT Logical
ASEQ	Assert Equal To
ASGE	Assert Greater Than or Equal To
ASGEU	Assert Greater Than or Equal To, Unsigned
ASGT	Assert Greater Than
ASGTU	Assert Greater Than, Unsigned
ASLE	Assert Less Than or Equal To
ASLEU	Assert Less Than or Equal To, Unsigned
ASLT	Assert Less Than
ASLTU	Assert Less Than, Unsigned
ASNEQ	Assert Not Equal To
CALL	Call Subroutine
CALLI	Call Subroutine, Indirect
CLZ	Count Leading Zeros
CONST	Constant
CONSTH	Constant, High
CONSTN	Constant, Negative
CONVERT	Convert Data Format
CPBYTE	Compare Bytes
CPEQ	Compare Equal To
CPGE	Compare Greater Than or Equal To
CPGEU	Compare Greater Than or Equal To, Unsigned
CPGT	Compare Greater Than
CPGTU	Compare Greater Than, Unsigned
CPLE	Compare Less Than or Equal To
CPLEU	Compare Less Than or Equal To, Unsigned
CPLT	Compare Less Than
CPLTU	Compare Less Than, Unsigned
CPNEQ	Compare Not Equal To
DADD	Floating-Point Add, Double-Precision
DDIV	Floating-Point Divide, Double-Precision
DEQ	Floating-Point Equal To, Double-Precision
DGE	Floating-Point Greater Than or Equal To, Double-Precision
DGT	Floating-Point Greater Than, Double-Precision
DIV	Divide Step
DIV0	Divide Initialize
DIVIDE	Integer Divide, Signed
DIVIDU	Integer Divide, Unsigned
DIVL	Divide Last Step
DIVREM	Divide Remainder
DMUL	Floating-Point Multiply, Double-Precision
DSUB	Floating-Point Subtract, Double-Precision
EMULATE	Trap to Software Emulation Routine
EXBYTE	Extract Byte
EXHW	Extract Half-Word
EXHWS	Extract Half-Word, Sign-Extended
EXTRACT	Extract Word, Bit-Aligned
FADD	Floating-Point Add, Single-Precision
FDIV	Floating-Point Divide, Single-Precision
FEQ	Floating-Point Equal To, Single-Precision
FGE	Floating-Point Greater Than or Equal To, Single-Precision
FGT	Floating-Point Greater Than, Single-Precision
FMUL	Floating-Point Multiply, Single-Precision
FSUB	Floating-Point Subtract, Single-Precision

Table 8.1 *(cont'd)*

Mnemonic	Instruction Name
HALT	Enter Halt Mode
INBYTE	Insert Byte
INHW	Insert Half-Word
INV	Invalidate
IRET	Interrupt Return
IRETINV	Interrupt Return and Invalidate
JMP	Jump
JMPF	Jump False
JMPFDEC	Jump False and Decrement
JMPFI	Jump False Indirect
JMPI	Jump Indirect
JMPT	Jump True
JMPTI	Jump True Indirect
LOAD	Load
LOADL	Load and Lock
LOADM	Load Multiple
LOADSET	Load and Set
MFSR	Move from Special Register
MFTLB	Move from Translation Look-Aside Buffer Register
MTSR	Move to Special Register
MTSRIM	Move to Special Register Immediate
MTTLB	Move to Translation Look-Aside Buffer Register
MUL	Multiply Step
MULL	Multiply Last Step
MULTIPLU	Integer Multiply, Unsigned
MULTIPLY	Integer Multiply, Signed
MULU	Multiply Step, Unsigned
NAND	NAND Logical
NOR	NOR Logical
OR	OR Logical
SETIP	Set Indirect Pointers
SLL	Shift Left Logical
SRA	Shift Right Arithmetic
SRL	Shift Right Logical
STORE	Store
STOREL	Store and Lock
STOREM	Store Multiple
SUB	Subtract
SUBC	Subtract with Carry
SUBCS	Subtract with Carry, Signed
SUBCU	Subtract with Carry, Unsigned
SUBR	Subtract Reverse
SUBRC	Subtract Reverse with Carry
SUBRCS	Subtract Reverse with Carry, Signed
SUBRCU	Subtract Reverse with Carry, Unsigned
SUBRS	Subtract Reverse, Signed
SUBRU	Subtract Reverse, Unsigned
SUBS	Subtract, Signed
SUBU	Subtract, Unsigned
XNOR	Exclusive-NOR Logical
XOR	Exclusive-OR Logical

the *Current Processor Status* register (SPR2) have the same format and they contain the status bits of the processor indicating whether an interrupt is pending, whether the processor is in the supervisor or user mode, and other details. The Old Processor Status stores a copy of the Current Processor Status when an interrupt or trap is taken. The Current Processor Status will then be modified to reflect

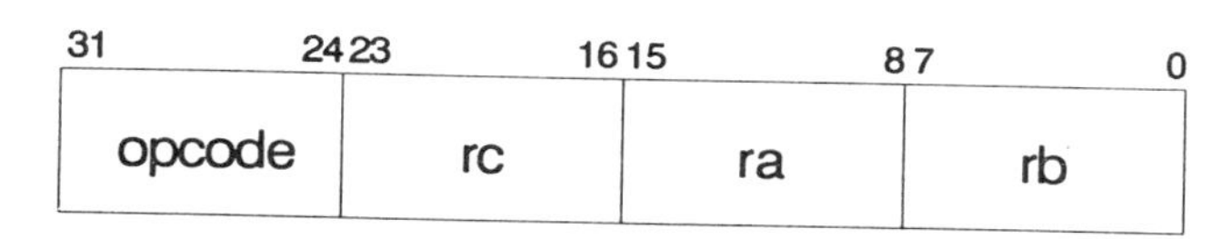

Figure 8.3 Am29000 Instruction Format

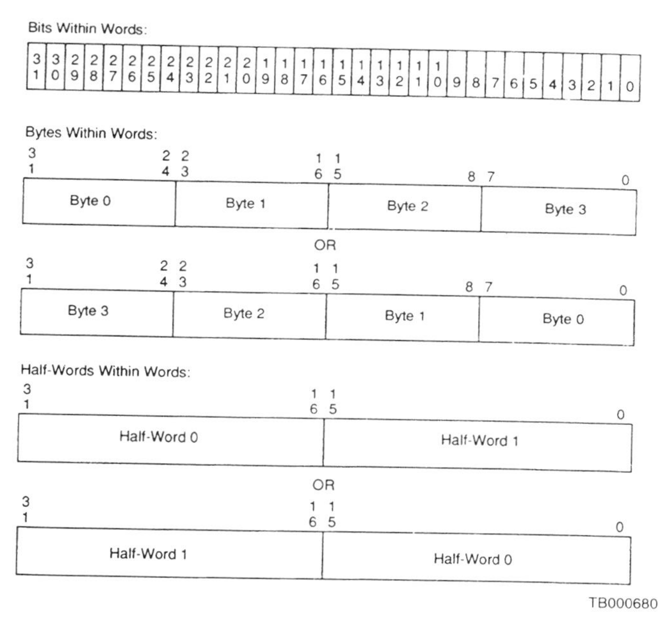

Figure 8.4 Data Unit Numbering Conventions

the status of the interrupt/trap handler. During an interrupt return the Old Processor Status is copied into the Current Processor Status. The *Configuration* register (SPR3) controls certain processor and system options, such as control of the interrupt/trap vector area, byte ordering in a word, coprocessor and cache control: all that using 5 bits, 4-0. The upper 8 bits 31-24 contain a read-only identification number which specifies the processor version.

The *Channel Address* register (SPR4) is used to report exceptions during external accesses or coprocessor transfers. It is also used to restart interrupted load-multiple and store-multiple operations, and to restart other external accesses. It is updated on the execution of every load and store instruction, and it contains the address of the current channel transaction. For transfers to the coprocessor it contains data transferred to the coprocessor. The *Channel Data* register (SPR5)

Special Purpose Reg. No.	Protected Registers
0	Vector Area Base Address
1	Old Processor Status
2	Current Processor Status
3	Configuration
4	Channel Address
5	Channel Data
6	Channel Control
7	Register Bank Protect
8	Timer Counter
9	Timer Reload
10	Program Counter 0
11	Program Counter 1
12	Program Counter 2
13	MMU Configuration
14	LRU Recommendation

Special Purpose Reg. No.	Unprotected Registers
128	Indirect Pointer C
129	Indirect Pointer A
130	Indirect Pointer B
131	Q
132	ALU Status
133	Byte Pointer
134	Funnel Shift Count
135	Load/Store Count Remaining

Figure 8.5 Special Purpose Registers

is used in a similar manner to that of the Channel Address register, and it contains the data (if any) associated with the current channel transaction. The *Channel Control* register (SPR6) is used to report status details of exceptions during external accesses or coprocessor transfers.

The *Register Bank Protect* register (SPR7) can be used to restrict user-mode program accesses to banks of general purpose registers. Each of its least 16 bits (15-0) is associated with one of the 16 register banks. When a bit is set, the corresponding bank is protected from access by programs executing in the user mode. The *Timer Counter* register (SPR8) contains the counter for the timer facility. The *Timer Reload* register (SPR9) maintains synchronization of the Timer Counter register, enables timer interrupts, and maintains timer facility status information.

The *Program Counter 0* register (SPR10) is used on an interrupt return to restart the instruction which was in the *decode* stage when the original interrupt or trap was taken. The *Program Counter 1* register (SPR11) is used on an interrupt return to restart the instruction which was in the *execute* stage when the original interrupt or trap was taken. The *Program Counter 2* register (SPR12) reports the address of certain instructions causing traps.

The *MMU Configuration* register (SRP13) specifies parameters associated with the MMU. Its least significant 8 bits (7-0) are used as a process identifier. Bits 9,8 are used to establish a page size, according to the following encoding:

Bits 9,8	Page Size (KBytes)
00	1
01	2
10	4
11	8

The *LRU Recommendation* register (SPR14) assists the TLB by indicating the Least Recently Used (LRU) TLB entry in the required replacement line.

The *Indirect Pointer C* register (SPR128) provides the rc operand register number when an instruction rc field (Figure 8.3) has the value zero (i.e., when Global Register 0 is specified). Similarly, the *Indirect Pointer A* (SPR129) and the *Indirect Pointer B* (SPR130) registers provide the ra and rb operands respectively.

The *Q* register (SPR131) holds the low-order bits of the dividend in a divide operation and contains the quotient at the end of it. During a multiply operation register Q holds the multiplier, and the low-order bits of the product at the end. The *ALU Status* register (SPR132) holds information about the outcome of ALU operations as well as control of certain operations performed by the execution unit. The *Byte Pointer* register (SPR133), whose bits 1,0 are the only ones in current use, provides alternate access to the field of bits 6,5 in the ALU Status register. This allows a program to change this field without affecting other fields in the ALU Status register. The *Funnel Shift Count* register (SPR134) is used in a similar manner with respect to bits 4-0 in the ALU Status register.

The *Load/Store Count Remaining* register (SPR135) provides separate access to bits 23-16 in the Channel Control register. This allows a program to change the above field without affecting other fields in the Channel Control register, and is used to initialize the value before a Load Multiple or Store Multiple instruction is executed.

Interrupts on the Am29000 are caused by signals applied to any of the external inputs INTR0*-INTR3* (* means low asserted), or by the timer facility. There are a number of bits in the *Current Processor Status* register which can mask interrupts. Bit DA (Disable All) disables all interrupts and most traps when set. Bit DI (Disable Interrupts) disables external interrupts only when set. The two-bit field IM (Interrupt Mask) disables interrupts selectively, as follows:

IM	Enabled Interrupts
00	INTR0*
01	INTR0*-INTR1*
10	INTR0*-INTR2*
11	INTR0*-INTR3*

It should be noted that INTR0* is never disabled by the IM field.

Traps on the Am29000 are caused by signals applied to one of the inputs TRAP0*, TRAP1*, or by exceptional conditions such as protection violations. Except for Instruction Access Exception, Data Access Exception, and Coprocessor Exception traps, traps are disabled by the DA bit in the Current Processor Status register (when DA is set).

Interrupt and trap handling routines are pointed to by vectors residing in the *Vector Area*, which begins at an address specified by the *Vector Area Base Address* register. The Vector Area includes 256 vectors, as illustrated in Table 8.2.

One of the unique features of the Am29000 is its *Branch Target Cache*. Its organization is illustrated in Figure 8.6. It is two-way set associative. Its total size is 512 bytes (128 32-bit words), divided into two sets each containing 64 32-bit instruction words. The sets are divided into 16 blocks, numbered 0–15, which consist of 4 words each. Blocks in different sets with equivalent block numbers are organized into a unit called a line.

Each branch target is defined as a sequence of exactly four instructions, and is aligned on a cache block boundary. A branch target sequence may occupy at most one block.

A 28-bit cache tag is associated with each four-word block (Figure 8.6). Of the 28 bits, 26 are derived from the address of the instruction in the block, and

Table 8.2 Vector Number Assignments
(*© Copyright AMD, Inc. 1988*)

Number (decimal)	Type of Trap or Interrupt
0	Illegal Opcode
1	Unaligned Access
2	Out of Range
3	Coprocessor Not Present
4	Coprocessor Exception
5	Protection Violation
6	Instruction Access Exception
7	Data Access Exception
8	User-Mode Instruction TLB Miss
9	User-Mode Data TLB Miss
10	Supervisor-Mode Instruction TLB Miss
11	Supervisor-Mode Data TLB Miss
12	Instruction TLB Protection Violation
13	Data TLB Protection Violation
14	Timer
15	Trace
16	$\overline{INTR_0}$
17	$\overline{INTR_1}$
18	$\overline{INTR_2}$
19	$\overline{INTR_3}$
20	$\overline{TRAP_0}$
21	$\overline{TRAP_1}$
22 – 23	reserved
24 – 31	reserved for instruction emulation (opcodes D8-DF)
32	MULTIPLY
33	DIVIDE
34	MULTIPLU
35	DIVIDU
36	CONVERT
37 – 41	reserved for instruction emulation (opcodes E5-E9)
42	FEQ
43	DEQ
44	FGT
45	DGT
46	FGE
47	DGE
48	FADD
49	DADD
50	FSUB
51	DSUB
52	FMUL
53	DMUL
54	FDIV
55	DDIV
56 thru 63	reserved for instruction emulation (opcodes F8-FF)
64 thru 255	Assert and EMULATE instruction traps (vector number specified by instruction)

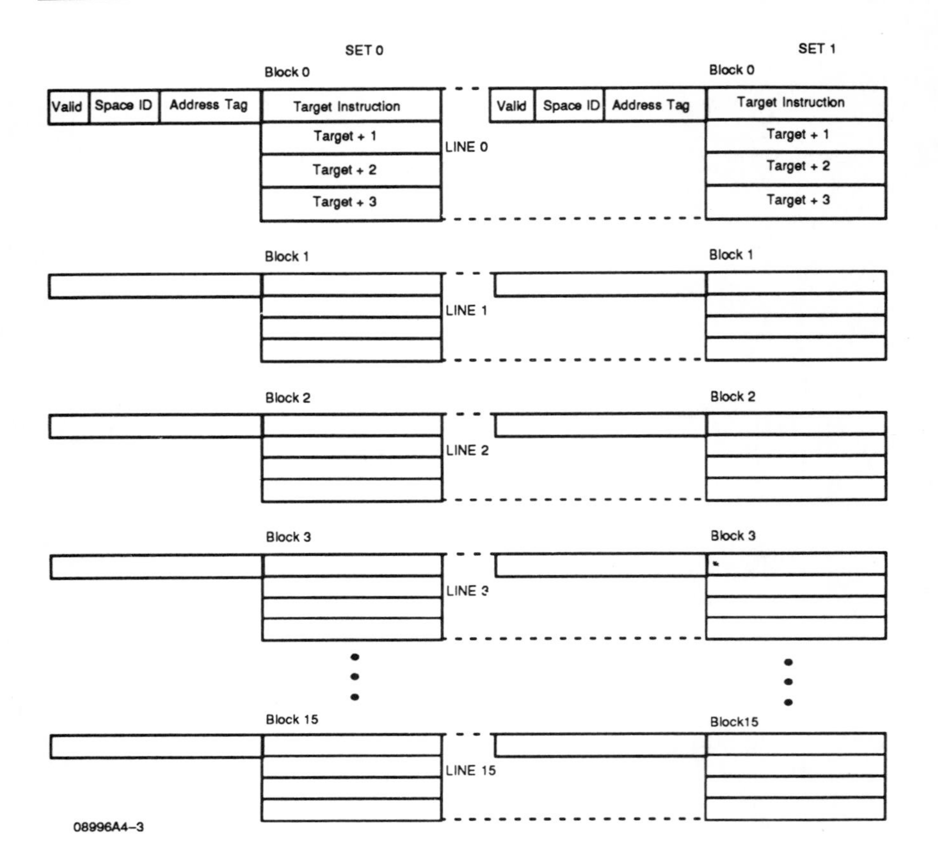

Figure 8.6 Branch Target Cache Organization
(*© Copyright Advanced Micro Devices, Inc. 1988. All AM29000 figures are reprinted with permission of copyright owner. All rights reserved.*)

are called the *Address Tag*. Two additional bits in the cache tag, called the *Space ID*, indicate the instruction memory from which the instructions were fetched and the program mode under which the instructions were fetched:

Space ID	Instruction Address Space
00	User Instruction/Data Memory
01	User Instruction ROM
10	Supervisor Instruction/Data Memory
11	Supervisor Instruction ROM

A *Valid* bit associated with *each cache word* indicates that the word contains a

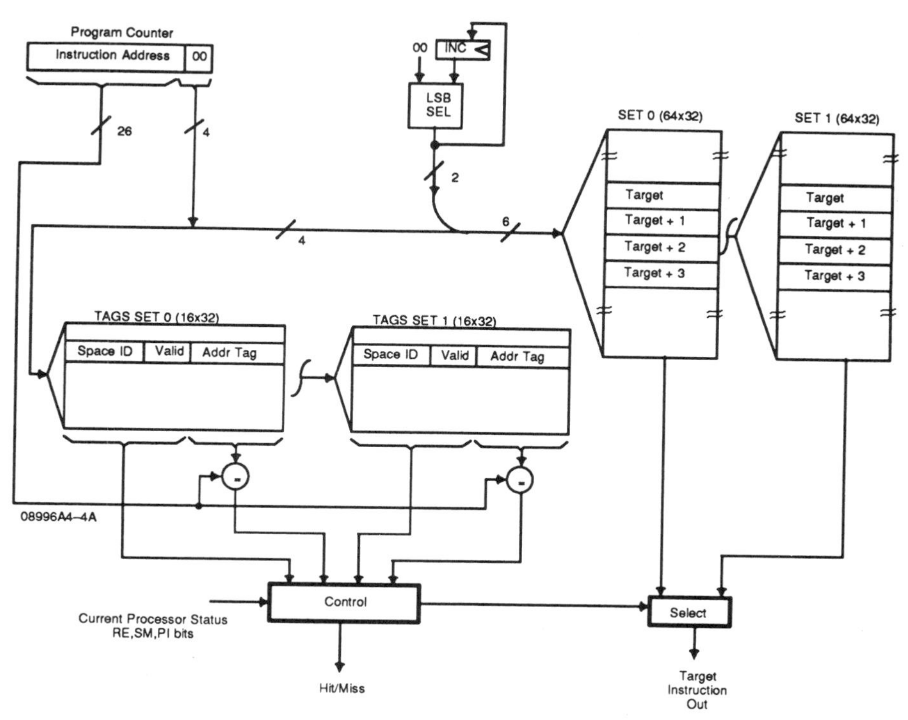

Figure 8.7 Branch Target Cache Lookup Process
(*© Copyright Advanced Micro Devices, Inc. 1988. All AM29000 figures are reprinted with permission of copyright owner. All rights reserved.*)

valid instruction in the branch target sequence. Cache invalidation instructions make it possible to reset all valid bits in a single processor cycle.

The Branch Target Cache lookup process is shown in Figure 8.7. Whenever a non-sequential fetch occurs (either for a branch instruction, an interrupt, or a trap), the address for the fetch is presented to the Branch Target Cache at the same time that the address is translated by the MMU. If the above target instruction is in the cache, it is presented for decoding in the next cycle. If the target instruction is not found in the Branch Target Cache, the address of the fetch selects a line to be used to store the instruction sequence of the new branch target. The replacement block within the line is selected at random, based on the processor clock. Instructions from the new fetch stream are stored into the selected cache block as they are issued to the decode stage. The Valid bit for each word is set as the instruction is stored.

For software support AMD offers a C cross-development package, a development and prototyping tool, a target resident debug monitor, and a symbolic debugger.

The Am29027 Floating Point Unit works with single (32 bits) and double precision (64 bits) IEEE 754-1985 Standard. There is also an Am29062 Integrated Cache Unit featuring an 8 KBytes RAM Cache. It can be programmed for two-way set associative or direct mapping, 4, 8, 16 or 32 word lines and LRU, random or external replacement algorithms. It is a CMOS, 25 MHz, 169 pin chip. Two Am29062 chips can be directly connected to the Am29000: one as an instruction, and the other as a data cache.

Future plans of AMD development include faster 1-micron CMOS versions of the Am29000:

40 MHz – 27 MIPS
55 MHz – 37 MIPS

The next chip Am29090 will include a Floating Point Unit on chip. The 1-micron CMOS versions will be:

40 MHz – 35 MIPS – 15 MFLOPS
47 MHz – 41 MIPS – 18 MFLOPS

and a 0.8 micron CMOS:

55 MHz – 48 MIPS – 21 MFLOPS.

The above MFLOPS figures are for single precision (32 bits) formats.

References

8.1 Am29000 32-Bit Streamlined Instruction Processor User Manual, AMD, 1988.
8.2 S. Silverstein, S. Adkar, 'VME Caches in on the 29000', *ESD*, Sept. 1988, pp. 53–58.
8.3 B. Case, 'Pipelined Processor Pushes Performance', *ESD*, March 1987, pp. 30–34.
8.4 B. Case, '32-Bit Microprocessor Opens System Bottlenecks', *Computer Design*, April 1, 1987, pp. 79–86.
8.5 Am29000 Performance Analysis, AMD, May 1988.
8.6 M. Johnson, 'System Considerations in the Design of the Am29000', *IEEE MICRO*, **7**, No. 4, pp. 28–41, Aug. 1987.

9

The Intel 80960 and 80860

9.1 The 80960 Architecture

The Intel 80960 was developed as a high-performance, RISC-type, 32-bit controller [9.1–9.9]. It actually represents a family of evolving controllers, designed in subsequent layers of architectural features. The currently announced architectures for the 80960 are [9.3]:

(1) Core Architecture (CA) – the basic integer RISC processor, implemented on the 80960KA chip.
(2) Numerics Architecture (NA) – adds an on-chip floating point unit to the CA, implemented on the 80960KB chip.
(3) Protected Architecture (PA) – adds to NA:

    Support for Virtual Memory, including memory protection and paging,
    Support for Task and Process Management,
    String Processing Instructions,
    Multiple-Processor support.
    The PA is implemented on the 80960MC chip, designed to fulfill military specifications.

(4) Extended Architecture (XA) – a future product: although details are not yet formally announced, there are indications that future versions of the 80960 will have an extended instruction cache on-chip with an 'always hit' ROM; a 128-bit instruction bus from the on-chip cache to parallel instruction sequencer capable of handling 4 instruction words concurrently. A multiply/divide and an address generation unit will be added [9.8].

The current discussion will focus primarily on the 80960KB model, featuring the Numerics Architecture.

The Intel 80960KB is a 32-bit RISC-type, 1.5 micron CHMOS III, 132 pin chip [9.1–9.4]. It is intended to serve as a high-performance, 32-bit, embedded controller. Its peak performance at 20 MHz is 20 MIPS (7.5 MIPS sustained) or 4 MWhetstones/sec. It has on-chip floating point processing and debugging functions, supporting 32- and 64-bit IEEE Standard and 80-bit extended floating point formats. A block diagram of the 80960KB model is shown in Figure 9.1. The 80960 has an on-chip 512 Byte, Direct-Mapped (16 Bytes/Block) Instruction Cache. The register set of the 80960 is shown in Figure 9.2.

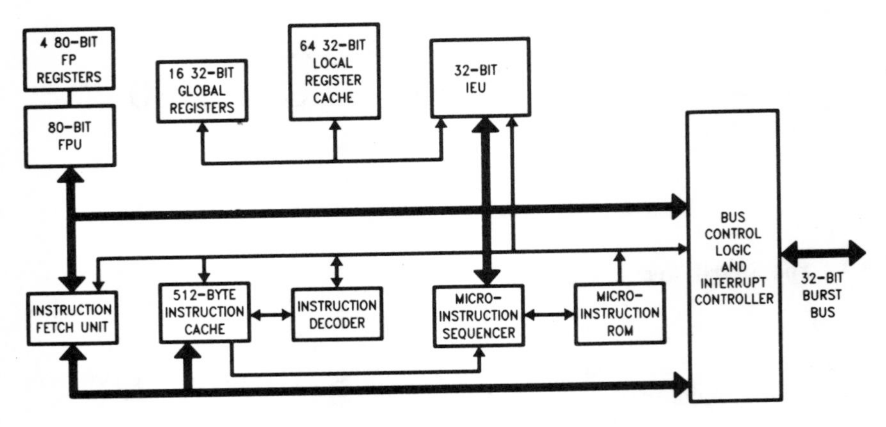

Figure 9.1 The 80960 KB Block Diagram
(Courtesy of Intel Corp.)

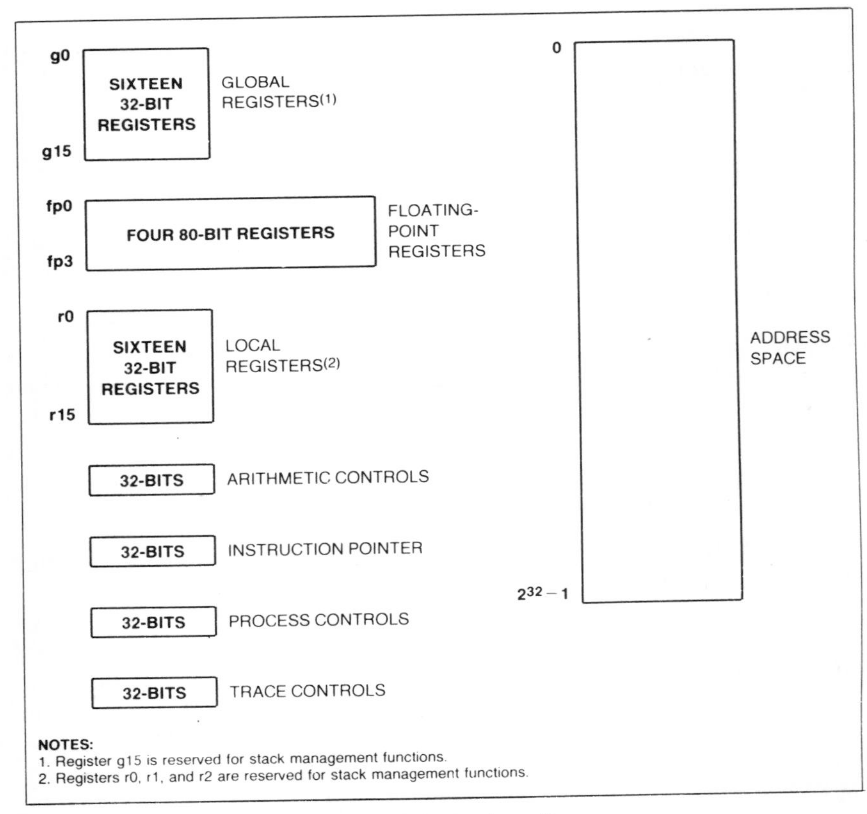

Figure 9.2 Register Set
(Courtesy of Intel Corp.)

The register set, available to any user procedure, is:

(a) g0–g15, Global 32-bit registers, 16,
(b) r0–r15, Local 32-bit registers, 16,
(c) fp0–fp3, Floating Point 80-bit registers, 4,

a total of 36. The global register g15 is used as a Frame Pointer (FP). It contains the address of the first byte in the current (topmost) stack frame. Local register r0 serves as the Previous Frame Pointer (PFP); r1 – as the Stack-Pointer (SP); and r2 – as the Return Instruction Pointer (RIP). Local registers r3 to r15 are intended for general purpose use, for a specific procedure. There is a total of four 16 local register sets, as illustrated in Figure 9.3. For each called procedure, the processor allocates a separate set of 16 local registers. Thus, on-chip nesting of up to 4 procedures is possible. When a CALL instruction executes, a new set of 16 local registers from a pool of register sets (4 sets, 64 registers) is allocated for the called procedure [9.9]. If the pool is depleted, a new register set is allocated by taking one associated with an earlier procedure and saving it in memory. A RET instruction causes the most recently stored register set to be restored, freeing a register set location. The 80960 implements scoreboarding of all of the procedure's registers to tag destination registers until the operation is complete (similarly to the M88000, as described in chapter 6).

The Instruction Pointer (IP, same as Program Counter, PC) contains the address of the currently executed instruction. Instructions, aligned on word (32-bit) boundaries, can be one or two words long. The IP specifies the address of the lowest order byte of the first word. During a call or an interrupt, the IP value of the next instruction is stored in the RIP(r2). Return addresses of subsequent

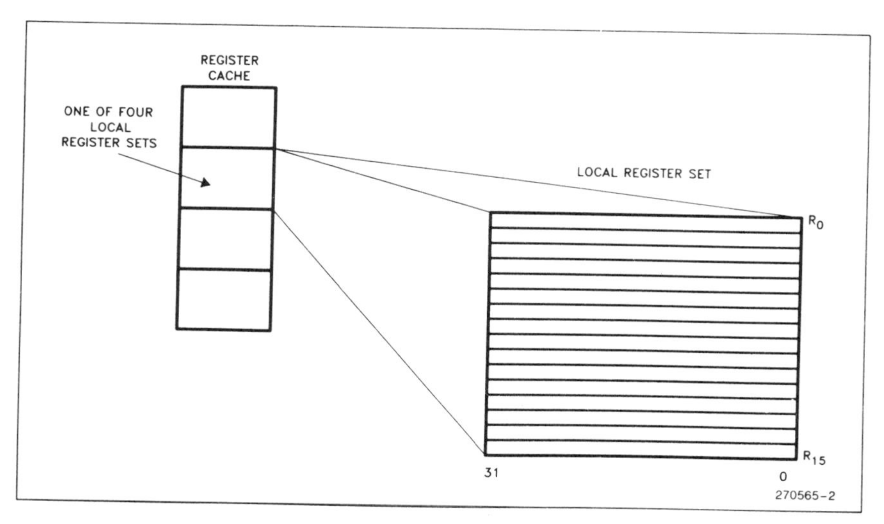

Figure 9.3 Local Register Sets
(Courtesy of Intel Corp.)

nested procedures are stored on stack. The overall unsegmented address space of the 80960 is 2^{32} Bytes, or 4 GBytes (Figure 9.2). Three other 32-bit registers (Figure 9.2) are used for storage of processor control and status information.

The 80960 family features three processors at the moment:

(1) The 20 MHz 80960KB, the current top performance chip with an on-chip floating point unit (NA).
(2) The lower cost 80960KA, without the floating point unit (CA).
(3) The 16 MHz 89060MC (PA), intended for military applications. Additional 89060MC features (not available on the other models):
  (a) On-Chip Memory Management Unit, 4 GBytes Virtual Address Space per task, 4 KByte pages with Supervisor/User protection.
  (b) Multitasking support, including Ada task management, automatic task dispatching, and prioritized task queues.
  (c) 164 Lead Ceramic Quad Flatpack packaging, in addition to the 132 Lead Ceramic Pin Grid Array (80960KB).
  (d) Military temperature range −55°C to +125°C.

The 80960 architecture recognizes the following data types:

(a) Numeric – 8, 16, 32 and 64-bit ordinals
8, 16, 24 and 64-bit integers
32, 64 and 80-bit real (floating point) numbers
Decimal, ASCII digits
(b) Non-numeric – Bit
Bit Field, 0 to 32 bits
Triple-Word (96 bits)
Quad-Word (128 bits)

The 80960 Addressing Modes are:

(1) Literal (immediate), value
(2) Register, Ri (can be gi or ri)
(3) Absolute, expression or value
(4) Register Indirect, RI, (Ri)
(5) RI + Offset (12 or 32-bit), expression (Ri)
(6) RI + Scaled Index + Displacement, expression (Ri)[Rj*scale]
(7) Index with Displacement, expression [Ri*scale]
(8) IP + Displacement, expression (IP).

There are five instruction formats shown in Figure 9.4. The instructions can have up to three operands.

EXAMPLE: addi src1, src2, dst; add integer
dst ← (src1) + (src2)

Control	Opcode | Displacement
Compare and Branch	Opcode | Reg/Lit | Reg | M | Displacement
Register to Register	Opcode | Reg | Reg/Lit | Modes | Ext'd Op | Reg/Lit
Memory Access—Short	Opcode | Reg | Base | M | x | Offset
Memory Access—Long	Opcode | Reg | Base | Mode | Scale | xx | Index
	Displacement

Figure 9.4 Instruction Formats
(*Courtesy of Intel Corp.*)

Unlike in other Intel products the destination is listed on the right.

The 80960 instruction set presented in Table 9.1 consists of the following groups:

		number
1.	Data Movement	4
2.	Arithmetic (Ordinal and Integer)	9
3.	Logical	12
4.	Bit and Bit Field	9
5.	Comparison	4
6.	Branch	3
7.	Call/Return	5
8.	Fault	2
9.	Debug	3
10.	Processor Management	4
11.	Miscellaneous	3
	Total	58

The 80960 has a memory-mapped I/O so there are no I/O-type instructions. In addition, there is an instruction set extension in the 80960 model, which consists of the following:

Table 9.1 80960KB Instruction Set
(Courtesy of Intel Corp.)

Data Movement	**Arithmetic**	**Logical**	**Bit and Bit Field**
Load Store Move Load Address	Add Subtract. Multiply Divide Remainder Modulo Shift Extended Multiply Extended Divide	And Not And And Not Or Exclusive Or Not Or Or Not Nor Exclusive Nor Not Nand Rotate	Set Bit Clear Bit Not Bit Check Bit Alter Bit Scan for Bit Scan over Bit Extract Modify
Comparison	**Branch**	**Call/Return**	**Fault**
Compare Conditional Compare Compare and Increment Compare and Decrement	Unconditional Branch Conditional Branch Compare and Branch	Call Call Extended Call System Return Branch and Link	Conditional Fault Synchronize Faults
Debug	**Miscellaneous**	**Decimal**	
Modify Trace Controls Mark Force Mark	Atomic Add Atomic Modify Flush Local Registers Modify Arithmetic Controls Scan Byte for Equal Test Condition Code	Move Add with Carry Subtract with Carry	
Conversion	**Floating-Point**	**Synchronous**	
Convert Real to Integer Convert Integer to Real	Move Real Add Subtract Multiply Divide Remainder Scale Round Square Root Sine Cosine Tangent Arctangent Log Log Binary Log Natural Exponent Classify Copy Real Extended Compare	Synchronous Load Synchronous Move	

1. Integer to Real Conversion	2
2. Floating Point	20
3. Synchronous	2
4. Decimal	3
Total	27

Thus, the total number of 80960KB instruction types is 85. The actual number of instructions amounts to 184, because for some operations several different instructions are provided to handle different operand sizes, data types, or branch conditions. Two of the miscellaneous instructions are indivisible Read-Modify-Write operations on operands in memory, intended for multiprocessing implementation:

atadd – atomic add
atmod – atomic modify (under control of a mask).

With a relatively large (compared to other RISC systems) number of instructions (some of which are microcoded, but most are hardwired), addressing modes, instruction and data formats, and two instruction sizes, the 80960 can be considered as a marginal RISC at most. The only RISC-type properties (see chapter 1) that it fully satisfies are load/store-only memory accesses and a relatively large (but not excessively large; smaller than in the Berkeley RISC) CPU register file.

The 80960MC, implementing the *Protected Architecture* (PA), contains basically the same subsystems as the 80960KB, shown in Figure 9.1, except that the 80960MC has in addition a Memory Management Unit (MMU) connected to the internal system bus. The PA recognizes the basic concept of a *process* (or, synonymously, *task*). The *state* of a process is described in a data structure called a *Process Control Block* (PCB). A process specifies a 4 GByte (2^{32} bytes) Virtual Address space [9.3]. The overall virtual address space is subdivided into four one GByte *regions*. The top address region 3 (C000 0000H to FFFF FFFFH; H = hexadecimal) is shared among all processes. Region 3 contains information not associated with specific processes, such as the interrupt stack and interrupt handling routines. The lower regions 0–2 (0000 0000H to BFFF FFFFH) can be subdivided between processes running on the system.

The PA standard page size is 4 KBytes (2^{12} bytes). Virtual addresses are translated to physical addresses by converting the upper 20 bits of the virtual (logical) address and using the lower 12 bits as an offset within the page frame in the physical (real) memory. The upper two bits (31, 30) of the virtual address denote one of the 4 regions, the next 18 bits denote a page within that region, and the 12 least significant bits denote a byte within that page [9.3]. A region can be mapped by 0, 1, or 2 levels of tables:

(a) *0-level.* A descriptor for the region points directly into a single page.
(a) *1-level.* The region descriptor points to a *Page Table*, which points to a maximum of 1024 physical pages. In this case, the region can be mapped into 4 MBytes of physical memory.
(c) *2-level.* The region is defined by the region descriptor pointing to a *Page Table Directory*, whose entries point to individual *Page Tables*, whose entries point to individual pages.

A diagram of valid Page Table Directory and Page Table entries and an invalid entry is shown in Figure 9.5 [9.3]. The *Page Rights* encoding is:

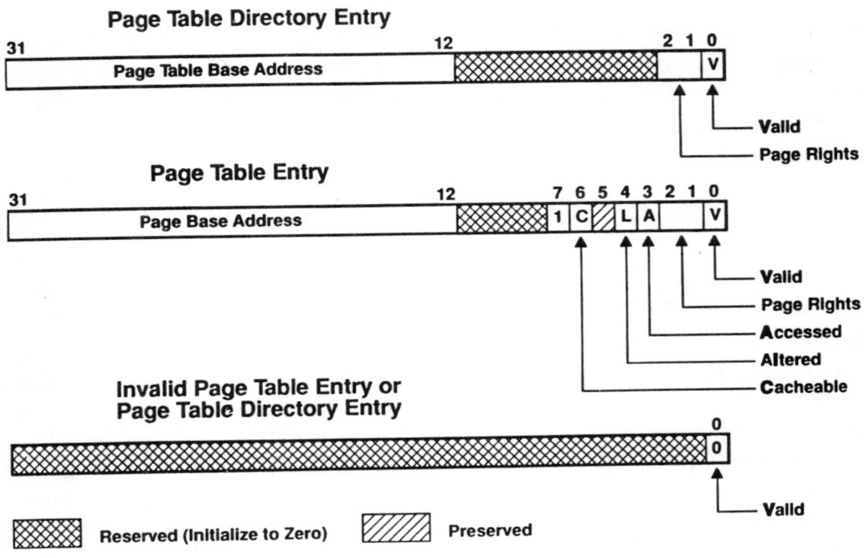

Figure 9.5 Page Table Directory Structure
(*Courtesy of Intel Corp.*)

00 : no user access, supervisor read only.
01 : no user access, supervisor read/write.
10 : user read only, supervisor read/write.
11 : user and supervisor read/write.

The 80960MC MMU contains a 64-entry Translation Lookaside Buffer, TLB, for fast, on-chip, virtual to physical address translation. For a 4 KBytes page size, the TLB maps $64 \times 4096 = 256$ KBytes of the address space.

9.2 The 80960 Interface

Although the 80960 has 132 pins, it is connected to a so-called Local Bus (L-bus) through multiplexed 32 Address/Data lines, LAD0–LAD31, as shown in Figure 9.6. The L-bus sustained bandwidth at 20 MHz is 53 MBytes/sec. The ALE signal enables the Address Latches, thus demultiplexing the address and data signals outside of the chip, in a similar manner to that implemented on the Intel 8085 or 8086. The DT/R*, Data Transmit/Receive, controls the direction of the data flow through the Data Transceivers, enabled by the DEN Data Enable signal. The ADS (Address/Data Status) identifies the address state to the external logic. The BE0-BE3 signals identify the byte to be transferred; BE0, the least significant; BE3, the most significant. Only adjacent bytes can be transferred. The READY signal generated by the Timing Control indicates that the LAD lines can be sampled.

The Burst Logic device controls memory burst transactions of up to 16 bytes (4 Words) at 1 Word/Clock cycle. It decrements the word count, increments the Local Address lines LAD3 and LAD2, and generates a CYCLE-IN-PROGRESS signal, connected to the Timing Control and DRAM Controller devices (Figure 9.6). The Timing Control device generates a READY signal and other memory enable signals. The DRAM Controller generates the DRAM refresh signals (CAS,RAS) and other control signals. The Byte Enable Latch holds the BE signals and the SRAM Interface generates enable signals (OE,WE) for the Static RAM.

The 80960 is fully compatible with most of the earlier Intel peripherals, such as:

8259A	Programmable Interrupt Controller (PIC)
8253,8254	Programmable Interval Timer (PIT)
8272	Floppy Disk Controller
82062,82064	Fixed Disk Controller
82510	Asynchronous Serial Controller
8274,82530	Multi-Protocol Serial Controller
8255	Programmable Peripheral Interface
82586	LAN (Local Area Network) Processor
82786	Graphics Processor

Two interface examples follow.

EXAMPLE 1 — Interface to the 82586 Local Area Network (LAN) Coprocessor, Figure 9.7. The 82586 controls access to LANs such as Ethernet or Starlan. The 82586 has only 16 Address Data Lines (AD0–AD15). Therefore one needs a 16–32 data-lines interface between the 82586 and the 80960. 16-Bit data are transmitted consecutively through the LAN Data Transceivers, controlled by the Byte Enable Converter, transmitting Byte Enable control signals BE0-BE3 to the LAN Data Transceivers. The Byte Enable Converter is controlled by the following signals:

A1 — selects between upper and lower 16-bit data lines
A0 — selects the lower byte of either 16-bit data
BHE — selects the upper byte of either 16-bit data.

The interface operation proceeds according to the following steps:

(a) Timing Control and external logic generate the Channel Attention (CA) signal, transmitted to the 82586.
(b) 82586 requests control of the L-Bus by asserting HOLD.
(c) 80960 grants control of the bus by asserting HLDA, which disables the

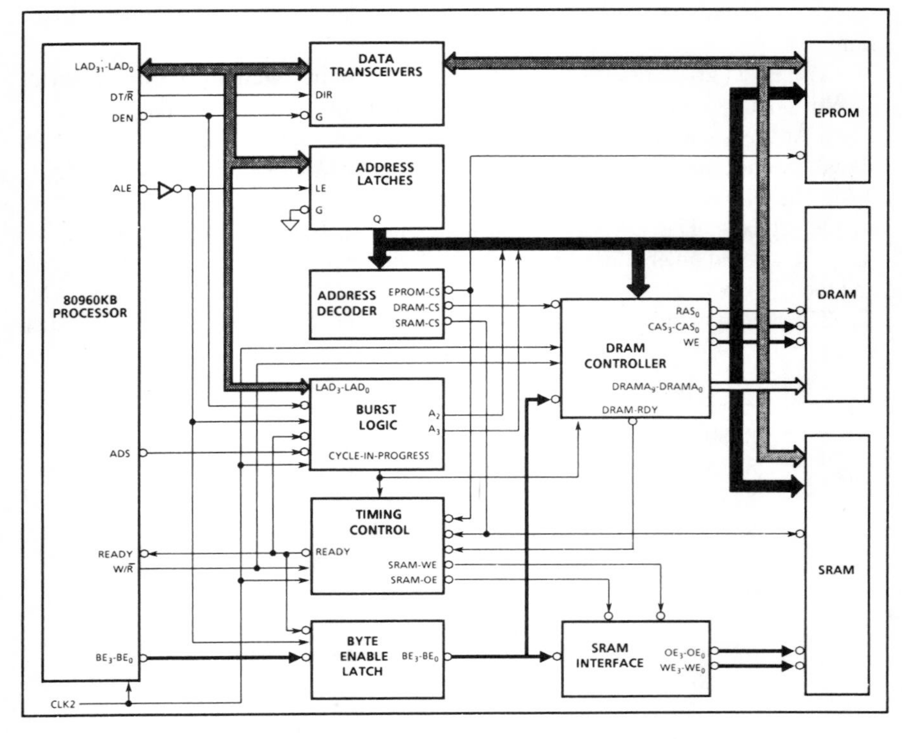

Figure 9.6 Simplified Block Diagram for Memory Interface Logic (*Courtesy of Intel Corp.*)

outputs of the 80960 address latches and enables the outputs of the 82586 address latches.

(d) 82586 generates a 16-bit address, a 16-bit data word and control signals for the interface circuit and memory controller.

(e) Interface circuit generates high-order address lines and controls the data flow to or from the DRAM Controller. Byte Enable signals determine which data lines are used.

(f) DRAM Controller terminates operation with DRAM-RDY.

(g) 82586 returns control of the bus to the 80960 by deasserting HOLD.

EXAMPLE 2 – Interface to the 82786 Graphics Coprocessor, Figure 9.8. The 80960 transfers a 32-bit data word to the 82786 16-bit data bus (D0–D15), a similar problem to that for the 82586. The Data Buffer Control circuit generates 4 output enable signals, controlling the Bidirectional Transceivers:

1. GABL – enables output on the B side for lower 16-bits

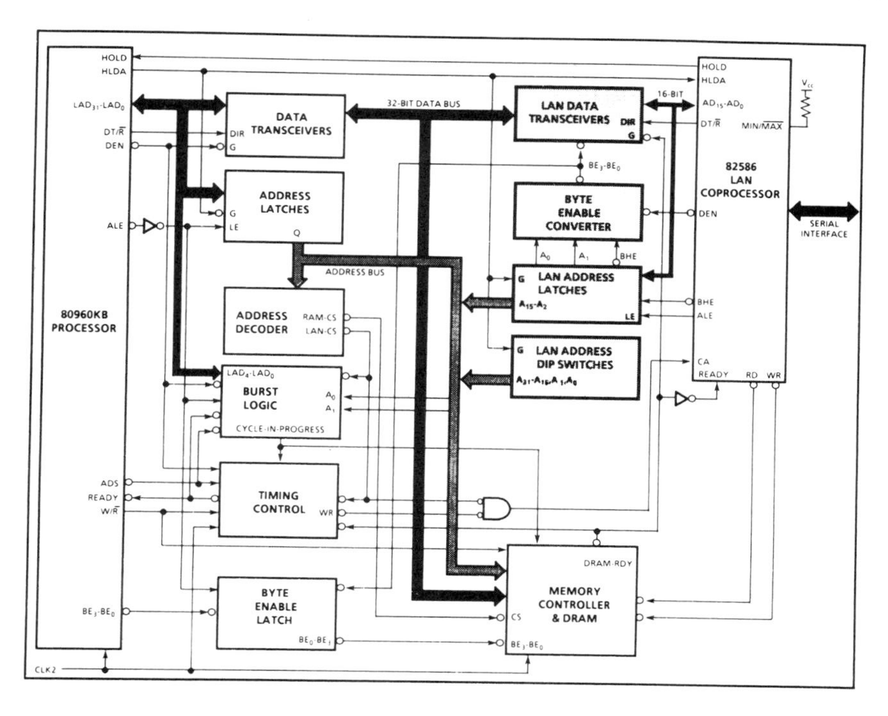

Figure 9.7 Block Diagram for LAN Controller Interface
(Courtesy of Intel Corp.)

2. GBAL – enables output on the A side for lower 16-bits
3. GABH – enables output on the B side for higher 16-bits
4. GBAH – enables output on the A side for higher 16-bits.

The above signals are derived from the BE signals and are asserted when the Slave Enable (SEN) signal is activated by the 82786. The Data Bus Controller provides Read (RD), Write (WR), M/IO*, and READY signals to the 82786. It generates two read or write commands for every 32-bit data transfer to or from the 80960.

The Address Translator:

Converts the BE0-BE3 signals to A0, A1 and BHE;

Increments A1 after receiving READY0 for the first 16-bit transfer;

Generates the clock signal CBAL that latches the first 16-bit data word in the Bidirectional Transceivers, for an 80960 read operation;

Generates the READY signal for the 80960 CPU.

The 82786 operation proceeds as follows:

(a) 80960 generates address and data.

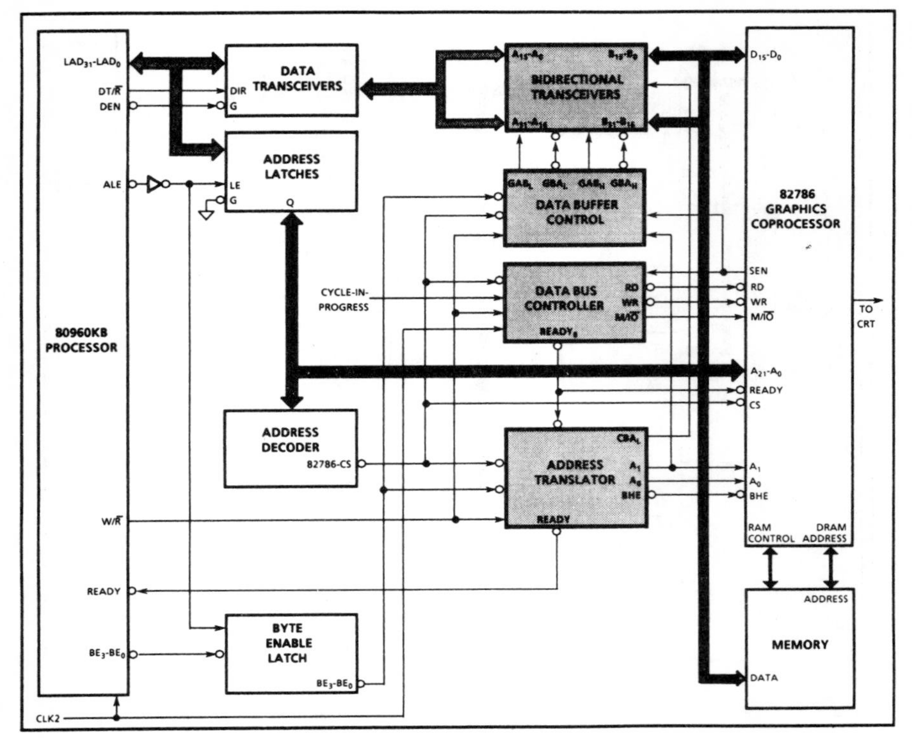

Figure 9.8 Block Diagram for 82786 Interface
(Courtesy of Intel Corp.)

First 16-Bit Data Transfer

(b) Interface circuit generates CS,RD (or WR), BHE and M/IO*.
(c) 82786 recognizes CS by asserting SEN.
(d) Interface circuit controls data flow. Generates READY0.
 1. Read operation – Latches data on lower 16-bits with GBAL signal
 2. Write operation – Enables output for data on *lower* 16-bits. Increments address A1.
(e) 82786 deasserts SEN.

Second 16-Bit Data Transfer

(f) Data Bus Controller generates RD (or WR), BHE and M/IO*.
(g) 82786 recognizes CS by asserting SEN.
(h) Interface circuit controls data flow. Generates READY0.
 1. Read-enables output for lower and higher 16 bits.
 2. Write-enables output for data on *higher* 16 bits.
(i) Interface circuit generates READY for 80960 and 82786, and deasserts SEN.

The 80960 development tools are hosted on IBM PC/AT and compatible computers. Future versions, hosted on VAX/VMS systems, are planned. Initial 80960 tools include:

(a) EVA-960KB Execution Vehicle. Plugs into an AT expansion slot and provides a complete 80960KB subsystem for architecture evauation, program execution, and software debugging. It includes an 80960KB CPU, 64 KBytes SRAM, 1 or 4 MBytes DRAM, DOS access libraries and a debug monitor.
(b) ASM-960 Assembler. Assembly language development environment. Includes an assembler, linker/loader, macro preprocessor, archiver, object module utilities, hex converter, PROM builder.
(c) iC-960 C Compiler. Includes: full C language with extensions, optimizing compiler, floating point library (IEEE-compatible) and inline assembly coding.
(d) Compilers for Ada, FORTRAN and Pascal.

9.3 The 80860

The most recent addition to the RISC systems family by Intel is the 80860 (also called i860 and formerly denoted as N10) microprocessor [9.10–9.14]. It is a 1 micron CHMOS IV, containing about one million transistors on-chip. Its current operating frequency is 33 MHz, yielding a peak 60 MFLOPS (single precision) performance. A future version of 40 MHz (80 MFLOPS, 120 MOPS peak) is being worked on, and 50 MHz operation has been attained in the laboratory. It has 168 pins. Its integer performance is 33 VAX 780 MIPS at 33 MHz.

The 80860 is a 64-bit data path processor. Its block diagram is shown in Figure 9.9. It includes the following on-chip units:

Integer Processor (32-bit),
Floating Point Unit (FPU), including floating point adder and multiplier pipelines and a floating point controller,
Instruction Cache – 4 KBytes,
Data Cache – 8 KBytes,
Memory Management Unit (MMU),
3D Graphics Controller.

The i860 architecture recognizes 4 basic addressing modes:

1. *Offset*. Absolute address into the first or last 32 KBytes of the logical address space.
2. *Register*. Operand in a CPU register.
3. *Register Indirect + Offset*. # const (reg)
   Effective address = const + (reg)
4. *Register Indirect + Index*. reg1 (reg2)
   Effective address = (reg1) + (reg2)

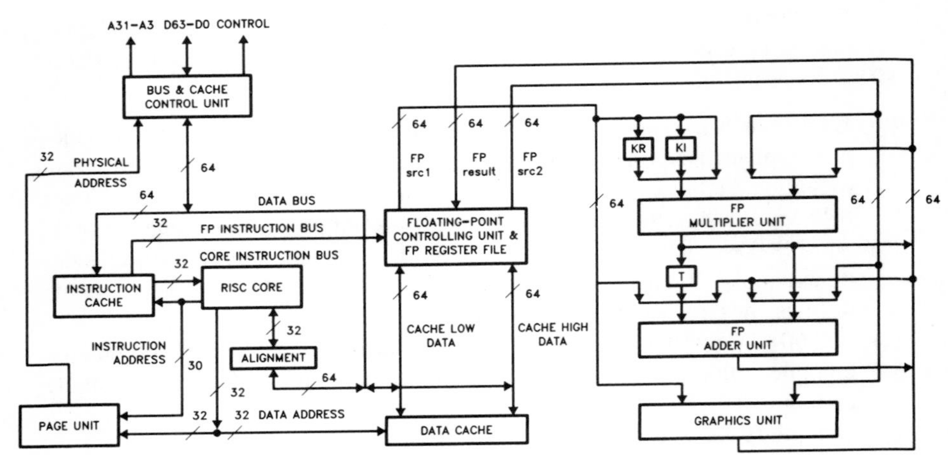

Figure 9.9 The 80860
(Courtesy of Intel Corp.)

The i860 instruction formats are illustrated in Figure 9.10.

The 80860 has 82 single-word (32 bits) instructions, subdivided into the following main groups:

Integer	42
Floating Point	24
Graphic	10
Assembler pseudo-operations	6

All instructions execute in a single cycle. The 80860 Instruction Set is shown in Table 9.2.

Examples of some instructions:

(1) adds src1, src2, rdest; add signed
rdest ← (src1) + (src2)

(2) subs src1, src2, rdest; subtract signed
rdest ← (src1) − (src2)

(3) ld.x src1(src2), rdest; load integer
.x = .b, 8 bits
= .s, 16 bits
= .l, 32 bits
src1 can be either a 16-bit immediate offset or an index register
src2 is an indirect address register
source memory address = (src1) + (src2)
rdest = destination CPU register.

(4) st.x src1, #const(src2); store integer
src1 = source register

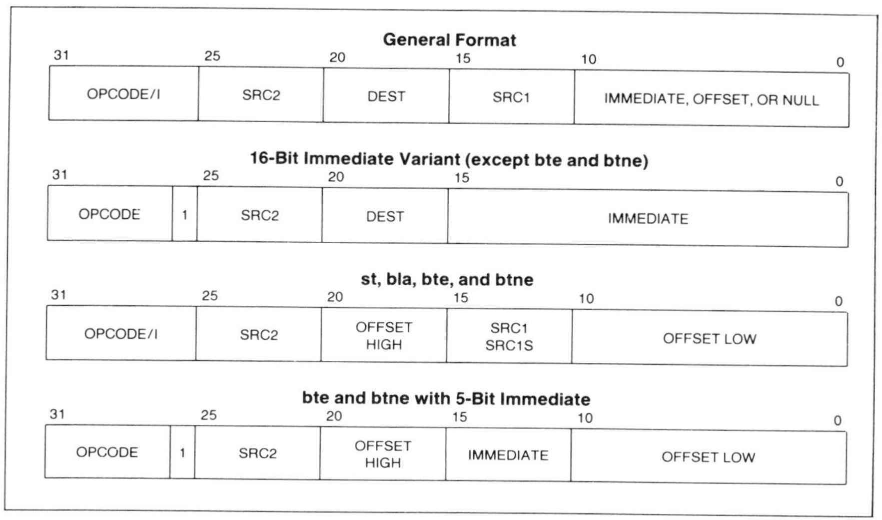

REG-Format Variations

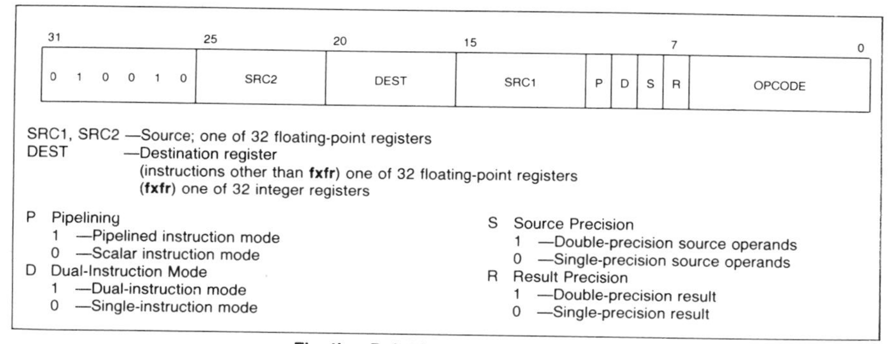

Floating-Point Instruction Encoding

Figure 9.10 80860 Instruction Formats
(*Courtesy of Intel Corp.*)

src2 = destination indirect address register (index register is not allowed for the store instruction).

#const = immediate constant

(5) shl src1, src2, rdest; shift left (logical)
rdest ← src2 shifted left by (src1) bits

(6) mov src2, rdest; register to register move
rdest ← src2
assembler pseudo-operation, equivalent to shl r0, src2, rdest.

Data are normally stored in memory in the little-endian format. The supervisor mode can also optionally select the big-endian format.

Table 9.2 The 80860 Instruction Set
(*Courtesy of Intel Corp.*)

Core Unit	
Mnemonic	**Description**
Load and Store Instructions	
ld.x	Load integer
st.x	Store integer
fld.y	F-P load
pfld.z	Pipelined F-P load
fst.y	F-P store
pst.d	Pixel store
Register to Register Moves	
ixfr	Transfer integer to F-P register
fxfr	Transfer F-P to integer register
Integer Arithmetic Instructions	
addu	Add unsigned
adds	Add signed
subu	Subtract unsigned
subs	Subtract signed
Shift Instructions	
shl	Shift left
shr	Shift right
shra	Shift right arithmetic
shrd	Shift right double
Logical Instructions	
and	Logical AND
andh	Logical AND high
andnot	Logical AND NOT
andnoth	Logical AND NOT high
or	Logical OR
orh	Logical OR high
xor	Logical exclusive OR
xorh	Logical exclusive OR high
Control-Transfer Instructions	
trap	Software trap
intovr	Software trap on integer overflow
br	Branch direct
bri	Branch indirect
bc	Branch on CC
bc.t	Branch on CC taken
bnc	Branch on not CC
bnc.t	Branch on not CC taken
bte	Branch if equal
btne	Branch if not equal
bla	Branch on LCC and add
call	Subroutine call
calli	Indirect subroutine call
System Control Instructions	
flush	Cache flush
ld.c	Load from control register
st.c	Store to control register
lock	Begin interlocked sequence
unlock	End interlocked sequence

Floating-Point Unit	
Mnemonic	**Description**
F-P Multiplier Instruction	
fmul.p	F-P multiply
pfmul.p	Pipelined F-P multiply
pfmul3.dd	3-Stage pipelined F-P multiply
fmlow.p	F-P multiply low
frcp.p	F-P reciprocal
frsqr.p	F-P reciprocal square root
F-P Adder Instructions	
fadd.p	F-P add
pfadd.p	Pipelined F-P add
fsub.p	F-P subtract
pfsub.p	Pipelined F-P subtract
pfgt.p	Pipelined F-P greater-than compare
pfeq.p	Pipelined F-P equal compare
fix.p	F-P to integer conversion
pfix.p	Pipelined F-P to integer conversion
ftrunc.p	F-P to integer truncation
pftrunc.p	Pipelined F-P to integer truncation
Dual-Operation Instructions	
pfam.p	Pipelined F-P add and multiply
pfsm.p	Pipelined F-P subtract and multiply
pfmam.p	Pipelined F-P multiply with add
pfmsm.p	Pipelined F-P multiply with subtract
Long Integer Instructions	
fisub.z	Long-integer subtract
pfisub.z	Pipelined long-integer subtract
fiadd.z	Long-integer add
pfiadd.z	Pipelined long-integer add
Graphics Instructions	
fzchks	16-bit Z-buffer check
pfzchks	Pipelined 16-bit Z-buffer check
fzchkl	32-bit Z-buffer check
pfzchkl	Pipelined 32-bit Z-buffer check
faddp	Add with pixel merge
pfaddp	Pipelined add with pixel merge
faddz	Add with Z merge
pfaddz	Pipelined add with Z merge
form	OR with MERGE register
pform	Pipelined OR with MERGE register

Assembler Pseudo-Operations	
Mnemonic	**Description**
mov	Integer register-register move
fmov.r	F-P reg-reg move
pfmov.r	Pipelined F-P reg-reg move
nop	Core no-operation
fnop	F-P no-operation
pfle.p	Pipelined F-P less-than or equal

The 80860 has separate (non-multiplexed) external 64-bit data and 32-bit address buses. It has 32 general purpose integer and floating point CPU registers, shown in Figure 9.11. The integer unit (RISC core, Figure 9.9) registers are r0 to r31. The r0 register is always zero. The 32 floating point registers (32 bits

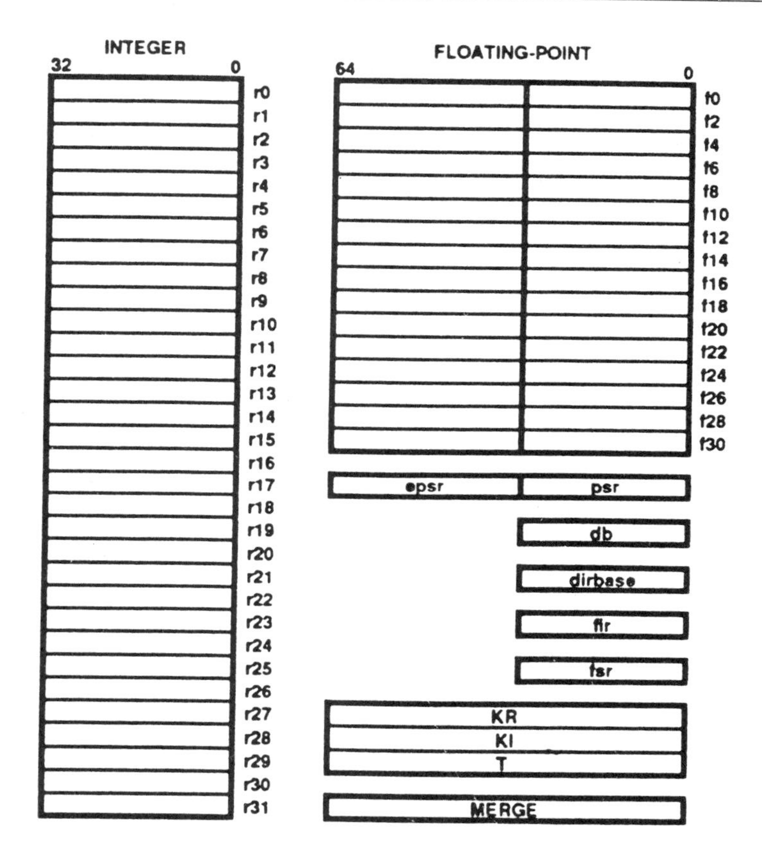

Figure 9.11 80860 Register Set
(*Courtesy of Intel Corp.*)

each) are f0, f1, f2, . . ., f31. They can be grouped into 16 64-bit registers for f0, f2, . . ., f30, as shown in Figure 9.11. The psr (processor status register) and the epsr (extended psr) registers (32 bits each) contain status information for the current process. The db (data breakpoint, 32 bits) register is used to generate a trap when the 860 accesses an operand at the address stored in this register. The dirbase (directory base, 32 bits) register controls address translation, caching, and bus options. The fir (fault instruction register, 32 bits) contains the address of the instruction that caused a trap. The fsr (floating-point status register, 32 bits) contains the floating-point trap and rounding-mode status for the current process. The KR, KI (constant) and the T (temporary) 64-bit registers are used by the dual-operation floating point instructions. The 64-bit MERGE register is used by the graphics instructions. The on-chip bus bandwidth is 960 MBytes/sec. The FPU has three 64-bit operand buses, interconnecting the FPU Controller to the adder, multiplier and graphics units. The 80860 has an operating mode in which it fetches an integer and a floating point instruction in one 64-bit cycle. These two instructions execute *in parallel* in their separate pipelined execution units. The interconnections of the floating point multiplier and adder units are shown on the right side of Figure 9.9. The two subunits can be effectively chained or otherwise reconfigured to produce pipelined results on every clock cycle. Given the operand data, the three units: Integer and the Floating Point Multiply and Add, can perform operations in parallel; three operations per cycle (in pipelined mode). The floating point performance is summarized in Table 9.3.

The on-chip 80860 MMU is compatible to the Intel 80386 Architecture [9.15]. It has a two-level page frame address translation mapping for a 4 KBytes page size. It uses User/Supervisor protection modes. It has a 64-entry, four-way associative Translation Lookaside Buffer (TLB).

The Instruction (4 KBytes) and Data (8 KBytes) on-chip caches are two-way set associative, using a Write-Back policy and a 32-byte line size. There are 64- and 128-bit internal cache paths. The instruction cache can issue a 32-bit integer and a 32-bit floating point instruction simultaneously. The data cache can issue 128 bits of data. The caches are user controllable, as a part of the 80860 system architecture. The internal cache bandwidths are (in MBytes/sec):

Frequency:	33 MHz	40 MHz
Instruction Cache	266	320
Data Cache	532	640

Table 9.3 80860 Floating Point Performance

Operation	Performance			
	Latency Clocks		Pipelined Clocks/Result	
	SP	DP	SP	DP
Adder, OP1+OP2	3	3	1	1
Multiplier, OP1*OP2	3	4	1	2
Dual Floating Point				
OP1+OP2; OP1*OP2			1	2
Divide				
Non IEEE format	22	38	7.5	18
IEEE format	50	76		

SP = Single Precision, 32 bits

DP = Double Precision, 64 bits

The graphics unit has a special 64-bit integer logic that supports three-dimensional (3D) graphics drawing algorithms. The unit can operate in parallel with the core unit. It contains a special purpose MERGE register, and performs multiple additions on integers stored in the floating-point register file. The graphics features assume that:

(a) The surface of a solid object is drawn with polygon patches whose shapes approximate the original object.
(b) The color intensities of the vertices of the polygon and their distances from the viewer are known, but the distances and intensities of the other points must be calculated by interpolation.

The 80860 software features at the moment FORTRAN-77 and C compilers. Green Hills Software (Glendale, CA) is working on an optimizing C compiler, and Pacific Sierra Research (Los Angeles, CA) is preparing a vectorizing preprocessor for FORTRAN code for the 80860 [9.12]. A Unix V, version 4 OS is planned for imminent release. The expected performance under the above optimizing compilers is 85 KDrhystones and 13 Linpack MFLOPS (at 40 MHz). A multiprocessor system, using 80860s as individual processors is planned for the future.

References

9.1 80960KB Hardware Designer's Reference Manual (Order number 270564-001), Intel Corp., Santa Clara, CA, 1988.

9.2 80960KB Programmer's Reference Manual (Order number 270567-001), Intel Corp., Santa Clara, CA, 1988.

9.3 G.J. Myers, D.L. Budde, *The 80960 Microprocessor Architecture*, Wiley, 1988.

9.4 R. Wilson, 'New CPUs Spearhead Intel Attack on Embedded Computing', *Computer Design*, April 15, 1988, pp. 22–28.

9.5 P. Bride, 'Embedded Controllers Push Printer Performance', *ESD*, Jan. 1989, pp. 75–82.

9.6 D. Schoebel, B. Lakey, 'Full House of 80960 Tools', *ESD*, Sept. 1988, pp. 92–95.

9.7 S. McGeady, 'A Programmer's View of the 80960 Architecture', *Proc. COMPCON 89*, pp. 4–9, San Francisco, CA, March 1989.

9.8 G. Hinton, '80960 – Next Generation', *Proc. COMPCON 89*, pp. 13–17, San Francisco, CA, March 1989.

9.9 D.P. Ryan, 'Intel's 80960: An Architecture Optimized for Embedded Control', *IEEE MICRO*, **8**, No. 3, pp. 63–76, June 1988.

9.10 T.S. Perry, 'Intel's Secret is Out', *IEEE Spectrum*, April 1989, pp. 22–28.

9.11 R. Wilson, '80860 CPU Positions Intel to Take On Supercomputers', *Computer Design*, April 1, 1989, pp. 20–23.

9.12 L. Kohn, S.W. Fu, 'A 1,000,000 Transistor Microprocessor', *Proc. 1989 International Solid-State Circuits Conf.*, New York, Feb. 15–17, 1989.

9.13 i80860 64-Bit Microprocessor (Order number 240296-002), Intel Corp., Santa Clara, CA, April 1989.
9.14 i80860 64-Bit Microprocessor Programmer's Reference Manual (Order number 240329-002), Intel Corp., Santa Clara, CA, 1989.
9.15 J.L. Turley, *Advanced 80386 Programming Techniques*, Osborne-McGraw Hill, Berkeley, CA, 1988.

10
The Intergraph CLIPPER

The CLIPPER system was not originally intended to be a RISC. The primary goal of its development, initiated by Fairchild in 1982, was to produce a microprocessor with supercomputer level performance. The CLIPPER was indeed the first microprocessor featuring an on-chip floating point unit and starting its operation at 33 MHz. The CLIPPER features some RISC properties, such as a relatively low instructions count (101), most of the instructions execute in a single cycle, register-to-register operation, and memory access by load/store instructions only [10.1–10.5]. For this reason it was also advertised as a RISC-type system although, as will be seen from the following discussion, it possesses some very definite CISC properties (see chapter 1). In 1987 the CLIPPER operation was acquired by Intergraph Corporation.

The CLIPPER is structured as a chipset *Module*, consisting of three chips:

1. CPU,
2. Cache (Instruction) and MMU (I-CAMMU),
3. Cache (Data) and MMU (D-CAMMU).

A block diagram of the CLIPPER C300 Module with its main interconnections is shown in Figure 10.1. The current C300 Module (CMOS) operating frequency is 50 MHz with 14 MIPS sustained performance. The current top performance CPU/FPU chip is C311, achieving 20 MIPS at 50 MHz. The C300 Module is also featured at 40 MHz (10 MIPS). Thre is also a lower performance product C100, achieving 8 MIPS at 33 MHz.

A detailed block diagram of the CLIPPER CPU/FPU chip (132 pins), showing its internal data flow and subsystems, is presented in Figure 10.2. The CPU has two séparate 32-bit bus outlets, one to the Instruction Cache and one to the Data Cache. However, on each of those buses, the 32-Bit Data and the 32-Bit Address are *multiplexed*. This structure is very similar to that of the Motorola M88000 family described in chapter 6. However, the MC88100 data and instruction buses (PBUS) have separate (non-multiplexed) 32-bit data and address parts.

The CPU integer and floating point subunits are capable of parallel execution. The CPU contains a Macro Instruction Unit, implemented on a 2 KByte ROM, intended for exception processing instructions, interrupt handling instructions and macrocoded instructions. A three-stage pipeline, illustrated in Figure 10.3, is implemented. The main pipeline stages are:

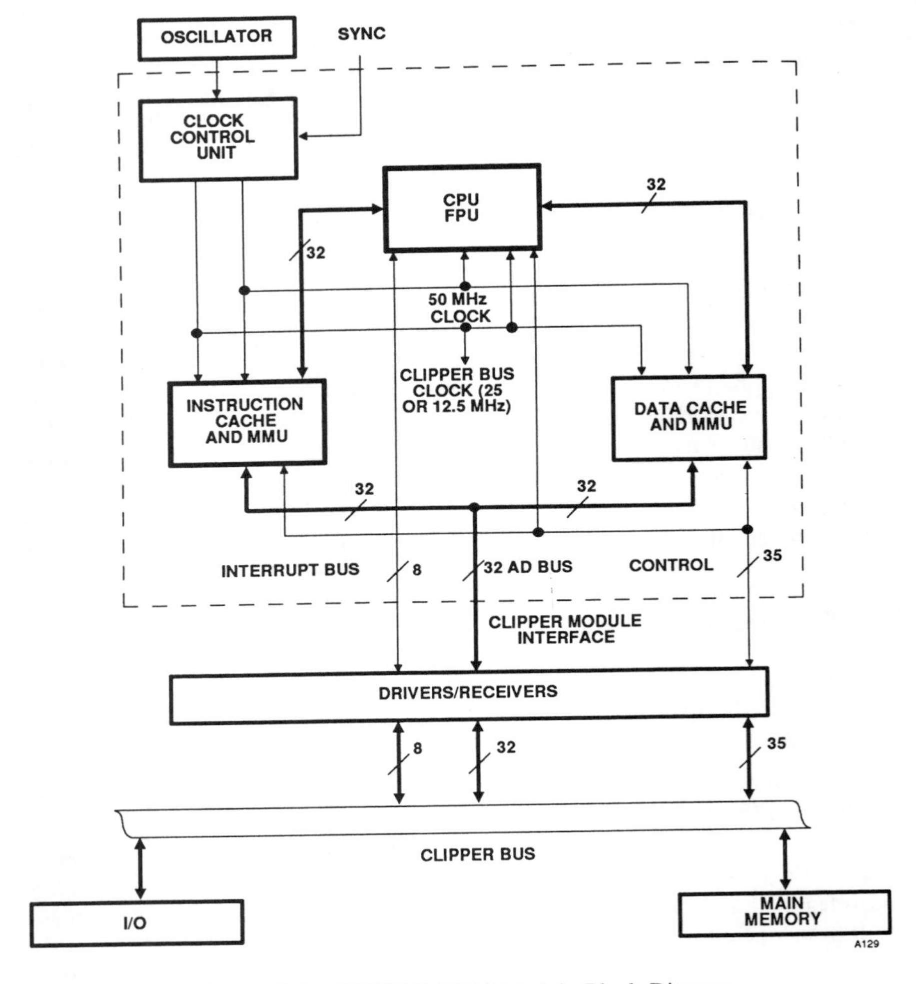

Figure 10.1 CLIPPER C300 Module Block Diagram
(Courtesy of Intergraph Corp.)

1. Fetch,
2. Decode,
3. Execute.

Each pipeline stage is subdivided into substages, as shown in Figure 10.3. The Fetch stage contains two substages:

(a) Cache prefetch, ahead of actual CPU request;
(b) Forwarding the information to the CPU's 8-byte Instruction Buffer, which

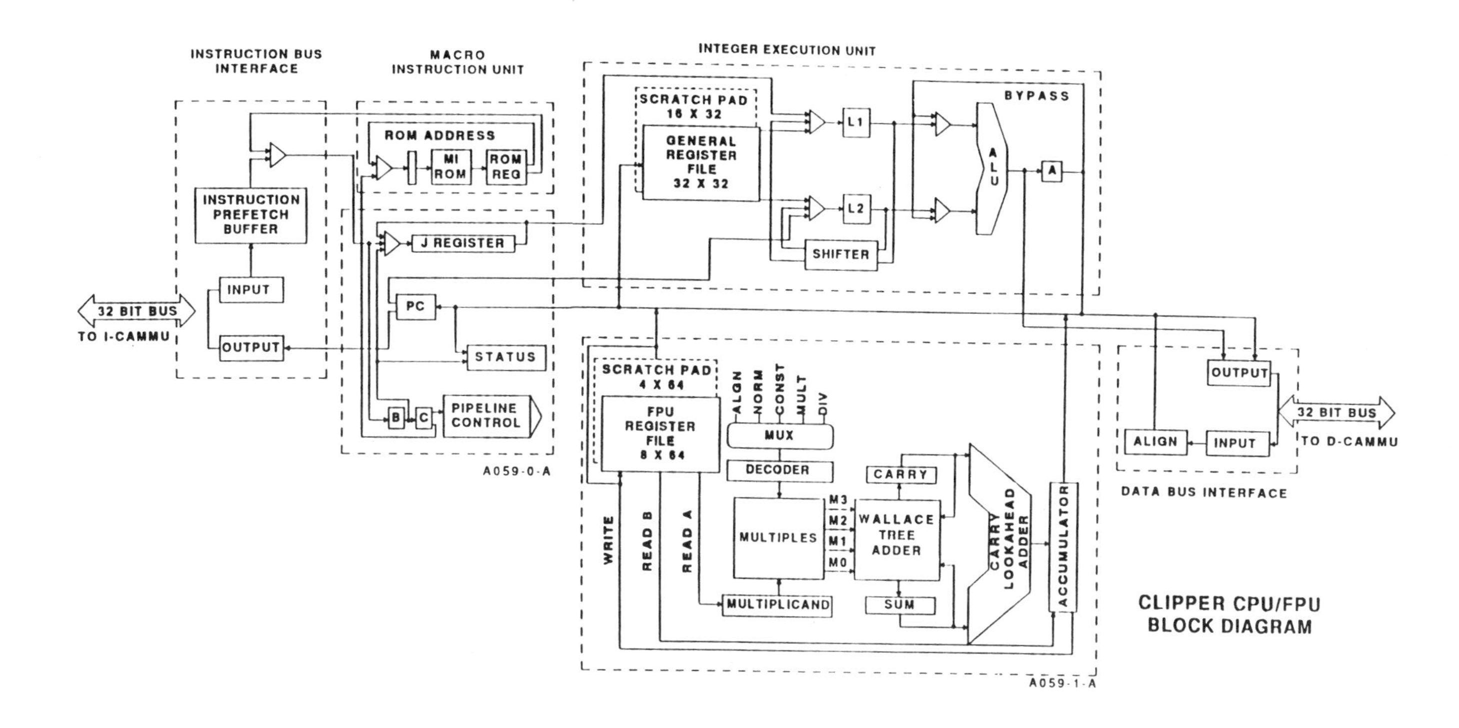

Figure 10.2 C300 CPU/FPU Block Diagram
(*Courtesy of Intergraph Corp.*)

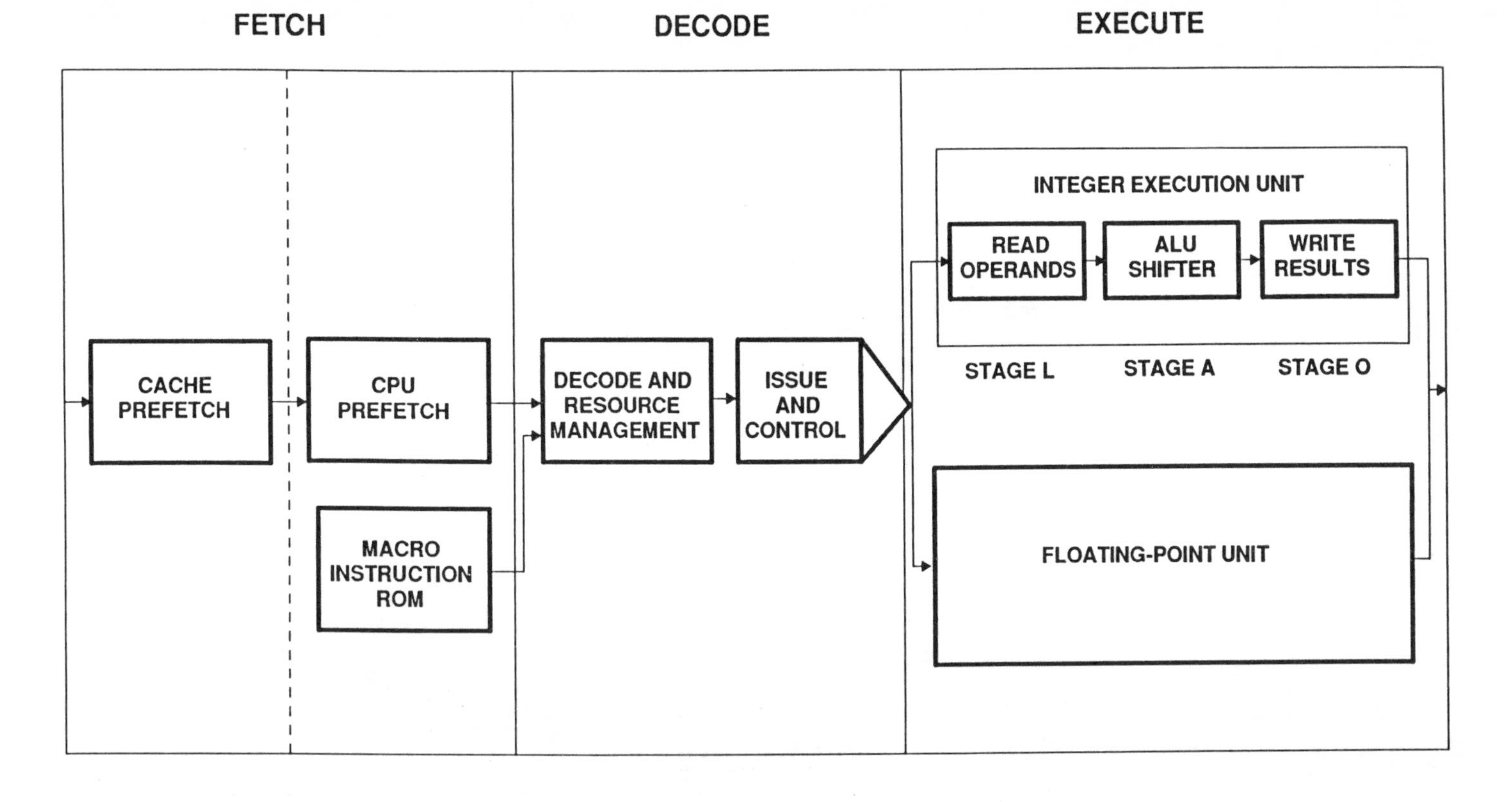

Figure 10.3 CPU Pipeline
(*Courtesy of Intergraph Corp.*)

can hold up to four instructions. Immediate values are sent from the Instruction Buffer via the J register to an L register (L1 or L2) in the ALU (see Figure 10.2).

The Decode stage consists of two parts: B and C, shown in Figure 10.2. The B part obtains instruction parcels from either the Instruction Buffer or the Macro Instruction Unit and decodes them. The C stage issues decoded instructions for execution to the integer or the floating point units in the Execute stage. The integer execution unit is subdivided into three substages:

(a) Read operands from the 3-port register file.
(b) ALU operation with the result going either to register A (Figure 10.2) or to the D-CAMMU interface.
(c) Transmit result from the A register.

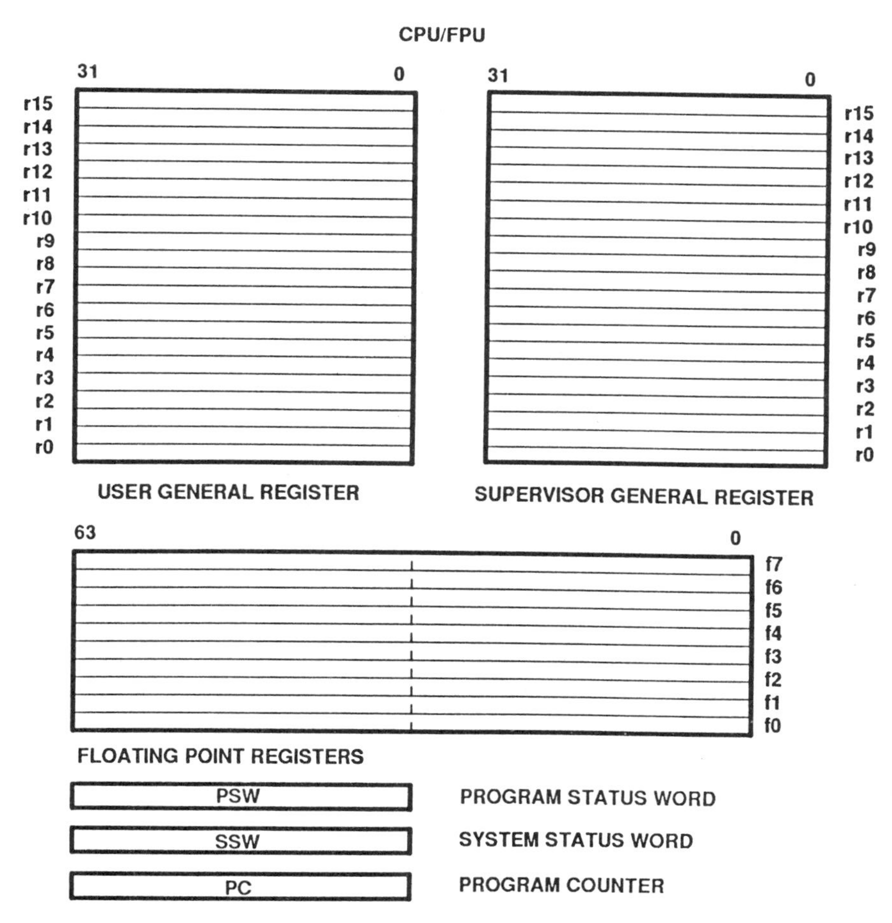

Figure 10.4 Programming Model
(Courtesy of Intergraph Corp.)

The processor programming model is shown in Figure 10.4. It consists of:

16 32-Bit User General Register Set
16 32-Bit Supervisor (OS) General Register Set
8 64-Bit Floating Point Registers

The PC, the SSW (System Status Word), and the PSW (Program Status Word) are separate 32-bit registers. The on-chip 64-Bit Floating Point Unit (FPU) operates on 32- and 64-Bit Floating Point values, according to the IEEE 754 Standard.

The CLIPPER architecture features a total of 10 Data Types, *9 Addressing Modes* (shown in Figure 10.5), and *6 Instruction Formats* (shown in Figure 10.6), which include 4 *Instruction Lengths* of 16, 32, 48 and 64 bits. The last three properties are most definitely those of a CISC; but then, the CLIPPER was not really intended to be a RISC to begin with, as noted earlier. The C300 data types are shown in Figure 10.7 and the representation of data in memory, in Figure 10.8. The little- or big-endian options can be implemented (as in M88000, chapter 6, or in the commercial MIPS, chapter 4). There is a control pin called BIG. If BIG=0, the big-endian ordering is selected, and if BIG=1, the little-endian ordering is in effect.

The CLIPPER instruction set is summarized in Table 10.1. The integer instructions (with the exception of integer multiply and divide) are executed by the Integer Execution Unit (IEU). The floating point instructions and the integer multiply and divide are executed by the FPU (Figure 10.2).

Most instructions are fetched from main memory. Each instruction is fetched through the instruction cache, decoded, then executed either by the IEU or by the FPU. The only exceptions are the *macro* instructions. A macro instruction opcode selects a sequence of instructions in the macro instruction ROM (MI ROM, Figure 10.2). When a macro instruction is decoded, execution control is switched to the MI ROM, and the sequences of the macro instruction are executed.

The information encoded in each instruction specifies the operation to be performed, the type of operands to use (if any), and the location of the operands. The mnemonic and operands of the assembly language source statement determine the instruction format (Figure 10.6) used.

All instructions are constructed in multiples of halfwords (16 bits) called *parcels*. Depending on the instruction format used, the size of an instruction varies from one to four parcels (64 bits, Relative + 32 bit Displacement, Figure 10.5). The instruction formats are divided into two main categories: non-memory referencing instructions (no address) and memory referencing instructions (with address), as illustrated in Figure 10.6.

In the assembly syntax (Table 10.1) the left letter of the operand code specifies the operand's type and size, as follows:

b – byte   s – single floating
h – halfword   d – double floating
w – word   p – processor register
l – longword

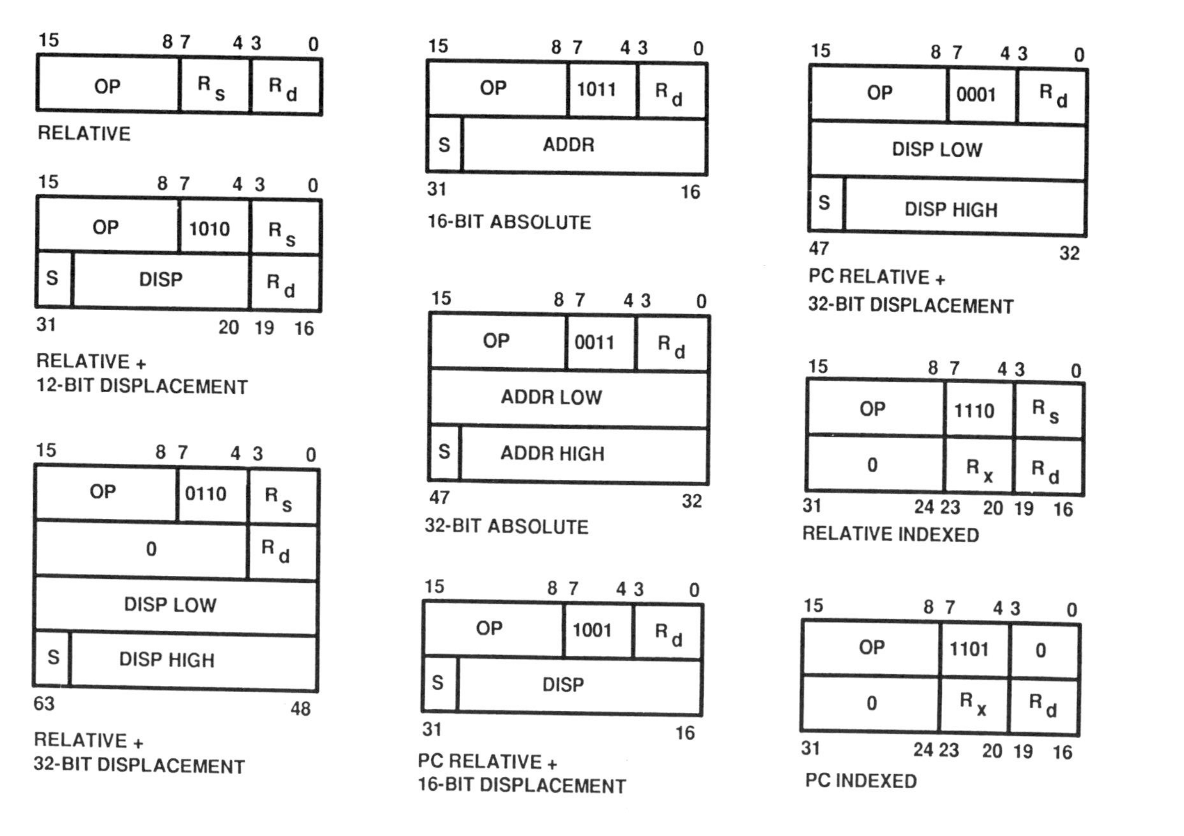

Figure 10.5 Address Modes
(Courtesy of Intergraph Corp.)

Instruction Formats

INSTRUCTION FORMATS - NO ADDRESS

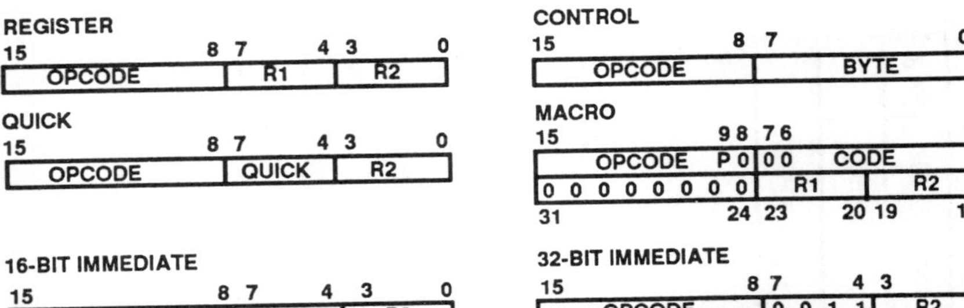

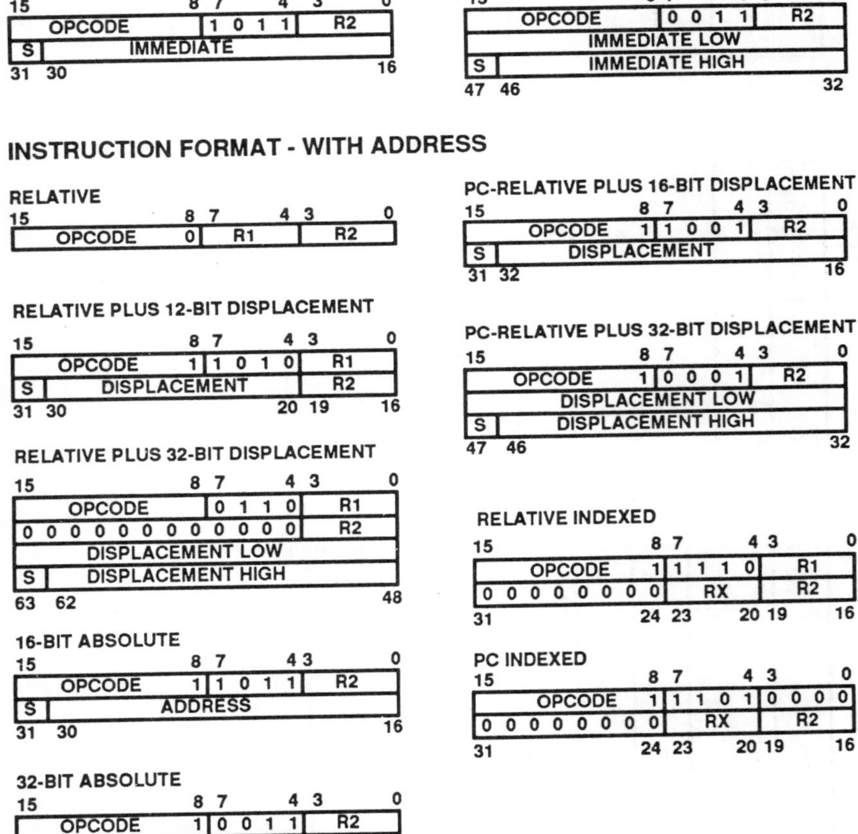

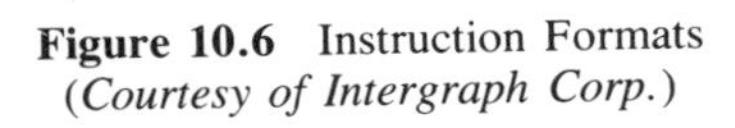

Figure 10.6 Instruction Formats
(Courtesy of Intergraph Corp.)

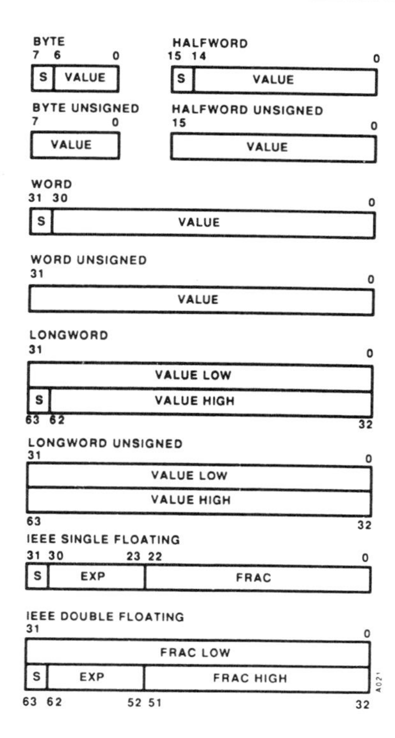

Figure 10.7 C300 Primitive Data Types
(*Courtesy of Intergraph Corp.*)

LITTLE ENDIAN

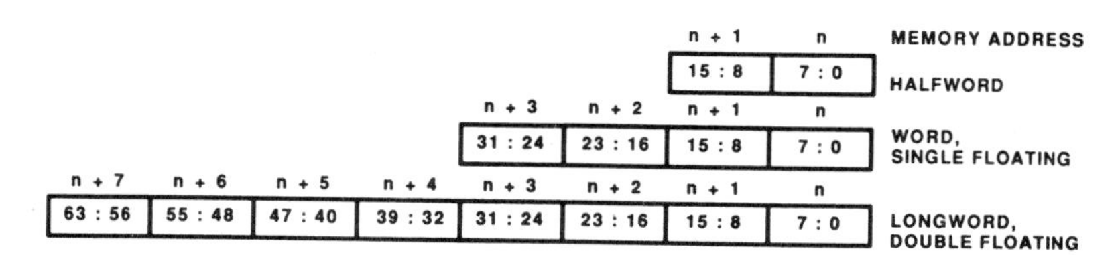

BIG ENDIAN

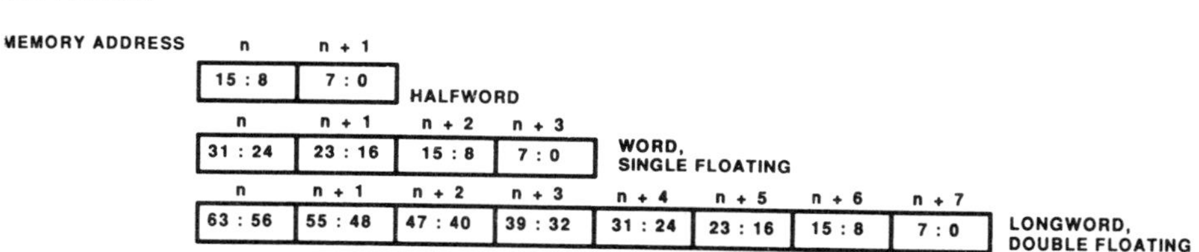

Figure 10.8 Representation of Data in Memory
(*Courtesy of Intergraph Corp.*)

Table 10.1 Instruction Operations
(Courtesy of Intergraph Corp.)

Instruction Name	Syntax		Opcode	Format	Operation	FFFFF IVDUX	CVZN	Traps
Add Double Floating	addd	d1,d2	22	Register	d2 ← (d2) + (d1)	* * . * *	. . . .	
Add Immediate	addi	wi,w2	83	Immediate	w2 ← (w2) + wi	. . . . .	* * * *	I
Add Quick	addq	wq,w2	82	Quick	w2 ← (w2) + wq	. . . . .	* * * *	
Add Single Floating	adds	s1,s2	20	Register	s2 ← (s2) + (s1)	* * . * *	. . . .	
Add Word	addw	w1,w2	80	Register	w2 ← (w2) + (w1)	. . . . .	* * * *	
Add Word with Carry	addwc	w1,w2	90	Register	w2 ← (w2) + (w1) + C	. . . . .	* * * *	
And Immediate	andi	wi,w2	8b	Immediate	w2 ← (w2) & wi	. . . . .	0 0 * *	I
And Word	andw	w1,w2	88	Register	w2 ← (w2) & (w1)	. . . . .	0 0 * *	
Branch on Conditional	b*	ha	48,49	Address	IF cond, PC ← ha	. . . . .	. . . .	A,I
Branch on Floating Exception	bf*	ha	4c,4d	Address	IF cond, PC ← ha	. . . . .	. . . .	A,I
Call Routine	call	w2,ha	44,45	Address	w2 ← (w2) − 4, (w2) ← (PC), PC ← ha	. . . . .	. . . .	A,P,W
Call Supervisor	calls	bb	12	Control	trap 400 + 8 × bb<7:0>	. . . . .	. . . .	
Compare Characters r0=length, r1=string1, r2=string2	cmpc		b4 0f	Macro	while [(r0)≠0] & [((r2))=((r1))], r0 ← (r0) − 1, r1 ← (r1) + 1, r2 ← (r2) + 1	. . . . .	* * * *	C,U,P,R
Compare Double Floating	cmpd	d1,d2	27	Register	(d2) − (d1)	. . . . .	0 0 * *	
Compare Immediate	cmpi	wi,w2	a7	Immediate	(w2) − wi	. . . . .	* * * *	I
Compare Quick	cmpq	wq,w2	a6	Quick	(w2) − wq	. . . . .	* * * *	
Compare Single Floating	cmps	s1,s2	25	Register	(s2) − (s1)	. . . . .	0 0 * *	
Compare Word	cmpw	w1,w2	a4	Register	(w2) − (w1)	. . . . .	* * * *	
Convert Double Floating to Single	cnvds	d1,s2	b4 39	Macro	s2 ← (d1)	* * . * *	. . . .	
Convert Double Floating to Word	cnvdw	d1,w2	b4 34	Macro	w2 ← (d1)	* . . . *	. . . .	
Convert Rounding Double to Word	cnvrdw	d1,w2	b4 35	Macro	w2 ← (d1)	* . . . *	. . . .	
Convert Rounding Single to Word	cnvrsw	s1,w2	b4 31	Macro	w2 ← (s1)	* . . . *	. . . .	
Convert Single Floating to Double	cnvsd	s1,d2	b4 38	Macro	d2 ← (s1)	*	. . . .	
Convert Single Floating to Word	cnvsw	s1,w2	b4 30	Macro	w2 ← (s1)	* . . . *	. . . .	
Convert Truncating Double to Word	cnvtdw	d1,w2	b4 36	Macro	w2 ← (d1)	* . . . *	. . . .	
Convert Truncating Single to Word	cnvtsw	s1,w2	b4 32	Macro	w2 ← (s1)	* . . . *	. . . .	
Convert Word to Double Floating	cnvwd	w1,d2	b4 37	Macro	d2 ← (w1)	. . . . .	. . . .	
Convert Word to Single Floating	cnvws	w1,s2	b4 33	Macro	s2 ← (w1)	. . . . *	. . . .	
Divide Double Floating	divd	d1,d2	2b	Register	d2 ← (d2) ÷ (d1)	* * * * *	. . . .	
Divide Single Floating	divs	s1,s2	29	Register	s2 ← (s2) ÷ (s1)	* * * * *	. . . .	
Divide Word	divw	w1,w2	9c	Register	w2 ← (w2) ÷ (w1)	. . . . .	0 * 0 0	D
Divide Word Unsigned	divwu	w1,w2	9e	Register	w2 ← (w2) ÷ (w1)	. . . . .	0 0 0 0	D
Initialize Characters r0=length, r1=dest, r2=pattern	initc		b4 0e	Macro	while (r1)≠0, (r1) ← (r2<7:0>), r0 ← (r0) − 1, r1 ← (r1) + 1, r2 ← (r2) rot −8	. . . . .	. . . .	P,W
Load Address	loada	ba,w2	62,63	Address	w2 ← ba	. . . . .	. . . .	I
Load Byte	loadb	ba,w2	68,69	Address	w2 ← (ba)	. . . . .	. . . .	C,U,A,P,R,I
Load Byte Unsigned	loadbu	ba,w2	6a,6b	Address	w2 ← (ba)	. . . . .	. . . .	C,U,A,P,R,I
Load Double Floating	loadd	da,d2	66,67	Address	d2 ← (da)	. . . . .	. . . .	C,U,A,P,R,I
Load Floating Status	loadfs	w1,d2	b4 3f	Macro	w1 ← (FP PC), d2 ← (FP dest)	. . . . .	. . . .	
Load Halfword	loadh	ha,w2	6c,6d	Address	w2 ← (ha)	. . . . .	. . . .	C,U,A,P,R,I
Load Halfword Unsigned	loadhu	ha,w2	6e,6f	Address	w2 ← (ha)	. . . . .	. . . .	C,U,A,P,R,I
Load Immediate	loadi	wi,w2	87	Immediate	w2 ← wi	. . . . .	0 0 * *	I
Load Quick	loadq	wq,w2	86	Quick	w2 ← wq	. . . . .	0 0 * 0	
Load Single Floating	loads	sa,s2	64,65	Address	s2 ← (sa)	. . . . .	. . . .	C,U,A,P,R,I
Load Word	loadw	wa,w2	60,61	Address	w2 ← (wa)	. . . . .	. . . .	C,U,A,P,R,I
Modulus Word	modw	w1,w2	9d	Register	w2 ← (w2) mod (w1)	. . . . .	0 * 0 0	D
Modulus Word Unsigned	modwu	w1,w2	9f	Register	w2 ← (w2) mod (w1)	. . . . .	0 0 0 0	D
Move Characters r0=length, r1=source, r2=dest	movc		b4 0d	Macro	while (r0) = 0, (r2) ← ((r1)), r0 ← (r0) − 1, r1 ← (r1) + 1, r2 ← (r2) + 1	. . . . .	. . . .	C,U,P,R,W
Move Double Floating	movd	d1,d2	26	Register	d2 ← (d1)	. . . . .	. . . .	
Move Double Floating to Longword	movdl	d1,l2	2e	Register	l2 ← (d1)	. . . . .	. . . .	
Move Longword to Double Floating	movld	l1,d2	2f	Register	d2 ← (l1)	. . . . .	. . . .	
Move Processor Register to Word	movpw	p1,w2	11	Register	w2 ← (p1)	. . . . .	. . . .	
Move Single Floating	movs	s1,s2	24	Register	s2 ← (s1)	. . . . .	. . . .	
Move Supervisor to User (privileged)	movsu	w1,w2	b6 01	Macro	w2 ← (w1)	. . . . .	0 0 * *	S
Move Single Floating to Word	movsw	s1,w2	2c	Register	w2 ← (s1)	. . . . .	. . . .	
Move User to Supervisor (privileged)	movus	w1,w2	b6 00	Macro	w2 ← (w1)	. . . . .	0 0 * *	S
Move Word	movw	w1,w2	84	Register	w2 ← (w1)	. . . . .	0 0 * *	
Move Word to Processor Register	movwp	w2,p1	10	Register	p1 ← (w2)	. . . . .	* * * *	
Move Word to Single Floating	movws	w1,s2	2d	Register	s2 ← (w1)	. . . . .	. . . .	
Multiply Double Floating	muld	d1,d2	2a	Register	d2 ← (d2) × (d1)	* * . * *	. . . .	
Multiply Single Floating	muls	s1,s2	28	Register	s2 ← (s2) × (s1)	* * . * *	. . . .	
Multiply Word	mulw	w1,w2	98	Register	w2 ← (w2) × (w1)	. . . . .	0 * 0 0	
Multiply Word Unsigned	mulwu	w1,w2	9a	Register	w2 ← (w2) × (w1)	. . . . .	0 * 0 0	
Multiply Word Unsigned Extended	mulwux	w1,l2	9b	Register	l2 ← (w2) × (w1)	. . . . .	0 * 0 0	
Multiply Word Extended	mulwx	w1,l2	99	Register	l2 ← (w2) × (w1)	. . . . .	0 * 0 0	

Table 10.1 *(cont'd)*

Instruction Name	Syntax		Opcode	Format	Operation	FFFFF IVDUX	CVZN	Traps
Negate Double Floating	negd	d1,d2	b4 3b	Macro	d2 ← − (d1)	. . . . .	. . . .	
Negate Single Floating	negs	s1,s2	b4 3a	Macro	s2 ← − (s1)	. . . . .	. . . .	
Negate Word	negw	w1,w2	93	Register	w2 ← − (w1)	. . . . .	* * * *	
No Operation	noop	bb	00	Control	none	. . . . .	. . . .	
Not Quick	notq	wq,w2	ae	Quick	w2 ← ~wq	. . . . .	0 0 0 1	
Not Word	notw	w1,w2	ac	Register	w2 ← ~(w1)	. . . . .	0 0 * *	
Or Immediate	ori	wi,w2	8f	Immediate	w2 ← (w2) | wi	. . . . .	0 0 * *	I
Or Word	orw	w1,w2	8c	Register	w2 ← (w2) | (w1)	. . . . .	0 0 * *	
Pop Word	popw	w1,w2	16	Register	w1 ← (w1) + 4, w2 ← ((w1) − 4)	. . . . .	. . . .	C,U,A,P,R
Push Word	pushw	w2,w1	14	Register	w1 ← (w1) − 4, (w1) ← (w2)	. . . . .	. . . .	A,P,W
Restore Registers *fn* .. f7 0 ≤ *n* ≤ 7	restd*n*		b4 28 .. b4 2F	Macro	*fn* .. f7 ← ((r15)) .. ((r15) + 8 × [7−*n*]), r15 ← (r15) + 8 × [8−*n*]	. . . . .	. . . .	C,U,A,P,R
Restore User Registers (privileged)	restur	w1	b6 03	Macro	r0 .. r15 ← ((w1)) .. ((w1) + 60)	. . . . .	. . . .	C,U,A,P,R,S
Restore Registers *rn* .. r14 0 ≤ *n* ≤ 12	restw*n*		b4 10 .. b4 1C	Macro	*rn* .. r14 ← ((r15)) .. ((r15) + 4 × [14−*n*]), r15 ← (r15) + 4 × [15−*n*]	. . . . .	. . . .	C,U,A,P,R
Return From Routine	ret	w2	13	Register	PC ← ((w2)) w2 ← (w2) + 4	. . . . .	. . . .	C,U,A,P,R
Return From Interrupt (privileged)	reti	w1	b6 04	Macro	Restore SSW, PSW and PC	. . . . .	* * * *	S
Rotate Immediate	roti	wi,w2	3c	Immediate	w2 ← (w2) rot wi	. . . . .	0 0 * *	I
Rotate Longword	rotl	w1,l2	35	Register	l2 ← (l2) rot (w1)	. . . . .	0 0 * *	
Rotate Longword Immediate	rotli	wi,l2	3d	Immediate	l2 ← (l2) rot wi	. . . . .	0 0 * *	I
Rotate Word	rotw	w1,w2	34	Register	w2 ← (w2) rot (w1)	. . . . .	0 0 * *	
Save Registers *fn* .. f7 0 ≤ *n* ≤ 7	saved*n*		b4 20 .. b4 27	Macro	(r15) − 8 × [8 − *n*] .. (r15) − 8 ← (*fn*) .. (f7), r15 ← (r15) − 8 × [8 − *n*]	. . . . .	. . . .	A,P,W
Save User Registers (privileged)	saveur	*w1*	b6 02	Macro	(w1) − 4 .. (w1) − 64 ← (r15) .. (r0)	. . . . .	. . . .	A,P,W,S
Save Registers *rn* .. r14 0 ≤ *n* ≤ 12	savew*n*		b4 00 .. b4 0C	Macro	(r15) − 4 × [15 −*n*] .. (r15) − 4 ← (*rn*) .. (r14), r15 ← (r15) − 4 x [15 - n]	. . . . .	. . . .	A,P,W
Scale by, Double Floating	scalbd	w1,d2	b4 3d	Macro	d2 ← (d2) × $2^{(w1)}$	* * . * *	. . . *	
Scale by, Single Floating	scalbs	w1,s2	b4 3c	Macro	s2 ← (s2) × $2^{(w1)}$	* * . * *	. . . .	
Shift Arithmetic Immediate	shai	wi,w2	38	Immediate	w2 ← (w2) sha wi	. . . . .	0 * * *	I
Shift Arithmetic Longword	shal	w1,l2	31	Register	l2 ← (l2) sha (w1)	. . . . .	0 * * *	
Shift Arithmetic Longword Immediate	shali	wi,l2	39	Immediate	l2 ← (l2) sha wi	. . . . .	0 * * *	I
Shift Arithmetic Word	shaw	w1,w2	30	Register	w2 ← (w2) sha (w1)	. . . . .	0 * * *	
Shift Logical Immediate	shli	wi,w2	3a	Immediate	w2 ← (w2) shl wi	. . . . .	0 0 * *	I
Shift Logical Longword	shll	w1,l2	33	Register	l2 ← (l2) shl (w1)	. . . . .	0 0 * *	
Shift Logical Longword Immediate	shlli	wi,l2	3b	Immediate	l2 ← (l2) shl wi	. . . . .	0 0 * *	I
Shift Logical Word	shlw	w1,w2	32	Register	w2 ← (w2) shl (w1)	. . . . .	0 0 * *	
Store Byte	storb	w2,ba	78,79	Address	ba ← (w2)	. . . . .	. . . .	A,P,W,I
Store Double Floating	stord	d2,da	76,77	Address	da ← (d2)	. . . . .	. . . .	A,P,W,I
Store Halfword	storh	w2,ha	7c,7d	Address	ha ← (w2)	. . . . .	. . . .	A,P,W,I
Store Single Floating	stors	s2,sa	74,75	Address	sa ← (s2)	. . . . .	. . . .	A,P,W,I
Store Word	storw	w2,wa	70,71	Address	wa ← (w2)	. . . . .	. . . .	A,P,W,I
Subtract Double Floating	subd	d1,d2	23	Register	d2 ← (d2) − (d1)	* * . * *	. . . .	
Subtract Immediate	subi	wi,w2	a3	Immediate	w2 ← (w2) − wi	. . . . .	* * * *	I
Subtract Quick	subq	wq,w2	a2	Quick	w2 ← (w2) − wq	. . . . .	* * * *	
Subtract Single Floating	subs	s1,s2	21	Register	s2 ← (s2) − (s1)	* * . * *	. . . .	
Subtract Word	subw	w1,w2	a0	Register	w2 ← (w2) − (w1)	. . . . .	* * * *	
Subtract Word with Carry	subwc	w1,w2	91	Register	w2 ← (w2) − (w1) − C	. . . . .	* * * *	
Test and Set	tsts	wa,w2	72,73	Address	w2 ← (wa), wa ← 1	. . . . .	. . . .	C,U,A,P, R,W,I
Trap on Floating Unordered	trapfn		b4 3e	Macro	IF PSW<ZN> indicates unordered, illegal instruction trap	. . . . .	. . . .	I
Wait for Interrupt (privileged)	wait		b6 05	Macro	Wait for interrupt	. . . . .	. . . .	S
Exclusive-OR Immediate	xori	wi,w2	ab	Immediate	w2 ← (w2) ⊕ wi	. . . . .	0 0 * *	I
Exclusive-OR Word	xorw	w1,w2	a8	Register	w2 ← (w2) ⊕ (w1)	. . . . .	0 0 * *	

Legend:

PSW Flags Field
- . = Flag not affected by instruction
- * = Flag set according to operation
- 0 = Flag set to 0
- 1 = Flag set to 1

Traps Field
- D = Divide-by-zero
- I = Illegal instruction
- M = Memory fault
- P = Page fault
- R = Read protect fault
- S = Supervisor only (priviledged) instruction
- W = Write protect fault

The right letter of the operand code specifies the operand's field within the instruction and its location in the system, as follows:

1 – R1 (field in Figure 10.6)	i – immediate
2 – R2 (field in Figure 10.6)	a – address
q – quick	b – byte

EXAMPLE: The operand code *w1* indicates a word operand in the general register whose number is encoded in the R1 field of the instruction. The code *sa* indicates a single floating-point operand in the memory location whose address is given by one of the addressing modes (Figure 10.5).

Quick and immediate operand types are always w because these directly encoded values are always zero or sign extended to a word before use.

The column in Table 10.1, denoted by FI, FV, FD, FU, FX, specifies the effect of the instruction on the floating-point exception flags in the Program Status Word (PSW). Similarly, the CVZN (condition flags in PSW) specify the effect of the instruction on these condition flags.

The last column specifies the traps that can be caused by the instruction:

C – Corrected memory error
U – Uncorrectable memory error
A – Data Alignment fault
P – Page fault
R – Read Protect fault
W – Write Protect fault
D – Divide by zero
I – Illegal operation
S – Supervisor only (privileged) instruction.

The CLIPPER architecture supports 404 exception conditions: 20 hardware traps, 128 programmable supervisor call traps, and 256 vectored interrupts. Traps are exceptions recognized by the CPU during execution of single instructions (divide by zero, page faults). A trap causes all instructions in both the upper and lower pipelines to be either backed out or completed in a manner consistent with program restart. Interrupts are events signalled by devices external to the CLIPPER module and are transmitted to the module via the interrupt pins.

The address of the service routine for each trap, supervisor call and interrupt is stored in an *Exception Vector Table* (EVT), located in the first real page of main memory. The EVT is shown in Table 10.2. It contains a two-word (64 bits) entry for each exception, consisting of the starting address of the exception's service routine and a System Status Word (SSW) value associated with the routine. The SSW controls the routine's mode of operation and provides status and control for program protection and the response to interrupts. Unassigned EVT addresses are reserved for future use by Intergraph and must be initialized to point to a valid handler routine.

Table 10.2 Exception Vector Table
(*Courtesy of Intergraph Corp.*)

Real Address (Hex)	Description
Data Memory Trap Group	
108	Corrected Memory Error
110	Uncorrectable Memory Error
120	Alignment Fault
128	Page Fault
130	Read Protect Fault
138	Write Protect Fault
Floating-Point Arithmetic Trap Group	
180	Floating Inexact
188	Floating Underflow
190	Floating Divide by Zero
1A0	Floating Overflow
1C0	Floating Invalid Operation
Integer Arithmetic Trap Group	
208	Integer Divided by Zero
Instruction Memory Trap Group	
288	Corrected Memory Error
290	Uncorrectable Memory Error
2A0	Alignment Fault
2A8	Page Fault
2B0	Execute Protect Fault
Ilegal Operation Trap Group	
300	Illegal Operation
308	Privileged Instruction
Diagnostic Trap Group	
380	Trace Trap
Supervisor Calls	
400	Supervisor Call 0
408	Supervisor Call 1
.	
.	
.	
7F8	Supervisor Call 127
Prioritized Interrupts:	
800	Non-Maskable Interrupt
808	Interrupt Level 0 Number 1
810	Interrupt Level 0 Number 2
.	
.	
.	
878	Interrupt Level 0 Number 15
880	Interrupt Level 1 Number 0
888	Interrupt Level 1 Number 1
.	
.	
.	
FF8	Interrupt Level 15 Number 15

The priority of exceptions is the order shown in the EVT (Table 10.2) in the order from highest to lowest priority, except that the Trace Trap (380) has the lowest priority. The CLIPPER Module's internal priority logic ensures that exception service is always granted to the highest priority event.

The CLIPPER Module interface with memory and I/O is shown in Figure 10.9. With 32 address lines there is a 4 GByte Virtual Address (VA) space per process and also 4 GBytes of Real (Physical) Memory. Demand-Paged (page size 4 KBytes) Virtual Memory Management is implemented, with separate User and Supervisor Modes. The Memory Management logic is realized on the two CAMMU chips mentioned above. Each such chip contains a 4 KByte Cache and the MMU logic. The MMU logic contains a 128 entries 2-way Set-Associative (2 entries/set) Translation Lookaside Buffer (TLB) to translate Virtual to Physical or Real Addresses (RA). The TLB, along with its entries, is illustrated in Figure 10.10.

The Cache of one CAMMU chip is used for Instructions and the other for Data. Both Caches are identical in their structure and management policies. Each 4 KByte (2^{12}) cache is subdivided into 256 (2^8) Blocks (lines) with 16 (2^4) Bytes/

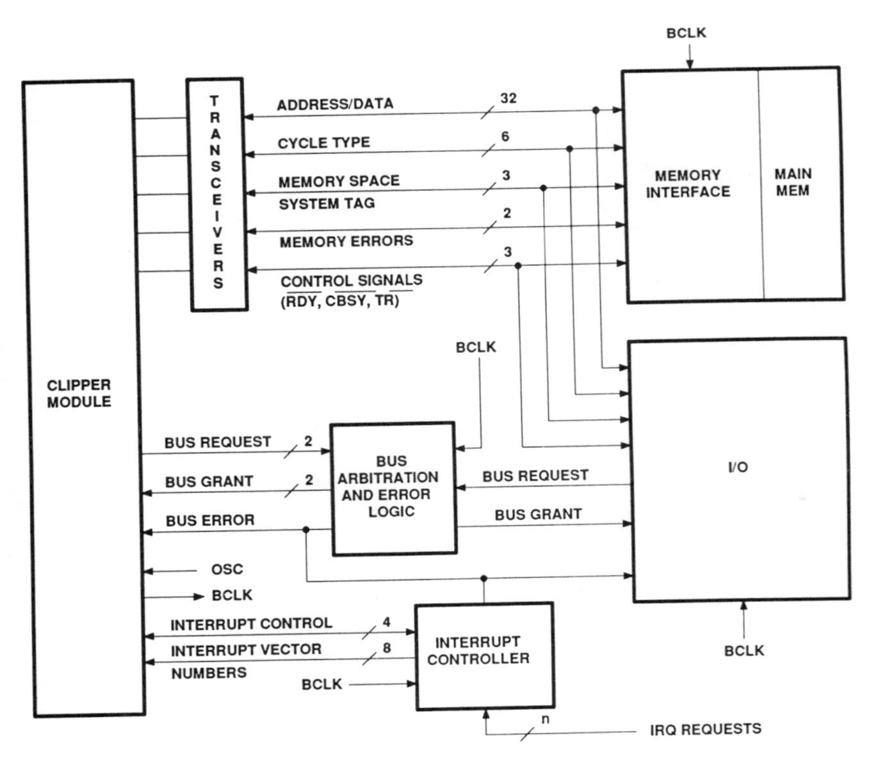

Figure 10.9 Example CLIPPER Configuration
(Courtesy of Intergraph Corp.)

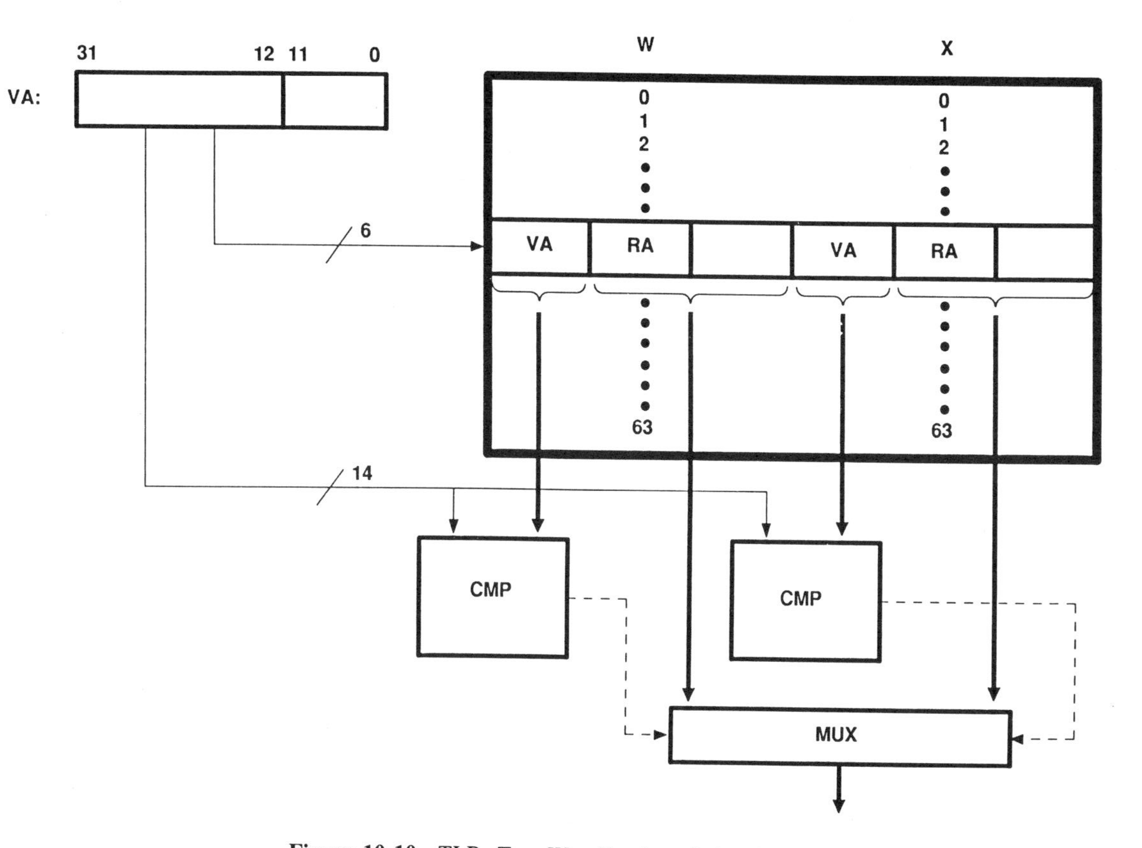

Figure 10.10 TLB: Two-Way Set-Associative Cache
(*Courtesy of Intergraph Corp.*)

Block. Each cache is 2-way Set-Associative. A Least Recently Used (LRU) replacement policy is implemented. Both the Instruction and Data Caches operate with a demand (by the CPU) block-fetching policy. Optionally, the Instruction Cache can operate with a block-prefetch algorithm. Write-through, copy-back and nocacheable data policies can be implemented on a per-page basis. A higher-size cache implementation (up to 256 KBytes per CAMMU) is planned in future Intergraph products.

The CLIPPER supports multiprocessing implementation by the following features:

(1) Bus Watch checks (bus 'snooping') of all caches in the system.
(2) Global writes access to all caches and TLBs in the system.
(3) Global system clock synchronization.
(4) Atomic Test-And-Set operation for semaphore handling.
(5) Multiple caching strategies.

The CLIPPER OS is the CLIX System V 3.0, derived from AT&T's UNIX System V, Release 3.0. The CLIX new capabilities include:

(a) STREAMS: a general facility for developing communication and networking services.
(b) Remote File Sharing: allows transparent sharing of files and directories among computers that are linked by a network.
(c) Shared Libraries of routines that are accessed dynamically at run-time rather than being combined with applications at link-time.

Intergraph provides three optimizing compilers for the CLIPPER system:

(1) C – implements the entire C language as defined originally, including AT&T and Berkeley extensions.
(2) FORTRAN – implements the full ANSI FORTRAN-77 language.
(3) Pascal – implements the ANSI Pascal standard and ISO Pascal, level 0.

All three compilers make use of optimization techniques to generate compact CLIPPER code that executes quickly. They are hosted on the CLIX System V OS.

References

10.1 C.B. Hunter, 'Introduction to the CLIPPER Architecture', *IEEE MICRO*, **7**, No. 4, pp. 6–26, Aug. 1987.

10.2 W. Hollingsworth, H. Sachs, A.J. Smith, 'The CLIPPER Processor: Instruction Set Architecture and Implementation', *Comm. ACM*, **32**, No. 2, pp. 200–219, Feb. 1989.

10.3 N. Mokhoff, 'New RISC Machines Appear as Hybrids with both RISC and CISC Features', *Computer Design*, April 1, 1986, pp. 22–25.

10.4 *CLIPPER C300 Data Sheet Manual*, Intergraph Corp., Palo Alto, CA, Sept. 1988.

10.5 *Introduction to the CLIPPER Architecture*, Intergraph Corp., Palo Alto, CA, Jan. 1989.

11
The Acorn and VLSI Technology System

The Acorn (UK) and VLSI Technology (Phoenix, AZ) microprocessor system was originally intended to be a simple, low cost, 32-bit system to be used in high-performance personal computers [11.1–11.6]. As the development progressed, it was realized that the system possesses some very definite RISC properties, such as a low number of instructions (46), addressing modes (2), and instruction formats (6), almost all instructions execute in a single cycle, memory access is performed by load/store instructions only, and the control is hardwired (see section 1.3). The Acorn RISC Machine (ARM) was designed to provide a superior cost/performance ratio and to maintain a low real-time interrupt latency. This makes the system particularly attractive for real-time controller applications.

The Acorn system operates with a 24 MHz clock that yields a basic processor frequency of 8 MHz (125 ns cycle). Higher frequency models are under development. The current VLSI Technology system is a 2-micron CMOS with up to 6 MIPS performance. The following chips are currently featured:

VL86C010	CPU, 84 pins,
VL86C110	Memory Controller, MEMC, 68 pins,
VL86C310	Video Controller, VIDC, 68 pins,
VL86C410	I/O Controller, IOC, 68 pins.

A block diagram of the VL86C010 CPU is shown in Figure 11.1. Its interface signals are shown in Figure 11.2.

The Acorn architecture recognizes only two basic data types:

Byte	8 bits
Word	32 bits.

All instructions are 32-bit words, aligned on word boundaries in memory. All instructions are fetchable in one clock cycle (125 ns). All instructions are executed in one cycle, except for a multiply and a multiple-register load/store. However, the latter is executed on the basis of one cycle per register. All operations are performed on 32-bit quantities. Bytes can be extracted and zero-extended to 32 bits. Load and Store operations can be performed also on bytes.

There exist 46 basic instruction codes, subdivided into five categories:

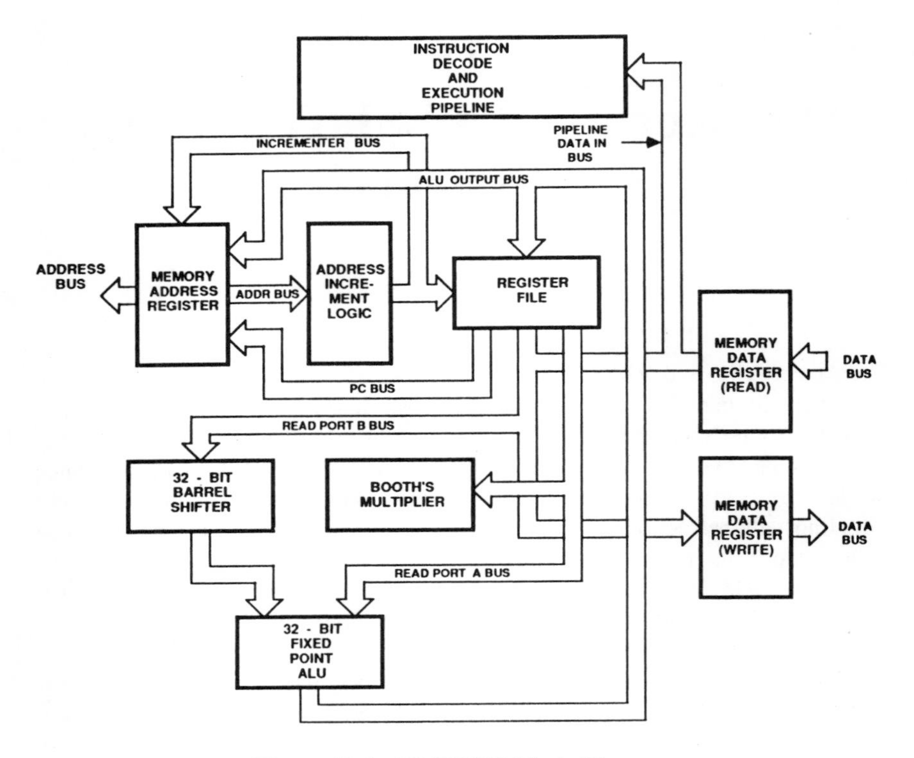

Figure 11.1 VL86C010 Block Diagram
(Courtesy of VLSI Technology, Inc.)

(1) Load/Store single register.
(2) Load/Store multiple registers.
(3) Arithmetic/Logic – all register-to-register.
(4) Branch.
(5) Software interrupt.

The VL86C010 instructions are summarized in Table 11.1. The Load and Store instructions are the only ones that access the main memory. Divide and Floating Point operations are not supported by the system. *All instructions are conditional*; they include a test that must be true before they will execute. The first four bits of each opcode select one of 16 possible conditions. This skip-on-test feature avoids pipeline delays. The instructions can have up to three operands. All instructions have conditional execution implementing a type of *skip architecture*. Unexecuted instructions require a single processor cycle and keep the three-stage pipeline intact. This approach was taken as opposed to the delayed branch approach (chapter 1) to simplify the virtual memory page fault recovery process. When the branch and delayed instruction are contained on separate physical pages and

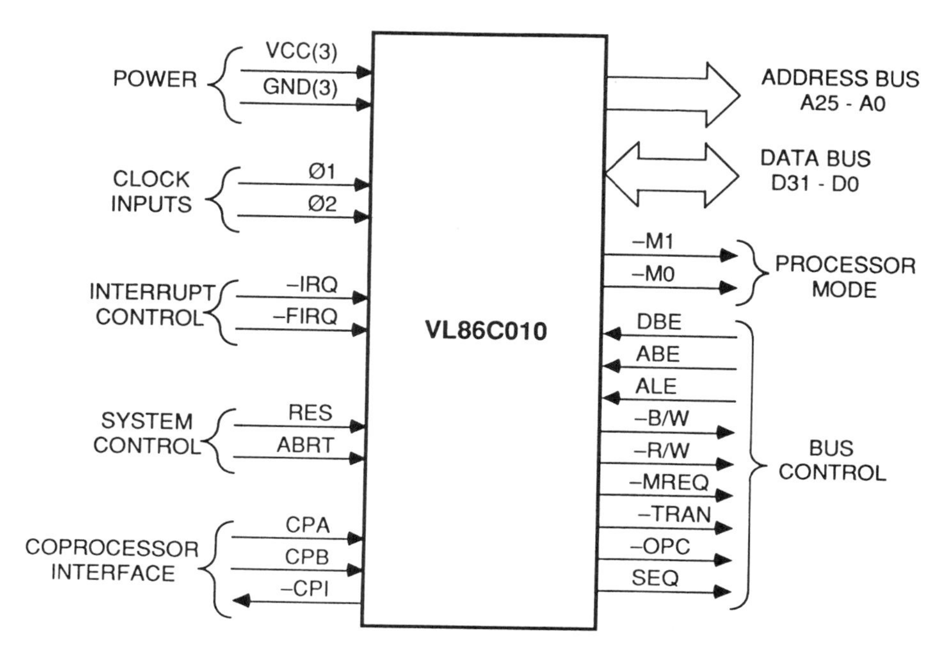

Figure 11.2 VL86C010 Functional Interface Signals
(*Courtesy of VLSI Technology, Inc.*)

a fault occurs on the fetch after the taken branch, the recovery process can be extremely expensive in both software and hardware complexity.

Two types of branch instructions are supported: branch and branch-with-link for subroutine calls. Both branch types offer conditional execution. For subroutine calls, the current value of the machine state contained in register R15, program counter and status register, is copied into register R14. Linking subroutine calls through the registers instead of the memory stack reduces the call/return overhead. For a single-level linkage, the state is saved within the machine in a single clock and can be restored also in a single clock. For multi-level call sequences, full machine state is contained in a single word, requiring only a single memory reference for stacking.

Two types of data transfer instructions are supported for memory references. A single register can be read or written to memory in two clock cycles. In order to exploit sequential memory access modes, the processor also performs load and store multiple operations. For these instructions more than one register is transferred, taking two clocks for the first register and one clock for each additional one. This instruction enhances the processor's ability to move large blocks of memory and context switches that save the entire machine state. A block transfer instruction of all 16 registers is the largest instruction and, therefore, is the limiting factor in interrupt response time.

Table 11.1 VL86C010 Instructions
(*Courtesy of VLSI Technology, Inc.*)

FUNCTION	MNEMONIC	OPERATION	PROCESSOR CYCLES
Data Processing			
Add with Carry	ADC	Rd:=Rn + Shift(Rm) + C	1S
Add	ADD	Rd:=Rn + Shift(Rm)	1S
And	AND	Rd:=Rn • Shift(Rm)	1S
Bit Clear	BIC	Rd:=Rn • Not Shift(Rm)	1S
Compare Negative	CMN	Shift(Rm) + Rn	1S
Compare	CMP	Rn – Shift(Rm)	1S
Exclusive - OR	EOR	Rd:=Rn XOR Shift(Rm)	1S
Multiply with Accumulate	MLA	Rn:=Rm * Rs + Rd	16S max
Move	MOV	Rn:=Shift(Rm)	1S
Multiply	MUL	Rn:=Rm * Rs	16S max
Move Negative	MVN	Rd:=NOT Shift(Rm)	1S
Inclusive - OR	ORR	Rd:=Rn OR Shift(Rm)	1S
Reverse Subtract	RSB	Rd:=Shift(Rm) - Rn	1S
Reverse Subtract with Carry	RSC	Rd:=Shift(Rm) - Rn - 1 + C	1S
Subtract with Carry	SBC	Rd:=Rn - Shift(Rm) - 1 + C	1S
Subtract	SUB	Rd:=Rn - Shift(Rm)	1S
Test for Equality	TEQ	Rn XOR Shift(Rm)	1S
Test Masked	TST	Rn • Shift(Rm)	1S
Data Transfer			
Load Register	LDR	Rd:=Effective address	2S + 1N
Store Register	STR	Effective address:= Rd	2N
Multiple Data Transfer			
Load Multiple	LDM	Rlist:=Effective Address	(n**+1)S + 1N
Store Multiple	STM	Effective Address:=Rlist	(n**+1)S + 2N
Jump			
Branch	B	PC:=PC+Offset	2S + 1N
Branch and Link	BL	R14:=PC, PC:= PC+Offset	2S + 1N
Software Interrupt	SWI	R14:=PC, PC:= Vector #	2S + 1N

*Shift() denotes the output of the 32-bit barrel-shifter. One operand can be shifted in several manners on every data processing instruction without requiring any additional cycles.

** - n is the number of registers in the transfer list.

N denotes a non-sequential memory cycle and S a sequential cycle.

The processor cycles column in Table 11.1 is expressed in terms of N (Non-sequential) and S (Sequential) cycles. The processor is able to take advantage of memories that have faster access time when accessed sequentially. These faster cycles are designated as S-cycles, while the N-cycles typically take twice as long. If faster static memory is used, the N and S cycles would be equal.

There are only two Addressing Modes:

1. Base Relative, with a 12-bit immediate source or a second register;
2. Program Relative.

The CPU has a 27 32-bit, partially overlapped, Register File; however, only 16 of the registers are normally available to the programmer. The CPU register model is illustrated in Figure 11.3. The extra 9 registers become available to the processor during interrupts to simulate a Direct Memory Access (DMA) channel,

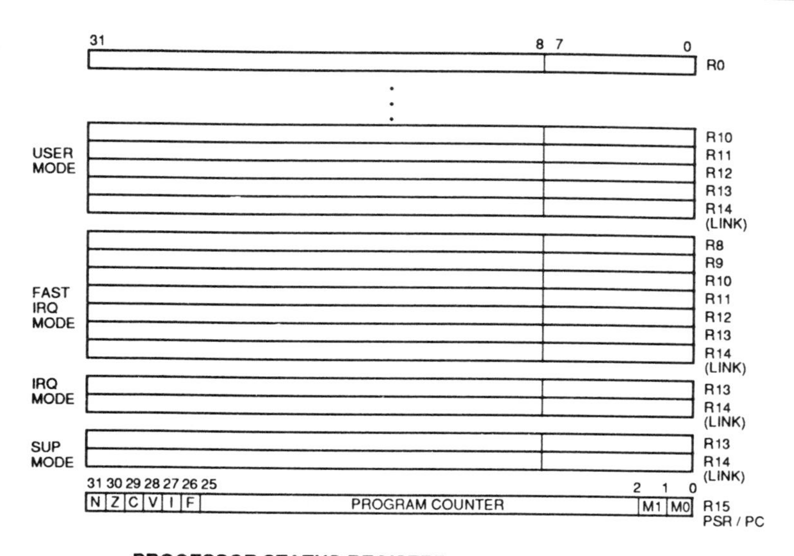

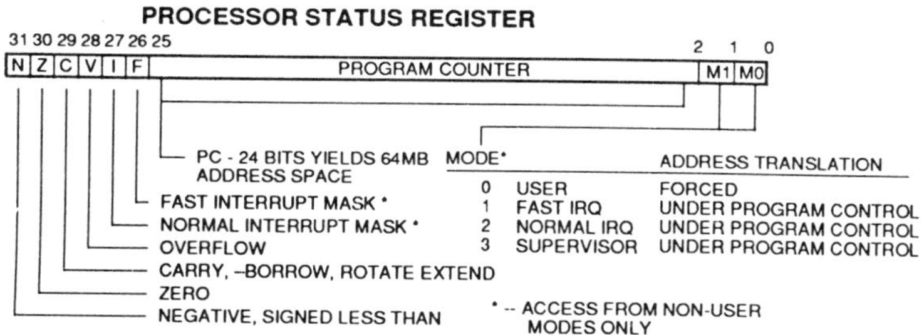

Figure 11.3 VL86C010 Register Model
(Courtesy of VLSI Technology, Inc.)

without needing to save any of the user's registers. In this way, a faster interrupt handling is achieved.

Out of the 16 general purpose registers available to the user, two have special assignments. Register R15 serves as a Program Counter (PC) and a Processor Status Register (PSR). Its most significant six bits serve as Status Flags. The PSR/PC structure is shown in Figure 11.3.

The CPU has four operating modes:

mode	M1, M0 (Figure 11.3)	
1. User	0	0
2. Supervisor	1	1
3. Normal Interrupt	1	0
4. Fast Interrupt	0	1

Table 11.2 Acorn Register by Mode Allocation

Mode:	00	01	10	11
	User	FIRQ	IRQ	SVC
	R0	R0	R0	R0
	R1	R1	R1	R1
	--	--	--	--
	--	--	--	--
	--	--	--	--
	R9	R9	R9	R9
	R10	R10-FIRQ	R10	R10
	--	--	R11	R11
	--	--	R12	R12
	R14	R14-FIRQ	R13-IRQ	R13-SVC
	R15	R15	R14-IRQ	R14-SVC
			R15	R15

SVC - Supervisor mode call
IRQ - Interrupt Request
FIRQ - Fast Interrupt Request

The register by mode assignment is shown in Table 11.2. Registers R10-FIRQ to R14-FIRQ are private registers used in the FIRQ processing state; registers R13-IRQ and R14-IRQ are used in the IRQ processing state; and R13-SVC and R14-SVC are used in the SVC processing state. Register R14 is called the *Subroutine Link Register*. It receives a copy of R15 (PC) on a Branch-and-Link instruction. The seven registers in the FIRQ mode (R8–R14) can be used to hold status, DMA pointers and DMA word counts, eliminating the need to save state and reload these values during exception or interrupt processing. The processor's worst case interrupt latency is 22.5 clock cycles, or 1.87 ms at 12 MHz operation [11.1]. The processor exception vector map is shown in Table 11.3. The FIRQ mode of the Acorn eliminates the need of a DMA Controller (DMAC). This

Table 11.3 Exception Vector Map
(*Courtesy of VLSI Technology, Inc.*)

Address (Hex)	Function	Priority Level
000 0000	Reset	0
000 0004	Undefined Instruction Trap	6
000 0008	Software Interrupt	7
000 000C	Abort (Prefetch)	5
000 0010	Abort (Data)	2
000 0014	Address Exception	1
000 0018	Normal Interrupt (IRQ)	4
000 001C	Fast Interrupt (FIRQ)	3

decreases the cost of the system while improving performance, since the DMA operations are managed on-chip.

The Acorn CPU has a three-stage pipeline and a barrel shifter, particularly useful in graphics.

The CPU chip has a 32-bit Data Bus and a 26-bit Address Bus (Figure 11.2). Both are separate (unmultiplexed). The Acorn can address directly 64 MBytes of memory. The processor to memory bandwidth is 18 MBytes/sec. The Acorn control system is hardwired. A PLA serves as a decoder and bits of the actual instruction word provide most of the control information.

The VL86C110 Memory Controller (MEMC), whose block diagram is shown in Figure 11.4, generates the timing and control signals for memory, including Dynamic RAM (DRAM) and acts as the main interface between the other system components by providing the critical timing signals for all elements from a single clock input. The MEMC provides full Virtual Memory support, drives up to 32 memory devices, provides 3 DMA generators, arbitrates the system bus and offers three levels of access protection. It has a 128-entry, content-addressable Logical-to-Physical address translator. The page size is optionally selectable; it can be 4, 8, 16 or 32 KBytes.

The VL86C310 Video Controller (VIDC) provides a flexible choice of display formats in both color and high resolution monochrome. Horizontal timing is controlled in units of two pixel times, and vertical timing is controlled in units of raster times. The VIDC can also generate high quality stereo sound with up to 8 channels of separate stereo position.

The VL86C410 I/O Controller (IOC), whose block diagram is shown in Figure 11.5, provides the system with several general I/O support functions. It contains four 16-bit counter/timer circuits, two configured as general purpose timers and two as baud rate generators. One baud rate generator is dedicated to the Keyboard Asynchronous Receiver-Transmitter (KART) and the other controls

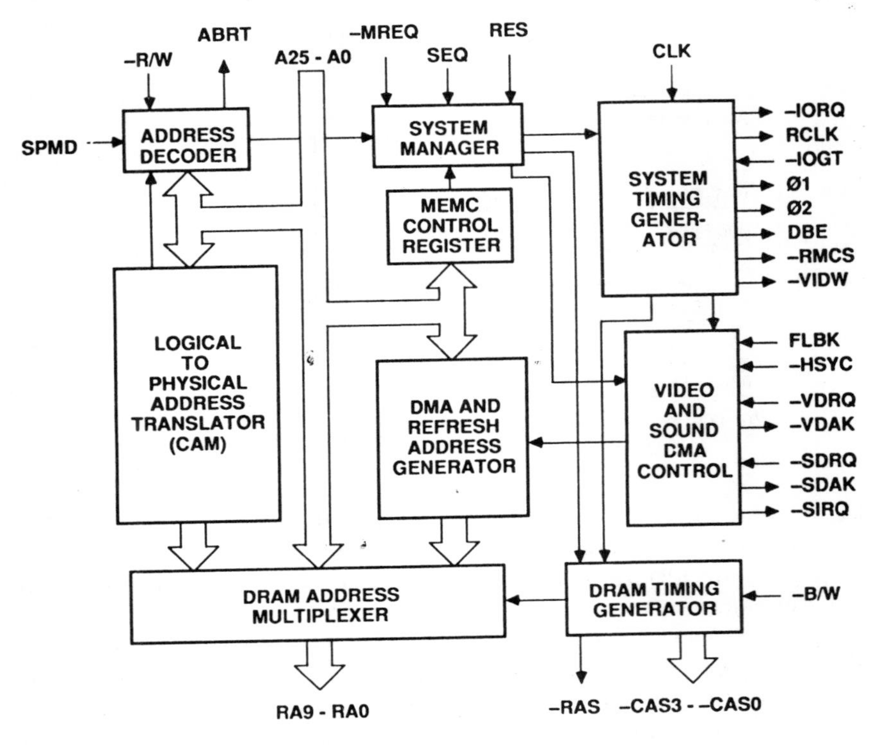

Figure 11.4 VL86C110 Block Diagram
(*Courtesy of VLSI Technology, Inc.*)

the BAUD output pin of the IOC for other communication tasks. The IOC contains six programmable bidirectional I/O pins for implementing special processor control. Interrupts are supported for both normal (IRQ) and fast (FIRQ) interrupts through mask, request and status registers. Sixteen interrupt sources are supported. A block diagram of a microcomputer containing all four chips of the Acorn family is shown in Figure 11.6.

Future implementations of the VL86C010 CPU and its supporting chips will feature 1.6 micron CMOS at 20 MHz and 1 micron CMOS at 33 MHz. An upgraded version of the VL86C010 will be the VL86C020, 1.6 micron at 20 or 25 MHz, 1 micron at 25 or 33 MHz, 300,000 transistors, with an on-chip 4 KByte cache (instruction and data, direct mapped, 4 words or 16 bytes/line, write-through for data references). The expected performance of the C020 is up to three times that of the C010 [11.7].

VLSI Technology features a number of development platforms and evaluation boards for the VL86C010. They feature the Acorn assembler, MS-DOS interface, PC cards for XT or AT-compatibles and compilers for C, Basic, FORTRAN-77, Cambridge LISP and Prolog. VLSI Technology also provides additional support

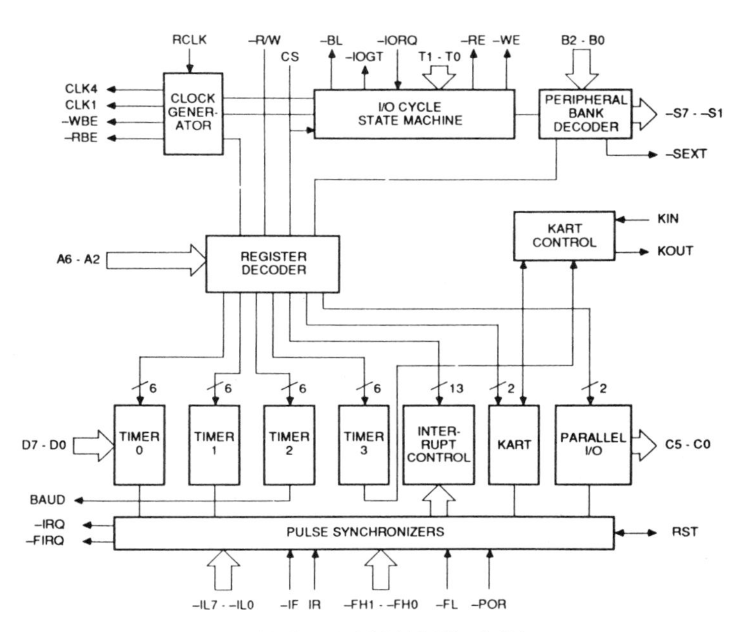

Figure 11.5 VL86C410 Block Diagram
(Courtesy of VLSI Technology, Inc.)

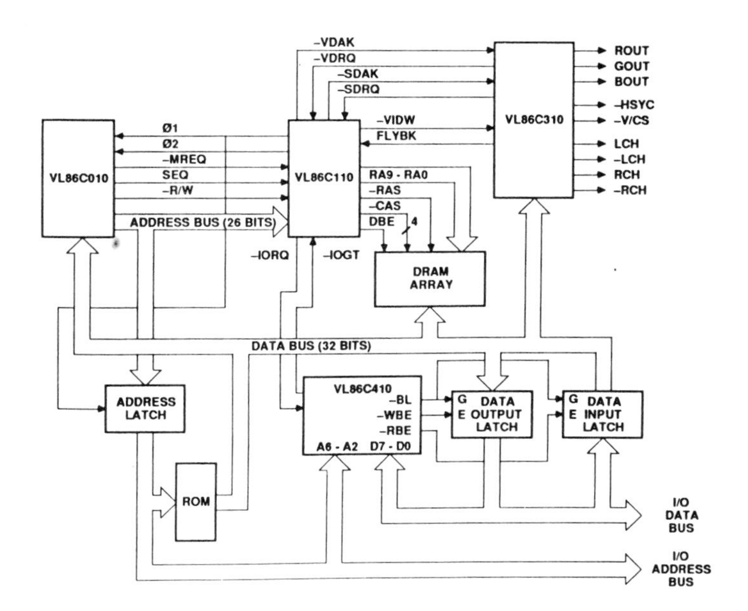

Figure 11.6 VL86C010 System Interconnect Diagram
(Courtesy of VLSI Technology, Inc.)

software, such as ROM-based debug monitor, cross assembler-linker for IBM PC and MacIntosh, and a Real-Time OS Kernel.

References

11.1 R. Cates, 'Processor Architecture Considerations for Embedded Controller Applications', *IEEE MICRO*, **8**, No. 3, pp. 28–38, June 1988.

11.2 J.F. Stockton, J.J. Farrell, III, '32-bit RISC Processor Executes at Full Throttle', *Electronic Products*, May 15, 1986, pp. 44–51.

11.3 S.B. Furber, A.R. Wilson, 'The Acorn RISC Machine – An Architectural View', *IEE Electronics & Power*, June 1987, pp. 402–405.

11.4 R. Wilson, 'Acorn Processor Opens Second Front in Battle for RISC Acceptance', *Computer Design*, Nov. 1, 1988, pp. 42–43.

11.5 D. Pountain, 'The Archimedes 310', *BYTE*, Oct. 1987, pp. 125–130.

11.6 *VL86C010 32-Bit RISC MPU and Peripheral User's Manual*, Prentice Hall, Englewood Cliffs, NJ, 1989.

11.7 R. Wilson, 'RISC CPUs Tune Up for Embedded Computing', *Computer Design*, May 1, 1989, pp. 36–38.

12

Alternate Commercial RISC Systems

12.1 The Pyramid

The Pyramid 90x is a 32-bit universal computing system manufactured by Pyramid Technology Corp. (Mountain View, CA), implemented in Schottky TTL MSI on three boards, with an 8 MHz clock (125 ns cycle). It supports a multiuser environment with up to 128 users. It was the first commercial RISC-type system when it was announced in 1983. The 90x is the first basic product of the Pyramid family. Other products are surveyed at the end of this section [12.1–12.3].

Practically the only Berkeley RISC feature, that has been implemented by Pyramid, is the idea of the multiple CPU register set and the Register Window. Indeed, the Pyramid CPU has a 528 32-bit register file. Out of all the 528 registers, 16 are *global*, and seen by all procedures (10 in RISC II). Each procedure sees a total of 64 registers:

16 global, denoted by GR0–GR15,
48 window registers (22 in RISC II).

The 48 window registers are subdivided into three equal groups of 16 registers each, as follows:

PR0–PR15 16 Parameter Registers. Contain:
14 32-bit parameters passed to the current procedure by the calling procedure.
Two registers are dedicated to store the:
Saved PC
Saved PSW

LR0–LR15 16 Local Registers. Contain the local parameters of the procedure.

TR0–TR15 16 Temporary Registers. Contain the parameters passed by the current procedure to the called procedure.

The 16 Parameter Registers are comparable to the six High Registers of the RISC II window, while the 16 Local Registers correspond to the 10 Local Registers of RISC II, and the 16 Temporary Registers correspond to the six Low Registers of RISC II (chapter 3).

Three of the 16 Global Registers of the Pyramid are dedicated to specific tasks:

GR15 serves as the Program Counter (PC).
GR14 serves as the Stack Pointer (SP) of the Data Stack.
GR13 serves as the Current Frame Pointer (CFP), pointing to the Base of the Current Stack Frame.

As can be easily seen, the Pyramid CPU Register File can support up to 15 levels of nested procedures (512/32 = 16; main procedure + 15 nested), without accessing the memory.

The architectural properties of the Pyramid border on the violation of most of the points of RISC definition (see section 1.3). In fact, the Pyramid can be regarded as a somewhat reduced CISC machine. Directly supporting floating point operations, the Pyramid has six data types:

1. *Byte Integer* 8 bits, 2's complement
   The *memory* is *byte-addressed*.
2. *Halfword Integer* 16 bits
   The addresses of halfwords in memory are established by their most significant byte and they must be *even*.
3. *Word Integer* 32 bits
   The word addresses in memory are multiples of 4. The most significant byte has the lowest address (big-endian).
4. *Longword* 64 bits
   The address of a longword in memory is established by the address of its most significant byte, aligned on a word boundary (multiple of 4).
   A longword residing in two CPU registers is placed so that its most significant 32 bits are in register Rn and the least significant, in register R(n+1). It is addressed by Rn.
5. *Floating Point* 32 bits, IEEE 754-1985 Standard
6. *Double Floating Point* 64 bits, IEEE 754-1985 Standard

The Pyramid has over 100 instructions. Although the majority of the instructions are one word (32 bits) long, there are also 2-word (64 bits) and a few 3-word (96 bits) instructions. The general Instruction Format of the Pyramid is shown in Figure 12.1. Both Op1 and Op2 fields are 6 bits wide and can specify up to 64 registers each (each procedure sees $64 = 2^6$ registers). The Op1 (source) can also specify an immediate signed integer value from -32 to $+31$.

31 28	27 20	19 18	17 12	11 6	5 0
Class	Function	T	X	Op1	Op2
Displacement 1 (optional)					
Displacement 2 (optional)					

Figure 12.1 Pyramid Instruction Format

The Op2 (destination) always represents a CPU register. The six-bit X field represents an index register (one of the CPU registers) if $X \neq 0$. If $X = 0$, there is no indexing. The two-bit T field specifies the operand size:

decimal	binary	Operand (bytes)
0	00	1
1	01	2
2	10	4
3	11	8

The index value (contents of the index register) is multiplied by the operand size (in bytes). The 8-bit *Function* field represents the Opcode, specifying the operation to be performed by the instruction. Only values 0–127 are used, values 128–255 are reserved for future use. The 4-bit *Class* field specifies the *Addressing Modes* and there are 16 of them. Examples:

Class		Meaning
0	RR	Both operands registers
1	I1R	First operand immediate, second operand register
1	I2R	First operand immediate, specified by Displacement 1, second operand register

An example of an assembly language specification of an instruction:

MOVx Op1, Op2; Op2 ← Op1

x can be B, H, W, L representing the different length data types.

The Pyramid control unit is microprogrammed (as opposed to the hardwired Berkeley and Stanford RISC machines, IBM 801, and many other RISC systems). The CPU is organized as a three-stage Instruction Pipeline:

1. Instruction Fetch,
2. Operand Fetch,
3. Execute.

There are two Caches with an access time of 125 ns (a single CPU cycle):

1. Data Cache, 32 Kbytes,
2. Instruction Cache, 4 Kbytes.

A Virtual Memory of 4 Gbytes = 2^{32} is supported. A fixed page size of 2 Kbytes is implemented. The total size of the Real (Physical) main memory is 8 Mbytes. An auxiliary MC68000-based system is used for system support and diagnostics.

The initial Pyramid 90 family was extended to feature additional models, whose properties are summarized in Table 12.1. All models work under the Pyramid OSx Unix-based OS which integrates 4.2BSD and AT&T System V versions of Unix. All models support C, FORTRAN, Pascal and Franz LISP. An Ethernet and a Network File Systems (NFS) interface is available in all models. All models have floating point units. Models 90Mx and 98x are dual-processors.

The Pyramid latest product families, with the same architecture as the 90x, are the series 9000 and 9000-TA. The 9000 models are 9810, 9820, 9830, 9840 and the 9000-TA models are 9815, 9825, 9835, 9845 with 1, 2, 3 and 4 CPUs respectively. Both series work with a 100 ns cycle time, feature a floating point accelerator, 4 GBytes virtual address space with 2 KBytes page size, up to 128 MBytes main memory, and 40 MBytes/s I/O bandwidth. Both series work under the OSx and offer C, FORTRAN 77, ANSI Pascal, COBOL 85 compilers, and Common LISP development system. They differ primarily in their instruction cache/CPU:

	9000	9000-TA
Instruction Cache/CPU (KBytes)	16	256
Data Cache/CPU (KBytes)	64	64

Table 12.1 Pyramid 90 Series Specifications

Model: Feature	90x	98xe	90Mx	98x
Relative performance	1	1.25	1.7	2.1
Cycle Time (nsec)	125	100	125	100
CPUs	1	1	2	2
Memory (MBytes)	2-16	4-32	4-32	8-32
Terminals (max.)	128	256	256	256
Data Cache Units, 32KBytes	Optional	1Standard	2Standard	2Standard

12.2 The Ridge

The Ridge 32 is the second commercial, universal RISC-type system, declared as such by its manufacturer, the Ridge Computers Co., Santa Clara, CA [12.4, 12.5]. It is realized by the Schottky TTL Bipolar Logic, using a multichip design. The Ridge 32S is a smaller, single user system, while Ridge 32C provides multiuser capabilities. Its Operating System (OS) is called ROS, a derivative of UNIX System V and 4.2BSD. It supports the C, Pascal, FORTRAN 77, Mainsail and an assembly language. The Ridge operates at a frequency of 8 MHz (125 ns CPU cycle). The CPU-Memory cycle is 3 × 125 ns = 375 ns. The overall throughput is 10.7 Mbytes/s. The Ridge provides full 32-bit data and address paths. The Virtual Memory per process is 4 GBytes for code and 4 GBytes for data. The fixed page size for Virtual Memory is 4 KBytes. The maximal size of the currently available Real (Physical) Main Memory (MM) is 8 MBytes.

The Ridge architecture supports (as in the Pyramid) 4 integer data types:

Byte	8 bits
Halfword	16 bits
Word	32 bits
Double Word	64 bits

and 2 Floating Point:

Real, 32 bits, 8-bit exponent, 23-bit mantissa with an implicit leading 1. Bias: 127.

Double Real, 64 bits, 11-bit exponent, 52-bit mantissa. Bias: 1023.

Two's complement notation for signed numbers is used. The bits in integers are numbered so that the Most Significant Bit (MSB) is 0. A Word is packed in memory as shown in Figure 12.2(a). A Double Word is stored in a pair of CPU registers as shown in Figure 12.2(b).

The Ridge has three *instruction formats*, shown in Figure 12.3.

The 8-bit opcode field contains all of the information pertaining to the instruction type, operand type and addressing mode.

There are only two *Addressing Modes*:

Direct

Indexed (indicated by one bit of opcode)

The effective address for a memory reference instruction is calculated as follows:

Address

Space	Indexed	Effective Address
Data	No	Displacement
Data	Yes	Ry + Displacement
Code	No	PC + Displacement
Code	Yes	PC + Ry + Displacement

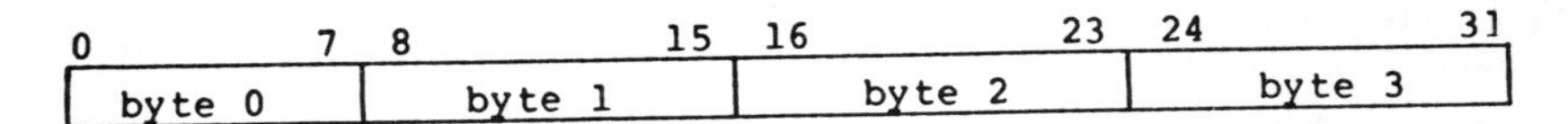

(a) Word in Memory

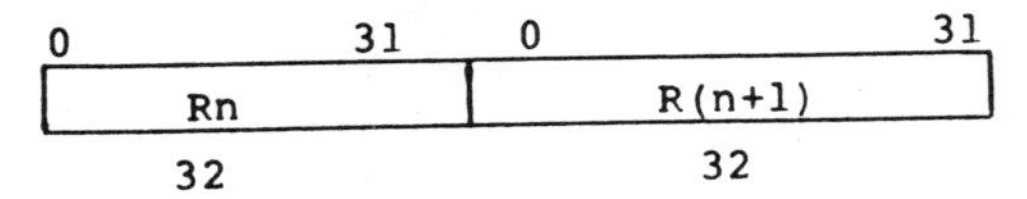

(b) Doubleword in CPU Registers

Figure 12.2 Ridge Data Storage

(1) Register, 16 bits

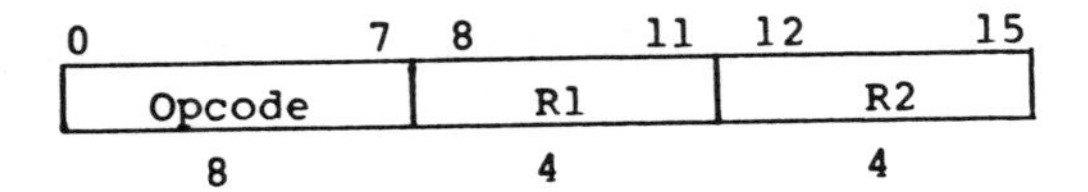

(2) Short Displacement, 32 bits

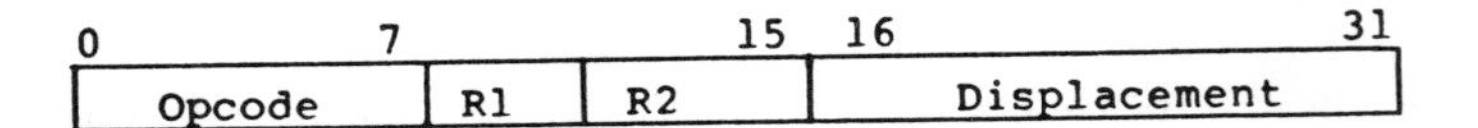

(3) Long Displacement, 48 bits

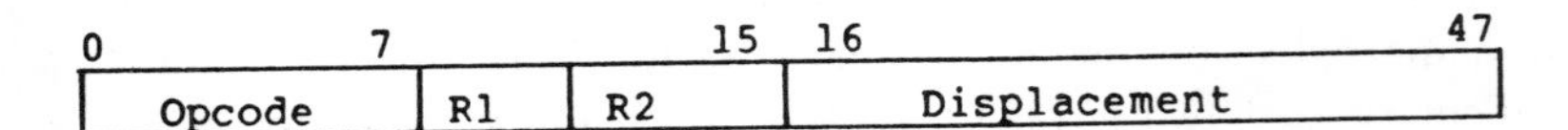

Figure 12.3 Ridge Instruction Formats

Ry is any of the CPU general purpose registers.

The basic instruction structure is the following:

$$\text{OPR dst, src; dst} \leftarrow \text{(dst) opr (src)}$$

EXAMPLE:

$$\text{Add R1, R2; R1} \leftarrow \text{(R1)} + \text{(R2)}$$

Although the Ridge architecture is not as simple as that of the Berkeley RISC (more options and different instruction sizes are offered), it is certainly simpler and 'more reduced' than that of the Pyramid. Some of the major reasons for calling Ridge a RISC (see section 1.3) are:

(a) Simplicity and Regularity of the Instruction Set.

(b) Computations are Register-to-Register only.
(c) Memory access by Load/Store only.

The Ridge system is illustrated in Figure 12.4.

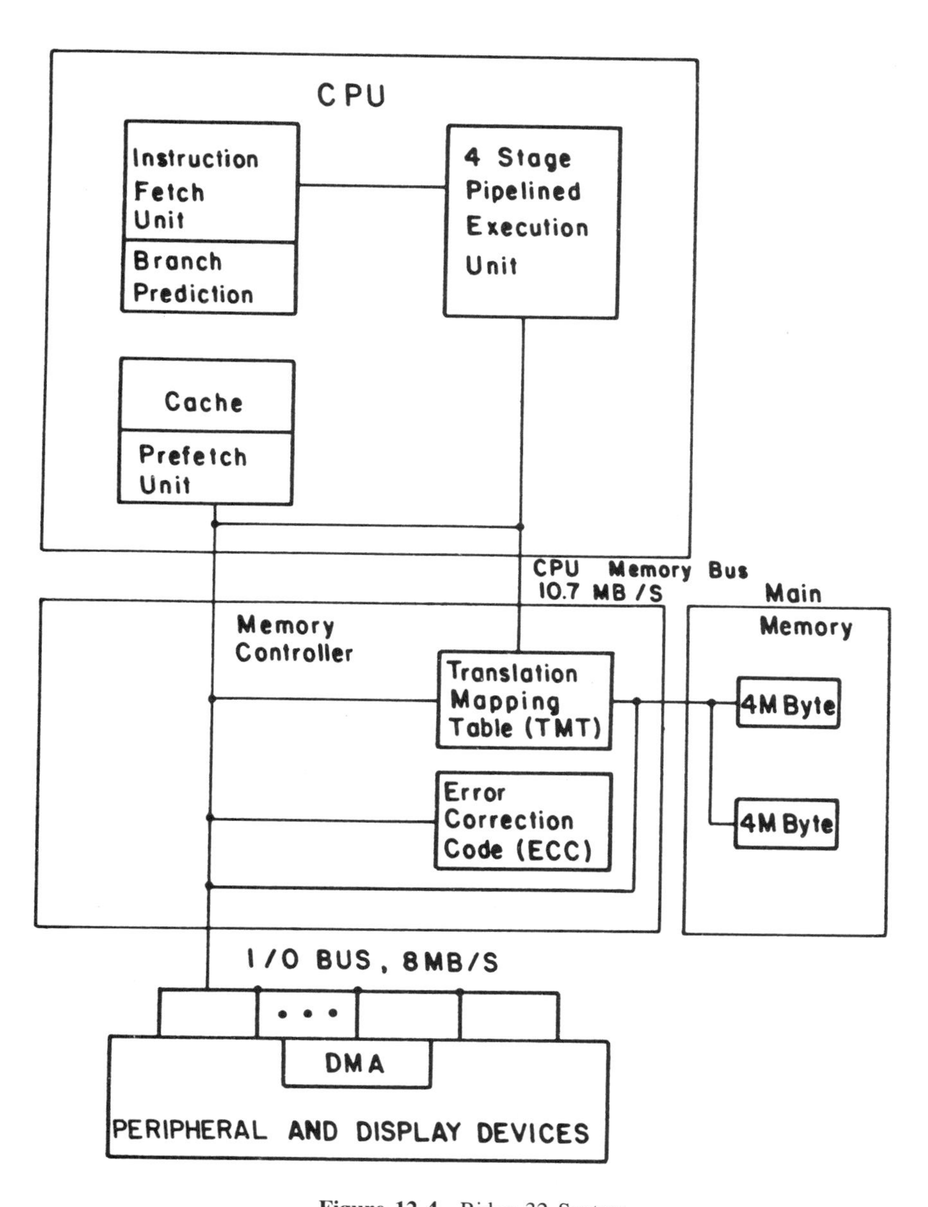

Figure 12.4 Ridge 32 System

The CPU is subdivided into two major units, each of which can access memory independently:

1. *Execution Unit* (EU) contains:
   16 32-bit General Registers
   A 32-bit ALU
   A 32-bit Barrel Shifter
2. *Instruction Fetch Unit* (IFU), capable of fetching two instructions ahead of the present instruction. It incorporates a *Cache* and a *Branch Prediction Unit*. It is capable of initiating one instruction every machine cycle (125 ns).

The CPU is microcoded. Its Execution Unit is organized as a four-stage pipeline. The stages are:

1. Instruction Fetch and Decode.
2. Operand Fetch.
3. Execute.
4. Store Result.

In addition, a *Register Bypass* capability is featured, better explained by the following example. Consider a sequence of the following two instructions:

ADD R6, R7; R6 ← (R6) + (R7)
AND R5, R6; R5 ← (R5) AND (R6)

The details of the Instruction Pipeline operation:

Clock Cycle	ADD	AND
1	ADD instruction fetched	—
2	R6 and R7 fetched from the register file	AND instruction fetched
3	ALU adds R6 and R7, puts the new R6 value on the bus	R5 is fetched from the register file, R6 taken from the bus, *bypassing* the register file
4	New R6 value stored in the register file	ALU ANDs R5 and R6, puts the new R5 value on the bus
5	—	New R5 value is stored in the register file

The Branch Prediction Unit works in such a way that if the prediction is wrong, the pipeline is cleared, causing a 4-cycle delay. Statistical studies indicate that a correct prediction (and no loss of time) occurs in 80% of the times.

There are several Ridge 32 models, all identical from the architectural standpoint, summarized in the following table:

Model	Winchester MBytes	Slots for I/O and M expansion	Main Memory MBytes
32/110	78	4	4 (1 board)
32/130	150	4	4 (1 board)
32/310	150	9	4 (1 board)
32/330	150	8	8 (2 boards)

The top model among the above is Ridge 32/330 with an 8 MBytes Real Main Memory, 8 I/O or Memory expansion slots and a Secondary (Winchester Disk) Memory of 150 MBytes.

The subsequent Ridge model is the Ridge 3200, featuring the same architecture as the 32. It works with an 83.3 ns clock and features up to 128 MBytes main memory and 16 KBytes cache. Its CPU-memory bandwidth is 28 MBytes/s and DMA-I/O bandwidth is 18.3 MBytes/s. The Ridge 3200 contains a 64-bit floating point operation and a 64-bit barrel shifter.

A more recent product, announced in 1987, is the supermini Ridge 5100 [12.5], which is completely object-code compatible with its Ridge predecessors. The 5100 is realized on a pair of 20000-gate, 1.5 micron CMOS VLSI chips running at 16 MHz (manufactured by Fujitsu). Future extensions include 24 MHz Bi-CMOS and 32 MHz ECL implementations. The 5100 system features 64 KBytes data and code caches (for a total of 128 KBytes). The cache bandwidth is 128 MBytes/s. The system can support 128 interactive users. Its sustained performance is 14 VAX MIPS. It runs under the Ridge RX/V implementation of the Unix System V OS.

12.3 The Apollo PRISM

The Apollo Computer, Inc. (Chelmsford, MA; now a subsidiary of Hewlett-Packard) has announced a 64-bit, 1.5 micron CMOS RISC Integer Processor (IP) [12.6, 12.7]. The IP is hardwire controlled and it features fixed lengths instructions, delayed branching, single cycle execution and interlocked multistage pipelines:

	Stages
Register-to-Register	4
Load/Store	5
Macro branches	2
Call	4

The IP has a 32 × 32 register file and a Power Shifter which can insert, extract or shift a 32-bit value 0–31 places in one cycle and merge with ALU output. The IP interconnects to 64-bit wide 128 KByte instruction and 64 KByte data caches.

Apollo Computer, Inc. also produces a Floating Point Unit (FPU) CMOS chip, including a 64 × 32 (or 32 × 64) register file, ECL-based ALU and Multiplier and featuring IEEE 754-1985 Standard single and double-precision floating-point.

The system contains a 64-bit, 150 MBytes/s synchronous system bus. There is 128 MBytes main memory and up to 3 GBytes local mass storage.

Four of the above processors are configured into a multiprocessor, called Parallel Reduced Instruction Set Multiprocessor, PRISM. Its overall throughput is about 100 times that of the VAX 11/780. The PRISM system is also called the Series 10000 Supercomputer.

The Apollo OS is called Domain/OS, a distributed UNIX-type OS, offering the users a choice of three OS environments: AT&T Unix system V.3; Berkeley Unix 4.3BSD; and Apollo's Aegis.

12.4 The INMOS Transputer

The original INMOS Transputer was announced as a 32-bit, VLSI chip, developed and manufactured by INMOS Ltd, Bristol, UK [12.8–12.14] as a component for scalable parallel processors. In addition to a full CPU, it contains a *4 KBytes* Static RAM *Main Memory on-chip*. In fact, it is a computer, or rather a micro-computer on a single chip. It has some definite properties of a RISC-type machine, although initially (1983) it was not advertised as such by INMOS. It has been intended to be a highly dense VLSI chip (main memory on-chip) and this should explain its higher density compared to other RISC-type chips. Its architectural properties will be explored further in this section.

Since there is a significant part of the main memory (4 KBytes) on-chip, it has been decided by the INMOS designers that there is no need to have a large CPU register file.

There are only *six CPU registers*:

(a) The *Workspace Pointer* which points to an area of memory for *local variables*.
(b) The *Instruction Pointer* which points to the next instruction to be executed (same as the PC in other systems).
(c) The *Operand Register* which is used in the formation of instruction operands.
(d) Three registers A, B and C which form an *Evaluation Stack*. The Evaluation Stack is used for expression evaluation, to hold the operands of scheduling and communication instructions, and to hold parameters of procedure calls.

Although the machine language has a total of 111 instructions (approximately as in the Pyramid or Ridge), there is only a *single instruction format*, and a very simple one. It is one byte long, divided into two 4-bit fields:

Function field, bits 7-4 (most significant)
Data field, bits 3-0 (least significant)

Since the Transputer is a 32-bit system and it has a 32-bit data bus, four instructions can be fetched simultaneously.

The four-bit Function field (0–15) provides for 16 functions. Thirteen of these values are used to encode the most important functions, as envisaged by the Transputer designers. These include:

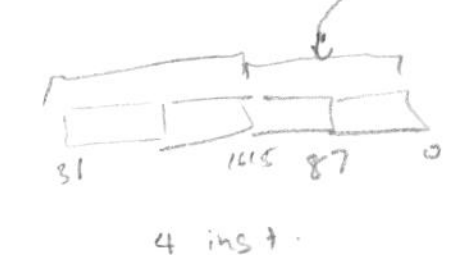

load constant
load local
add constant
store local
load local pointer
load non local
store non local
jump
conditional jump
call

The *load constant* instruction enables values between 0 to 15 to be loaded onto the *evaluation stack* with a single byte instruction. The *load local* and *store local* access locations in memory relative to the *workspace pointer*. The first 16 locations can be accessed using a single byte instruction. The *load non local* and *store non local* instructions behave similarly, except that they access locations in memory relative to the A register. The use of the above simple instructions *eliminates the need* for *complicated addressing modes*.

Two additional function codes, *prefix* and *negative prefix*, are used to allow the operand of any instruction to be extended in length. In both cases, the 4-bit Data field of the instruction is loaded into the least significant 4 bits of the *Operand Register*. For the *prefix* function, the Operand Register is shifted 4 bits to the left (up) and then it is used as the instructions operand. The *negative prefix* function works similarly, except that the Operand Register is *complemented* before being shifted. Consequently, operands can be extended to any length up to the length of the Operand Register by a sequence of prefixing instructions.

The 16th function code, *operate*, causes its operand to be interpreted as an operation on the values held in the *Evaluation Stack*. Up to 16 such operations can be encoded in a single byte instruction. However, the prefixing instructions can be used to extend the operand of an operate function as that of any other function. This allows the number of operations in the machine to be extended indefinitely. The encoding of the indirect functions is chosen so that the most frequently occurring operations are represented without using the prefixing instruction (arithmetic, logic, comparison, control, register manipulation).

Loading a value onto the *Evaluation Stack* pushes B into C, and A into B, before loading A. Storing a value from A pops B into A and C into B. The A, B and C registers are the sources and destinations for arithmetic and logic operations.

EXAMPLE: The *add* instruction causes the following:

$$A \leftarrow A + B$$
$$B \leftarrow C$$

The Evaluation Stack removes the need for instructions to specify registers explicitly. About 80% of the executed operations are encoded in a single byte, and many of these execute in a single cycle.

It should be stressed that the regular user is not supposed to program in the machine language. A special High Level Language (HLL), Occam [12.9], has been developed by INMOS for all applications programming on the Transputer. The Occam language has been designed for parallel processing implementations of the Transputer. It is a process-oriented language with parallel constructs.

EXAMPLE: Occam statement

$$(v + w) \times y$$

Equivalent machine language subprogram:

Instruction	Detailed form	Comment	Bytes	Cycles
load local v	LDL #7	offset of v	1	2
load local w	LDL #7	offset of w	1	2
add	OPR ADD #F #5	Register 0:#5 operands in stack	1	1
load local y	LDL #7	offset of y	1	2
multiply	PFIX #2 #5	most significant part of code for MUL	2	8
	OPR #F #3	least significant part of code for MUL. Register 0:#53 operands in stack		

The direct addressing space of the Transputer is 4 GBytes (2^{32} Bytes). The address space is linear and the architecture does not differentiate between on-chip or off-chip memory. The memory-CPU bandwidth is 25 MBytes/s. The chip has 4 serial links with 10 MBits/s on each link. This unique feature permits the interconnection of a number of Transputer chips in a multiprocessing configuration.

The top Transputer product is the 1.5 micron CMOS T800 [12.11–12.14]. Its current top frequency is 30 MHz for a 15 MIPS sustained performance. It has an on-chip 64-bit Floating Point Unit (FPU), operating by the IEEE 754-1985 Standard, attaining a 2.25 MFLOPS sustained performance for single precision (32 bits). It has 4 KBytes main memory RAM on-chip, with a 120 MBytes/s bandwidth, at 30 MHz. The T800 can directly access a linear address space of 4 GBytes. The external 32-bits memory interface uses multiplexed data and address lines, with a 40 MBytes/s bandwidth, at 30 MHz. The T800 has four serial communication links operating at a maximal 20 Mbits/s rate. Each link can transfer data bidirectionally. The Transputer was designed to be programmed in Occam; however, INMOS also provides support for C, Pascal and FORTRAN.

INMOS also features a lower level chip, the T414, with only 2 KBytes of RAM on-chip and no on-chip FPU. It is a 1.5 micron CMOS, 84 pins, and top frequency of 20 MHz chip. The T800-20 (20 MHz) is pin compatible with the T414-20. The T800-20 can be plugged directly into a circuit designed for a 20 MHz version of the T414. Software should be recompiled, although no changes to the source code are necessary [12.11].

12.5 The IBM ROMP

The IBM features its commercial RISC-type product on the 6150 and 6151 RT PC workstations which use two custom made chips [12.15–12.20]:

(1) The RISC Processor chip, called ROMP (Research Office products division MicroProcessor).
(2) The Memory Management Unit (MMU) chip.

Both chips implement a 1.8 micron NMOS technology, and both are packaged in 175-pin ceramic pin-grid arrays. The RISC Processor chip is a 52000 transistors, 32-bit, pipelined system. The MMU chip contains 61500 transistors. There is no direct connection between the RT and the IBM 801 experimental system (section 5.1). More on this at the end of this section.

There is a total of 118 machine language instructions. Out of those, 65% are 2-byte (16 bits), and the rest 4-byte (32 bits) long: 84 of the instructions (71%) execute in a single machine cycle of 170 ns. There is a total of 16 32-bit general purpose registers.

The logical (virtual) memory addressing space is One Tera Byte = 1 TByte = 2^{40} Bytes. Naturally, the Virtual Address is 40 bits long. The virtual memory space is subdivided into 4096 segments, 256 MBytes each. The maximal Real (Physical) Memory is 16 MBytes. The current 6150 model actually provides up to 4 MBytes of Real Memory, while the 6151 has 3 MBytes. The memory is two-way interleaved; that is, two words can be fetched from it simultaneously.

The Virtual Addresses, issued by the Processor, are 32-bits long. They are transmitted into the MMU: 28 Least Significant Bits (LSB) of the Processor Virtual Address are used by the MMU without any change. The upper 4 bits of the Processor Virtual Address are used as a pointer to a set of 16 12-bit Segment Identifiers, stored in the MMU. Thus, a 12-bit identifier is selected and concatenated (serving as upper 12 bits) with the 28 bits, transferred from the processor, thus creating a 40-bit MMU Virtual Address.

The Operating System (OS) used in the RT is the Advanced Interactive Executive (AIX), a multiuser, multitasking OS, based on the UNIX System V, with Berkeley 4.2BSD and Interactive Systems Corp. enhancements. Some of the currently supported languages are: C, FORTRAN 77, BASIC, Pascal and Assembler.

The RT can work with a NS32081 Floating Point Coprocessor, achieving 20000 Whetstones/s. As a comparison, an Apollo system based on the MC68020 + MC68881 achieves 50000 Whetstones/s. Optionally, the RT can use an Intel 80286 as a parallel coprocessor, achieving compatibility with the IBM AT PC.

Is the RT an extension of the 801 system? Let us compare some of their properties:

Property	801	RT
Primary designation	Experimental, HLL support	Commercial, Workstation
Technology	Off-the-shelf MSI	Custom-made NMOS VLSI
Word size, bits	32	32
Instruction length, bits	32	16 (65%), 32 (35%)
Number of instructions	120	118
Single cycle execution?	Yes	Yes, 71% only
Machine cycle, ns	66	170
CPU Registers (32-bit)	32	16
Virtual Memory, Bytes	2^{32}	2^{40}
Cache?	Yes	No

The systems differ on most of the points. In fact, the RT satisfies the RISC definition points (section 1.3) to a smaller degree than the 801. That is, the RT is less of a RISC-type mahine than the 801. So the IBM development has been going away from the RISC idea, rather than towards it.

12.6 The Hewlett-Packard Precision Architecture

The Hewlett-Packard Co. has announced its new RISC-type system under the general label of HP *Precision Architecture* [12.16, 12.21, 12.22]. The principles on which the Precision Architecture is based are as follows:

1. Reduced Instruction Set.
2. Fixed Length and Fixed Format Instruction.
3. Load/Store only memory access.
4. Hardwired instructions.
5. Single-Cycle execution of instructions.
6. Optimizing Compilers.

Comparing the above with the nine points of RISC definition in section 1.3, it is easy to see that there is a perfect fit, with the exception that the HP Precision Architecture does not stress a large CPU register file. Otherwise, it has fully adopted the RISC principles. As a matter of fact 32 32-bit general purpose registers have been implemented. On the other hand, there are 140 instructions – not a very 'reduced' figure.

In addition to the above basic RISC principles the following *additional features* have been added within the HP Precision Architecture (features not connected with the RISC idea):

(1) *Extended Addressing*
There are three Virtual Addressing options offered:
2^{32} Bytes
2^{48} Bytes (2^{16} Virtual Address spaces of 2^{32} Bytes each)
2^{64} Bytes (2^{32} Virtual Address spaces of 2^{32} Bytes each)

(2) *Support for Coprocessors and Multiprocessors*
Coprocessors for Floating Point or I/O handling can be added to operate in parallel with the CPU. Their interconnection and management are directly supported by the machine design. Moreover, several CPUs can be used in the system in a Multiprocessing configuration.

(3) *Memory-Mapped I/O*
In addition to the regular properties of memory-mapped I/O, the HP Precision Architecture stresses the *added security* involved in this feature. Each I/O device is handled by the same *memory protection* scheme as any other module of the main memory.

The HP Precision Architecture first commercial RISC-type system was realized by two products:

(a) *HP 3000 Series 930*
The 930 Processor is realized on five boards using high-speed Schottky

TTL logic. 4.5 MIPS performance, up to 24 MBytes main physical memory.

(b) *HP 3000 Series 950*
The 950 Processor is single-chip, 1-micron NMOS III VLSI. 6.7 MIPS performance, up to 64 MBytes main physical memory.

The architecture and the basic organization of the 930 and 950 systems is essentially the same.

The *Data Types* recognized by the architecture are:

Integers: 2's complement used
16-bit, aligned at even byte addresses
32-bit, aligned on word (32 bits) boundaries
Characters: 8-bit, ASCII code used
Floating Point: ANSI/IEEE 754-1985 Standard
Single-word Precision, 32 bits, aligned on word boundaries
Double-word Precision, 64 bits, aligned on double-word boundaries
Quad-word Precision, 128 bits, aligned on double-word boundaries

It should be noted though, that Floating Point operations are performed by a Floating Point Coprocessor. The CPU can perform only Software Emulations of floating point operations.

There is a total of 140 instructions. Each instruction has *a fixed size* of 32 bits and there is a *fixed format*. There is a total of 32 32-bit *general purpose* CPU registers and 32 32-bit *control registers*. In addition, there are 8 *Space Registers*, which point to the Virtual Space to be accessed.

The Virtual Memory is organized as a set of linear spaces. Each space has 4 GBytes = 2^{32} Bytes. Demand-paged memory management is implemented. Each memory space is subdivided into pages of 2 KBytes each.

A 128 KByte Cache is included in the system. It can contain both instructions and data. As an option, the Cache can be subdivided (see Figure 12.5) into:

1. A 64 KByte Instruction Cache
2. A 64 KByte Data Cache

Each of the above two caches is subdivided into 4096 blocks (lines) of 16 bytes/block. Both caches are *Directly Mapped* (one-way associative). The *Instruction Cache* is *Read Only*, as code is typically assumed to be non-modifiable. A *Write-to-Cache* management scheme is utilized with the *Data Cache*. Modified data in the Cache is written to main memory only when the CPU requires other data to be in that cache location, or when a DMA operation is performed within that data area, or upon a power fail.

The CPU is organized as a three-stage instruction pipeline:

Fetch
Execute
Store.

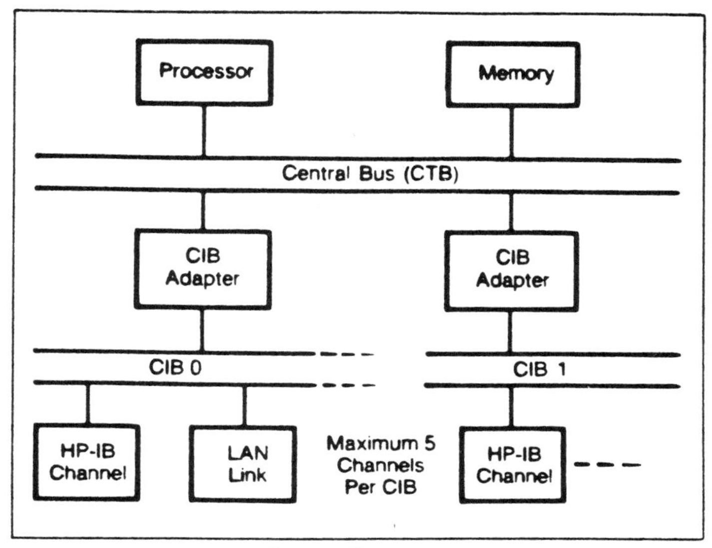

System Structure

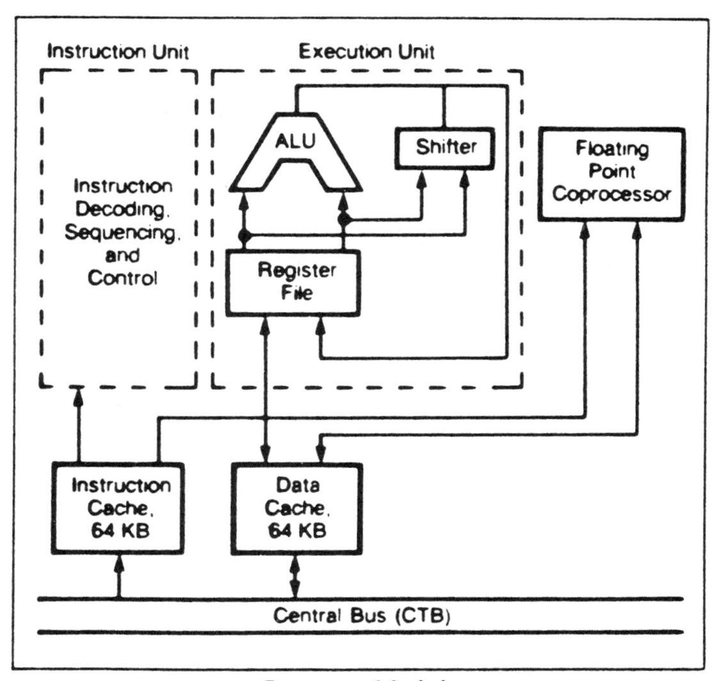

Processor Module

Figure 12.5 The Hewlett Packard HP3000 Series 930 System
(*Courtesy of the Hewlett-Packard Co.*)

Each stage has a 125 ns cycle. A Delayed Branch policy, similar to the one of the Berkeley RISC, is implemented.

The Operating System (OS) implemented on the 930 is the MPE XL (MultiProgramming Executive), a Unix-based system.

The 930 and the 950 are compatible with the previous HP 3000 products, Series 37, 42, 58 and 70. Programs written for the previous machines can run on the 930 or the 950 without modification.

Hewlett-Packard has subsequently announced another Precision Architecture product family, the HP9000 Series 800, featuring models 825, 840 and 850. The top model of this series, HP9000/850S has a 73 ns cycle, 48-bits virtual addressing (281000 GBytes), a 512 MBytes physical address space, and a 128 KBytes cache. Its average memory to CPU bandwidth is 100 MBytes/s. Its 40 instruction floating point coprocessor implements the IEEE 754-1985 Standard. The OS is Unix System V, supporting FORTRAN 77, C and Pascal HLLs.

References

12.1 R. Ragan-Kelley, R. Clark, 'Applying RISC Theory to a Large Computer', *Computer Design*, Nov. 1983, pp. 297–301.

12.2 N. Mokhoff, 'Second Generation RISC Superminis Excel in Price/Performance', *Computer Design*, Jan. 15, 1987, pp. 19–20.

12.3 R. Wilson, 'Application Tuning: A Key to RISC System Development', *Computer Design*, Aug. 1, 1988, pp. 21–22.

12.4 E. Basart, D. Folger, 'Ridge 32 Architecture – A RISC Variation', *Proc. ICCD 83*, pp. 315–318, New York, Oct. 1983.

12.5 T.C. Shannon, 'Ridge Promises Unparalleled Supermini Speed', *Digital Review*, Oct. 12, 1987, p. 10.

12.6 D.W. Haskin, 'At the Speed of Light Through a PRISM', *Digital Review*, Dec. 19, 1988, pp. 39–42.

12.7 P. Bemis, 'PRISM with a Million Gates', *ESD*, Jan. 1989, pp. 55–59.

12.8 I.M. Barron *et al.*, 'The Transputer', *Electronics*, Nov. 17, 1983, p. 109.

12.9 R. Pountain, 'The Transputer and its Special Language OCCAM', *BYTE*, Aug. 1984, pp. 361–366.

12.10 C. Whitby-Strevens, 'The Transputer', *Proc. 12th Annual Int. Symp. on Computer Architecture*, pp. 292–300, Boston, MA, June 17–19, 1985.

12.11 *IMS T800 Transputer, Preliminary Data*, INMOS, Bristol, UK, March 1988.

12.12 P. Wilson, 'Parallel Processing Comes to PCs', *BYTE*, Nov. 1988, pp. 213–218.

12.13 R.M. Stein, 'T800 and Counting', *BYTE*, Nov. 1988, pp. 287–296.

12.14 R. Wilson, 'British Microprocessors: A Lesson in Innovation', *Computer Design*, Nov. 1, 1988, pp. 32–42.

12.15 H.J. Hindin, 'IBM RISC Workstation Features 40-bit Virtual Addressing', *Computer Design*, Feb. 15, 1986, pp. 28–30.

12.16 N. Mokhoff, 'New RISC Machines Appear as Hybrids with both RISC and CISC Features', *Computer Design*, April 1, 1986, pp. 22–25.

12.17 R.O. Simpson, 'The IBM RT Personal Computer', *BYTE Extra Edition, Inside the IBM PCs*, 1986, pp. 43–78.

12.18 D.E. Waldecker, P.Y. Moon, 'ROMP/MMU Technology Introduction', *IBM RT PC Technology*, IBM Publ. No. SA23-1057, pp. 44–47, 1986.

12.19 P.D. Hester, R.O. Simpson, A. Chang, 'The IBM RT PC ROMP and MMU Architecture', *IBM RT PC Technology*, IBM Publ. No. SA23-1057, pp. 48–56, 1986.

12.20 M.E. Hopkins, 'Compiling for the RT PC ROMP', *IBM RT PC Technology*, IBM Publ. No. SA23-1057, pp. 76–82, 1986.

12.21 J.S. Birnbaum, W.S. Worley, 'Beyond RISC: High Precision Architecture', *Hewlett-Packard Journal*, **36**, No. 8, pp. 4–10, Aug. 1985 (also in *Proc. COMPCON 86*, pp. 40–47, San Francisco, March 1986.

12.22 R.B. Lee, 'HP Precision: A Spectrum Architecture', *Proc. Hawaii Int. Conf. on System Science, HICSS-22*, **1**, pp. 242–251, Jan. 1989.

13

Comparison and Performance of RISC Systems

13.1 Introductory Comments

A number of experimental and commercial RISC systems have been described in the preceding chapters. This chapter summarizes the properties of these systems, compares them and presents some experimental results on their performance.

A considerable amount of experimentation was conducted in conjunction with the first RISC system to be denoted by the name 'RISC' – the Berkeley RISC I and II (see chapter 3). Subsequently, the properties of the commercial RISC systems are compared and experimental results, conducted by some of the RISC manufacturers, are reported.

13.2 Performance Evaluation of the Berkeley RISC

Because of the inherent properties of the RISC architecture (small choice of instructions, formats and addressing modes), it is rather difficult and time consuming to program in its assembly language. The Berkeley RISC developers adopted an efficient C language compiler for the RISC at an early stage of the study [1.2, 1.17]. The main benchmark programs, used in the RISC performance evaluation, were written in (or translated into) the C language. The following computing systems were compared with the RISC:

Digital	VAX 11/780
Digital	PDP 11/70
Motorola	MC68000
Zilog	Z8002
BBN	C/70

The C compilers for all systems, except the PDP 11/70, were based on the Unix portable C compiler [13.1]. The C compiler for the PDP 11/70 was based on the Ritchie C compiler [13.2].

Eleven benchmark programs (in C language) were used [1.17]:

E – Character String Search
F – Bit Set, Reset, Test
H – Linked List Insertion
K – Bit Matrix Transposition
I – Quicksort
Ackerman
Puzzle (Subscript)
Puzzle (Pointer)
Recursive Qsort
SED (Unix-environment Batch Text Editor)
Towers of Hanoi (game program)

The first five benchmark programs are C versions of the so-called EDN benchmarks [13.3].

The *Character String Search* (E) program examines a long character string for the first occurrence of a substring. If the search is successful, the procedure returns the substring's starting position. Otherwise, the procedure returns a 'not found' indicator. The starting addresses and the lengths of the string and substring are passed as parameters to the benchmark. This benchmark exercises an architecture's ability to move through character strings sequentially. The *Bit Set, Reset, Test* (F) benchmark tests, sets or resets a bit within a tightly packed bit string beginning at a word boundary. This benchmark tests, sets, and then resets three bits. It checks an architecture's bit-manipulation capabilities. The *Linked List Insertion* (H) benchmark inserts five new entries into a doubly linked list. This benchmark tests pointer manipulation. The *Bit Matrix Transposition* (K) program takes a tightly packed, square bit matrix and transposes it. The matrix is of variable size and starts on a word boundary. This benchmark exercises an architecture's bit manipulation and looping capabilities. The *Quicksort* (I) performs a nonrecursive quick sorting algorithm on a large vector of fixed-length records. It contains no procedure calls. It thoroughly tests an architecture's addressing modes and character and stack manipulation capabilities. A recursive version of Quicksort, the *Recursive Qsort*, frequently used in Unix, has also been used as one of the benchmark programs. It sorts 2600 fixed-length character strings. The *Puzzle* is a recursive bin-packing program that solves a three-dimensional puzzle. Two versions of this program have been used: the Puzzle-Subscript, denoted sometimes as Puzzle and the Puzzle-Pointer, denoted as Ppuzzle. The *SED* (Stream-oriented text EDitor) is one of the Unix software tools. It copies files to the standard output after they have been edited according to a script of commands. The *Ackerman* and the *Towers of Hanoi* are programs stressing recursive procedure calls; particularly the Ackerman which requires more than 170,000 procedure calls [13.4].

The average relative code size for the above 11 C benchmark programs is:

Machine	Code Size Relative to RISC
RISC I, II	1.0
VAX 11/780	0.8 ± 0.3
MC68000	0.9 ± 0.2
Z8002	1.2 ± 0.6
PDP 11/70	0.9 ± 0.4
BBN C/70	0.7 ± 0.2

Even in the worst case (C/70), the RISC code is no more than 50% larger on the average. In the case of Z8002, the RISC code is even 20% smaller. The results should have been expected. Since RISC uses the most frequently used instructions, the penalties of having a reduced instruction set are not excessive.

As far as execution speed is concerned, we have the following results [13.4]:

Machine	Clock; MHz	Reg-to-Reg add; ns	b
RISC I	12	330	0.67
RISC II	8	500	1.00
VAX 11/780	5	400	1.7 ± 0.9
PDP 11/70	7.5	500	2.1 ± 1.2
MC68000	10	400	2.8 ± 1.4
BBN C/70	6.7	—	3.2 ± 2.2
Z8002	6	700	3.3 ± 1.3

where b = (Execution Time)/(8 MHz RISC Execution Time) averaged over 11 C programs

As one can see, for the benchmarks chosen, the RISC is superior on the average. For the particular add instruction, the 12 MHz RISC is also superior.

Data-Memory (M) traffic due to Call and Return instructions has also been monitored and expressed in units of words transferred and the percentage of all data-memory references:

Benchmarks:		Puzzle	Quicksort
VAX 11/780:	words	440K	700K
	% of all data-M ref.	28%	50%
RISC:	words	8K	4K
	% of all data-M ref.	0.8%	1%

The extensive savings of Data-Memory traffic on the RISC contributes considerably to its overall enhancement of the throughput.

Another measurement, concerning the HLL performance of the RISC, was made in [13.4]. The average of the following ratio was measured:

$$a = \text{average} \quad \frac{\text{Assembly Code Execution Time}}{\text{Compiler Code Execution Time}}$$

The results were:

Machine	a
RISC	0.90 ± 0.1
PDP 11/70	0.50 ± 0.2
Z8002	0.46 ± 0.3
VAX 11/780	0.45 ± 0.2
MC68000	0.34 ± 0.3

The lower this ratio, the more the programmer is tempted to program in assembly code. The above results indicate that the RISC programmer has a higher incentive to program in HLL [1.2].

The RISC does not have any floating point supports in its architecture. Any floating point calculations, to be performed on a RISC, are to be taken care of in two possible ways:

(a) Using a floating point coprocessor
(b) By software subroutines

Both approaches have been experimented with by the Berkeley RISC researchers [13.5]. The Weitek floating point two-chip set was used as a coprocessor. The Whetstone benchmark program [13.6, 13.7], translated into C, has been implemented. The Whetstone benchmark, developed by the Central Computer Agency of the British Government, is a synthetic program which tests numerical computing by executing a substantial amount of floating point arithmetic. The results were as follows:

Machine	Floating Point Implementation	Time (sec.)
VAX 11/780	hardware (FPA)	2.2
VAX 11/750	hardware	3.4
RISC II (12 MHz)	hardware (coprocessor)	4.5
VAX 11/780	microcode	5.5
RISC II (8 MHz)	hardware (coprocessor)	6.4
VAX 11/750	microcode	8.4
68010 (10 MHz)	software (assembly)	41.5
RISC II (12 MHz)	software (C)	67.1
RISC II (8 MHz)	software (C)	101.7

While the RISC performance with a coprocessor is quite competitive, its purely software performance for floating point calculations is quite poor. The use of a coprocessor seems to be the most reasonable way of treating floating point on the Berkeley RISC.

The compile time for C benchmarks has also been evaluated running the VAX C compiler and the RISC C compiler *both* on the VAX 11/780 and on the RISC II at 8 and 12 MHz. The total compile time for 3 benchmark programs in C (1d, sort, puzzle) is summarized below:

VAX C Compiler		Compile Time (sec.)	$\frac{\text{VAX}}{\text{RISC}}$ Compile Time
on VAX		50.5	
on RISC II	8 MHz	37.8	1.3
	12 MHz	25.0	2.0
RISC C Compiler			
on VAX		62.5	
on RISC II	8 MHz	40.4	1.5
	12 MHz	26.7	2.3

We can see that the RISC C Compiler or the VAX Compiler, run on the RISC II at 12 MHz, is twice as fast as the VAX C Compiler run on the VAX.

The Lisp and PSL (dialect of Lisp) performances were also tested for the RISC [13.5]. The programs tested were translated into the RISC machine code from the output of VAX Lisp compilers. The results were:

TAK Lisp benchmark in Franz Lisp		TAK Lisp benchmark in PSL	
Machine	Time (sec.)	Machine	Time (sec.)
MC68010 (10 MHz)	13.7 no optimization	VAX 11/750	7.1 no optimization
VAX 11/780	8.3 no optimization	RISC II (8 MHz)	2.6
RISC II (8 MHz)	4.4	RISC II (12 MHz)	1.7
VAX 11/750	3.6	VAX 11/750	1.4
RISC II (12 MHz)	2.9		
MC68010 (10 MHz)	2.5		
VAX 11/780	1.1		

The performance of RISC is quite competitive, at least compared to the VAX 11/750.

In the performance evaluation of RISC one has to note two aspects not directly associated with the idea of a reduced instruction set:

(a) Use of an optimized C compiler;
(b) The presence of a large CPU register file and the 'register window' approach.

Both of the above contribute considerably to the enhancement of the RISC throughput and both can be implemented in a CISC system as well. In other words, the above two aspects are not necessarily connected with the RISC general philosophy (see section 1.4). One has to add here the following points though:

(1) Looking from the VLSI standpoint, it is precisely because of the RISC small control area (up to 10%) that it is possible to allocate a large CPU register file on the chip, as argued in section 2.2.
(2) The presence of a large CPU register file is one of the RISC defining points, as stated in section 1.3.

Some researchers took up performance evaluation studies where the above aspects (a) and (b) of RISC were put to the test. Heath [13.8] has applied the optimized C compiler, running the same EDN benchmarks, to the MC68000 and the Z8002, with the following run time results (in msec.):

Benchmark	RISC I	MC68000	Z8002
Character string (E)	460	1228 (2.8)	421 (0.9)
Bit set (F)	60	288 (4.8)	242 (4.0)
Linked list (H)	100	160 (1.6)	137 (1.4)
Quicksort (I)	50400	206640 (4.1)	149760 (3.0)
Bit matrix (K)	430	1720 (4.0)	1278 (3.0)
average		(3.5)	(2.5)

The numbers in parentheses indicate the number of times slower than the RISC I program.

Next, the programs were recoded in the RISC assembly code and run on a RISC I simulator and the other two machines. The RISC run assumed that the CPU has a total of 32 registers, eliminating the 'register window' concept. The running time (msec.) results were:

Benchmark	RISC I	MC68000	Z8002
E	417	244 (0.59)	134 (0.32)
F	83	70 (0.84)	70 (0.85)
H	66	153 (2.32)	135 (2.05)
I	39449	33527 (0.85)	66000 (1.67)
K	772	368 (0.48)	369 (0.45)
average		(1.01)	(1.07)

As should have been expected, the RISC performance dropped compared to the Berkeley results. Notwithstanding this drop of performance in the above experiments, they still indicate that even eliminating the large register file and 'register window' edge, the RISC is still comparable and competitive with some CISC microprocessors. One should also keep in mind that a large CPU register file is an integral part of the RISC attributes.

Similar studies were also reported in [13.9]. One of the main conclusions of that project was that 'performance gains due to multiple register sets are independent of instruction set complexity'. As argued earlier in this section, this is a very logical statement and it does not really require a lengthy simulation study to support it.

To summarize, most of the performance evaluation studies point to the superiority (or at least non-inferiority) of the RISC with respect to other comparable computing systems. No study has demonstrated RISC inferiority, with or without the register window or the optimized C compiler.

13.3 Comparison of Commercial RISC Systems

The properties of a sample of leading RISC systems MIPS R3000 (chapter 4), Motorola M88000 (chapter 6), Sun SPARC (chapter 7), AMD 29000 (chapter 8) and Intel 80860 (chapter 9), are presented in Table 13.1 [13.10]. The MC88100 and i80860 have an on-chip Floating Point Unit (FPU), while the others have a coprocessor for this purpose. With the increase in VLSI chip density (1.2 million transistors on the 80860), the trend is to place the FPU on the CPU chip (also in the T800, see section 12.4). Indeed, the future AMD chip 29090 will include an on-chip FPU instead of the 29027 coprocessor.

While SPARC architects have chosen the Berkeley window registers feature, scaling the architecture in the direction of increasing the number of implemented windows, the Motorola designers have chosen the extra on-chip Special Function Unit (SFU) scalability. Motorola, Intel and MIPS have adopted the rather modest 32 Register File design. AMD has implemented a large register file; however, it did not adopt the register window feature as in the Berkeley RISC (chapter 3),

Table 13.1 RISC Systems Comparison

System: / Feature	M88000	i80860	SPARC Cypress	Am29000	MIPS
CPU	MC88100	80860	CY7C601	Am29000	R3000
FPU	on CPU	on CPU	CY7C609	Am29027	R3010
Clock, MHz	20	40	33	25	25
CPU GP Registers	32	32	136	192	32
Cache	MC88200 16KB Code 16KB Data	on CPU 4KB Code 8KB Data	CY7604 64KB	AM29062 8KB Code 8KB Data	external 256KB Code 256KB Data
MMU	MC88200	on CPU	CY7604	on CPU	on CPU
CPU Bus Bandwith MBytes/sec.	160	960	133	200	200
Main Memory Bandwidth, MBytes/sec.	64	160	266	--	100
Number of instructions	51	65	89	124	74
Peak VAX MIPS	17	33	24	17	20
Microns CMOS	1.2	1.0	0.8	1.2	1.2*
Pins	180	168	244	168	144
1000-unit price, $ (CPU+MMU)	1113	750	1275	331	200
$/MIPS	65	23	53	19	10

CPU = Central Processing Unit

FPU = Floating Point Unit

MMU = Memory Management Unit

GP = General Purpose

* LSI Logic and Performance Semiconductor second-sourced R3000 are 1 micron CMOS. The Performance Semiconductor price is $415 and the corresponding $/MIPS figure is 21.

Pyramid (section 12.1) and SPARC (chapter 7). All in all, the performance of the above systems is quite comparable within a 2:1 factor. The real test will come when software packages, run in a HLL, will eventually be made available to the users by the above companies. MIPS and Sun have already made significant progress as far as software is concerned. Others will follow soon.

The relative merits and shortcomings of a large register file were given in section 2.6. The merits of a register file, compared to a cache, were also discussed in section 2.6. With the advent of large on-chip caches, such as the 12 KBytes on i80860, we can attain a fast access cache with a reasonable hit ratio. Under those circumstances, one can afford a smaller register file as the designers of the i80860 have done (32 registers). But is it really the best possible solution? This is a problem yet to be investigated: what is the optimal on-chip register file vs. cache ratio? Future comparative experimentation with the i80860 and other systems may offer an answer.

The i80860, Am29000 and R3000 contain the Memory Management Unit (MMU) on chip. The others have it on a separate chip. Having the MMU on chip certainly speeds up any memory related operations. Putting the MMU on the CPU chip is a current trend also in CISC chips, such as MC68030, Intel 80386 and NS32532. From the memory interface point of view, the i80860 has a definite edge: it has both the MMU and a significant cache on-chip. This is also one of the reasons for its exceedingly large CPU bus bandwidth of 960 MBytes/s and 33 MIPS performance – almost double compared to the others.

Looking at the bottom line in Table 13.1 we can see that using the MIPS and the Am29000 one has to pay less per MIPS of performance. However, the cost of the i80860 is not much more, considering the additional benefits of an FPU and a large cache on-chip, and 33 MIPS performance. If one leans towards the large CPU register set solution, then the Am29000 and the SPARC are the only contenders. From the price/performance point of view, the Am29000 has a definite edge. Its large and almost unconstrained register set (192×32) permits on-chip task switching, making the Am29000 very attractive for real-time embedded applications. The i80860 with its on-chip 8 KByte data cache and superior performance is certainly a very serious contender in similar applications.

The Intel 80960 (chapter 9) and the Acorn (chapter 11) were intended primarily to serve as embedded subsystems, such as controllers. Their properties are therefore compared separately in Table 13.2. Although the performance of the 80960 is considerably superior to that of the Acorn, its price per MIPS is by an order of magnitude higher. In a large number of embedded control applications, 4 MIPS performance and a 64 MBytes address space would be quite adequate. In these cases, using the Acorn would make much more sense from the economic standpoint. If higher performance and a larger address space are important, then the 80960 should be used, at a much higher cost.

13.4 Performance Evaluation Reports

The Dhrystone benchmark program [13.12] has become an accepted industry standard for comparing integer processing performance of different systems. A summary of Dhrystone performance of some RISC systems, as reported by their manufacturers, is summarized in Table 13.3 [13.11]. For obvious reasons (large on-chip cache, higher frequency) the i80860 performance is considerably superior.

A set of integer processing experiments was conducted by AMD [13.13] using three benchmark sets:

(1) Dhrystone [13.12]
(2) AMD Unix Benchmarks
   diff – find the differences between two 20 KByte files with a total of 7 differences.
   grep – look for a regular expression in a 17 KByte file.
   nroff – format an input 10 KByte file with hyphenation, justification and pagination.

Table 13.2 Intel 80960 and Acorn

Feature	System: Intel 80960	Acorn
CPU	80960	VL86C010
FPU	on CPU	off chip
Clock, MHz	25	12
CPU Registers	84	27
Cache	512B on CPU	external
Address space	4GBytes	64MBytes
Microns	1.5	2
Pins	132	84
Peak MIPS	20	4
1000-unit price, $	2400 (80960 MC)	35
$/MIPS	120	9

Table 13.3 Dhrystone Performance of RISC Systems

System	Dhrystones/sec
MIPS R3000	42300 (25 MHz)
Motorola M88000	46000 (25 MHz)
SPARC - Cypress	42000 (33 MHz)
SPARC - Fujitsu	19000 (16.67 MHz)
AMD 29000	42000 (30 MHz)
Intel 80960	13000 (20 MHz)
Intergraph CLIPPER	35000 (33 MHz)
Intel 80860	85000 (40 MHz)
VL86C010	11820 (12 MHz)

(3) Stanford University benchmark suite, consisting of a number of small programs, collected by J. Hennessy:
perm – computes all permutations of 7 elements 5 times.
towers – solves the Towers of Hanoi problem for 14 disks.
queen – solves the 8 queens problem 50 times.
intmm – calculates the product of two 40 × 40 integer matrices.
puzzle – solves Forrest Basket's puzzle cube.
quick – uses quicksort to sort 5000 elements.
bubble – uses bubblesort to sort 500 elements.
tree – does a binary tree sort of 5000 elements.

The systems compared were:

Am29000 with 8 KBytes Cache, 25 MHz.
Am29000 with Video RAM (VRAM), 25 MHz.
Sun 4/200 (SPARC)
Sun 3/60 (MC68020)
VAX 11/780

The benchmark results, expressed in values relative to the VAX 11/780, are summarized in Table 13.4 and illustrated in Figure 13.1, which also includes a comparison with the MIPS Computer Systems, Inc. M/1000 (R2000) system. All benchmarks are written in C and were compiled using AMD's HIgh C29K optimizing C compiler, developed by Metaware.

AMD also reported experimentation results on the frequency of memory address computations for its Am29000 with a 192 CPU register file, compared to other systems with only 32 CPU registers. The results are summarized in Figure 13.2, demonstrating a lower address computation overhead in the Am29000. It should be remembered that even in the on-chip fast cache access on the i80860, a full memory address has still to be formed.

Experimentation conducted by Intel for integer performance (Dhrystones [13.12]) is illustrated in Figure 13.3, and that for floating point performance (Whetstones [13.6, 13.7]) in Figure 13.4. For the integer performance the

Table 13.4 Summary of AMD Benchmark Results

System:	Am29000				
Benchmark	Cache	VRAM	Sun 4	Sun 3	VAX 11/780
Dhrystone	20.32	14.26	11.71	2.65	1.0
AMD Unix Mean	15.31	11.35	7.64	3.21	1.0
Stanford Aggregate	20.60	16.72	8.64	2.51	1.0

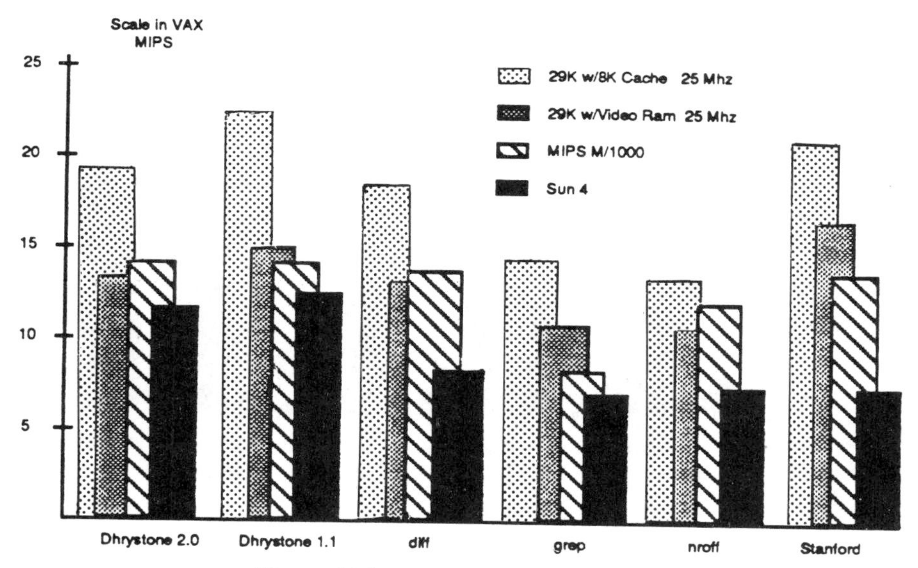

Figure 13.1 AMD Benchmark Results
(Courtesy of AMD, Inc.)

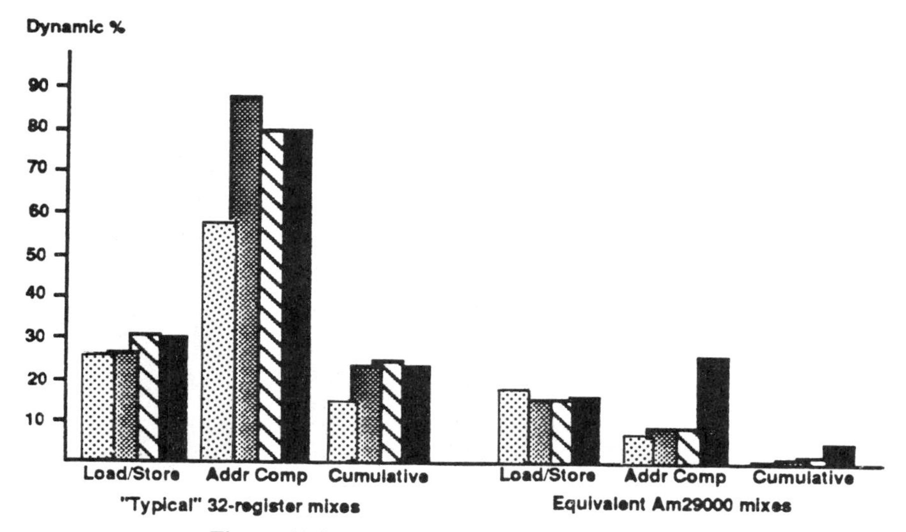

Figure 13.2 Frequency of Address Computation
(Courtesy of AMD, Inc.)

comparison is made with CISC microprocessors, such as Intel 80386 and Motorola MC68030 and MC68020. The top performance for the 80960 at 25 MHz is 157000 Dhrystones/sec. As can be seen from Table 13.3, this is well below other RISC systems (but then, as argued in chapter 9, the 80960 is only a marginal

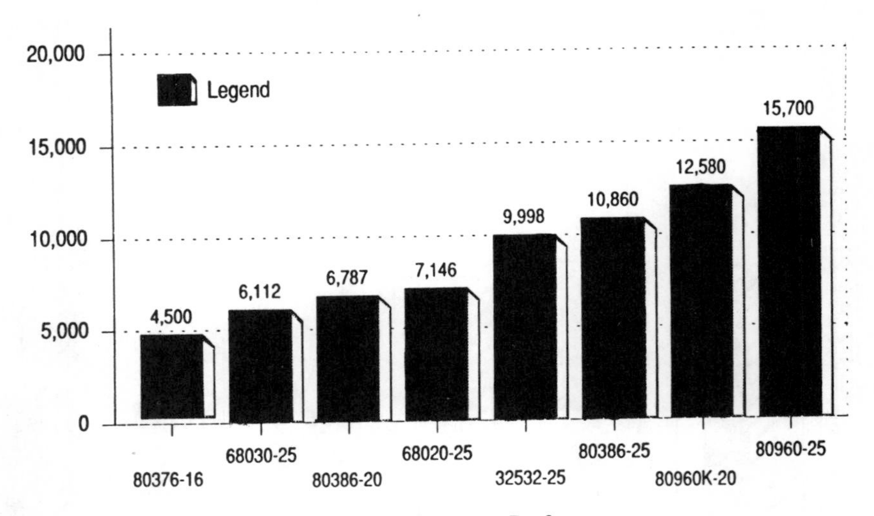

Figure 13.3 Dhrystone Performance
(*Courtesy of Intel Corp.*)

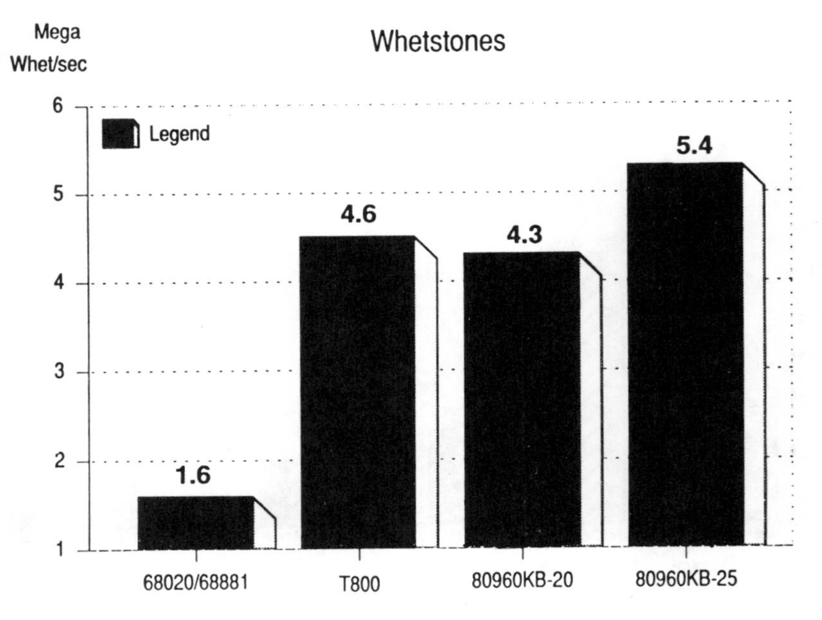

Figure 13.4 Whetstone Performance
(*Courtesy of Intel Corp.*)

RISC). In the floating point performance, illustrated in Figure 13.4, the 80960 performance at 25 MHz exceeds somewhat that of the T800 (section 12.4), but not at 20 MHz.

Benchmark results, reported by Intel for the 80860 at 40 MHz, are

Peak performance	120 MOPS
Dhrystones/sec.	85000
Whetstones/sec., double precision	24000
Stanford suite [13.13]	33 VAX MIPS
Linpack [13.14], double precision	13 MFLOPS

Some benchmark comparison results conducted for the CLIPPER (chapter 10) were reported in [13.15]. The results, normalized with respect to the VAX 8600 (assumed as 1.0), are shown in Table 13.5. One can see a considerable step-up from the first CLIPPER product C100 to the next C300. The SPARC chip used in the Sun 4 workstation is the Fujitsu at 16.67 MHz, while the CLIPPER operates at a double frequency of 33 MHz. Thus, the results reported in Table 13.5 do not constitute a completely fair comparison. Even so, the SPARC has a slight edge over the C100. It should also be remembered that the CLIPPER has an on-chip FPU while the SPARC uses a coprocessor (a powerful Weitek, however).

A comparison of the code size for a number of benchmarks, compared to the VAX (assumed as 1.0), was also reported in [13.15]. The average relative code size is shown in Table 13.6. The results fit quite well with the discussion in section 2.6. The code length for the CISC systems (VAX, MC68020, NS32032, Intel 80386) is relatively shorter than that of the RISCs. The CLIPPER code length is shorter than that of the other RISCs compared (ROMP, SPARC). This can be attributed to the following reasons:

(a) The CLIPPER instructions are of different lengths (see chapter 10), allowing better code compaction.
(b) The CLIPPER is only a marginal RISC, with a number of CISC properties (chapter 10).

Table 13.5 Benchmark Results for the CLIPPER

System: Benchmark	Sun 4 (SPARC)	CLIPPER C100	CLIPPER C300
Dhrystone	1.78	1.47	2.89
Whetstone (double)	1.68	1.24	3.19
Whetstone (single)	2.07	1.77	3.63
Linpack	1.09	1.48	2.61
Stanford Integer	1.24	1.50	2.49
Stanford Fl.Pt.	1.32	1.34	2.28
Average:	1.37	1.32	2.53

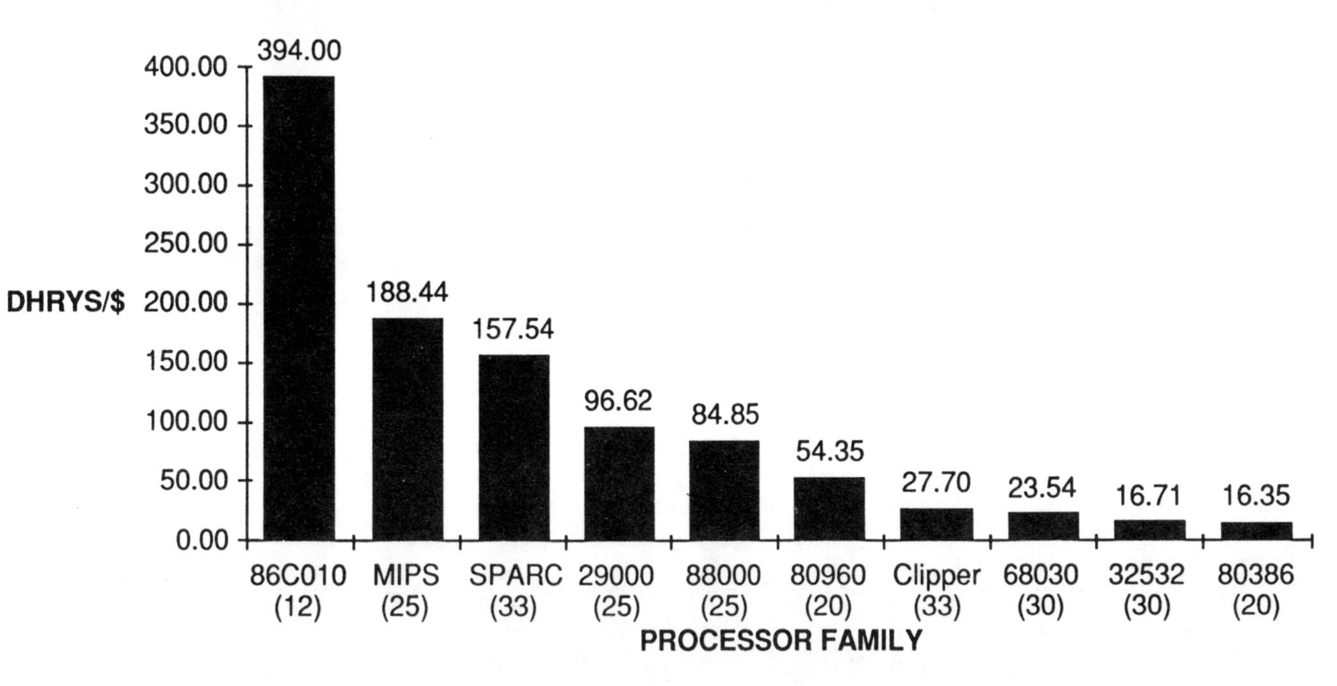

Figure 13.5 VL86C010 RISC Performance Measures
(*Courtesy of VLSI Technology, Inc.*)

Table 13.6 Average Code Size of Several Benchmarks

System	Average relative code size
VAX (Unix 4.3 BSD)	1.00
IBM PC RT (ROMP)	1.63
Sun 3 (MC68020)	1.23
Sun 4 (SPARC)	1.53
Sequent (NS32032)	0.81
Sequent (80386)	1.05
CLIPPER	1.11

As a matter of fact, the CLIPPER code size is smaller than that of the MC68020 CISC.

The absolute Dhrystone performance of the VL86C010 (Table 13.3) is rather low. However, if one makes the comparison in units of Dhrystone per dollar cost, as reported by VLSI Technology, Inc. and illustrated in Figure 13.5, the picture is completely different. The Acorn VL86C010 has a definite advantage as far as the cost of performance is concerned.

Some recent performance comparison studies were conducted by the Intel Corp. for the new 80860 processor. The integer performance, compared to the MIPS R3000, Motorola M88000 and the Sun SPARC, is summarized in Figure 13.6. The floating-point performance, compared to the same processors, is summarized in Figure 13.7 [13.16].

References

13.1 S.C. Johnson, 'A Portable Compiler: Theory and Practice', *Proc. Fifth Annual ACM Symp. on Programming Languages*, pp. 97–104, Jan. 1978.

13.2 B.W. Kernighan, D.M. Ritchie, *The C Programming Language*, Prentice-Hall, Englewood Cliffs, NJ, 1978.

13.3 R.G. Grappel, J.E. Hemmengway, 'A Tale of Four Microprocessors: Benchmarks Quantify Performance', *Electronic Design News*, **26**, No. 7, pp. 179–265, April 1, 1981.

13.4 D.A. Patterson, R.S. Piepho, 'Assessing RISCs in HLL Support', *IEEE MICRO*, **2**, No. 4, pp. 9–19, Nov. 1982.

13.5 D.A. Patterson, 'RISC Watch', *Computer Architecture News*, **12**, No. 1, pp. 11–19, March 1984.

13.6 H.J. Curnow, B.A. Wichmann, 'A Synthetic Benchmark', *Computer Journal*, **19**, No. 1, 1975.

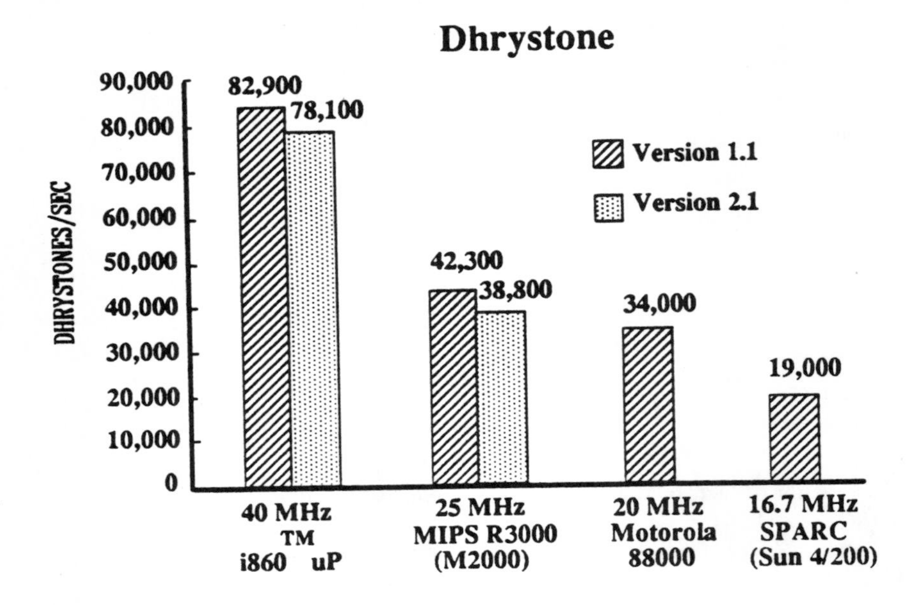

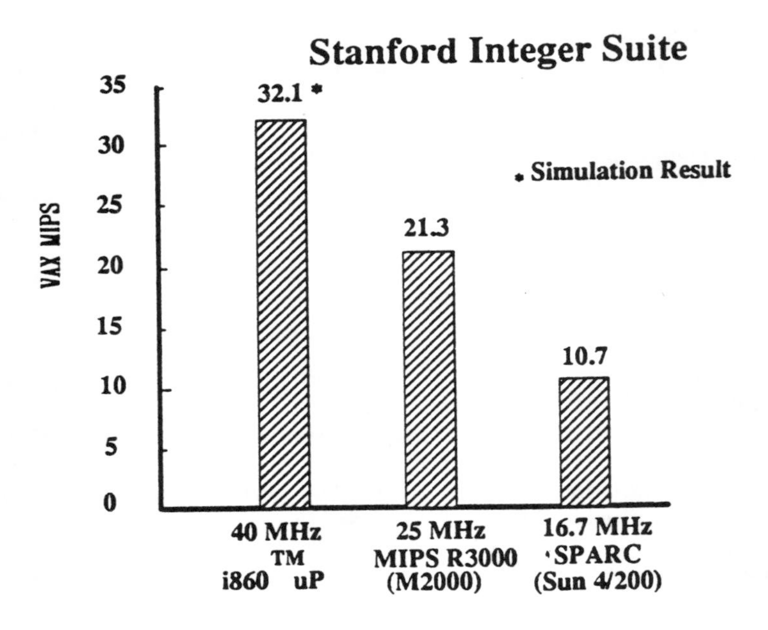

Figure 13.6 Summary of Integer Benchmark Results
(*Courtesy of Intel Corp.*)

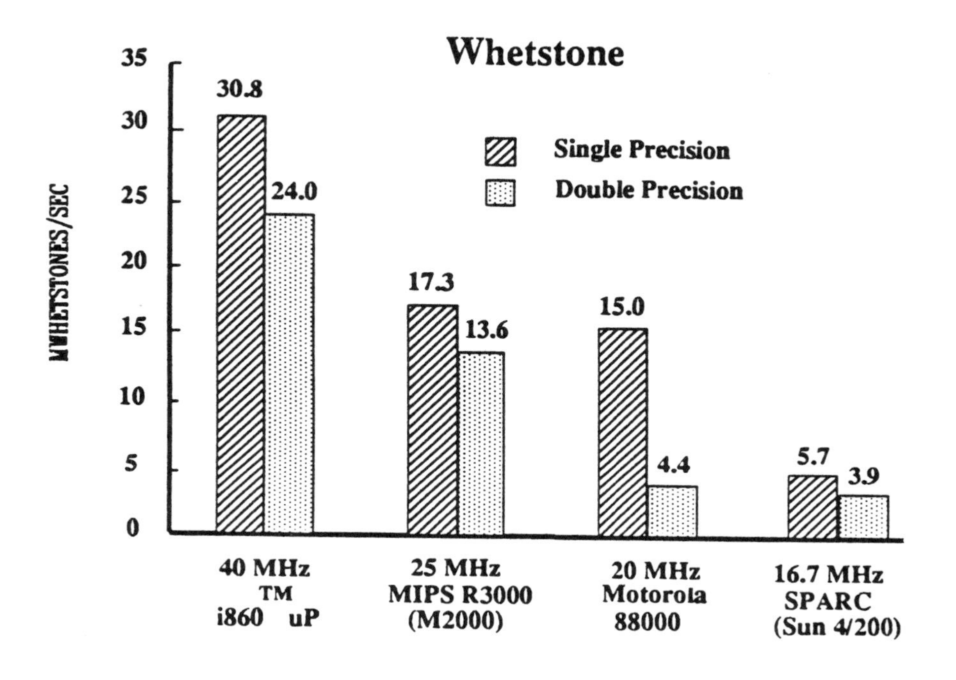

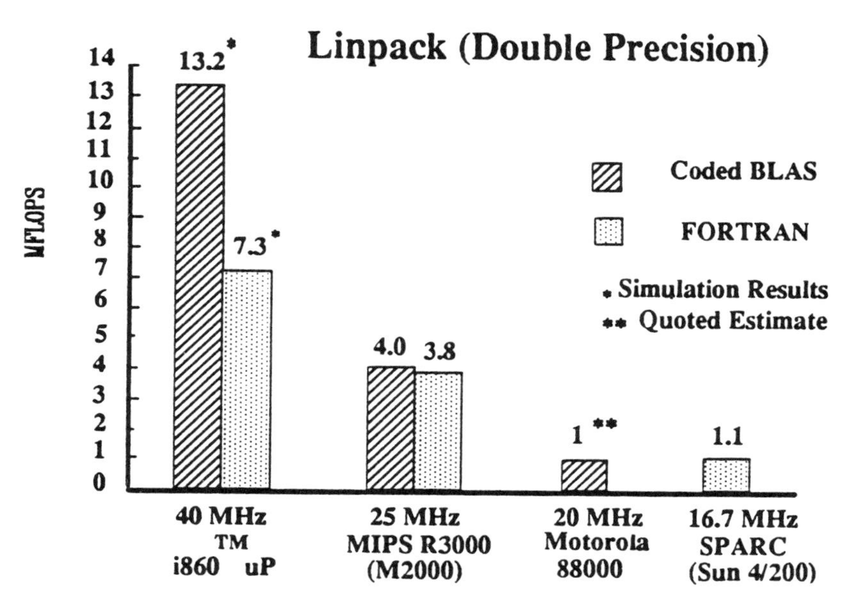

Figure 13.7 Summary of Floating-Point Benchmark Results
(*Courtesy of Intel Corp.*)

13.7 B.A. Wichmann, H.J. Curnow, 'The Design of Synthetic Programs', in *Benchmarking: Computer Evaluation and Measurement*, pp. 89–114, Wiley, London, 1975.

13.8 J.L. Heath, 'Reevaluation of the RISC I', *Computer Architecture News*, **12**, No. 1, pp. 3–10, March 1984.

13.9 C.Y. Hitchcock, H.M.B. Sprunt, 'Analyzing Multiple Register Sets', *Proc. 12th Annual Int. Symp. on Computer Architecture*, pp. 55–63, Boston, MA, June 17–19, 1985.

13.10 B. Furlow, 'RISC – The Sound and the Fury', *ESD*, March 1989, pp. 49–57.

13.11 T. Marshall, J.M. Tazelaar, 'Worth the RISC', *BYTE*, Feb. 1989, pp. 245–249.

13.12 R.P. Weicker, 'Dhrystone: A Synthetic Systems Programming Benchmark', *Comm. ACM*, **27**, No. 10, pp. 1013–1030, Oct. 1984.

13.13 *Am29000 Performance Analysis*, AMD, Sunnyvale, CA, May 1988.

13.14 J.J. Dongarra, 'Performance of Various Computers Using Standard Linear Equations Software in a Fortran Environment', *Computer Architecture News*, **13**, No. 1, pp. 3–11, March 1985.

13.15 W. Hollingsworth, H. Sachs, A.J. Smith, 'The CLIPPER Processor: Instruction Set Architecture and Implementation', *Comm. ACM*, **32**, No. 2, pp. 200–219, Feb. 1989.

13.16 *i860 Processor Performance, Release 1.0*, Intel Corporation, March 1989.

14
RISC Applications

14.1 Introductory Comments

When the development of the first RISC systems was contemplated (by IBM, Berkeley, Stanford; chapter 1), there was no specific field of application in mind. In fact, most of the existing RISC systems were developed as universal computing systems. Therefore, when the question is asked: what are the applications of RISC?, the answer is that RISCs can be applied to any problem and to all tasks without limitation. The mere fact that RISC systems are actually implemented in a number of areas, attests to their universality.

Although there are no basic limitations imposed on the potential areas of RISC applications, there are three fields in which RISC systems implementation is notable:

(1) Workstations (including graphics workstations) and personal computers;
(2) Multiprocessors;
(3) Real-time applications.

The reason for the above is the high throughput, relative simplicity, relatively low cost/performance ratio, and relatively short development time. RISC designers have taken particular care in endowing the systems with multiprocessing capabilities such as cache coherency mechanisms (as in MC88200; chapter 6) and atomic instructions for semaphore handling in virtually all RISCs. The large CPU register set (as in MULTRIS, chapter 5, or SPARC, chapter 7, or AM29000, chapter 8) or a large on-chip cache (as in Intel 80860, chapter 9), make some RISC systems particularly attractive for multitasking real-time applications. As pointed out in section 2.6, not all CPU registers have to be saved on a context switch, and with a large register set the context switch can be accomplished entirely within the CPU register file, avoiding CPU-memory traffic.

A number of actual examples of RISC applications are presented in the following sections of this chapter. Workstations, boards and personal computers are described in section 14.2. Multiprocessor applications of RISCs are presented in section 14.3. Real-time and robotics applications of RISCs are discussed in section 14.4.

14.2 Workstations and Personal Computers

The Digital Equipment Corporation, DEC (Maynard, MA), famous for its PDP and VAX systems, decided to adopt the *MIPS* Computer Systems R2000 processor (section 4.3) as the CPU of its new DECstation 3100 workstation [14.1–14.3]. Interestingly enough, it announced, in parallel, a new VAXstation based on its MicroVAX as a CPU [14.1]. There is also a DECstation 2100, using a 12.5 MHz R2000.

The block diagram of the 3100 is shown in Figure 14.1. It contains a 16.67 MHz R2000 as a CPU, R2010 FPU, R2020 buffer, Ethernet (DEC Local Area Network, LAN) and SCSI interfaces, LK301 keyboard, DEC mouse, serial communications port with modem control, and a graphics monitor. It features 25 ns SRAM, 64 KByte Data and 64 KByte Instruction caches. Its main memory can be configured up to 32 MBytes in 4 MByte increments.

The 3100 integer performance ranges from 10 to 14 MIPS. Its floating point performance is 3.7 MFLOPS single precision Linpack (compared to 2.7 MFLOPS on DECstation 2100 and 1.3 MFLOPS on Sun 4/260) and 10 MWhetstones/s, double precision (compared to 4 on the Sun 4/260) [14.1]. A set of benchmarks was run by the authors of [14.1], comparing the 3100 with other systems in MVUP (MicroVax II Units of Processing) units:

System	MVUPs
MIPS M/120-5 (section 4.3)	13.72
DECstation 3100	12.78
Sun 4/260 (chapter 7)	5.91
Solbourne 4/601 (SPARC)	5.60
Sun 4/110 (chapter 7)	4.29

The M/120 and the 3100 are both R2000-based. The Sun 4 and Solbourne are SPARC-based.

The implementation of the higher level R3000 on future DEC workstations is contemplated. This will certainly yield higher performance.

The 3100 runs under Ultrix Worksystem Software (UWS) version 2 [14.1]. UWS includes Ultrix-32 version 3, DEC's version of Unix OS. Ultrix-32 version 3 is based on the Berkeley 4.2BSD (Berkeley Software Distribution) with version 4.3BSD enhancements. It also includes many Unix System V features, such as the Bourne shell, the interprocess communication mechanism, the C runtime and math libraries, and demand-paged shared memory support and page locking [14.1]. It is also compliant with the IEEE 1003.1 Posix specification for applications portability [14.1].

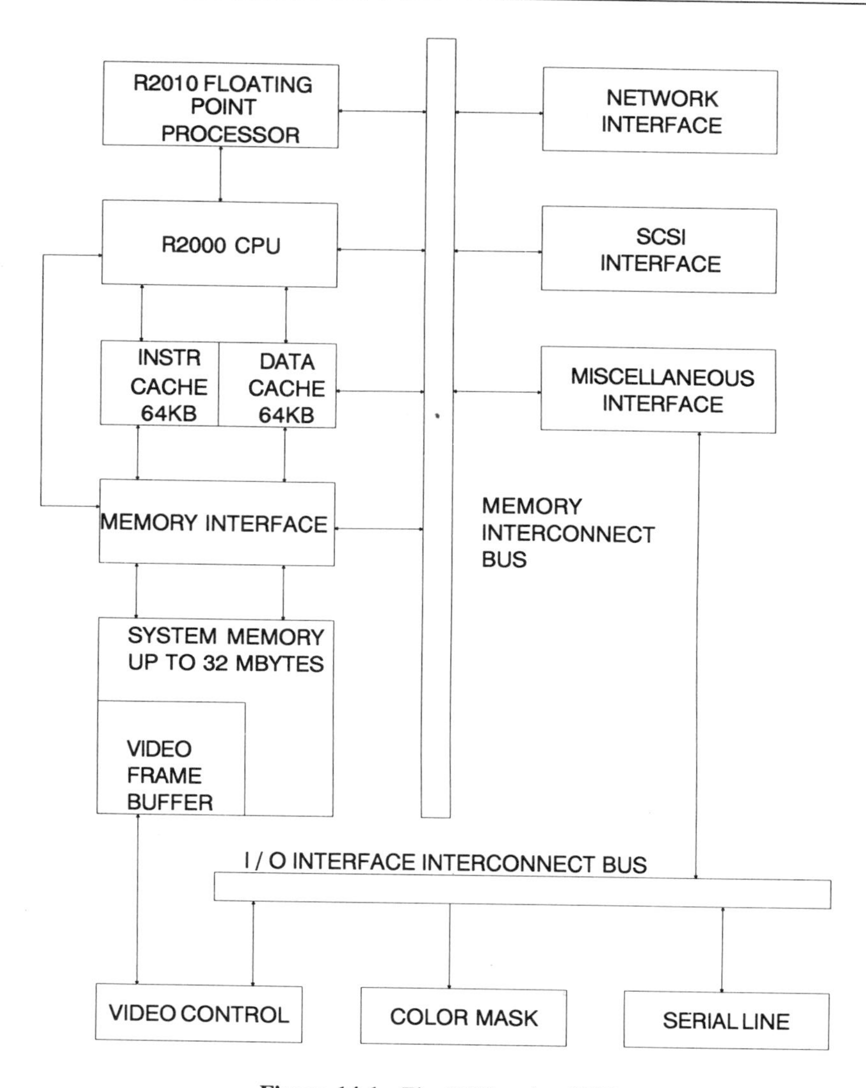

Figure 14.1 The DECstation 3100

The 3100 is priced from $12,000 to $24,000* depending on the main memory size and other options [14.1].

Silicon Graphics Co. (Mountain View, CA) has developed a number of *MIPS*-based workstations. One of its products is the *IRIS Power Series*, based on the

*Prices given in this chapter, for comparative purposes, are those of mid-1989.

16.67 MHz R2000 and 25 MHz R3000. Some of the products of this series are configured as multiprocessors (see section 14.3). A recent product is the *Personal Iris* 4D/20 workstation [14.4]. It is a 3-D Graphics workstation, based on the 12.5 MHz R2000 CPU. Its block diagram is shown in Figure 14.2. The Personal Iris main memory can be 8, 12, or 16 MBytes. The main memory is dual-ported between the CPU and I/O subsystems. The I/O subsystem is based on a 10 MHz, 32-bit I/O bus and provides the system with Ethernet, SCSI, audio and parallel interfaces, as well as a connection to the graphics subsystem [14.4].

The Personal Iris CPU Controller (Figure 14.2) manages the CPU and I/O

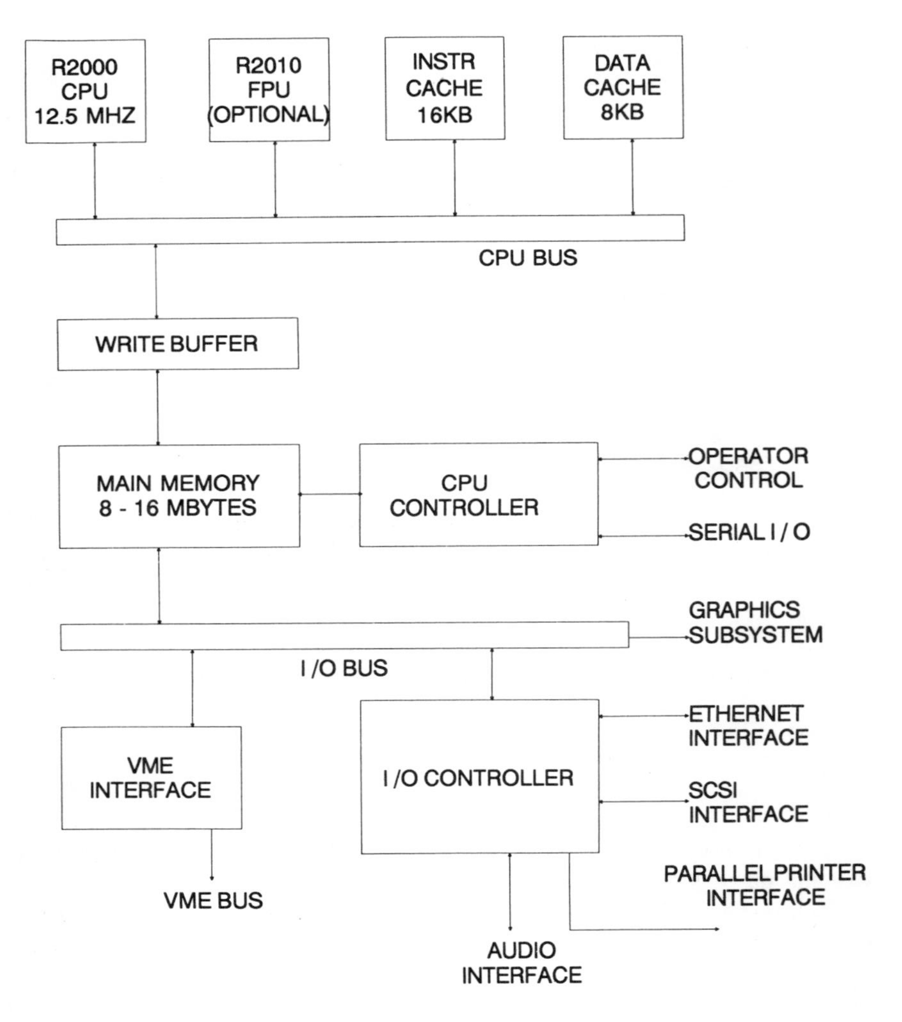

Figure 14.2 The Personal Iris

subsystems' access to main memory and handles the DMA transfers between the CPU and graphics subsystems. The CPU Controller also handles the keyboard, mouse and other serial I/O interfaces. There are also two RS-232-C ports, both having full modem control. The I/O Controller handles all I/O tasks, managing the I/O bus as well as the Ethernet, SCSI, audio and parallel interfaces. There is a single VME bus slot.

The Personal Iris graphics subsystem is organized as a four-stage pipeline:

(1) host interface subsystem;
(2) geometry subsystem;
(3) raster subsystem;
(4) display subsystem.

The *host interface* section receives graphics commands and data from the CPU through the I/O bus, performs some processing on these commands and data, and passes them on to the other stages. It also serves as the controller for the geometry subsystem and manages all data flow to and from the host CPU. The *geometry* subsystem consists of the *Geometry Engine*, 16 KBytes of microcode RAM and 8 KBytes of data RAM. The Geometry Engine receives graphics commands and data from the host interface and applies transformations, lighting calculations, clipping and the beginning of scan conversion, then passes the results to the raster stage. The *raster* subsystem performs the final stage of scan conversion and controls the buffers, interfacing with the next stage. The *display* subsystem sends the values stored in the buffer to the D/A converters for display on the monitor. It uses 5 Multimode Graphics Processors (MGP) to read the color and window planes of the buffer. As many as 16 different windows can be displayed simultaneously in different color modes.

The Personal Iris runs a version of Unix System V.3 called *Irix*, which includes networking features of the 4.3BSD version. Irix is divided into two configurations:

(a) the application environment,
(b) the development environment.

The *application environment* is intended for *end users* who will not do any programming or development. The *development environment* includes the C language compiler and all files and libraries necessary to develop applications on the system in any language, including graphics applications. Irix has several extensions that are not derived from Unix System V or 4.3BSD; these include a modified file system (the Extent File System, EFS), non-degrading processing priorities and high-resolution timers for quasi-real-time applications, library and kernel primitives for multiprocess applications and concurrent programming, a version of the dbx debugger that can examine multiple processes, and memory-mapped files [14.4].

The performance of the Personal Iris was compared to that of other systems, using a set of benchmarks, in MVUP units (as for the 3100) [14.4]:

System	MVUPs
Apollo DN10010	16.60
MIPS M/120	13.72
DECstation 3100	12.88
Personal Iris	8.40
Sun 4/260	5.91
HP9000/Model 3	4.88
VAXstation 3100	3.43

The entry price of the Personal Iris is $16,000.

The Silicon Graphics also features an R2000-based workstation Iris 4D/60, which is identical to the Prime Computer (Natick, MA) 3D graphics workstation PXCL 5500. It has up to 12 MBytes of memory and is currently priced at $75,000.

An additional family of Silicon Graphics R2000-based workstations is the Iris 4D GT Series, featuring the following models:

Model	MIPS
4D/50 GT	7
4D/70 GT	10
4D/80 GT	13

Microcomputers and workstations, using the R2000 or R3000, offered by the MIPS Computer Systems, Inc., are described in subsection 4.3.4.

Integrated Solutions, Inc. (San Jose, CA) features a 16.67 MHz R2000-based Advantedge 2000 desktop workstation. It includes the R2010 FPU, 32 KBytes Data and 32 KBytes Instruction caches, up to 16 MBytes main memory (4 MBytes increments), Ethernet, 2 RS-232-C serial ports and a Centronics parallel port interfaces. It runs under MIPS RISC/OS (see section 4.3) and Integrated Solutions OS based on Unix System V.3 and 4.3BSD. Its performance is 12 MIPS and its price, $12,000, offering $1,000/MIPS.

Sony Microsystems (Palo Alto, CA) is planning to use the MIPS R3000 for its next generation of the NEWS workstation.

The *M88000* family components (chapter 6) have already been implemented in a number of industrial products. For instance, the Tadpole Technology Co. of Cambridge, England, features a TP8800M Multibus II-based CPU board, using the MC88100 CPU and two MC88200 CMMUs. An MC68000 is used as an I/O Processor. The on-board memory contains 4 MBytes, 100 ns DRAM, allowing CMMU-DRAM bandwidths of 35 MBytes/sec. [14.5]. It is expected to reach 50 MBytes/sec. for a 25 MHz processor clock.

Tektronix (Wilsonville, Oregon) has announced 88000-based graphics workstations [14.6, 14.7]. This endeavor is particularly helped by the 88000 capability to include Special Function Units (SFUs), such as for graphics data processing, in a future version of the MC88100. The workstations are identified by the XD88 label.

The following products are featured in particular:

XD88/30 3-D workstation	for $35,000,
XD88/20 2-D workstation	for $30,000,
XD88/01 Applications Processor	for $25,000,
XD88/05 File Server	for $75,000.

The XD88 series offers performance of up to 17 VAX MIPS and 12 MFLOPS [14.7]. There is one 88100 CPU and four 88200 CMMUs (chapter 6) for a total of 64 KBytes cache on the processor board. The standard configuration includes 8 MBytes of main memory, a 156 MByte disk drive and a 150 MByte streaming tape. A separate I/O board includes a SCSI port that connects to both the VME and the internal buses. The internal bus bandwidth is 100 MBytes/sec.

Data General (Westborough, MA) announced an 88000-based workstation called AViiON [14.8]. It contains an 88100 CPU (16.67 or 20 MHz versions), two CMMUs, and from 4 to 28 MBytes main memory. Its performance is 17 MIPS and its price is around $12,000. The system works under the DG/UX 4.1 revision of Data General's Unix OS.

An 88000-based, 17 MIPS coprocessor boad is featured by Opus Systems (Cupertino, CA). It is called 400 Personal Mainframe and it is intended to be used with PC/XT or AT. It includes an 88100 CPU, two 88200 CMMUs and 4 MBytes main memory. There are sockets for up to 40 MBytes of main memory. It runs under a ported AT&T Unix System V OS.

The Opus board is used by the Everex Systems (Fremont, CA) Step 8820 workstation [14.9]. It is also called Personal Mainframe/8000. It has two processors:

(1) MC88100 on the Opus board, under AT&T System V.4 Unix OS,
(2) Intel 80386, under MS-DOS.

Both can run simultaneously. The system contains from 4 to 16 MBytes main memory. Its price is $13,000. Other companies adopting the M88000 family in their products are Aitech (Sunnyvale, CA), Beacon Technologies (Valparaiso, FL), Convergent Technologies, Inc. (San Jose, CA), and Encore Computer Corp. (Marlborough, MA).

The Unix C library and library functions for Pascal and FORTRAN are available to developers of 88000-based systems [14.10].

The UniSoft Co. is porting the Unix System V.3 OS, called SYSTEM V/88 for M88000-based products. A number of companies are working on various compilers for the 88000-based systems. For instance: TeleSoft, Ada; Tadpole

Technology, Inc., C; Green Hills Software, Inc., C, FORTRAN and Pascal [14.11].

Motorola, Inc. features its own 88000-based single board microcomputer, the MVME181 [14.12]. The board contains an 88100 CPU (20/25 MHz, 16–20 MIPS), two 88200 CMMUs, a full 32-bit VME bus interface, 8 MBytes RAM, two serial communications ports, a 16-bit Counter/Timer, and a battery-backed calendar clock. The system functional block diagram is shown in Figure 14.3.

A recent arrival on the RISC-workstations scene is the Motorola Delta Series 8000. The single processor Model 8608 features a 20 MHz MC88100, two MC88200 (32 KBytes cache), 8 to 32 MBytes main memory, one to four SCSI Winchester disk drives (up to 2.4 GBytes of storage capacity per controller), and 150 MByte streaming tape drive. It has 12 VME card slots and up to 98 serial ports. Its performance is 17 to 20 MIPS.

Sun Microsystems, Inc. has implemented, so far, the Fujitsu chip (chapter 7) on its Sun-4/200 series workstations. It has adopted as its OS the SunOS, a converged version of Unix System V and Berkeley 4.3BSD [7.2, 7.6]. Sun provides compilers for C, FORTRAN, Pascal, Ada and LISP [7.3].

Sun features several versions of its SPARC-based Sun-4/260 workstations (a lower model, Sun-4/110 is also available). The above workstations use the Fujitsu 16.67 MHz MB86900 IU and a set of Weitek 1164/1165 chips. It also features a 128 KByte virtual-address, write-back cache and 8 to 128 MBytes of main memory, managed by the Sun-4 Memory Management Unit (MMU), which provides complete mapping for 16 processes. A process occupies 1 GByte (2^{30}) of virtual address space.

A new addition to the Sun workstations is the SPARCstation 1 [14.13]. It includes a 20 MHz LSI Logic (chapter 7) SPARC CPU, a FPU, 64 KBytes cache, up to 16 MBytes main memory, an Ethernet port, two serial ports, one SCSI port, an optical mouse, and an IBM PC AT-compatible keyboard (type 4 keyboard). It has three expansion slots controlled by a new proprietary bus called the *S-bus*. The S-bus is a synchronous 32-bit bus that operates at the CPU speed of 20 MHz and features DMA capability. It includes separate channels for the SCSI, Ethernet, and serial ports, which all have DMA access through the S-bus. The SPARCstation 1GX version contains the GX graphics board for interactive 2-D and 3-D graphics. The system runs under the SunOS version 4 [7.2]. Its performance is 12.5 MIPS and 1.5 double precision Linpack MFLOPS. Its price is about $10,000 ($800/MIPS).

Sun also features the SPARCsystem 300 workstation which uses the Cypress 25 MHz SPARC chip (section 7.3). Its performance is 16 MIPS with prices starting at $30,000.

Metaflow Technologies, Inc. (San Diego, CA) is developing a new workstation which will implement a Metaflow version of SPARC, utilizing BiCMOS technology at 50 MHz (20 ns clock period) [14.14]. The new processor is designated as MFT 2I/2O. It will feature a high level of internal parallelism, capable of fetching two instructions and issuing up to four instructions for

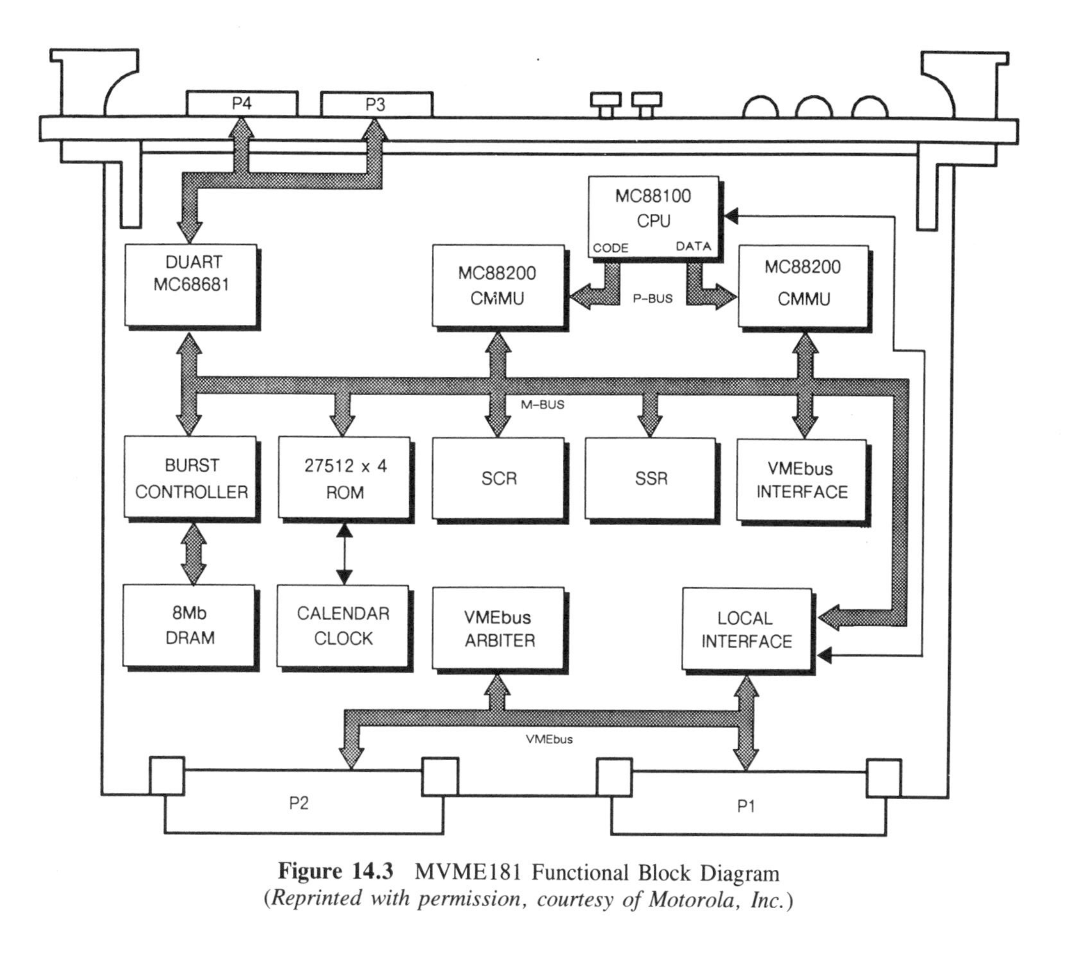

Figure 14.3 MVME181 Functional Block Diagram
(Reprinted with permission, courtesy of Motorola, Inc.)

execution, each clock period. Additional 48 'invisible' registers will be added to the CPU register file by dynamic register allocation logic.

The Am29000 (chapter 8) was implemented by the Yarc Systems Corp. (Westlake Village, CA) on a number of boards. The NuSuper Macintosh-II RISC Coprocessor System features a 25 MHz Am29000 CPU with 17 MIPS sustained performance. The Am29027 FPU is optional. The NuSuper board can have up to 6 MBytes main memory on board with direct access to 32 MBytes of DRAM on the NuBus. The NuSuper operates under the Macintosh MULTIFINDER OS. Up to 4 NuSupers can be run concurrently with one Macintosh host. The NuSuper price is about $5,000. A predecessor of NuSuper, the McCray, has the same properties, however, less main memory on-board [14.15].

Yarc Systems also features the AT-Super PC-AT Coprocessor System [14.16], using the same Am29000 CPU as the NuSuper. It has 512 KBytes of data and 2 MBytes of instruction memory on board. It operates under MS-DOS. Up to 4 AT-Supers can be run concurrently with one PC AT host. Its price is about $5,000. Yarc Systems has conducted a performance comparison with the following results:

System	Dhrystones/sec.
Yarc At/NuSuper (Am29000, 25 MHz)	31000
Sun 4/200 (SPARC, 16.67 MHz)	15600
VAX 8600	7100

Adage Inc. (Billerica, MA) implements a 25 MHz *Am29000* in its *Adage 200* Graphics Processor [14.17]. The Adage 200 connects to Q-bus and Unibus systems, as well as to other minicomputers. It includes the Extended Graphics OS graphics language, which incorporates many 2-D graphics primitives and functions. Its price range is $18,000–$30,000. Its software drivers are compatible with DEC's VMS version 5.

Step Engineering Co. has announced a development system called Adapt II 29K which supports 40 MHz Am29000-based systems. It includes a breakpoint facility, an interface to external logic state analyzers, an additional 32 bits of logic state analysis outputs, and a ROM simulator pod for debugging and patching of ROM-based code. The Adapt II 29K is controlled by a user-provided PC or ASCII terminal. The system comes with a hex debugger, a macro assembler with linking loader and library, an ANSI C compiler, and a source-level debugger. It costs $13,500.

The Acorn Co. (UK) has used its own *Acorn* chip (chapter 11) in its Archimedes 310 personal computer [14.18]. The A310 uses the Acorn CPU and the MEMC, VIDC, and IDC chips, described in chapter 11. It features 1 MBytes RAM and a single 3.5 inch floppy disk drive. The 310 runs under a proprietary

OS called Arthur, contained in a 512 KBytes ROM, along with a BASIC interpreter. The system comes standard with parallel printer and RS-423 serial interfaces. Its price is $1,600 (£875 in the UK). The performance of A310 was compared to that of Compaq Deskpro 386 which uses a 16 MHz Intel 80386 CPU with an 8 MHz 80287 FPU, running a number of benchmarks. The A310 achieved 4901 Dhrystones/sec., while the Deskpro achieved 3748 Dhrystones/sec. [14.18].

The Apollo Computer, Inc. (Chelmsford, MA) uses its PRISM (section 12.3) in its 10000 VS (Visualization System) graphics system. It can have from 1 to 4 processors, each with graphics capability of up to 1.5 million 3-D graphic transforms per second. The graphics subsystem is tightly integrated with the CPU via a 64-bit 150 MByte/sec. bus. The main memory ranges from 8 to 128 MBytes. There is a 128 KBytes instruction and a 64 KBytes data cache. The performance is 15 to 30 MIPS, 31000 Dhrystones, or 5.8 double precision Linpack MFLOPS (single processor). The system runs under a Unix-based Aegis OS. The basic single processor configuration price is $95,000 with $20,000 for each additional processor.

Cogent Research, Inc. (Beaverton, OR) uses two T800, 20 MHz *Transputer* chips (section 12.4) in its XTM workstation [14.19]. There is a total of 8 MBytes main memory, 3 slots of NuBus interface, a PC AT compatible port, and 2 Macintosh II compatible ports. The lowest configuration XTM costs about $20,000. The total performance is 10 VAX MIPS or 3 MFLOPS, sustained.

Two special issues of the journal *Microprocessors and Microsystems* (**13**, No. 2, March, No. 3, April 1989) were dedicated to the topic 'Applying the Transputer'. Some of the articles in these issues will be mentioned in the next sections.

Hewlett-Packard (HP) has announced its HP 9000 Model 835 superworkstation, based on its Precision Architecture CPU (section 12.6) [14.39]. The processor board of the Model 835 contains the CPU, instruction and data caches (64 KBytes each), a 4096 entry TLB, an FPU supplied by Bipolar Integrated Technology, and the system interface unit, connecting to the workstation's central bus and to the Processor Dependent Hardware (PDH) board. All of the processor board units are interconnected by a 32-bit 120 MBytes/sec. cache bus. The TLB entries are equally divided between instruction and data addresses. The 32-bit, 21 MBytes/sec. central bus has nine slots. Two are occupied by the processor and PDH boards and one by the display controller interface. Six slots are available for memory boards. Each memory board can have 8 or 16 MBytes, for a total of up to 96 MBytes. The PDH has two channel adapters. One interconnects to an 8-slots I/O expander. The other is connected to the central bus and to a 7-slots internal Channel I/O (CIO) bus. One slot of the CIO bus is occupied by the display controller interface. One more CIO slot each is taken by a standard Ethernet interface card and an HP-IB interface card. The remaining four CIO slots are available for future expansion. HP-IB is HP's I/O channel, based on the IEEE 754-1985 Standard, and provides a transfer rate of about 1.2 MBytes/sec.

The Model 835 runs the HP-UX OS. The HP-UX is a port of Unix AT&T

System V release 3.0. It includes many features from 4.3BSD. The following HLLs are supported: FORTRAN (with VAX extensions), BASIC, Pascal, Ada, LISP and APL.

A comparative run was made using a set of benchmarks [14.39], with performance expressed in MicroVAX II Units of Processing (MVUP):

System	Average MVUPs
MIPS M/2000	20.98
Apollo DN 10010	16.60
DECstation 3100	12.88
HP9000 Model 835	11.68
Personal Iris	8.46
VAXstation 3500	3.37

The price of the lowest version of the 835 is about $60,000 (about $5,000/MVUP).

At the time of writing no Intel 80860-based workstations have yet been announced. However, considering the 80860 properties (section 9.3), such as FPU, MMU and a 3-D Graphics subsystem on-chip, and its relatively low cost (section 14.3), there is no doubt that it will be extensively used in workstations and particularly in graphics workstations, in the near future. Because of its low cost and high performance, one can predict that 80860-based graphics workstations will offer the performance of 3-D workstations at a price of 2-D workstations. Some workstations described in this section are summarized in Table 14.1.

14.3 Multiprocessors

Silicon Graphics Co. (see section 14.2) features two families of graphics multiprocessors, using the MIPS R2000 and R3000 CPUs:

(1) Power Iris Graphics Supercomputing Workstation; 3 models,
(2) Power Station that can be used as a Supercomputer server or as a general purpose technical computer in a networked environment; 4 models [14.40, 14.41].

All of the above are fully binary compatible with all Silicon Graphics 4D systems (section 14.2). The multiprocessor models are:

CPU	MHz	No. of CPUs	Power Iris	MIPS	MFLOPS
R3000	25	8	4D/280	160	32
R3000	25	4	4D/240GTX	80	16
R3000	25	2	4D/220GTX	40	8
R2000	16	2	4D/120GTX	20	2

Table 14.1 Workstations Summary

System	MM (MB)	Cache (KB)	MIPS	$1000	$1000/MIPS
DECstation 3100 (16.67 MHz R2000)	32	128	14	24	1.71
Personal Iris (12.5 MHz R2000)	16	-	10	16	1.60
Advantedge 2000 (16.67 MHz R2000)	16	64	12	12	1.00
Tektronix XD88 (M88000)	8	64	17	30	1.76
D.G. AViiON (M88000)	28	-	17	12	0.70
Everex Step 8820 (M88000)	16	-	17	13	0.76
SPARCstation 1 (20 MHz LSI Logic)	16	64	12.5	10	0.80
Yarc NuSuper (25 MHz 29000)	6	-	17	5	0.30
Apollo 10000 VS (PRISM)	128	192	30	155	5.17
Cogent XTM (20 MHz T800)	8	-	10	20	2.00

MM - Main Memory

MB - Mega Bytes

KB - Kilo Bytes

MIPS - Millions of Instructions Per Second (sustained)

$1000 - Price in thousands of US $.

The performance values above are sustained. Upgrading from a 120 to a 220 model requires one board swap; and from a 220 to a 240, an addition of one new board. All of the above models include a floating point coprocessor; R3010 with the R3000 CPU and R2010 with the R2000 CPU. On all models, each processor operates on its own processor bus, with its own two-level caches and read/write buffers. The processor bus bandwidth is 100 MBytes/sec. The first level cache is 64 KBytes instruction and 64 KBytes data. The second level cache is 256 KBytes data. All caches employ fast Static RAMs (SRAMS). The main memory is configured in 8 MByte increments up to 128 MBytes.

All systems operate under Unix System V.3 OS with 4.3BSD and Silicon Graphics enhancements. Standard software offered:

C Compiler
Iris edge visual debugger
Iris graphics library
4 Sight Window Manager.

Optional software:

Power FORTRAN accelerator
FORTRAN compiler
Network File System (NFS)
Documentor's Workbench
EMACS text editor.

All systems work with Ethernet LAN with the TCP/IP protocol. Optional communications features:

RS-232-C port for serial communications (up to 19.2K baud)
IBM coax 3270 emulation
IBM 5080 emulation
IBM PC emulation
DECnet connectivity
Hyperchannel connectivity.

The BBN Advanced Computers, Inc. (Cambridge, MA) manufactures a powerful multiprocessor, called the Butterfly [14.20–14.22]. The current models are denoted as GP1000 and TC2000. The Butterfly is organized as a set of N processor nodes. Each node contains a CPU, FPU, MMU, main memory, I/O controller and interfaces. All main memories of all nodes form a pool of *shared memory*, directly accessible by all processors through the system's logarithmic, packet-switched communication network, the Butterfly switch. An average access time to other node's memory is 4 microseconds. The switch bandwidth is 32 MBits/sec. per path. A sketch of a Butterfly switch configuration, for the case of N=16 nodes, is illustrated in Figure 14.4. The CPUs on the GP1000 models are Motorola MC68020 and, on the TC2000, MC88100 (chapter 6).

The TC2000 can optionally feature from 8 to 504 processors [14.42, 14.43]. The processors are located on *function cards*. Each function card contains an MC88100 CPU, 2 MC88200 CMMUs (32 KBytes cache), memory, and interface logic. There are two types of function cards. The TC/FP function card can have 16 to 32 MBytes of main memory. The TC/FPV function card has 4 to 16 MBytes

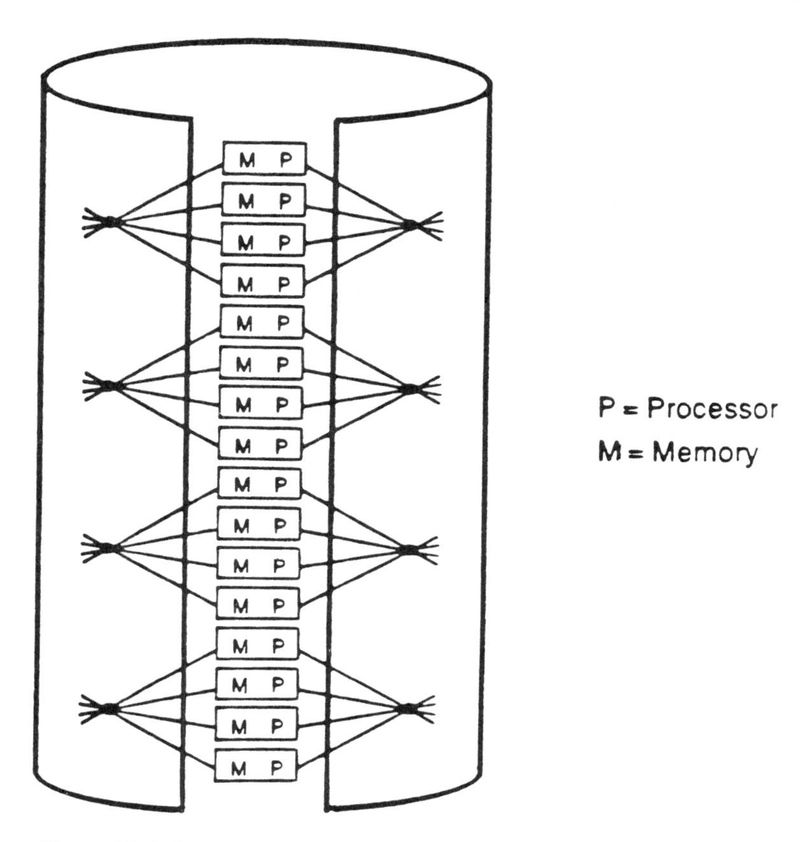

Figure 14.4 Processor Nodes and Switch for a 16-Processor Configuration (*Courtesy of BBN Advanced Computers, Inc.*)

of main memory and a VME I/O interface. Both the 20 MHz and 33 MHz versions of the 88000 can run interchangeably in the same machine. All function card subsystems are connected to an internal 32-bit, 80 MBytes/sec. Tbus.

The TC2000 OS is the BBN nX, based on Unix 4.3BSD, for general purpose software development, and pSOS+m, a real-time, multitasking, multiprocessing executive from Software Components Group, Inc. The system supports FORTRAN, C and Ada languages.

The system performance is up to 9000 VAX 780 MIPS, 152 to 9576 Dhrystone MIPS, 104 to 6553 MWhetstones, and 160 to 10080 MFLOPS, for 8 to 504 processors respectively. The total shared memory, distributed among the function cards is 240 to 16096 MBytes. The VME bus-based I/O bandwidth is 40 to 2560 MBytes/sec.

A similar case can be observed with the Encore Computer Corp. (Marlborough, MA), the creator of the Multimax multiprocessor [14.21]. The current

Multimax top product is the Multimax 520 which uses the National Semiconductor NS32532 as a CPU. Up to 20 CPUs can be configured on a single system. Encore is now developing, under a DARPA contract, a new general purpose multiprocessor, based on the Multimax structure, using M88000 family chips. The initial product will feature 4 MC88100 CPUs, up to 128 MBytes main memory and 3 GBytes of secondary memory. It will also feature 2 cache levels; the first, inside the MC88200 CMMUs, and the second, external. The system will run on the MACH OS [14.21].

Tadpole Technology (Waltham, MA) produces in cooperation with Motorola a VME bus board set, based on the HYPERmodule (section 6.6) [14.23]. The system consists of 4 board modules:

(1) Processor module, includes 4 MC88100 CPUs, 8 MC88200 CMMUs, a 50 MBytes/sec. intermodule MBUS (chapter 6) and up to 32 MBytes DRAM with parity check.
(2) Base module, includes the set's VME bus interface, MBUS arbiter and interrupt handler, nonvolatile up to 4 MBytes EPROM, real time clock, I/O subsystem containing a synchronous RS-232 port, 3 asynchronous RS-232 ports, an Ethernet interface and 2 SCSI interfaces.
(3) DRAM module (optional), additional 16 to 64 MBytes of DRAM.
(4) Custom module (optional), can include additional processors and interfaces.

The expected performance of the processor board is about 50 MIPS.

Motorola features its own multiprocessor board MVME188 with up to 4 CPUs, 128 KBytes cache and up to 64 MBytes main memory. The performance at 20 MHz will be 15 VAX MIPS and 3.75 MFLOPS per CPU. The 4-processor version price will be $33,500. Motorola's Delta Series 8000 workstation features a 20 MHz up to 4-processor model 8864. Its performance is 17 to 50 VAX 780 MIPS. It features a 128 KByte cache, 16 to 64 MBytes main memory, one to four SCSI Winchester disk drives for up to 2.4 GBytes of storage per controller, and 150 MBytes streaming tape drive [14.24].

Solbourne Computer, Inc. (Longmont, CO) features a fully Sun-4 binary compatible multiprocessor, called Series 4/600 [14.25]. It runs under SUN OS 4.0 (chapter 7). The system contains up to 4 SPARC Fujitsu, 16.67 MHz processors with Weitek floating point coprocessors and a 64 KBytes cache per CPU. One CPU is designated as the primary CPU (the master), while all other CPUs are secondaries (slaves). The primary CPU distributes the workload among the CPUs, handles all I/O, and runs any kernel-level tasks of the OS. The 4 CPU boards, up to 80 MBytes of main memory, the color graphics subsystem, and the System Board are connected to the proprietary 64-bit, 128 MBytes/sec. K-bus. The System Board includes an I/O processor, a monochrome graphics subsystem, and Ethernet, SCSI and VME bus interfaces. A seven-slot, 25 MBytes/sec. VME-Bus can be interconnected to the System Board.

A multiple benchmark performance comparison is reported in [14.25] in units of MVUPs (MicroVAX II Units of Processing). The average results are:

System	MVUPs
MIPS M/120-5 (R2000)	15.10
Personal Iris (R2000)	8.32
Series 4/600 (1 SPARC CPU enabled)	5.60
Sun 4/260 (SPARC)	5.43
Sun 4/110 (SPARC)	3.76
MicroVax 3200	3.53

The performance of the 4/600 with all 4 CPUs enabled was 4 times the above, that is, about 22 MVUPs. The price of a four-processor 4/600 with 16 MBytes RAM is $65,500.

A large-scale experimental multiprocessor is under development at the New York University [14.26–14.28]. It is called the NYU Ultracomputer. It is designed to be extendable to 4096 processors, however, only a 64-processor prototype is contemplated for construction. The individual processor selected for the Ultracomputer is the Am29000 (chapter 8).

The INMOS Transputer (section 12.4) was designed from the start with multiprocessing applications in mind. Each Transputer chip has, in addition to the regular 32-bit bus interface, four serial communication links, enabling it to be interconnected to four other neighboring processors, forming a multiprocessor configuration. This property was fully utilized by many developers in numerous projects. Only a sample of the existing work will be mentioned here.

A *Transputer*-based dataflow multiprocessor system for robot arm control was developed at MODCOMP (Ft. Lauderdale, FL) [14.29]. The system, which explores the maximum parallelism, consists of 1834 processing elements, using 20 MHz T414 transputers (section 12.4). It is programmed in OCCAM. A T800-based multiprocessor was developed in the 'ESPRIT Project 1085', with a large consortium lead by the Royal Signals and Radar Establishment [14.30]. The total number of processor boards can be optionally changed. The system is marketed by Parsys (UK) and Telmat (France).

Intel and DARPA are developing an 80860-based multiprocessor prototype that will ultimately contain as many as 2000 processors. It is called the Touchstone project. A fully configured system will contain up to 128 GBytes of high-speed memory, more than a terabyte of fast disk storage, animated 3D graphics displays, and connections to high-speed, optical data networks. Peak performance is expected to exceed 128 billion, 64-bit floating-point operations per second (128 DP GFLOPS).

14.4 Real-time Applications

As argued in section 14.1, RISC systems can be useful in real-time applications

[14.31]. Indeed, several commercial, RISC-based products are available and will be described in this section.

Mizar Co. (Carrollton, TX) features a real-time, SPARC-based, two-board system MZ 7170 [14.32]. It is intended for real-time and embedded control applications. The two-board set includes a SPARC CPU (20 or 25 MHz), 1 MByte SRAM, up to 4 MBytes of EPROM, two RS-232 serial ports, a real-time clock with battery backup, a VME bus interface, a system controller with four-level arbitration, an interrupt handler, an interrupt generator, and a mailbox interrupt facility. A block diagram of MZ 7170 is shown in Figure 14.5.

The system performance is 15 MIPS, sustained at 25 MHz (12 MIPS at 20 MHz). Its price is $7,000.

Development of MZ 7170-based applications is provided through the Sun OS (chapter 7), either via a Sun workstation, or with a Mizar Hybrid Development system. Software support for the MZ 7170 includes a complete debug monitor as well as Wind River Systems, Inc. (Emeryville, CA) VxWorks Real-time OS, specifically designed to work in partnership with Unix. VxWorks can handle up to 64 tasks and up to 256 priority levels. In the VxWorks environment, Unix is used as a high-level software development platform to develop real-time code that will run and be debugged under VxWorks, which resides on the real-time processor and handles the testing and running of real-time applications. Mizar also offers the VADS Ada Development Environment which includes an Ada compiler, developed by the Verdix Corporation.

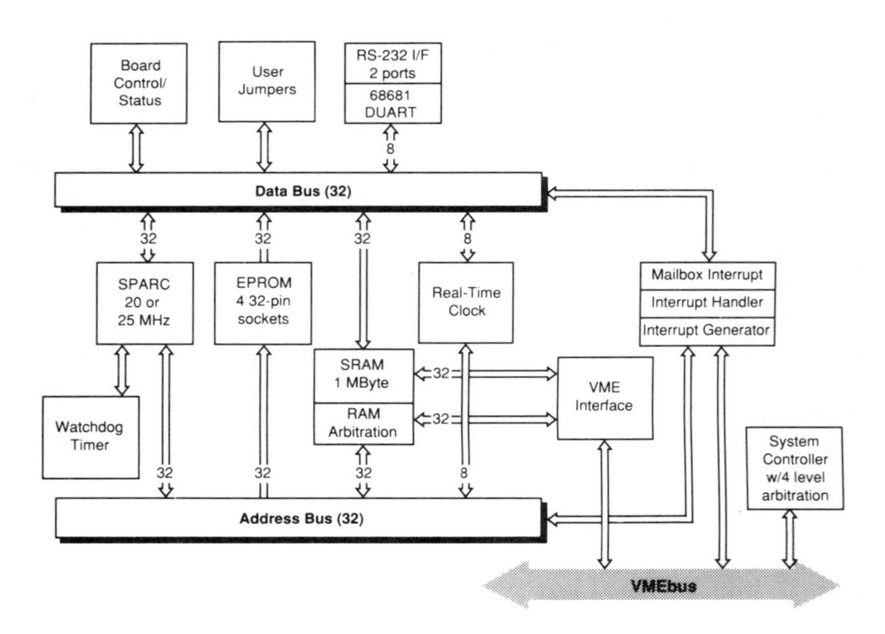

Figure 14.5 MZ 7170 Block Diagram
(Courtesy of Mizar Co.)

A Real-time OS, intended for Fujitsu SPARC-based systems (chapter 7), was developed by JMI Software Consultants, Inc. (Spring House, PA) [14.33]. It is called C Executive and it is a multitasking, ROMable OS kernel for the Fujitsu SPARC-based real-time system. The C language is used to write portable embedded real-time applications software which can be used on a variety of processors. Time critical sections, such as context switching, task scheduling, interrupt handling, and block data moves, are written in optimized assembly language.

Ironics, Inc. (Ithaca, NY) manufactures a single-board, Am29000-based (chapter 8) computer called IV-9001 [14.34], which can be used in single, or multiprocessor real-time applications. Am29000 is 25 MHz, 17 MIPS sustained performance. The AM29027 FPU is optional. The board includes 16 KBytes data cache, up to 16 MBytes DRAM main memory, VME bus controller interface, 100 MBytes/sec. I/O board interface, and 2 serial I/O ports. Multiprocessing is supported by guaranteeing an inherent cache coherency mechanism. The IV-9001 software includes a debug monitor, real-time kernel, cross-compilers and development support tools on Ironics Performer 32 Unix Systems. The Ironics Performer runs an optimized C compiler with an assembler, linker, loader for IV-9001 cross development. Applications can be developed under Unix and downloaded over the backplane to an IV-9001 in the same chassis. Other software support for the IV-9001 includes optimizing compilers for Pascal, FORTRAN, Ada. Unix V.3 and VRTX32 real-time kernel are also provided. The system costs about $6,500.

Intel offers an 80960-based (chapter 9) controller card, called iLASER III, for driving laser printers [14.35]. It uses a 16 MHz 80960KB or 80960KA. The iLASER III is a PC or PC AT compatible card and it supports connections to common Laser Beam Print (LBP) systems, such as Canon SX or Ricoh. The LBP interface includes a 1 KBytes FIFO (First-In, First-Out) buffer storage. A similar 1 KByte FIFO buffer is also provided for the PC-compatible interface port. The card has up to 8 MBytes of on-board DRAM and a DRAM controller.

The Inmos Transputer, with its on-chip FPU, 4 KBytes of main memory, four serial communication links, 600 ns worst case context switch (30 MHz T800), and 1.9 ms interrupt latency, is well suited for real-time applications, particularly in robotics [14.13]. It was indeed applied in this manner in a number of projects.

Yale University researchers, in cooperation with Evergreen Design Co. (Branford, CT) produced a T800-based (section 12.4) board XP/DCS. It includes a 128 KBytes SRAM and a fiber-optic interface. It was used as a processor for a planar juggling robot apparatus [14.36]. A set of 20 MHz T414 Transputers was used in the control of the loading of roller mounted containers with parcel post [14.37]. The parallel implementation was developed and tested on a board with four 20 MHz T414s using a TDS2 transputer development system. The link speeds were 20 MBits/sec. Measurements were conducted with up to 36 transputers. The performance acceleration for various numbers of processors, N, was measured and compared to that using a single processor. For N=4 the acceleration factor was 3.95. For N=8 it was about 7.7. With more processors the performance continued to increase, although the acceleration factor decreases. The average acceleration factor is 25 for 36 processors. A board with 4 T800s (or 4 T414s) was used in a controller for a flexible robot arm [14.38].

References

14.1 D.W. Haskin, J.A. Steinberg, 'DECstation 3100', *Digital Review*, Feb. 6, 1989, pp. 55–62.
14.2 K. Sorensen, 'Outlook on RISC', *Digital Review*, March 10, 1989, pp. 1, 8.
14.3 D. Wilson, 'Technology Trends', *ESD*, Feb. 1989, p. 22.
14.4 D.W. Haskin, 'A 3-D Homerun', *Digital Review*, May 8, 1989, pp. 43–54.
14.5 G. Grey, 'The 88000 Faces of Multibus II', *ESD*, Sept. 1988, pp. 45–50.
14.6 R. Wilson, 'Motorola Unveils New RISC Microprocessor Flagship', *Computer Design*, May 1, 1988, pp. 21–24.
14.7 E. Smalley, 'Tektronix Uses 88000 Chip to Power Latest Line', *Digital Review*, April 10, 1989.
14.8 E. Smalley, S. Kovsky, 'Data General RISC Offering Due at Uniforum', *Digital Review*, Feb. 27, 1989, p. 3.
14.9 E. Smalley, 'Dual-Processor System Supports Unix, MS-DOS', *Digital Review*, April 17, 1989, p. 24.
14.10 H. Falk, '88000 Designed for Use with Optimizing Compilers', *Computer Design*, May 1, 1988, pp. 30–32.
14.11 *The Source-88000 Update, Motorola Document No. BR506AD/D*, Motorola, Inc., Phoenix, AZ, 1988.
14.12 *MVME 181 RISC Microcomputer, Motorola Document MVME 181/DD, Rev. 1*, Motorola, Inc., Phoenix, AZ, 1989.
14.13 N. Baran, 'Two Powerful Systems from Sun', *BYTE*, May 1989, pp. 108–112.
14.14 M. Slater, 'Parallelizing SPARCs and Clones', *ESD*, Feb. 1989, p. 24.
14.15 T. Marshall, 'Standard DRAMs Get 15 MIPS from RISC', *ESD*, Dec. 1988, pp. 52–56.
14.16 D. Lieberman, 'RISC Coprocessor Gives AT a Boost', *Computer Design*, April 1, 1989, p. 105.
14.17 E. Smalley, 'RISC-Based Subsystem Zips Through Graphics', *Digital Review*, March 13, 1989, pp. 31–32.
14.18 D. Pountain, 'The Archimedes A310', *BYTE*, Oct. 1987, pp. 125–130.
14.19 F. Hayes, 'The Crossbar Connection', *BYTE*, Nov. 1988, pp. 278–279.
14.20 *Butterfly GP1000 Overview*, BBN Advanced Computers, Inc., Nov. 10, 1988.
14.21 D. Tabak, *Multiprocessors*, Prentice Hall, Englewood Cliffs, NJ, 1990.
14.22 G.E. Schmidt, 'The Butterfly Parallel Processor', *Proc. 2nd Int. Conf. on Supercomputers, ICS 87*, **I**, pp. 362–365, Santa Clara, CA, May 4–8, 1987.
14.23 D. Lieberman, 'Multiprocessing RISC Boards Fend Off Bus Obsolescence', *Computer Design*, Feb. 1, 1989, pp. 41–42.
14.24 E. Smalley, 'Motorola Hopes RISC Boards Set Stage for High-End Gain', *Digital Review*, Feb. 20, 1989, p. 62.

14.25 D.W. Haskin, 'Dawn of the First Sun Clone', *Digital Review*, Jan. 16, 1989, pp. 35–37.

14.26 A. Gottlieb *et al.*, 'The NYU Ultracomputer – Designing an MIMD Shared Memory Parallel Computer', *IEEE Trans. on Computers*, **C-32**, No. 2, pp. 175–189, Feb. 1983.

14.27 G.S. Almasi, A. Gottlieb, *Highly Parallel Computing*, Benjamin/Cummings, Redwood City, CA, 1989.

14.28 A. Gottlieb, 'An Overview of the NYU Ultracomputer Project', *Ultracomputer Note #100*, NYU, April 1987.

14.29 S. Geffin, B. Furht, 'Transputer-Based Dataflow Multiprocessor for Robot Arm Control', *Microprocessors and Microsystems*, **13**, No. 3, pp. 219–226, April 1989.

14.30 D.A. Nicole, 'Reconfigurable Transputer Processor Architectures', *Proc. Hawaii Int. Conf. on System Sciences, HICSS-22*, **1**, pp. 365–374, Jan. 1989.

14.31 R. Wilson, 'Real-time Executives Take On Newest Processors', *Computer Design*, Feb. 1, 1989, pp. 88–105.

14.32 M. Donlin, 'SPARC Module Targets Real-time Applications', *Computer Design*, Dec. 1988, p. 100.

14.33 D. Wilson, 'SPARC Goes to Harvard', *ESD*, Jan. 1989, p. 26.

14.34 S. Silverstein, S. Adkar, 'VME Caches in on the 29000', *ESD*, Sept. 1988, pp. 53–58.

14.35 *iLASER III Manual*, Intel Corp., March 1989.

14.36 F. Levin *et al.*, 'Transputer Computer Juggles Real-time Robotics', *ESD*, Feb. 1989, pp. 77–82.

14.37 W. van den Broek, M. deBoer, 'Adaptation of a Robotics Algorithm for a Distributed Implementation Using Transputers', *Microprocessors and Microsystems*, **13**, No. 3, pp. 195–202, April 1989.

14.38 A.C.J. Stavenuiter, G. Ter Reehorst, A.W. Bakkers, 'Transputer Control of a Flexible Robot Link', *Microprocessors and Microsystems*, **13**, No. 3, pp. 227–232, April 1989.

14.39 D.W. Haskin, 'The Power of Precision Architecture', *Digital Review*, June 26, 1989, pp. 31–33.

14.40 S. Kovsky, 'Silicon Graphics' RISC System Doubles Forerunner's 80 MIPS', *Digital Review*, July 17, 1989, p. 3.

14.41 J.A. Steinberg, 'Unparalleled 3-D Power', *Digital Review*, Aug. 14, 1989, pp. 33–35.

14.42 *TC2000 Technical Product Summary, Rev: 1.0*, BBN Advanced Computers, Inc., Cambridge, MA, July 1989.

14.43 G. Grygo, 'BBN's Expandable Minisuper Capitalizes on Motorola 88000', *Digital Review*, July 31, 1989, pp. 25–26.

15 Concluding Comments

Looking at the recent rapid development of RISC systems one can predict that, over the next few years, some new RISC systems, unknown today, will be announced.

With the development of the current VLSI technology, more and more resources will be put on the processor chip. We already have the Intel 1.2 million transistors, 80860 chip today, with its 12 KBytes on-chip cache. Other manufacturers will follow and eventually the number of transistors on-chip will exceed 2 millions. Undoubtedly, all manufacturers will put the Floating Point Unit and more cache on-chip. Some will also increase the number of CPU registers.

With the increase of chip densities, we should also expect an expansion in the standard word length. The 80860 has a 64-bit external and internal data bus, although its integer unit is a 32-bit processor. Its data cache transmits 128 bits simultaneously. There are current and future applications which could definitely benefit from 64-bit standard word computation. It is expected that some new RISC systems will indeed be full-scale (including the ALU) 64-bit machines.

The RISC applications will undoubtedly expand even more. In addition to the increase in the number of RISC systems, used in current applications, new applications areas will appear. The Intel 80860 already includes a 3D graphics subsystem on the processor chip. This trend is expected to spread with other manufacturers as well. In a few years, the graphics workstations market may well be completely dominated by RISC-type processors, because of their relative high performance, low cost, and faster design turnaround.

The GaAs RISC systems, while being still in the experimental stage, will eventually offer very high performance commercial alternatives. The CMOS technology is also being perfected. While at the moment, the offered frequency range is around 20–33 MHz, we are going to attain 40–60 MHz products in the near future. There is also a parallel effort along ECL technologies, which might yield practical products at around 100 MHz. No doubt, some exciting technological developments are just around the corner.

Problems

1. In a given computing system assume that any fetch (F) takes only one CPU cycle T. An execute stage (E) involving memory access, such as load, takes 2 CPU cycles. All other execute stages take only a single cycle. Draw a time-space pipeline diagram for a two-stage instruction pipeline: stage 1, Fetch (F); stage 2, Execute (E). Discuss any problems encountered for the following instruction sequence:

```
load memrloc, r10  ; (memrloc) → r10
add  r10, r11, r12 ; (r10) + (r11) → r12
sub  r4, r3, r1    ; (r4) − (r3) → r1
cmp  r12, r2       ; (r12) − (r2), flags affected
bz   addr1         ; branch on zero (if r12 = r2) to addr1
dcr  r12           ; if (r12) ≠ (r2), (r12) − 1 → r12
```

   addr1 next instruction.
   memrloc is an address in memory.

2. Explain the method of scoreboarding and discuss in detail how it would be implemented for the program sequence in problem 1.

3. Repeat problem 1 for a three-stage pipeline, whose stages are:
   Fetch, F
   Execute, E
   Write Back result, WB

4. Implement, in the most efficient way, the delayed branch principle to the instruction sequence in problem 1. Is it necessary to insert a 'no operation' (nop) instruction?

5. Given the following instruction sequence:

```
load  memloc1, r1  ; (memloc1) → r1
load  memloc2, r2  ; (memloc2) → r2
add   r1, r2, r4   ; (r1) + (r2) → r4
add   r1, r5, r6   ; (r1) + (r5) → r6
sub   r7, r4, r3   ; (r7) − (r4) → r3
store r6, memloc3  ; (r6) → memloc3
cmp   r1, r10      ; (r1) − (r10), flags affected
bz    addr1        ; branch on zero to addr1
dcr   r1           ; (r1) − 1 → r1
```

   addr1 next instruction.
   Assume a three-stage pipeline as in problem 3. Draw a detailed time-space diagram and discuss the problems encountered. Assume that each stage in the pipeline takes a single CPU cycle, and memory access takes 2 CPU cycles.

6. Present in detail the scoreboarding sequence for the program in problem 5.

7. Apply in the most efficient way the delayed branch principle to the program in problem 5.
8. A RISC and a CISC computer run at the same basic CPU cycle of 50 ns (20 MHz). A given program contains 150 instructions on the RISC and 100 instructions on the CISC. All RISC instructions execute in one CPU cycle. In the CISC program 20 instructions execute in one cycle, 40 instructions execute in two cycles, and the remaining 40 instructions in three cycles. Calculate the total program time for both systems and discuss the results.
9. Assume that window 7 of the Berkeley RISC II is taken up by the main program. Four nested subroutines are called subsequently. Which registers will be seen by the last (4th) nested subroutine?
10. Write a simple 8 × 8-bits multiply subroutine for the Berkeley RISC. Implement the delayed branch whenever appropriate.
11. Design a Berkeley RISC II-based microcomputer, interfacing to a floating point coprocessor, 16 KBytes cache (instruction and data), and 16 MBytes main memory (DRAM).
12. Write a simple subroutine to add 64-bit values on the MIPS 2000.
13. Analyze in detail the treatment of the program you have written in problem 12, by the R2000 pipeline.
14. Write a small program for a floating point scalar product of two floating point vectors (dimension up to 100) on the MIPS R2000 and R2010. Use the mnemonics of instructions listed in Table 4.1.
15. Analyze in detail the treatment of the program you have written in problem 14, by the R2010 pipeline.
16. Design a MIPS R2000-based system with 64 KBytes Data and 64 KBytes Code caches, 128 MBytes main memory, and eight I/O interfaces.
17. Design an M88000-based system with 32 KBytes Data and 32 KBytes Code caches, 64 MBytes main memory, and eight I/O interfaces.
18. Expand the system, designed in problem 16, into a dual-processor (two MC88100 chips), doubling its cache, main memory, and I/O interfaces.
19. Design a SPARC Cypress-based computer, including the floating point unit. The cache, main memory and I/O interfaces specifications are as in problem 17.
20. Expand the system in problem 19 into a dual processor, doubling the system resources.
21. Design an Am29000-based system, including the floating point unit Am29027, with 8 KBytes Data and 8 KBytes Code caches, 16 MBytes main memory, and four I/O interfaces.
22. Expand the system, designed in problem 21, into a dual processor, doubling the system resources.
23. Design an 80960KB-based controller, interfacing to 2 KBytes SRAM, 64 KBytes DRAM, and eight I/O devices. All I/O devices have interrupt privileges through an 8259A chip.

24. Modify the system, designed in problem 23, to allow DMA privileges for two of the I/O devices.

25. Design the interface circuitry between the 80960KB and two 8-bit 8255 Programmable Peripheral Interface chips.

26. Complete the details of the logic design of the following subsystems in Fig. 9.7 Block Diagram for LAN Controller Interface:
    (a) LAN Data Transceiver;
    (b) Byte Enable Converter;
    (c) LAN Address Latches.

27. Complete the details of the logic design of the following subsystems in Fig. 9.8 Block Diagram for 82786 Interface:
    (a) Bidirectional Transceivers;
    (b) Data Buffer Control;
    (c) Data Bus Controller;
    (d) Address Translator.

28. Design an 80860-based system with a dual cache hierarchy. The on-chip cache will be considered as the first cache level. The second cache level should contain 64 KBytes Data and 64 KBytes Code caches. The main memory is 128 MBytes. There are eight I/O interfaces.

29. Expand the system, designed in problem 28, into a dual processor, doubling the system resources.

30. Design an Acorn-based controller, with 2 MBytes main memory and four I/O interfaces with interrupt privileges.

Glossary of Abbreviations

AIX – Advanced Interactive Executive
ALU – Arithmetic Logic Unit
AMD – Advanced Micro Devices
AMU – Arithmetic Move Unit
ANSI – American National Standards Institute
AP – Argument Pointer
ARM – Acorn RISC Machine
ASCII – American Standard Code for Information Interchange
ATC – Address Translation Cache

B – Byte
BATC – Block ATC
BBN – Bolt, Beranek and Newman
BCD – Binary Coded Decimal
BE – Byte Enable
BGU – Ben Gurion University
BIT – Bipolar Integrated Technology
BSD – Berkeley Software Distribution

C – Carry
CA – 1. Core Architecture
 2. Channel Attention
CAD – Computer Aided Design
CAMMU – Cache and MMU (also CMMU – see below)
CDC – Control Data Corp.
CFP – Current Frame Pointer
CIO – Channel Input/Output
CISC – Complex Instruction Set Computer
CLA – Carry Look Ahead
CMMU – Cache/MMU
CMOS – Complementary MOS
CMOVE – Conditional Move
CP – Control Parity
CPU – Central Processing Unit
CU – Control Unit
CWP – Current Window Pointer

DARPA – Defense Advanced Research Project Agency
DCL – DEC's Command Language

DEC – Digital Equipment Corporation
DEN – Data Enable
DES – Data Execution Section
DI – Disable Interrupt
DIP – Dual In-line Packages
DIR – Data Input Register
DM – Data Memory
DMA – 1. Direct Memory Access
2. Data Memory Address
DMAC – DMA Controller
DMD – Data Memory Data
DMT – Data Memory Transaction
DOR – Data Output Register
DRAM – Dynamic RAM
DST – Destination

EA – Effective Address
ECL – Emitter Current Logic
EFS – Extended File System
EPROM – Extended PROM
EPSR – 1. Exception-time PSR
2. Extended Process Status Register
EU – Execution Unit
EVT – Exception Vector Table

FCOP – Floating-point Coprocessor
FCR – Floating-point Control Register
FGR – Floating-point General-purpose Register
FIFO – First In, First Out
FIP – Fetch Instruction Pointer
FIR – Fetch Instruction Register
FP – Frame Pointer
FPA – Floating Point Accelerator
FPC – Floating Point Controller
FPP – Floating Point Processor
FPR – Floating Point Control Register
FPU – Floating Point Unit
FQ – Floating-point Queue
FSR – Floating-point Status Register
FW – Free Window
FWB – Floating-point Write Back

G – Giga (times 10^9)
GaAs – Gallium Arsenide
GMU – George Mason University
GR – General Register

HLL – High Level Language

HP – Hewlett Packard
Hz – Hertz

IAR – Instruction Address Register
IBM – International Business Machines
IC – Integrated Circuit
ICR – Interrupt Control Register
ICU – Interrupt Control Unit
ID – Instruction Decode
IDT – Integrated Device Technology
IEEE – Institute of Electrical and Electronic Engineers
IEO – Integer Execution Unit
IF – 1. Instruction Fetch
   2. Instruction Format
IFU – Instruction Fetch Unit
IO – Input/Output
IOC – I/O Controller
IOP – Input/Output Processor
IP – 1. Instruction Pointer
   2. Integer Processor
IR – Instruction Register
IRQ – Interrupt Request
ISO – International Standards Organization
ISR – Interrupt Service Routine
IU – Integer Unit

JAL – Jump And Link (also JMPL)

K – Kilo (times 10^3)
KART – Keyboard Asynchronous Receiver-Transmitter
KHz – Kilo Hertz (10^3 Hertz)

L – Longword
LAN – Local Area Network
LBA – Logical Block Address
LBP – Laser Beam Print
LIFO – Last-In, First-Out
LPA – Logical Page Address
LR – Logical Register
LRU – Least Recently Used
LSB – Least Significant Bit
LSI – Large Scale Integration
LSW – Logical Status Word

M – 1. Memory (also MEM)
   2. Mega (times 10^6)
MAG – Memory Address Generator
MAR – Memory Address Register

MBUS – Memory Bus
MC – Motorola Company
McD – McDonnell-Douglas
MEM – Memory (also M)
MEMC – Memory Controller
MFLOPS – Millions of Floating-point Operations Per Second
MHz – Mega Hertz (10^6 Hertz)
MIMD – Multiple Instruction, Multiple Data
MIPS – 1. Microprocessor without Interlocked Pipeline Stages
2. Millions of Instructions Per Second
MIRIS – Microcoded RISC
MM – Main Memory
MMU – Memory Management Unit
MOPS – Millions of Operations Per Second
MOS – Metal Oxide Semiconductor
MPE – Multiprogramming Executive
MSB – Most Significant Bit
MSI – Medium Scale Integration
MULTRIS – Multitasking RISC
MVUP – MicroVAX II Units of Processing
MW – Map Window
MWI – Map Window Index

N – 1. Negative
2. Non-sequential
NA – Numerics Architecture
NEC – Nippon Electric Co.
NFS – Network File System
NIP – Next Instruction Pointer
NMOS – N-channel MOS
NOP – No(n) oPeration
NS – National Semiconductor
ns – nanosecond (10^{-9})
NWINDOWS – Number of Windows
NYU – New York University

OB – Overflow Bit
OD – Operand Decode
OF – Operand Fetch
OPR – Overflow Pointer Register
OS – 1. Operating System
2. Operand Store
OT – Overflow Type
OW – Object Window

PA – Protected Architecture
PARIS – Parallel RISC
PATC – Page ATC

PBA – Physical Block Address
PBUS – Processor Bus
PC – Program Counter
PCB – Process Control Block
PCS – Program Control Section
PCU – Program Control Unit
PDH – Processor Dependent Hardware
PFA – Page Frame Address
PFP – Previous Frame Pointer
PIC – Programmable Interrupt Controller
PIT – Programmable Interval Timer
PM – Program Memory
PMOS – P-channel MOS
PPUs – Peripheral Processing Units
PR – Parameter Register
PRISM – Parallel Reduced Instruction Set Multiprocessor
PROM – Programmable ROM
PSCU – Program Status Control Unit
PSR – Process Status Register
PSW – Processor Status Word
PT – Program Time

RA – Real Address
RAM – Random Access Memory
RCA – Radio Corp. of America
RD – Read
RE – Result Even
RET – Return Instruction
RF – Register File
RIP – Return Instruction Pointer
RISC – Reduced Instruction Set Computer
RISCS – Reduced Instruction Set Computer Space
RO – Result Odd
ROM – Read Only Memory
ROMP – Research Office product division MicroProcessor
RTN – Register Transfer Notation
RWM – Read Write Memory

S – 1. Sign
    2. Sequential
SAPR – Supervisor Area Pointer Register
SB – Scoreboard
SCSI – Small Computer Systems Interface
SFIP – Shadow FIP
SFU – Special Function Unit
SIC – Single Instruction Computer
SIMD – Single Instruction, Multiple Data
SMD – Storage Module Device

SNIP – Shadow NIP
SOAR – Smalltalk On A RISC
SP – Stack Pointer
SPARC – Scalable Processor Architecture
SPR – Special Purpose Register
SPUR – Symbolic Processing Using RISC
SQW – Stack/Queue Window
SQWI – Stack/Queue Window Index
SR – Status Register
SRAM – Static RAM
SSW – System Status Word
SWP – Saved Window Pointer
SX – Storage and Execution
SXIP – Shadow XIP

T – Temporary
TBR – Trap Base Register
TI – Texas Instruments
TLB – Translation Lookaside Buffer
TR – Temporary Register
TTL – Transistor-Transistor Logic

UAPR – User Area Pointer Register
UCLA – University of California at Los Angeles
USP – User Stack Pointer
UWS – Ultrix Worksystem Software

V – oVerflow
VA – Virtual Address
VADS – Verdix Ada Development System
VBR – Vector Base Register
VIDC – Video Controller
VLSI – Very Large Scale Integration
VM – Virtual Memory
VRAM – Video RAM

W – Word
WB – Write Back
WIM – Window Invalid Mask
WR – Write
WT – Windows Transferred

XA – Extended Architecture
XIP – Execution Instruction Pointer

Z – 1. Zero
2. Zilog

Glossary of Basic Definitions

Absolute Address – A binary number that is permanently assigned as the address of a memory location.

Addressing Mode – The way in which an operand is specified, or the way in which the effective address of an instruction operand is calculated.

ALU – Arithmetic Logic Unit – The component of a computer where arithmetic and logic operations are performed.

Array – A set or list of elements, usually variables or data.

Array System – An array is generally understood to be a collection of N processors, $P_1, \ldots, P_n$, handling the same instruction issued by a single control unit. Each processor, P_i, is equipped with a local memory, M_i, used by P_i for storing both its operands and the computational results it obtains. An array composed of N processors may concurrently execute N identical operations with one program instruction. Each instruction handles a data vector made of operands handled by $P_1, \ldots, P_n$, respectively. An array of N processors thus implements data parallelism but no instruction parallelism.

Assembler – A program which translates symbolic opcodes into machine language and assigns memory locations for variables and constants.

Assembly Language – The machine-oriented programming language used by an assembly system.

Base Address – A given address from which an absolute address is derived by combination with a relative address.

Catastrophic Failure – A failure within a system causing a complete breakdown and a cessation of its operation.

Compiler – A code that translates a program written in a High Level Language (HLL) into an object program.

Control Unit (CU) – The unit responsible for sequencing, fetching, decoding and producing all of the necessary control signals to execute an instruction in a computer.

CPU – Central Processing Unit – The unit of a computing system that includes the circuits controlling the interpretation and execution of instructions and the ALU.

Decoder (n to 2^n) – A multiple output combinational logic network with n input lines and 2^n output lines. For each possible input condition one and only one signal will be logic 1.

Destination Address – Address of a storage location in memory or a register, into which an information item is to be stored.

Direct Addressing – An addressing mode using an absolute address within the instruction.

Effective Addressing – The address obtained after indirect or indexing modifications are calculated.

High Level Languages (HLL) – Problem-oriented languages such as Pascal, PL/1, Ada, FORTRAN, ALGOL, COBOL, which have a powerful set of operational and control statements which are substantially above the basic statement types provided in assembly languages. In conventional computers, transformed into assembly languages by a compiler.

Immediate Addressing – An addressing mode where the operand is actualy a part of the instruction.

Index Register – A register used to contain an address offset.

Indexed Addressing – An addressing mode where the effective address is calculated by adding the contents of a special register, called an 'index register' to another address value, given in the direct or any other mode.

Indirect Address – An address in a computer instruction which indicates a location where the address of the referenced operand is to be found.

Instruction Execution – The process of actually executing the instruction by the CPU, after it has been decoded.

Instruction Fetch – The process of the transfer (move) of the instruction from its memory storage into the CPU, and its decoding (some texts put the decoding within the instruction execution period).

Interrupt – An event that changes the normal flow of instruction execution. Generally external to the process executing when the interrupt occurs.

I/O Port – A junction between the main bus and the I/O device. It is a part of a device interface; a group of bits accessed by the processor during I/O operations.

Latch – A logic circuit to which an input action must be applied to a specified input to cause the device to assume one of two logic conditions. Further application of the latch input signal has no effect; the latch remains in the latched position. Release of the latch must be accomplished by application of an input signal to another input location.

Machine Language – Information that can be directly processed by the computer.

Master Controller – One of the subsystems, in a multiprocessing system, which assumes control of all the others.

Memory-to-memory Organization of the Processor – An organization in which each instruction has its operands fetched from the memory and the result is sent back to the memory.

Microoperation – The most elementary processing done in a computer consists of executing a microoperation during a word transfer between registers. To execute a microoperation, a data path between registers must contain the control circuit and may or may not contain an execution circuit. An execution circuit implements a Boolean function that transforms input data word(s) stored in one or several source registers into an output data word broadcast to one or several destination registers. Since a microoperation necessarily includes one control circuit, it is activated by the microcommand that opens this control circuit.

MIMD – Multiple Instruction Multiple Data – A parallel processing configuration where multiple processors execute different processes simultaneously.

Multiprocessing – Utilization of several computers or processors to logically or functionally divide jobs or processors, and to execute them simultaneously.

Multiprogramming – Execution of two or more programs in core at the same time. Execution switches between programs.

Opcode – The pattern of bits within an instruction that specify the operation to be performed.

Operand – A quantity which is affected, manipulated or operated upon.

Parallel Processing – Simultaneous execution, or any other treatment, of more than one instruction, or more than one data item at a time.

Parallel System – A parallel system generally means a system that implements either instruction parallelism, or both types of parallelism, instruction and data, in a single system.

Pipelining – In general, pipelining requires partitioning of the instruction handling sequence into several phases and allows for the overlapped execution of consecutive phases assigned to consecutive instructions. If the instruction handling sequence is partitioned into K phases, F_1, F_2, . . ., F_k, then the pipeline that executes it contains k stages, S_1, S_2, . . ., S_k, so that S_i executes phase F_i of the instruction handling sequence.

Procedure – The course of action taken for the solution of a problem.

Process – The smallest unit of programming activity which can be scheduled to run on a processor.

Processing Element (PE) – A general purpose ALU capable of executing a conventional instruction set.

Processor – A physical device performing data processing tasks.

Program – The counter sequence of instructions and routines necessary to solve a problem.

Program Counter (PC) – The counter that stores a current (macro-) instruction address in the main memory.

Register Transfer Notation (Language) – A method which describes the information flow and processing tasks among the data stored in registers of a computer system. Uses a set of expressions and statements which resemble the statements used in programming languages.

Relative Address – The number that specifies the difference between the actual address and a base address.

Reliability, R(t) – The probability that a given system will continue to function faultlessly up to a time t.

SIMD – Single Instruction, Multiple Data – A parallel processing configuration where multiple Processing Elements (PE) perform the same instruction on different data simultaneously.

Single-Address Instruction – An instruction whose format contains a single operand address reference.

Software – The collection of programs and routines associated with a computer.

Source Address – Address of a storage location in memory, or a register, containing an information item which is to be transferred to another location.

Survivability – The ability of a system to continue to function properly, despite existing conditions which may possibly cause a failure.

Task – Synonymous to 'process' (on some systems, but may consist of a number of processes on others).

Three-Address Instruction – An instruction whose format contains references to the addresses of two operands and of the destination of the operation result.

Two-Address Instruction – An instruction whose format contains references to the addresses of two operands.

Virtual Memory – A hierarchical storage system of at least two levels, which is managed by an Operating System to appear to a user as a single large directly addressable main memory.

VLSI – Very Large Scale Integration is the fabrication of 100,000 or more gates on a single wafer.

Von Neumann Architecture – Forms the basis of the design of a digital computer with the following properties:

(1) It is composed of five basic units: ALU, Memory (M), Control, Input, Output.
(2) The M is single, linear, sequentially addressed. The M is one-dimensional, a vector of words, with addresses starting from 0.
(3) Both the program and data are stored in the single M.
(4) There is no explicit distinction between instructions and data or between various data types.

Index